From a Thankful Nation

FROM A THANKFUL NATION

*Latin American Medals & Orders in
the Robert L. Ross Collection
Princeton University*

Robert L. Ross   Alan M. Stahl

PRINCETON, NEW JERSEY
PRINCETON UNIVERSITY LIBRARY

2014

✳

TITLE-PAGE IMAGE:

Argentina, *La Toma de Montevideo* (Ar5d)

FRONT-COVER IMAGE:

Cuba, *La Orden Nacional de Mérito "Carlos Manuel de Céspedes"* (Cu61a)

SPINE IMAGE:

Brazil, *A Ordem Imperial da Rosa* (Br62)

BACK-COVER IMAGES:

Top: Guatemala, *La Orden del Quetzal* (Gt18). *Middle row, left*: Chile, *La Estrella por la Campaña de Bolivia y el Peru* (Ch19). *Middle row, right*: Dominican Republic, *La Orden del Mérito Duarte, Sánchez, y Mella* (Do11). *Bottom row, left*: Paraguay, *La Cruz de Corrales* (Py2). *Bottom row, center*: Mexico, *La Estrella de Bejar y El Salado* (Mx26). *Bottom row, right*: Cuba, *La Orden "Ernesto Che Guevara"* (Cu79).

CONTENTS

PREFACE:
NOT JUST BAUBLES AND TRINKETS

C'est avec des hochets que l'on mène les hommes.
(It is with baubles that one leads men.)
—NAPOLEON BONAPARTE, 1802

FROM OUR very first accounts of complex societies, we see indications that symbols and decorations played an important role in establishing and honoring status. The articles of clothing or the particular accessories that one was permitted to wear could easily map out the hierarchy of any society. Honoring individuals with some special sign of privilege allowed rulers to make distinctions and to reward specific behavior. No matter the value of the decoration, its cost would pale next to the assurances and demonstration of loyalty that it could provide.

At least as early as the Roman Empire, we have records of such awards made in the form we would now recognize as a medal. Metal decorations had the advantage of being difficult to counterfeit, and their durability also assured a significant period of enjoyment for the person so honored and his (largely) or her family. As political entities became more complex and the identities of retainers and favorites became more difficult to establish, these institutions came to rely on medals as ways of recognizing individuals who could otherwise become lost in the large masses of soldiers and subjects.

Interestingly, while they are a sign of distinction and honor, medals and such decorations are very much a product of increasing democracy. As family lineages and class distinctions became harder to identify, the need to recognize individuals in a public manner became ever more important. This was especially true for states that rejected aristocratic titles and the granting of noble status. It should be no surprise that two of the earliest and most prominent examples of military decorations may be found in the revolutionary armies of the United States and of France. The practice spread widely, and examples such as the Prussian Iron Cross (1813) became an expected part of military uniforms and a recognized symbol of distinction.

As the new republics of Latin America arose and developed in the nineteenth century, it should not surprise us that they emulated this European custom and began creating their own honors. As was the case with previous revolutions, the new Latin American republics needed to create these forms of honorifics while avoiding the noble titles and grants associated with the Spanish Empire. The relatively low cost and ease of producing such medals made them ideal tools for governments and political groups that often had few resources to make more than symbolic acts. Not surprisingly, in societies concerned with status and recognition, but deprived of other forms of distinction, medals became an important part of any important personage's wardrobe. As in ancient times, the simple act of being able to adorn oneself with a piece of metal and a bit of ribbon automatically provided and required recognition.

In a time when one can find practically any information about anyone through a hand-held electronic device, it is difficult to imagine how important these relatively small objects were. The military retains the custom of wearing medals, and as any soldier will tell you, the set of awards and accomplishments displayed are an important part of intramilitary personal relations. Academics may no longer wear their equivalent honors (but note the lingering popularity of Phi Beta Kappa keys and the like), but the prominence they give to their various awards and accomplishments reveals that they are not above such distinctions.

What can these objects tell a scholar? It is hard to imagine a better way of reading a society and defining its values than by studying how and what it honors. The list of those who have received one sort of award or another tells a great deal about what and whom a society most holds dear. Much of what we know of premodern societies comes from what remains of their monuments and celebrations. Similarly, we can best understand what a modern state considers essential by studying what and whom deserves recognition. Societies at war will focus on military valor; those at peace might recognize statesmanship. In times of scientific progress, medals will be awarded for distinguished scholarship. Those societies seeking to promote growth or philanthropy will honor those who produce bounty. The social equality of a society may be gauged by the composition of its rolls of honor. Basic indications of ethnic homogeneity, racial and class differences, and the extent of patriarchy can be extrapolated from the names and visages of those who are honored. Similarly, the kinds of symbols used in such honorifics also tell us a great deal about what societies hold most sacred. We can track the symbolic history of a country by tracing the figures that adorn its medals, from classical busts to abstract designs.

Three examples demonstrate how this perspective can illustrate the scholarly worth of these objects.

Cuba established a new set of honorific Orders of the Revolutionary State in 1979. The statutes of the new orders clearly state that any deviation from revolutionary principles by the recipient can lead to his or her being stripped of membership in the order. It is further very clear that the order has been awarded by the Republic of Cuba (patriotism) and the Council of State (collective leadership). It was precisely at this time that the revolutionary government sought to institutionalize its rule and to clearly define the overriding principles of the regime.

Similarly, Rafael Trujillo created the Dominican Republic's first order in 1930, shortly after taking power, and his rule lasted for more than thirty years. He created the Heraldic Order of Trujillo, the Order of the Generalissimo, and the Order of the Benefactor of the Nation, whose reverse legend celebrates "25 Years of the Glorious Era of Trujillo." The central theme of these awards was personal loyalty to Trujillo, and it is not surprising that every medal and order related to his person was rescinded shortly after his assassination.

Panama had practically no national medals or orders until recently. As the country sought to take over control of the Panama Canal in the wake of World War II, discussions were held of what it meant to be Panamanian and what attributes the nation wished to promote. Consequently, the government set out to create an array of orders (no medals) recognizing the accomplishments of distinguished Panamanians: intellectuals, journalists, writers, artists, diplomats, folklorists—each group with its own order and usually named after a respected Panamanian from the past.

In the end, these decorations are also aesthetic and symbolic objects. One of the Cuban orders carries the iconic image of Che Guevara, whereas those of Trujillo feature his profile and an emblematic representation of the ships from Columbus's voyages to the Americas.

These medals and orders allow us a unique perspective on the development of Latin American states and the qualities they have chosen to represent and reward. As such, they are an invaluable historical catalogue of patriotism and nationalism in the Americas.

—MIGUEL ANGEL CENTENO
Chair, Department of Sociology, Princeton University
Professor of International Affairs, Woodrow Wilson School

HISTORICAL INTRODUCTION

TWO HUNDRED years ago, newly independent Latin American republics began creating orders and medals to sustain their fight for sovereignty and individual political ambitions. Republican military victories at Chacabuco in Chile, Ayacucho in Peru, Pichincha in Ecuador, Boyacá in Colombia, and Carabobo in Venezuela inspired the victorious generals to reward their officers and troops with medals for their accomplishments. These medals reflected the common gratitude of a thankful nation (*la patria agradecida*) for advancing the cause of independence. The medals also helped to record individual bravery and sacrifice on the battlefield.

The royalists fought in allegiance to the Spanish Crown and looked to their king to recognize their bravery. The republicans fought for their political independence, and their people joined together in a nation-state. The title of this book, *From a Thankful Nation*, conveys succinctly who the republicans were fighting for and who awarded the medals.

When creating military medals, beginning with the wars of independence, Latin Americans were inspired by contemporary European practices. The wearable military medal as a reward for loyalty and bravery on the battlefield and an ethos of entitlement for the victors proliferated during the Napoleonic Wars. Modern warfare bypassed the chivalrous knight who was rewarded with titles and heraldic shields. The new battlefield hero became the common soldier with his rifle, who could kill even an armored knight at long distance. England designed its ubiquitous round, silver medals with the name of the recipient engraved on the rim. Prussia produced its Iron Cross patterned after the cross of the Teutonic Knights that Napoleon had abolished. The French invented their elegant Legion of Honor with its five grades, which became the standard of the modern order. Many medals were given for specific battles or wars, a precedent that Latin America followed for the rest of the century. England placed bars for specific battles on its ribbons, a practice that Chile adopted during its two wars with Peru.

The new Latin America nations produced a profusion of bejeweled gold medals for its highest-ranking generals, plain gold medals for senior officers, silver ones for other officers, and bronze for enlisted men. Each class was awarded by rank rather than the degree of bravery on the battlefield. Latin America did not readily take to the more formal order with its long silk sash and resplendent breast star. Republicans looked askance at awarding orders as being too closely associated with European nobility and privilege.

Latin America's first orders were instituted by officers who had once fought for the Spanish Crown. Argentina's General San Martín, who created the Peruvian Order of the Sun, had served in Ferdinand VII's army in Spain and Italy. Mexico's Agustín de Iturbide had led the Spanish viceroy's army against republican insurgents until he conspired with Vicente Guerrero to turn on the viceroy. San Martín and Iturbide were both royalists. Iturbide even proclaimed himself emperor.

Once independence had been assured, designers were asked to create medals as liberals killed conservatives, federalists cut down unitarians, and caudillos eliminated their rivals. When the new leaders had no need to fight each other, they could always send an expedition to subjugate restive Indians. As usual, it was the victors who designed and awarded most of the medals for these conflicts.

By the middle of the nineteenth century, major foreign wars allowed the producers of medals to operate overtime. Mexico fought the Texas Rebellion, the Mexican-American War, and the French Intervention. Chile fought the War of the Confederation and the War of the Pacific against Bolivia and Peru. Paraguay lost the Triple Alliance War against its more powerful neighbors but later redeemed itself by defeating Bolivia in the Chaco War. All of these wars caused significant border adjustments. However, as nations became accustomed to the new borders, wars between neighbors became a phenomenon of the past. Liberals gained power and promoted trade and investment; higher tax revenues allowed governments to maintain professional armies, which "pacified" rebellious provinces.

The twentieth century brought with it a new wave of medals associated with social revolutions such as the 1910 Mexican Revolution, the 1959 Cuban Revolution, and the Sandinista Revolution in 1979. These revolutionary medals extolled ideological zeal rather than bravery in a specific battle.

As the need for recognition for bravery and loyalty on the battlefield receded, other needs surfaced. Red Cross societies began to be created at the end of the nineteenth century, and today all of the Latin American nations have active societies affiliated with the International Committee of the Red Cross. These societies provide a range of services for natural disasters, ambulance services, health and nutrition clinics, and vaccination programs manned by volunteers. Most of these societies award medals and even orders, some of them quite elegant in their design and meaningful in their purpose.

World War II created the need for civil defense brigades, which evolved during peacetime into first responders for natural disasters such as earthquakes and hurricanes. These civil defense organizations often give medals for merit. After World War II, many Latin

American countries went through periods of violent insurrections and terrorism. National police forces are increasingly assuming responsibility for internal order at personal risk to their members. Most countries now award police medals for bravery, merit, and distinguished service, similar to the military.

The military forces themselves have adapted their system of awards in peacetime to recognize loyal and professional service. As the level of violence diminished, so did the need for these medals. Although Latin America has more medals now than at any time in its history, they mainly recognize good conduct, length of service, and professional competency, rather than bravery on nonexistent battlefields. Because of their large numbers, we have limited this exhibit and catalogue to medals that fit the title: *From a Thankful Nation.* This definition reflects the purpose of the medals originally awarded during Latin America's wars of independence.

The history of Latin America's orders has differed from that of its medals. The region's leaders had an early need to reward military achievement, a need that lasted well into the twentieth century. Orders, in the minds of Latin America's early republican leaders, evoked images of monarchical privilege and religious military nobility, values that they were determined to overthrow. Most early orders in Latin America were instituted by emperors such as those of Pedro I and Pedro II in Brazil, Faustin I in Haiti, and Iturbide and Maximilian in Mexico. These orders respected their traditional purpose to reward loyalty to the monarch and recognize the regal status of a noble class. There were a few notable republican exceptions, like Bernardo O'Higgins's Legion of Merit and General San Martín's Order of the Sun. These original orders were awarded, like medals, for military merit during the wars of liberation. However, republican rejection of noble privilege prevented their proliferation during the nineteenth century.

Republican leaders changed their attitudes toward orders when they realized their usefulness as a tool to promote positive behavior and good international relations. This process began after World War I and accelerated after World War II, as officials sought ways to promote diplomacy, culture, the arts, science, and "good citizenship" in general. Orders were increasingly viewed as tools to change human behavior rather than to decorate the uniforms of the already high and mighty.

The model for this new generation of orders was the French Legion of Honor with its carefully structured hierarchy of grades. This enabled governments to reward individuals for meritorious behavior while at the same time to dignify each individual with the appropriate grade. The highest grade has always been the Collar. The Collar of a kingdom's highest order came to symbolize the head of a royal house, such as the Order of the Golden Fleece in the House of Hapsburg or the Order of the Holy Ghost for pre-revolutionary Bourbons. In a republican world, the Collar of a nation's most important order became a symbol of sovereignty, such as Venezuela's Order of the Liberator. Governments discovered new uses for the Collar by awarding them to heads of state or heads of government as an inexpensive way of promoting friendly international relations.

Governments also found it useful to award the Grand Cross of an order to a foreign ambassador or minister of state. This practice induced every Latin American nation to institute prestigious orders for foreign dignitaries, which are awarded on the basis of reciprocity. Ministries of foreign affairs, which award these orders, appoint a protocol officer whose sole function is to make certain that any exchange of orders based on reciprocity extends equal prestige to both nations. Bureaucracies regulate in great detail the rank of those eligible to receive each grade of an order. The regulations often specify the nature of the meritorious service being recognized. Sometimes the regulations are kept deliberately vague by describing the merit as being of "interest" or "importance" to the nation.

No Latin American military order recognizes wartime valor; in fact they are rarely even awarded to a nation's own military. Rather, they are bestowed on foreign military for meritorious service to the nation giving the award. Such orders are used to promote closer collaboration among the military of friendly nations.

All Latin American countries have instituted at least one order to promote the national interest, but in some cases recipients are limited to foreigners. Communist Cuba and the Nicaraguan Sandinistas boast the greatest number of orders, all of which are designed to glorify their revolution and to perpetuate their revolutionary ideology. Brazil has more than a dozen orders designed to promote good government and economic development. Panama has recently instituted its own array of orders to develop its national identity. Chile encourages the arts. Colombia promotes democracy. The political priorities of Latin American nations are unique to each country. Their orders tell the world what those priorities are. Individuals receiving these orders can legitimately feel that they have been recognized by a thankful nation.

—ROBERT L. ROSS
Princeton, New Jersey

THE MEDALLIC LEGACY OF
THE FILIBUSTERS

T HE second half of the nineteenth century attracted to Latin America a steady stream of foreign adventurers in search of power and fortune. The personal rivalries of caudillos, incompatible ideologies, conflicting economic interests, ethnic tensions, and poor communications complicated the consolidation of republican rule. Nature abhors a vacuum, but military adventurers thrive on it. The Latin American version of such an adventurer is called a *filibuster*. These foreign carpetbaggers came mainly from France, but also from the United States, Spain, Switzerland, and other Latin American countries. They were persuasive, resourceful, opportunistic, and persistent, but eventually they all failed. Had they succeeded, history would have remembered them as the founding fathers of a new nation rather than as filibusters. Most of them left behind a record of medals awarded (or sold) either by themselves or the governments that defeated them.

In 1852, a Frenchman, Gaston de Raousset-Boulbon from Avignon, landed in Guaymas, Mexico, with his armed followers to create an independent colony out of the state of Sonora in the northern part of the country. Under the guise of his Compañia Restauradora de la Mina de la Arizona, he took Sonora's capital city of Hermosillo but was soon defeated. The Mexicans executed him on August 13, 1854, in Guaymas.

In November 1860, another Frenchman, Orélie-Antoine de Tounens from Chourgnac, proclaimed himself king of the "Royaume d'Araucanie et de Patagonie" (kingdom of Araucanía and Patagonia), with its capital in Perquenco, Chile. His "kingdom" extended in Chile to the south of the Bío-bío River and also included all of Argentine Patagonia. The Chileans repeatedly expelled him, and he died of natural causes in Tourtoirac, France, on September 17, 1878. Tounens is known to have instituted at least one order, the Royal and Noble Order of the Steel Crown, in 1869. The name was changed to the Royal Order of the Star of the South in 1872. It came in six grades: Collar, Grand Cross, Grand Officer, Commander, Officer, and Knight. He awarded the order to people who supported him financially.

I will take a closer look at three filibusters. Like most such adventurers, they chose remote locations with weak governments in which to build their fiefdoms. Unlike Raousset-Boulbon and Tounens, these three actually succeeded in establishing executive power.

WILLIAM WALKER

William Walker (1824–60) was a well-educated young American mesmerized by his country's dream of Manifest Destiny. In 1853, following the Mexican-American War, he sought to gain control of the Mexican state of Sonora (while Raousset-Boulbon was still there) in the hope of eventually having it annexed by the United States, much as had happened with Texas eight years earlier. In October of that year he sailed down the

Republic of Lower California

coast of Baja California in Mexico with his armed followers and occupied La Paz, in the southern part of the peninsula. He proclaimed the Republic of Lower California, with himself as president. He put his new republic under the laws of Louisiana, the only American state using the Roman Code and also one where slavery was legal. The Mexican government sent troops to expel Walker, who was forced to return to the United States in May 1854. He never returned to Mexico, and no medals were produced in connection with this adventure.

In 1854, civil war broke out again in Nicaragua between conservatives based in Granada and liberals in León. The liberals, finding themselves on the defensive, reached out to William Walker for help. Walker arrived in Nicaragua in 1855 with his armed followers and joined the fight against the conservatives. By October, he occupied Granada and took effective control of Nicaragua under acting president Patricio Rivas. In March 1856, Walker's men invaded Costa Rica after it declared war on him, but he was defeated at the Battle of Santa Rosa and later at the Second Battle of Rivas. The Costa Ricans went home, and Walker set out to consolidate his political hold on Nicaragua. By July 1856, he was elected president of Nicaragua. He declared English to be the legal language and revoked an 1824 decree emancipating the slaves in Nicaragua. He invited pro-slavery southerners to immigrate to Nicaragua.

Walker's election and political initiatives alarmed the leaders of El Salvador, Guatemala, and Honduras, and they organized an army to unseat him. By December a large Central American army had surrounded Granada. In May 1857, Walker's men had abandoned Granada, and Walker himself surrendered to the United States Navy.

Walker was not a man to be deterred by defeat. He reappeared near Greytown six months after he escaped from Nicaragua but was soon apprehended by U.S. Marines, who again repatriated him back to the United States. In 1860, residents of the island of Roatán who were seeking independence invited Walker to help them. He accepted and arrived with his armed followers on the Honduran coast. While there Walker fell into the custody of the British Royal Navy, which turned him over to the Honduran authorities. Walker was executed by firing squad on September 12, 1860, and is buried in Trujillo, Honduras.

Walker's legacy is better known in Central America than in the United States, where some consider him an eccentric proponent of Manifest Destiny. The Central Americans are united in rejecting Walker's interference in their domestic affairs and his goal of annexing part of the region to the United States. On a more positive note, the fact that Central American troops defeated Walker's men has become a source of national pride. Costa Rica awarded a silver medal (Cr1) to its veterans. In my opinion, a gold medal (Cr2) was awarded by Costa Rica to its officers for defeating Walker at Santa Rosa and Rivas. Guatemala awarded a silver cross (Gt2) to its officers who expelled Walker from Granada. Honduras sent troops along with those of Guatemala and authorized a military medal for the same campaign (Hn1).

THE REPUBLIC OF COUNANI

The territory once called Counani covers an area of some 250,000 square kilometers (about 100,000 square miles) between the mouth of the Amazon River and French Guiana. The 1713 Treaty of Utrecht, which ended the War of the Spanish Succession, named the "Japoc" as the border between the Portuguese kingdom's colony of Brazil and the French monarchy's colony of Guiana. The French claimed that the word *japoc* was a generic term in the native language for "river" and that the border followed the Araguaia River, which flows into the northern reaches of the Amazon estuary. The Portuguese claimed that *japoc* referred to the Oyapock River, which is today's recognized border between Brazil and the French territory of Guiana.

Between the two rivers, the coastal village of Counani was founded by Jesuits in 1788, perhaps as a safe haven for escaped slaves from Brazil. Its inhabitants hoped to be administered by France rather than Portugal, because slavery was still legal in Brazil. Two filibusters, Jean Guigues from France and Paul Quartier from Switzerland, conspired to create a republic that would come under French protection and be administered from French Guiana. They persuaded a French journalist, Jules Gros, to become the republic's president for life, and he took the title of Gros I. He proclaimed the country's independence on July 23, 1886. Gros created the *Ordre de l'Étoile de Counani* (Order of the Star of Counani) for his supporters on April 29, 1887. Examples of such an order are not known to have existed, but the projected appearance of it can be inferred from a five-franc

République de la Guyane Indépendante

pattern coin struck in 1887 in the name of the République de la Guyane Indépendante (Republic of Independent Guiana), which displays a ball-tipped Maltese cross on the reverse. The order is believed to have had five grades: Grand Cross, Grand Officer, Commander, Officer, and Knight. It is possible that Gros took his inspiration for the order from the French king Jean le Bon, who created France's first monarchical Order of the Star in 1351. The obverse of that order featured a white star on a red enameled field, which coincides with Gros's design of his order, as well as that of his second flag for Counani with its white star in the middle of a red flag. Gros is believed to have founded two more orders: *l'Ordre du Mérite* (Order of Merit) and *l'Ordre de Notre Dame de Bon Secours* (Order of Our Lady of Good Help). Both orders are believed to have come in three grades: Commander, Officer, and Knight. Gros may have sold them and used the proceeds to defray his expenses. The literature does not describe them, and they, like the Order of the Star of Counani, have been left out of this catalogue.

Gros's publicity attracted the attention of the French Foreign Affairs Ministry, which refused to recognize any Republic of Counani. At the time, France sought to protect the

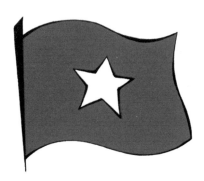

République Indépendante du Counani

integrity of official orders, and the ministry reportedly warned French citizens they could be penalized for wearing Gros's orders. In the face of this official rejection, Gros opted for full independence and created the République Indépendante du Counani (Independent Republic of Counani). Gros never actually set foot in Counani. He tried to go there in 1888 with his family but was intercepted by the English in Georgetown and forcibly sent to London. Gros returned to Paris, where he continued to administer his government, but no one paid any attention to him. At some point, he created two medals for his loyal supporters: *la Médaille des Bons Services* (Medal for Good Services) (Br55) and *la Médaille aux Organisateurs de la Patrie* (Medal to the Organizers of the Fatherland) (Br56). He died in 1891 of natural causes.

In 1901 (the exact date differs in the literature) a French adventurer, Adolphe Brezet, proclaimed himself president of the État Libre du Counani (the Free State of Counani), with its own constitution and a flag (also a white star on a red field). He lived in Counani and took the Indian name of Uayana Assu. He had no messianic dreams for his republic,

Etat Libre du Counani

and he is regarded as an unethical swindler. For several years he sought unsuccessfully to raise money in France and England. He appeared in public in an officer's uniform with the sash of a Grand Cross and a chest full of orders. He opened consulates in a number of European capitals, all for the purpose of raising money. The only country to recognize the Free State of Counani was the Orange Free State, where Brezet had once served as a mercenary. Brezet was more swindler than filibuster. When he failed to raise money for his venture, he seems to have vanished from the public eye. He continued the Order of Our Lady of Good Help. He created new orders for sale, such as the *Ordre du Saint Esprit* (Order of the Holy Spirit), *la Croix de Palestine* (Palestine Cross), *la Croix de la Couronne de Fer Militaire* (Military Cross of the Iron Crown), *l'Ordre de Mérite Commercial* (Cross of Commercial Merit), and the *Ordre de Mérite Agricole de S. Fiacre* (Agricultural Order of Merit of Saint Fiacre). It is not known when and under what circumstances he died.

Sovereignty over Counani was granted to Brazil by a Swiss arbitrator in 1900, and the territory has been incorporated into the Brazilian state of Amapá.

THE INDEPENDENT STATE OF ACRE

The Brazilian state of Acre once belonged to Bolivia. Part of it was ceded to Brazil by President Manuel Mariano Melgarejo in 1867. A much larger piece of territory was annexed as a result of the Treaty of Petrópolis between Brazil and Bolivia in 1903. As the nineteenth century was coming to a close, industrialized nations were buying ever larger quantities of natural rubber from huge forests of rubber trees in the region of Acre. The trees grew on both sides of the border, but the laborers were Brazilian, as were most of the plantation owners. The new economic activity and the arrival of many Brazilians attracted the attention of the Bolivian authorities, who opened a customs house in Puerto Alonso to collect a tax on rubber exports. The Brazilian rubber growers and their *seringueiros* (who tapped the trees for latex sap) opposed the tax. A visiting Spanish journalist, Luis Gálvez Rodríguez de Arias, led a secessionist movement with the *seringueiros* and occupied Puerto Alonso in July 1899. He proclaimed the Estado Independiente de Acre (Independent State of Acre), named himself president in December, created ministries, designed a new flag, and even printed stamps. Although it is likely that Gálvez received support from the governor of the neighboring state of Amazonas, the central

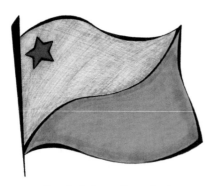

Estado Independiente de Acre

government in Rio de Janeiro disapproved of Gálvez's nation-building. In March 1900, Brazilian marines removed him from office and returned him to Europe.

In November 1900, a Brazilian filibuster, Rodrigo de Carvalho, proclaimed a second independent state of Acre, this one clearly Brazilian in sponsorship. Bolivia sent troops to the region, occupied Puerto Alonso, and deposed Carvalho in December. Gálvez's filibustering might have passed into history with no further consequences had Bolivia not signed an agreement with an American investor group called the Bolivian Syndicate to exploit the rubber resources in Acre. This agreement infuriated Brazil, which protested and sent troops to the region.

Bolivia's agreement with the Bolivian Syndicate caused the *seringueiros*, whose jobs were threatened, to create a revolutionary junta in protest. A Brazilian with some military training, José Plácido de Castro, assumed the leadership of an armed insurrection. The goal of the *seringueiros* was to create an independent republic of Acre and have it annexed by Brazil. Plácido launched the Acre Revolution in January 1903. By February he had defeated and expelled the Bolivian authorities from Puerto Alonso. Bolivian President José Manuel Pando personally led a military expedition to expel Plácido and retake Puerto Alonso. Brazil objected to both the Bolivian Syndicate and the Bolivian military response. It sent troops in warships up river and then blocked the border crossings with Bolivia. Faced with this new military reality, Bolivia decided to negotiate instead of fighting. Bolivia and Brazil negotiated and signed the Treaty of Petrópolis on November 17, 1903. Under the terms of the treaty, Bolivia ceded 190,000 square kilometers (about 75,000 square miles) of its territory to Brazil in exchange for two million pounds sterling, the building of a railroad, and the transfer of 3,000 square kilometers (about 1,150 square miles) of Brazilian territory elsewhere to Bolivia. Bolivia awarded a total of seven medals to its military in relation to Acre, three of which are in the catalogue (Bo31, Bo32, Bo33).

—ALLEN MENKE
Centralia, Washington

INTRODUCTION TO THE
CATALOGUE

WHEN Robert Ross first approached me in 2008 about the possibility of donating his collection of medals and orders to the Princeton University Numismatic Collection, we addressed the question of the potential use of this material for future research, teaching, and exhibition. I expressed my belief, on the basis of two decades as curator of the medals collection of the American Numismatic Society, that such objects did indeed provide material evidence for historical inquiry. Moreover, the need for such a collection at an academic institution was all the more acute, given the recent decision of the ANS to sell its entire collection of foreign medals and decorations. This left the scholarly world with no comprehensive public collection of such material, the Musée de la Légion d'Honneur in Paris limiting itself to Orders of Knighthood. We were assured as to the potential use of the collection for teaching purposes from faculty members in several departments of Princeton's Program in Latin American Studies. That left the issue of public exhibition, which is being actualized in the exhibition that this catalogue accompanies, held in Firestone Library, February 22 through August 3, 2014.

In the course of several decades of dedicated collecting, Robert Ross had built a general collection of world medals and orders. As a result of our ongoing discussions of how to form a collection with the depth necessary for serious research and teaching, we decided to focus on the primary interest of his collecting as well as professional life: Latin America. For the past five years, therefore, Mr. Ross has sold off part of the rest of his collection and used the proceeds to constitute a series of annual donations to fill in this area. The culmination of this effort is the acquisition this year of a significant number of pieces from the collection of Allen Menke, the builder of a major collection of such material.

While the primary purposes of this catalogue are to accompany the exhibition and to document the Ross Collection, we have responded to the lack of any comprehensive publication in this field since Gillingham's handbooks of the 1930s by attempting at least a summary description of all known pieces that meet our criteria, be they documented in catalogues, regulations, or even sales notices in auction catalogues or on websites. The criteria for the inclusion of pieces, which have grown out of the consideration of many possible examples, focus on whether the object in question can be said to be the result of a Latin American nation's efforts to reward outstanding service with a wearable insignia of distinction.

The first criterion is therefore Latin America, which includes Brazil and Haiti as well as the Spanish-speaking countries of North, Central, and South America. We are concerned basically with the pieces produced since independence from European powers, and have excluded colonial pieces, though we include the empires of Brazil, Haiti, and Mexico, which were based in the New World. Our criterion of national reward has been stretched to include awards by specific localities and institutions for service on a national level, but not local awards, those of private or educational institutions, or of branches of the military or bureaucracy. The criterion of outstanding service has meant the exclusion of routine rewards for periods of service (often expressed in Spanish as *perseverencia*) but inclusion of those for recognized loyalty (*constancia*). We include, with rare exception, only wearable awards and have generally limited ourselves to metallic insignia worn suspended from a ribbon, as opposed to metal pieces sewn onto a uniform (*escudos*) or to commemorative medals not intended for wear.

Within the listings of each country, we have distinguished between medals and orders, though there have been some cases where this distinction was more than a little arbitrary. We take medals to be those pieces whose award can be tied to participation in a specific historical event, often a battle, but sometimes the response to a natural disaster or other nonmilitary event. These are listed within each country in chronological order of the event to which they respond. Many medals have prescribed classes of recipients, which frequently correspond to the military rank of the individual; often the class of the recipient determines the material from which the medal is made.

Orders, which derive historically from medieval and early modern associations of chivalry, are organizations established and regulated by the state but (at least in theory) with their own internal organization and governance. Within each country, the orders are listed by the chronology of their institution. Members of orders are often grouped into grades, with differences in size and appearance of the insignia of the members of the grades. When possible, the Ross Collection has been built with the intention of representing the Grand Cross grade (which often comprises a badge hanging from a broad sash and a star pinned to the chest) and the Knight grade (usually a smaller badge suspended from a ribbon pinned to the chest).

Each catalogue entry that represents a piece in the Ross Collection is accompanied by a photograph of the piece, showing both faces for those pieces in which the back carries significant information; the particular classes or grades illustrated are indicated by an asterisk (*) in the listing. Each piece has been given a sequential number for its country and a name in the language of that country, which, when possible, corresponds to that by which the piece is generally known. Only those categories of information for which we have found trustworthy evidence are included in each listing. The listing of decrees and dates of institution, modification, and rescinding of awards corresponds to government documents, which are increasingly available on the Internet. There then follows a listing of the attested classes for medals and grades for orders, with the maximum number of recipients authorized given in parentheses.

The physical description of the piece follows. For those orders (and occasional medals) that comprise a star (usually uniface with a pin back) as well as a badge (suspended from a ribbon), the basic description is of the badge, with the star following. First comes the image on each face; for complex constructions this is focused on what appears on the central round disc (referred to in some catalogues as the medallion) of each face. We use the term *legend* for the text that follows the round of the disc, separating breaks and changes of direction with a short vertical line (|). We use the term *inscription* for horizontal text, again using the vertical division mark to indicate the separation of lines. Wreaths are described as *laurel, olive, palm,* and *oak* when such a term appears in regulations or is otherwise clear, but in truth it does not appear that all designers were consistent in such distinctions; see the accompanying illustration of wreaths kindly drawn up for us by Alexandra Welm.

The description of the complex shapes that these pieces take has been a source of considerable discussion and experimentation on our part (if no shape is given, the medal can be presumed to be round). The basic terms we use are cross (4-armed unless otherwise stated), star (5 to 8 points; 5 if not stated), and sun (8 or more points). For 8-pointed medals, if the points are distinct and well separated, we call it a star; if the overall effect is round rather than starlike, we call it a sun. Rather than adopt the arcane (and incomplete) vocabulary of heraldry in trying to describe the many forms of the cross that appear on these pieces, we have limited ourselves to three basic cross shapes: the default (no characterization given) is a cross of parallel sides and with arms of equal length (i.e., a *Greek cross*; the term *Latin cross* is used if the lower arm is longer than the other three). If the arms of the cross are formed by straight lines emanating diagonally from a central point, we use the term *Maltese cross,* and if the sides of the arms curve concavely, we use the term *cross pattée.* If no description is given of the ends of the cross, they can be presumed to be flat; the other ends are illustrated on the accompanying figure, as are the most common forms of texturing. For orders (and the occasional medals with

laurel

olive

tobacco

coffee

oak

palm

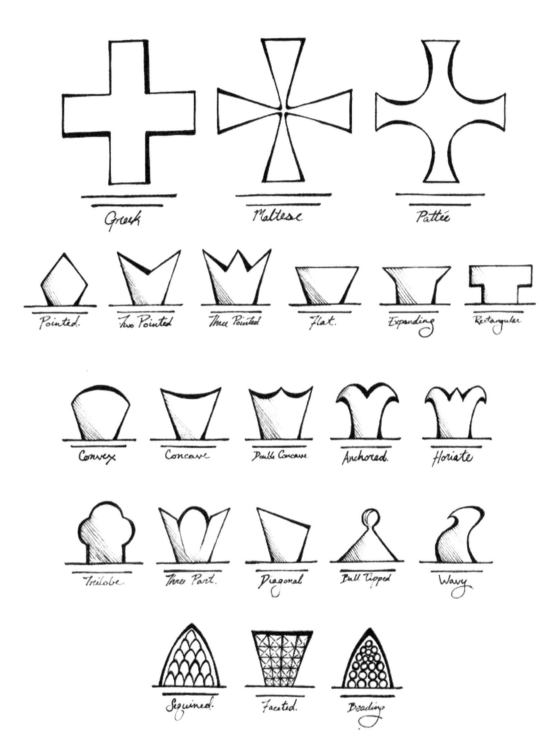

Greek   Maltese   Pattée

Pointed.   Two Pointed   Three Pointed   Flat.   Expanding   Rectangular

Convex   Concave   Double Concave   Anchored.   Horiate

Trilobe   Three Part.   Diagonal   Ball Tipped   Wavy

Sequined.   Faceted.   Beading

multiple pieces) the basic description given is for the badge; if the star has a different description, it follows.

Sizes do not include hinged hangers, but do include suspension devices that are soldered tight to the medal. Single sizes are the diameter for round pieces and the largest diagonal measurement for complicated but symmetrical pieces (i.e., the diameter of the circle in which they would fit). For all other pieces, the longest vertical measurement precedes the horizontal. Though the collection includes many miniature pieces (intended for wear in nonceremonial contexts), neither the size nor the picture of these is included in this catalogue, except when no larger piece is available.

The metal given is the apparent actual composition of known pieces; many medals prescribed in regulations to be gold were actually given as gilt silver or bronze (when the underlying metal is not discernible, pieces have been described simply as "gilt" or "silvered"). The name of the designer, engraver, or maker is often taken from the piece itself (or from the box in which the piece was purchased). In some cases, the recipient of an honor had the privilege of having the medal made by a private firm of choice; the makers identified in the catalogue are of those pieces illustrated here.

The colors of the ribbon are given from left to right; unless relative size is indicated, they can be presumed to appear in even vertical stripes. It is a well-known phenomenon of the field that pieces are re-ribboned for wear, exhibition, and sale; in cases where the ribbon on a piece in the collection does not correspond to that prescribed for it, we have removed the ribbon prior to photography.

The abbreviated references for each piece correspond to the listings in the bibliography at the end of the catalogue. The literature on these pieces varies enormously by country and period. For each piece, we have listed those that we believe to be accurate descriptions in what we believe to be the order of the authoritativeness of their information. Where no reference is given, the piece is known only from the example in the collection.

All pieces illustrated in this catalogue are in the Princeton University Numismatic Collection, Department of Rare Books and Special Collections, Firestone Library and (with the exception of Pa6) are donations of Robert L. Ross. Many have been acquired from the collection of Allen Menke, a preeminent collector in this area, who generously has shared his knowledge of the field and agreed to transfer to Mr. Ross key pieces from his collection for donation to Princeton; they are given a provenance listing of A. Menke. Some of the pieces are from the collection of the American Numismatic Society, until its dispersal in a series of sales in 2006 and 2007 the only public collection of world medals and orders, which itself derived from several major donations in the late nineteenth and early twentieth centuries; both Mr. Ross and Mr. Menke bought directly from the ANS auctions, and other pieces have come into this collection indirectly from it. With a few exceptions noted in the description, the pieces in the collection are not engraved to a recipient and were not acquired with an accompanying certificate or brevet indicating the individual to whom they were awarded.

We are very grateful for the outstanding work on this catalogue by its production editor, Gretchen Oberfranc; its copy editor, Beth Gianfagna; its photographers, John Blazejewski and Bruce White; and its designer, Mark Argetsinger. The collection, exhibition, and catalogue were aided to a great extent by the advice of Princeton faculty, the collector Allen Menke, and the veteran medals cataloguer David T. Alexander, but mostly they are the result of, and a lasting tribute to, the vision, patience, and generosity of Robert L. Ross.

—ALAN M. STAHL
Curator of Numismatics
Princeton University

From a Thankful Nation

ARGENTINA

THE CONGRESS of Tucumán declared Argentina's independence from Spain on July 9, 1816, following more than eight years of conflict. Independence did not bring peace. Argentina spent most of the nineteenth century at war: first to expel Spain from South America; then against Brazil and later Paraguay over control of Uruguay; throughout much of the century against itself, as regional forces, caudillos, and economic interests competed for political and economic power; and frequently against the indigenous tribes living on the frontier.

Buenos Aires inherited a mint from colonial times, which it used to strike medals for many of these conflicts. Its first medals recognized its military for fighting royalist forces coming down from Upper Peru (Bolivia) to defeat republicanism and independence. General José de San Martín awarded medals to his men for defeating royalist forces in Chile, allowing that country to declare its independence. He went on to occupy Lima, where he created Peru's first republican order and military medals for his forces and his allies.

Buenos Aires fought to extend its power internally, first against regional forces, as unitarians fought federalists. All political factions united to use military force to exterminate the Indians on the country's frontier and to expand Argentine settlements, particularly in the south. Argentina's medals document the violence that affected the nation throughout most of the nineteenth century.

During the twentieth century, Argentina engaged in one war with Great Britain over Las Malvinas (the Falkland Islands) in the South Atlantic, and it created new medals for the men who fought in that conflict. Argentina has also awarded medals for its military personnel who participated in the First Gulf War in the Middle East.

True to its republican origins, Argentina never created orders for its own nationals, regarding even republican orders as institutions that were associated with monarchy and nobility. The country's civilian and military orders are awarded only to foreign nationals, often in accordance with diplomatic protocol.

MEDALS

ARGENTINA's first medals were for the battles associated with independence, including its assistance in liberating Chile and Peru. The medals issued during the remainder of the nineteenth century were mainly for actions resulting from the struggle and the wars with Brazil and Paraguay over control of Uruguay, as well as expeditions against Indian tribes. Most of the medals of the twentieth century are related to the war against Great Britain in the Falkland Islands.

ARGENTINA'S WAR OF INDEPENDENCE (1810–1820)

SHORTLY after the May Revolution of 1810, the Argentine Army of the North marched into Charcas (in today's Bolivia) to intercept royalist forces advancing from Lima to suppress the rebellion in Buenos Aires.

Ar1. *La Medalla por la Batalla de Tupiza (Suipacha)*

This first battle of Argentina's War of Independence occurred on October 27, 1810, in Charcas. Spanish troops under the command of General José de Córdoba y Rojas fortified their position near the mining town of Tupiza. An Argentine force under the command of Colonel Antonio González Balcarce attacked the royalist lines. The Argentines, unable to dislodge the royalists, retreated and awaited reinforcements. On November 7, both sides resumed fighting near Suipacha. This time the Army of the North defeated the royalist expeditionary force. The Primera Junta in Buenos Aires authorized a medal for bravery, the first issued by the new government.

Instituted: By the Provincial Junta on November 29, 1810

Obverse: A small sun at the top

Obverse legend: ACCION DE GUERRA DEL 7 DE NOVIEMBRE DE 1810

Obverse inscription: LA | PATRIA | A LOS | VENCEDORs | DE | TUPIZA

Shape: Oval with 3 loops at the top

Size: 42 × 33 mm

Metal: Gilt

Ribbon: Light blue, white

Reference: Argentina 1910, 1:171–74; Gillingham 1932, 12–13

* * *

ANOTHER BATTLE took place a week later, on November 15, 1810, between the royalists and an untrained citizen militia fielded by the city of Cochabamba. Inspired by the success of the Argentine revolutionaries, the cities of Cochabamba and Oruro declared for the Primera Junta against the royalists. The Cochabambinos, reportedly armed mainly with macanas, carried the day. This was the only battle won by the Charcas citizenry against the royalist forces, who soon reestablished their control over Upper Peru.

*Ar2. *La Medalla por la Batalla de Aruhuma*

The United Provinces awarded a medal to Cochabambino officers and men who fought in the battle. The medal was struck at the Potosí mint in Charcas while the town was still in the hands of the rebels. There is no documentary proof of this sequence of events, as there is no mention of Aruhuma on the medal itself. However, this was the only battle won by the Cochabambinos.

Obverse: 8-pointed sun with branches below, within a wreath

Obverse legend: P· L· PATRIA A LOS FIELES L· D COCHABAMBA·

Shape: Oval

Size: 27 × 24 mm

Metal: Silver, bronze*

Ribbon: Blue with narrow white edge stripes

Reference: Argentina 1910, 1:189; Gillingham 1932, 13

Ar 2

Metal: Gilt copper

Reference: Argentina 1910, 1:202; Gillingham 1932, 13

Ar3. *La Medalla del Rio de las Piedras*

Royalist and republican forces fought frequent engagements on both sides of the border between the United Provinces and Charcas. Neither side made much progress. One battle pitted a royalist expeditionary force under General Juan Pio Tristan against General Manuel Belgrano as he retreated from Jujuy to Tucumán. The two sides fought near Tucumán on September 3, 1812. Belgrano won the battle, capturing arms and taking royalist prisoners. The Primera Junta authorized a medal for his troops in the battle.

Obverse: Sun above crossed branch and spear

Obverse legend: LA PATRIA RECONOCIDA A SUS NATUR[S]. BENEMERITOS HIJOS

Obverse inscription: LIBERTAD

Shape: Oval, holed at top

Size: 50 × 40 mm

Ar4. *La Medalla por la Batalla de Salta*

Both sides continued skirmishing. They met again on February 20, 1813, at Salta, where Belgrano had outflanked the royalist positions. Belgrano again defeated Tristan, forcing him to surrender unconditionally. Belgrano's victory allowed the Argentines to maintain their hold on the north at least temporarily. The Assembly of the United Provinces authorized a medal for the victors.

Instituted: By Law No. 100 of the National Assembly of the United Provinces on March 5, 1813

Obverse: Long tasseled pileus atop sabre surmounting joined hands, within olive and palm wreath

Obverse legend: LA PATRIA A LOS
   VENCEDORES EN SALTA EN 20. D.
   FEBRO. D. 1813
Shape: Oval
Size: 51 × 40 mm
Metal: Gold, silver
Reference: Argentina 1910, 1:301–14; Gill-
   ingham 1932, 14–15

* * *

MEANWHILE, the United Provinces laid siege
to Montevideo in 1811 but failed to overcome
the royalist defenses. The republican forces returned again late in 1812. They occupied Cer-
rito, a small hill near Montevideo. Royalist
forces under General Gaspar de Vigodet attacked in the morning of December 31, 1812,
but were eventually repulsed and retreated back
to Montevideo. The battle itself was inconclusive, but the royalist forces never again took
the offensive. The United Provinces forces continued to blockade Montevideo, without being
able to break through its defenses. The city was
able to hold out thanks to Spanish control of
the River Plate, which allowed the royalists to
resupply themselves by sea. In 1814, warships
of the United Provinces defeated the Spanish
navy, and the royalist forces were forced to surrender Montevideo to the United Provinces.

*Ar5. *La Medalla del Cerrito y Toma de Montevideo*

The United Provinces authorized a number of
medals in 1814, which it awarded to the participants in the siege and capture of Montevideo. A
number of variants were issued, including some
that were authorized and paid for by individual generals from the United Provinces. Some
referred only to the liberation of Montevideo.

Instituted: By Decree No. 158 on September
   9, 1814

Obverse: Palm and olive wreath
Obverse inscription: La Patria | alos
   vencedo | res del 31 de | Diciembre de | 1812
   y Liberta | dores de Mon | tevideo en | Junio
   de | 1814
Shape: Oval
Size: 41 × 31 mm
Metal: Gilt silver
Ribbon: Light blue, white

Ar5a. *La Medalla del Cerrito*

Instituted: September 9, 1814
Obverse: Sun above mountain
Obverse legend: LA PATRIA RECONOCIDA Á
   LOS LIBERTADORES DE MONTEVIDEO
Shape: Oval
Size: 32 × 30 mm
Metal: Gilt, silver
Ribbon: Light blue, white

Ar5b. *El Combate del Cerrito*

Obverse: Sun above mountain
Obverse legend: LA PATRIA RECONOCIDA
   A LOS LIBERTADORES DE MONTEVIDEO:
   DIC. 31 DE 1813
Shape: Oval with loop at top terminating in
   ribbons
Size: 39 × 31.5 mm
Metal: Gold, silver
Ribbon: Light blue, white

Ar5c. *La Toma de Montevideo*

Obverse: Palm and laurel branches
Obverse inscription: LA | PATRIA | ALOS |
   LIBERTADORES | DE | MONTEVIDEO |
   1814
Shape: Oval
Size: Gold: 39 × 31 mm; silver: 52 × 40.5 mm
Metal: Gold, silver
Ribbon: Light blue, white

*Ar5d. *La Toma de Montevideo*

Obverse inscription: LA | PATRIA | RECONOCIDA | A LOS | LIBERTAD.ˢ | D MONTEV.º | 1814.

Shape: Oval, olive branches beneath, suspended from a double bow

Size: 31 × 30 mm

Metal: Silver

Ribbon: Light blue, white

Ar5e. *La Toma de Montevideo*

Obverse inscription:
LA | PATRIA | ALOSLIBERT.ˢ | DE | MONTEVIº

Shape: Oval, olive branches beneath, bow above

Size: 38 × 28 mm

Metal: Gold, silver

Ribbon: Light blue, white

*Ar5f. *La Toma de Montevideo*

Obverse: Sun

Obverse legend: LA PATRIA RECONOCIDA A LOS LIBERTADORES DE MONTEVIDEO

Shape: Round, surrounded by oak wreath

Size: 26 mm

Metal: Gilt

Ribbon: White with light blue side stripes

Reference: Argentina 1910, 1:215–26; Gillingham 1932, 16–17

* * *

THE LOSS of Montevideo to the revolutionaries forced the royalist army marching south from Charcas to turn around. The Spaniards had hoped to link up their forces in Charcas with those in Montevideo. The United Provinces, for its part, was now able to turn its attention elsewhere.

Argentina's leading military figure at this time was General José de San Martín. Shortly after the United Provinces declared its independence,

Ar 5d

Ar 5f

he decided to attack the royalists in Chile as a prelude to expelling them from Lima. He moved to Mendoza near the Chilean border to organize his Army of the Andes. Chile had declared its independence in 1810, but royalist forces reoccupied the country and effectively controlled Chile by 1817. In January of that year, San Martín crossed the Andes with his army and his Chilean allies under the command of Bernardo O'Higgins. The combined armies met the royalists at Chacabuco in the Aconcagua Valley. The republican forces outnumbered the royalists and attacked first along two flanks on February 12. The royalists were quickly overwhelmed with no possibility of retreating. Royalist forces further south regrouped and marched north the following year. On March 5, 1818, San Martín again defeated the royalists at the Battle of Maipú just outside Santiago. This ended Spanish rule in Chile except for a few isolated garrisons in the south.

*Ar6. *La Medalla de Chacabuco*

The government of the United Provinces authorized medals for the Argentine troops under San Martín. It is known in three variants.

Ar6a. *Variant 1*

Instituted: By Decree No. 265 on April 15, 1817

Classes: Chiefs, generals, other officers, enlisted men

Obverse: The shield of the United Provinces within a wreath

Obverse inscription: 12 DE FEB⁰ DE 1817

Reverse inscription: LA | PATRIA | A LOS | VENCEDORES | DE LOS | ANDES

Reverse legend: CHILE RESTAURADO POR EL VALOR EN CHACABUCO

Shape: Pentagonal, rising sun above, suspended from an oval wreath

Metal: Chiefs and generals: gold; other officers: silver; enlisted men: white metal

Maker: London

Ribbon: White, light blue, yellow

Ar6b. *Variant 2*

Instituted: April 15, 1817

Obverse: The shield of the United Provinces within a wreath

Reverse inscription: LA | PATRIA | A LOS | VENCEDORES | DE LOS | ANDES

Reverse legend: CHILE RESTAURᵒ Pᴿ. EL VALOR EN CHABᶜᵒ.

Shape: Pentagonal, rising sun above

Metal: Silver

Maker: London

Ribbon: White, light blue, yellow

*Ar6c. *Variant 3*

Instituted: April 15, 1817

Obverse: The shield of the United Provinces in an oval disc surrounded by a laurel wreath

Reverse inscription: LA | PATRIA | ALOSVENCEDˢ | DE LOS | ANDES within a laurel wreath

Reverse legend: CHILE RESTAURADO POR EL VALOR EN CHACABUCO

Shape: Oval

Size: 40 × 35mm

Metal: Gold, silver*

Maker: Casa de Moneda, Santiago

Ribbon: White, light blue, yellow

Provenance: A. Menke

Reference: Argentina 1910, 1:255–709; Gillingham 1932, 17

Ar7. *La Medalla de Salta*

While the main republican armies were occupied on the other side of the Andes, royalist forces continued to occupy parts of the north-

Ar 6c

Ar 6c

ern United Provinces. Royalist forces attacked the city of Salta in the second battle for that city but were repulsed by its republican defenders. The United Provinces authorized a medal to those taking part in the battle.

Instituted: By Decree No. 284 of the United Provinces on November 28, 1817

Classes: Chiefs, other officers

Obverse inscription: AÑO DE 1817

Obverse legend: AL MERITO EN SALTA

Shape: 6-pointed star

Metal: Chiefs: gold; other officers: gold with a silver center

Ribbon: Light blue, white

Reference: Argentina 1910, 1:277–81; Gillingham 1932, 17–18

Ar8. *La Medalla de Humahuaca*

In early 1817, royalist forces commanded by Viceroy de la Serna advanced into northwestern Argentina. He left his rear guard in the town of Humahuaca and marched on to attack Salta. Republican troops under Colonel Manuel Arias defeated the rear guard and occupied Humahuaca. De la Serna was repelled at Salta and was forced to retreat back to Upper Peru, because he no longer had reinforcements in Humahuaca. Although the battle at Humahuaca was not a major one, it thwarted de la Serna's goal of retaking Buenos Aires. The United Provinces authorized a medal for the battle.

Instituted: By Decree No. 265 of the United Provinces on April 25, 1817

Classes: Generals, other officers

Obverse inscription: EL 2 | DE MARZO | DE 7 | EN | HUMAHUACA in an oval disc

Shape: 5-pointed star with notches at each point suspended from an oval laurel wreath. Each arm of the star represents one of the republican heroes of the battle. Starting from the top, they are: Manuel Eduardo

Arias, José G. Ontiveros, Juan P. Mariscal, Manuel del Portal, and Hilario Rodríguez.

Metal: Generals: gold; other officers: silver

Ribbon: Light blue, white

Reference: Argentina 1910, 1:273–76; Gillingham 1932, 18–19

* * *

EVEN as the United Provinces fought royalist forces in the northern part of their country and in Chile, their forces faced unexpected challenges behind their lines.

Ar9. La Medalla de San Luis

Following the Battle of Maipu, the royalist prisoners were taken to the town of San Luis in Argentina. On February 8, 1819, the prisoners tried to escape. However, local militia recaptured them with help from local residents.

The United Provinces authorized a medal for the local militia and the town council who prevented the escape.

Instituted: By Decree No. 332 of the United Provinces on August 6, 1819

Classes: Chiefs, other officers, enlisted men

Obverse: Rising sun

Obverse inscription: Alos que defendieron | el orden | en San Luis

Reverse: Large hand with sword fighting 3 hands with knives

Reverse inscription: El 8 de Febrero | de 1819

Shape: Oval, with narrow surrounding wreath

Size: 38 × 35 mm

Metal: Chiefs: gold; other officers: silver; enlisted men: bronze* or white metal

Ribbon: Light blue

Reference: Argentina 1910, 1:295–98; Gillingham 1932, 18–20

*Ar10. *La Medalla del Orden*

By 1819, the civil war between the unitarians and the federalists was beginning, as caudillo-led armies fought each other with regularity. In September of that year, forces from Santa Fe invaded Buenos Aires. Soldiers from the United Provinces repelled the attack, for which the United Provinces awarded a medal. The battles themselves were indecisive, as both sides continued fighting for many decades.

Instituted: October 9, 1819
Obverse: Wreath
Obverse inscription: LA | PATRIA | POR | MI AMOR | AL | ORDEN
Shape: Oval
Size: 53 × 42 mm
Metal: Silver, bronze*
Maker: Casa de Moneda, Santiago
Ribbon: Light blue
Reference: Argentina 1910, 1:299–301; Gillingham 1932, 20

Ar11. *La Medalla a las Partidas de Guerrilla*

General San Martín arrived in Peru in early 1821. The Spanish garrison in Lima withdrew into the mountains and Peruvian revolutionaries occupied the city in July. They named San Martín Protector of Peru. However, the Spanish forces in the mountains outnumbered San Martín's army, and he was reluctant to challenge them directly. Instead, he relied on irregular Peruvian forces to keep them away from Lima. In appreciation of their efforts, San Martín authorized a medal for his guerrilla allies.

Instituted: By Decree of General San Martín on October 1, 1822, in Lima
Classes: Officers, enlisted men
Obverse inscription: EL | VALOR | ES MI | DIVISA

Ar 10

Reverse: Sun with rays
Reverse inscription: A LAS PARTIDAS DE GUERRILLA
Shape: Oval, edged in a wreath at the top
Size: 40 × 37 mm
Metal: Officers: gold; enlisted men: silver
Ribbon: White, red
Reference: Argentina 1910, 3:53–55

* * *

AFTER EXILE as a result of the Spanish reconquest of Chile, General José Miguel Carrera Verdugo (1785–1821), one of the country's founders, tried to join San Martín in Mendoza, but did not get along with either San Martín or O'Higgins. He allied himself with the federalists against Buenos Aires. He tried to return to

Chile at the head of a small army, but the Argentine Province of Cuyo defeated Carrera at the Battle of Punta del Medano.

Ar12. *La Medalla de Punta del Medano*

Carrera was executed by the Province of Cuyo on September 4, 1821. The provincial governor authorized a medal for the officers and men who defeated Carrera at Punta del Medano. The governor had the medal struck in Santiago at the mint. Although Carrera's final hours properly belong to Chile's history, the medal for his defeat was authorized by the Province of Cuyo, whose arms appear on the medal's obverse. In addition to the version struck in the Santiago mint, variants of this medal appear to have been made by hand.

Ar12a. *Variant 1*

Instituted: February 28, 1822

Obverse: Cap of Liberty over mountains (Arms of Mendoza) within a wreath

Reverse inscription: ANIQUILE | LA | ANARQUIA | AG^{TO} 31 DE | 1821 within a wreath

Shape: Round

Size: 26 mm

Metal: Gold, silver

Maker: Casa de Moneda, Santiago

Ar12b. *Variant 2*

Obverse: Shield, sun above

Obverse inscription: PUNTA | DEL | MEDANO | MENDOZA | AGOSTO 1821

Obverse legend: ANIQUILE LA ANARQUIA

Shape: Shield within scroll, sun above

Size: 38 mm

Metal: Silver

Reference: Medina 1901, 120–29; Argentina 1910, 3:151–54; Gillingham 1932, 104–5; Barac 2009, 236; Brinkmann 2012, 1, 22–23

* * *

BRAZIL invaded Uruguay in 1825 and annexed it as the Cisplatine Province. Brazil also declared war on Argentina and sent its fleet south to blockade Montevideo and Buenos Aires. On land, neither side could win a decisive battle. England and France mediated the conflict, and both sides signed the Treaty of Montevideo on August 27, 1828, recognizing the independence and name of the Oriental Republic of Uruguay. Argentina awarded an *escudo* for the conflict, but no medals.

BUENOS AIRES AGAINST THE PROVINCES (1820–1861)

THIS PERIOD was marked by the ongoing civil war between the unitarians and the federalists. The unitarians favored a centralized government and were strongest in Buenos Aires itself. The federalists favored a looser federation and were strongest among the provinces. However, neither side was united. Alliances were made and broken with regularity. The battles during this period produced many campaign medals. All of the medals during this period were either struck at the Buenos Aires mint or the Banco de la Provincia.

*Ar13. *La Medalla por la Virtud Marcial*

Little is known about this medal, as it does not appear in the literature. It is probable that the medal was struck when the federalists controlled the Buenos Aires mint.

Ar13

Obverse: Arms of Argentina

Obverse legend: ¡MUERAN LOS UNITARIOS! | LA PROVINCIA DE B.ˢ AY.ˢ AL PATRIOTISMO, Y AL VALOR.

Reverse: Arms of the Province of Buenos Aires

Reverse legend: ¡VIVA LA FEDERACION! | EL GOBIERNO DE B.ˢ AY.ˢ RECONOCIDO À LA= | =VIRTUD MARCIAL.

Shape: Oval

Size: 36 × 30 mm

Metal: Silver

Provenance: A. Menke

*Ar14. *La Medalla del Salado*

As settlers moved south in search of land for their herds, they met resistance from Ranquel and other Indian tribes living there. The Indians often rustled cattle, which was duly denounced to the authorities in Buenos Aires. A punitive expedition by the Department of the North under the command of Colonel Angel Pacheco defeated an Indian force at El Salado on April 10, 1830. The colonel, his chiefs, and officers were awarded a medal by the Province of Buenos Aires. Many more military expeditions to expel the Indians would follow for the next half a century.

Ar13

Instituted: By Decree of the Province of Buenos Aires on July 23, 1830

Classes: Chiefs, other officers*

Obverse: Wreath of laurel and palm

Obverse inscription: A LOS | VENCEDORES |

SOBRE | EL SALADO | EL 10 DE ABRIL | DE | 1830 surrounded by laurel and palm branches

Reverse legend: Gold only: CORONEL DON ANGEL PACHECO, COMANDANTE EN GEFE DEL DEPARTAMENTO DEL NORTE

Shape: Oval

Size: 45 × 32 mm

Metal: Chiefs: gold; other officers: silver

Designer: Pedro Miranda

Maker: Banco de la Provincia, Buenos Aires

Reference: Argentina 1910, 2:161–65; Gillingham 1932, 22

Provenance: A. Menke

* * *

ANOTHER military expedition against the Indian tribes along the southern border of the Province of Buenos Aires was launched in 1833.

Ar15. *La Medalla por la Expedición al Rio Colorado*

Dictator Juan Manuel Rosas himself commanded his first expedition south to the Colorado River against Indians accused of rustling cattle from ranchers. The expedition left in 1833 and lasted for more than one year. The Province of Buenos Aires authorized a medal for its officers.

Instituted: By Decree No. 674 of the Province of Buenos Aires on May 6, 1834

Obverse: Arms of Argentina surrounded by a wreath of laurel and palm

Obverse legend: LA PROVᴬ DE BUENˢ AYs AL PATRIOTISMO Y AL VALOR

Shape: Oval

Size: 39 × 32 mm

Metal: Gold, silver

Ribbon: Red

Ar 14

Ar15a. *A variant was designed for those who died in action.*

Obverse: Arms of Argentina surrounded by a wreath of laurel and palm

Obverse legend: LA PROVᴬ DE BUENˢ AYs AL PATRIOTISMO Y AL VALOR

Reverse: A LOS QUE MURIERON POR LA SEGURIDAD DE SU PATRIA

Shape: Oval

Size: 40 × 30 mm

Metal: Copper

Ribbon: Red

Reference: Argentina 1910, 2:169–76; Gillingham 1932, 22–23

*Ar16. *La Medalla por un Triunfo sobre una Division de Indios Chilenos Sublevados*

The Province of Buenos Aires sent its Southern Division on yet another punitive expedition against the Borogas Indians in 1836, de-

feating them on October 1 of that year. The province authorized a Medal for a Triumph over a Division of Rebellious Chilean Indians to the members of the expedition. All the officers and men of the division were paid an extra two months salary. Chiefs were allotted one *legua* of land, captains received three quarters of a *legua*, while junior officers received one half a *legua*, all taken from the defeated Indians.

> Instituted: By Decree No. 714 of the Province of Buenos Aires on October 5, 1839
>
> Classes: Chiefs, other officers, enlisted men
>
> Obverse: Arms of Argentina surrounded by a wreath of laurel and palm
>
> Obverse legend: EL GOV^NO RECONOCIDO A LA VIRTUD Y AL VALOR MARCIAL-
>
> Reverse: Trophy of arms
>
> Reverse legend: VICTORIA CONTRA UNA FUERTE DIVISION DE INDIOS CHILENOS SUBLEVADOS.

> Reverse inscription: BUENOS AY.^S OCT^RE | -1.º DE 1836-
>
> Shape: Oval
>
> Size: 38 × 31 mm
>
> Metal: Chiefs: gold; other officers*: silver; enlisted men: white metal
>
> Ribbon: Red
>
> Reference: Argentina 1910, 2:199–202; Gillingham 1932, 23
>
> Provenance: A. Menke

Ar 17. *La Medalla por una Acción contra Indios Chilenos Enemigos*

Argentina sent another expedition under Colonel Antonio Ramírez in 1837. With its overwhelming firepower, the expedition defeated the Indians on October 2, 1837. A medal was duly authorized for the officers and men of the expedition.

Instituted: By Decree No. 708 on October 5, 1837

Classes: Chiefs, other officers enlisted men

Obverse: Arms of Argentina surrounded by a wreath of laurel and palm

Obverse legend: EL GOV^{NO} RECONOCIDO A LA VIRTUD Y AL VALOR MARCIAL

Reverse: Military trophies, laurel wreath above

Reverse legend: VICTORIA CONTRA UNA FUERTE DIVISION DE INDIOS CHILENOS ENEMIGOS

Reverse inscription: B.^S AY.^S OCT.^{RE} 2 DE 1837

Shape: Oval

Size: 37 × 30 mm

Metal: Chiefs: gold; other officers: silver; enlisted men: brass

Maker: Banco de la Provincia, Buenos Aires

Ribbon: Red

Reference: Argentina 1910, 2:185–87; Gillingham 1932, 24

Ar18. *La Medalla por un Triunfo contra Indios Ranqueles y Chilenos*

The government sent out yet another expedition in 1838 to suppress the Chilean and Ranquel Indians to the north. Argentine forces under the command of Colonel Hilario Lagos defeated a large force of Indians on December 22, 1838, at Loreto in the southern part of Santa Fe Province. This was the last major expedition against the Indians until after the Triple Alliance War.

Obverse: Arms of Argentina surrounded by a wreath of laurel and palm

Obverse legend: EL GOV^{NO} RECONOCIDO A LA VIRTUD Y AL VALOR MARCIAL

Reverse: Military trophies

Reverse legend: VICTORIA CONTRA UNA FUERTE DIVISION DE INDIOS RANQUELES Y CHILENOS ENEMIGOS

Reverse inscription: BUENOS AY^S DICI^E 22 DE 1838

Size: 37 × 30 mm

Metal: Silver, brass

Designer: José Massias

Maker: Banco de la Provincia, Buenos Aires

Ribbon: Red

Reference: Argentina 1910, 2:189–90; Gillingham 1932, 24

* * *

AS THE number of expeditions against the Indians fell off, the infighting between the unitarians and federalists increased, as reflected in the number of medals awarded.

*Ar19. *La Medalla de Pago Largo*

On March 31, 1839, a unitarian army from the Province of Corrientes commanded by Governor Genaro Berón de Astrada was defeated by federalist forces from the Province of Entre Rios under the command of General Pascual Echagüe. The unitarians lost two thousand men, including eight hundred prisoners whose throats were reportedly slit, among whom was General Berón. General Manuel Rosas authorized separate medals for the officers and men from Entre Rios.

Ar19a. *Officers*

Instituted: By Decree No. 711 on April 26, 1839

Classes: Division generals, chiefs, officers

Obverse: 4 flags, laurel wreath between surrounded by olive wreath

Obverse inscription: VALIENTE DEFENSOR EN LOS CAMPOS DE PAGO-LARGO, DE LA LIBERTAD DE LA CONFEDERACION ARGENTINA Y DE LA INDEPENDENCIA AMERICANA

Ar 19b

Ar 19b

Reverse: Arms of Argentina surrounded by wreaths above

Reverse inscription: MARZO 31 DE 1839 | EL GOBIERNO DE LA | CONFEDERACION ARGENT^A | AL PATRIOTISMO Y | AL VALOR

Shape: Oval

Size: 36 × 29.5 mm

Metal: Division generals: gold; chiefs and officers: silver

Designer: José Massias

Maker: Banco de la Provincia, Buenos Aires

Ribbon: Red

*Ar19b. *Enlisted men*

Instituted: On April 26, 1839

Obverse: 6 flags, laurel wreath above, surrounded by olive wreath

Obverse inscription: COMBATIO | POR LA LIBERTAD | Y HONOR AMERICANO | EN EL VALIENTE EXERC^TO | VENCEDOR EN LOS | CAMPOS | DEL PAGO-LARGO

Reverse: Arms of Argentina surrounded by olive wreath

Reverse inscription: MARZO 31 DE 1839 | EL GOBIERNO DE LA | CONFEDERACION ARGENT.^A | AL PATRIOTISMO Y | AL VALOR

Shape: Oval

Size: 36 × 30 mm

Metal: Bronze

Designer: José Massias

Maker: Banco de la Provincia, Buenos Aires

Ribbon: Red

Provenance: A. Menke

Reference: Argentina 1910, 2:191–97; Gillingham 1932, 24–26

Ar20. *La Medalla de Cayastá*

A renegade unitarian officer from a returning army in Santa Fe Province led his men on a brief rampage in neighboring provinces. Rosas's forces defeated them on May 26, 1839, near Cayastá stream. On April 2, 1840, General Rosas authorized the Cayastá Medal for his officers and men. The medal's inscriptions reflect the general's blunt syntax when referring to his enemies.

Instituted: By Decree No. 717 of General Rosas on April 2, 1840

Obverse: Arms of Argentina on military trophies

Obverse legend: ¡MUERAN LOS UNITARIOS! LA PROVINCIA DE B.ˢ AY.ˢ AL PATRIOTISMO Y AL VALOR

Reverse: Military trophies within a laurel wreath

Reverse legend: ¡VIVA LA FEDERACION! EL GOBIERNO DE B.ˢ AY.ˢ RECONOCIDO A LA VIRTUD MARCIAL

Shape: Oval

Size: Gold and silver: 31 × 29.5 mm; brass: 36 × 39 mm

Metal: Gold, silver, brass

Ribbon: Red

Reference: Argentina 1910, 2:203–5; Gillingham 1932, 26–27

Ar21. *La Medalla del Sauce Grande*

The unitarian General Juan Lavalle was defeated by an army commanded by General Pascual Echagüe, governor of Entre Rios Province at Sauce Grande in Entre Rios on July 16, 1840. General Rosas authorized a medal and also granted his officers and men cattle and sheep belonging to unitarian officers. General Echagüe received three thousand head of cattle and three thousand sheep, the largest grant. Enlisted men received fifty head of cattle and fifty-five sheep, the lowest grant.

Ar21a. *Officers*

Instituted: By Decree No. 719 of General Rosas on December 17, 1840

Classes: Chiefs, officers

Obverse inscription: ¡VIVA LA CONFEDERACION ARGENTINA! | VALIENTE DEFENSOR EN LOS CAMPOS DE SAUCE GRANDE DE LA LIBERTAD DE LA CONFEDERACION ARGENTINA Y DE LA INDEPENDENCIA DEL CONTINENTE AMERICANO

Reverse: Arms of Argentina between military trophies

Reverse inscription: ¡MUERAN LOS SALVAGES UNITARIOS! | JULIO 16 DE 1840 | EL GOBERNADOR DE LA CONFEDERACION ARGENTINA AL PATRIOTISMO Y AL VALOR

Metal: Chiefs: gold; officers: silver

Ribbon: Deep scarlet

Ar21b. *Enlisted men*

Obverse inscription: ¡VIVA LA CONFEDERACION ARGENTINA! | COMBATIÓ POR LA LIBERTAD Y HONOR AMERICANO EN EL VALIENTE EJÉRCITO VENCEDOR EN LOS CAMPOS DE SAUCE GRANDE

Reverse: Arms of Argentina between military trophies

Reverse inscription: ¡MUERAN LOS SALVAGES UNITARIOS! | JULIO 16 DE 1840 | EL GOBERNADOR DE LA CONFEDERACION ARGENTINA AL PATRIOTISMO Y AL VALOR

Metal: Bronze

Ribbon: Deep scarlet

Reference: Argentina 1910, 2:209–12; Gillingham 1932, 27–28; Barac 2009, 38

Ar22. *La Medalla del Quebrachito*

General Lavalle regrouped and fought another federalist army led by Uruguayan General Manuel Oribe, a member of his country's Blanco Party and a political ally of Rosas. The two sides fought at Quebrado Herrado in Santa Fe Province on November 28, 1840. Oribe won the battle, forcing Lavalle to retreat. Rosas awarded a medal to the victorious federalist troops.

Ar22a. *Officers*

Instituted: By Decree No. 720 of General Rosas on December 17, 1840

Classes: Chiefs, officers

Obverse legend: ¡VIVA LA CONFEDERACION ARGENTINA! | VALIENTE DEFENSOR EN LOS DESIERTOS DEL QUEBRACHITO DE LA LIBERTAD DE LA CONFEDERACION ARGENTINA Y DE LA INDEPENDENCIA AMERICANA

Reverse: Arms of Argentina between military trophies

Reverse legend: ¡MUERAN LOS SALVAJES UNITARIOS! | NOVIEMBRE 28 DE 1840 | EL GOBIERNO DE LA CONFEDERACION ARGENTINA AL PATRIOTISMO Y AL VALOR

Metal: Chiefs: gold; officers: silver

Ribbon: Dark red

Ar22b. *Enlisted men*

Obverse legend: ¡VIVA LA CONFEDERCION ARGENTINA! COMBATIÓ POR LA LIBERTAD Y HONOR AMERICANO EN EL VALIENTE EJERCITO VENCEDOR EN LOS DESIERTOS DEL QUEBRACHITO

Reverse: Arms of Argentina between military trophies and flags

Reverse legend: ¡MUERAN LOS SALVAJES UNITARIOS! | NOVIEMBRE 28 DE 1840 | EL GOBIERNO DE LA CONFEDERACION ARGENTINA AL PATRIOTISMO Y AL VALOR

Metal: Brass

Ribbon: Dark red

Reference: Argentina 1910, 2:213–17; Gillingham 1932, 28–29

Ar23. *La Medalla de San Cala*

After retreating from his defeat at Quebracho Herrado, General Lavalle split his army in two parts. One of the two units was set upon by a federalist army and decisively defeated on January 8, 1841, at San Cala. Most of the unitarian officers taken prisoner were shot. General Rosas authorized a medal for his men. Cattle belonging to the defeated officers were divided among the officers and men of the federalist army. The second unit was defeated in September of that year. The federalists captured six hundred unitarians, whose throats were reportedly slit, among whom was the governor of Catamarca. General Lavalle was later shot while trying to flee.

Ar23a. *Officers*

Instituted: By Decree No. 724 of General Rosas on February 28, 1841

Classes: Chiefs, officers

Obverse legend: ¡VIVA LA CONFEDERACION ARGENTINA! | VALIENTE DEFENSOR EN LOS CAMPOS DE SANCALA DE LA LIBERTAD DE LA CONFEDERACION ARGENTINA Y DE LA INDEPENDENCIA AMERICANA

Reverse: Arms of Argentina between military trophies

Reverse legend: ¡MUERAN LOS SALVAJES UNITARIOS! | ENERO 8 DE 1841 | EL GOBIERNO DE LA CONFEDERACION ARGENTINA AL PATRIOTISMO Y AL VALOR

Metal: Chiefs: gold; officers: silver

Ribbon: Scarlet

Ar23b. *Enlisted men*

Obverse legend: ¡VIVA LA CONFEDERCION ARGENTINA! COMBATIÓ POR LA LIBERTAD Y HONOR AMERICANO EN LA VALIENTE DIVISION VENCEDORA EN LOS CAMPOS DE SAN-CALA

Reverse: Arms of Argentina between military trophies and flags

Reverse legend: ¡MUERAN LOS SALVAJES UNITARIOS! | ENERO 8 DE 1841 | | EL GOBIERNO DE LA CONFEDERACION ARGENTINA AL PATRIOTISMO Y AL VALOR

Metal: Brass

Ribbon: Scarlet

Reference: Argentina 1910, 2:219–22; Gillingham 1932, 29

Ar24. *La Medalla de Corrientes*

In March 1843, troops commanded by the unitarian Colonel Joaquín Madariaga crossed into the province of Corrientes from Uruguay at a point that was later named "Paso de los Libres." Madariaga expelled the federalist governor and replaced him on August 30, 1843. The date on the medal refers to Madariaga's election. The General Congress of Corrientes authorized a medal for freeing the province.

Instituted: By the General Congress of Corrientes on September 19, 1843

Classes: Chiefs, officers, enlisted men

Obverse inscription: LIBERTÓ LA PÁTRIA | 30 DE AGOSTO DE 1843

Reverse: PROVINCIA DE CORRIENTES

Metal: Chiefs: gold; officers: silver; enlisted men: brass

Ribbon: Blue, white

Reference: Argentina 1910, 3:173–75; Gillingham 1932, 29–30

* * *

IN 1856, Argentina sent an exploratory force under the command of General Antonino Taboada from Matará up to the border with the province of Santa Fe. This region between the Rio Salado and the Pilcomayo River was a sparsely populated territory. General Taboada prepared an extensive report on his exploration. It would later become a contentious issue with Paraguay after the Triple Alliance War, when Paraguay was forced to give up its claim to the area.

*Ar25. *La Medalla por la Exploración del Rio Salado*

Argentina authorized one gold medal and one hundred silver medals to General Taboada and his men. Because of its heavy weight, it is believed that most of the silver medals were melted down by the poorly paid troops. Only a handful are believed to have survived.

Instituted: By Law No. 902 on December 19, 1856

Classes: Generals, officers,* enlisted men

Obverse: Arms of Argentina between trophies and flags

Obverse inscription: CONFEDERACION | ARGENTINA

Reverse: Allegorical figure of a river god between laurel and palm branches

Reverse inscription: RIO | SALADO | MDCCCLVI

Shape: Oval attached to ribbon by a scroll suspender

Size: 64 × 58 mm

Metal: Generals: gold; officers and enlisted men: silver

Designer: Baron du Graty

Engraver: Mayer

Maker: Thomas Ottley, Birmingham

Ribbon: Light blue, white

Reference: Argentina 1910, 2:111–14; Gillingham 1932, 30

Provenance: A. Menke

* * *

THE long-standing conflict between Buenos Aires and the provinces was not resolved by Urquiza's victory over Rosas at Monte Caseros in 1852. Still, there followed a period of relative peace with the approval of the 1853 constitution, which essentially remains in force today.

Urquiza replaced Rosas and moved the federal capital from Buenos Aires to Paraná in Entre Rios. His main rival was General Bartolome Mitre, the governor of Buenos Aires. These two first faced each other with their respective armies on October 23, 1859, in the Battle of Cepeda. Urquiza's men carried the day, and Mitre was forced to resign as governor. No medals were authorized by either side for this battle. Both men met again two years later at Pavón with different results.

Ar26. *La Medalla de Pavón*

On September 17, 1861, Urquiza and Mitre fought each other again at the battle of Pavón. This time Mitre won, and Urquiza retreated with his surviving forces to Entre Rios. The battle proved to be decisive in terms of consolidating the nation's unity. Mitre pressed his advantage and occupied Paraná, the unitarian capital. The following year, Mitre was elected president of the Argentine Confederation. The country was now finally united under a single national authority, although regional rebellions plagued Buenos Aires for several decades. The Argentine Confederation authorized a medal for Mitre's men.

Obverse: Arms of Argentina flanked by wreath and spears

Obverse legend: BATALLA DE PAVON 17
    SEPTIEMBRE DE 1861
Reverse: small sun above wreath
Reverse inscription: COMBATIO | CON
    GLORIA | POR LA LIBERTAD | DE LA
    REPUBLICA | ARGENTINA

Size: 35 mm
Metal: Silver
Ribbon: Light blue, white, light blue
Reference: Argentina 1910, 3:256; Gillingham
    1932, 30–31

THE TRIPLE ALLIANCE WAR (1864–1870)

IN 1865, Argentina and Brazil were both supporting the Uruguayan Colorado Party against its Blanco opponent, whose only external support came from Paraguay. Alleging border conflicts, Brazil invaded Uruguay to depose the Blanco government. In response, Paraguay invaded Brazil up the Paraguay River into Matto Grosso and soon marched south to link up with its Uruguayan allies. Paraguay asked permission from Argentina to transit its territory, but this was refused. Paraguay declared war on Argentina and invaded the Province of Corrientes on April 13, 1865. Paraguay defeated the Argentine river fleet, occupied Corrientes, and started marching down both sides of the Uruguay River toward Uruguay. The allies slowed the Paraguayan advance and briefly recaptured Corrientes on May 25.

*Ar27. *La Medalla a los Vencedores de Corrientes*

An allied force commanded by Argentine general Wenceslao Paunero advanced up the Paraná River and reoccupied Corrientes after heavy fighting. Argentina awarded the Medal to the Victors of Corrientes for its officers and men who retook the city on May 25, 1865. The victory was short-lived, however, as the Paraguayans soon reoccupied the city. It was not until three months later that the allies were able to retake and hold Corrientes definitively. The medal was awarded to both Argentine and Brazilian troops.

Instituted: By Law No. 1,162 on August 19, 1865
Classes: Chiefs, officers,* enlisted men*
Obverse: Arms of Argentina in an array of banners

Obverse legend: LA REPUBLICA ARGENTINA
    A LOS VENCEDORES EN CORRIENTES
Reverse: Tiny human head with extended
    multiple rays
Reverse legend: 25 DE MAYO | 1865
Shape: Oval
Size: 33 × 25 mm
Metal: Chiefs: gold; officers: silver;* enlisted
    men: copper* and bronze*
Ribbon: Light blue, white, light blue
Reference: Argentina 1910, 2:9–15; Gillingham 1932, 31–32; Pratt 2007, 79–82

* * *

HAVING stopped the Paraguayan advance toward Uruguay, the allies worked their way up the Paraná River and crossed into Paraguayan territory. Their first major objective was to take the key Paraguayan fort at Humaitá, which controlled river traffic up the Paraguay River

Ar 27

Ar 27

to Asunción. However, the Paraguayans had built another fort downstream at Curupaity, which the allies had to take if they were to move the Brazilian river fleet upstream to attack Humaitá.

*Ar28. *El Escudo al Valor por la Batalla de Curupaity*

The Battle of Curupaity took place on September 22, 1866. The powerful Brazilian river fleet commanded by the Marquis of Tamandaré launched a heavy bombardment of the Paraguayan positions. A joint expeditionary force of Argentines under the overall command of President Bartolomé Mitre and Brazilians under Manuel Marques de Souza III made a frontal attack on the Paraguayan fort. The Brazilian naval bombardment caused little damage to the Paraguayans, who had carefully prepared their defenses prior to the battle. The allied troops were caught in the open and suffered heavy losses. As a result, the allied effort to attack Humaitá was delayed for nearly a year. Argentina authorized the Escudo for the Battle of Curupaity to recognize the heroism of its men, who advanced in the face of withering fire from the Paraguayans.

> Classes: Chiefs, other officers,* enlisted men
> Obverse: Arms of Argentina surrounded by laurel branches
> Obverse legend: HONOR AL VALOR Y DISCIPLINA | REPUBLICA ARGENTINA
> Shape: Oval
> Size: 40 × 31 mm
> Metal: Chiefs: gold; other officers: silver; enlisted men: bronze
> Engraver: R. Grande
> Reference: Argentina 1910, 2:66–67; Gillingham 1932, 32
> Provenance: A. Menke

Ar 28

*Ar29. *La Medalla por la Terminación de la Campaña contra el Gobierno del Paraguay*

The Argentine Congress authorized the Medal for the End of the Campaign against the Government of Paraguay for the officers and men who fought the Paraguayan army on Argentine territory. By the time the medal was instituted, the fighting had moved north into Paraguay after the allies crossed the Paraná River. The war itself was far from over, but Argentina wanted to recognize the heroism and discipline of its officers and men who had completed their service in the war.

> Instituted: By Decree on September 28, 1866
> Modified: By Decree on November 17, 1871
> Classes: Chiefs,* officers,* enlisted men*
> Obverse: Arms of Argentina within a wreath, with small sun above, surmounting flags and weapons

Obverse legend: EJERCITO ARGENTINO | DE OPERACIONES CONTRA EL PARAGUAY

Reverse: Sun of May with multiple rays

Reverse legend: AL VALOR Y A LA CONSTANCIA | LA NACION AGRADECIDA

Shape: Round

Size: 27 mm

Metal: Chiefs: gold; officers: silver; enlisted men: bronze

Designer: J. T. Mundt

Ribbon: Light blue, white, light blue

Reference: Argentina 1910, 2:71–74; Gillingham 1932, 34–35; Pratt 2007, 102–17

* * *

Some twenty years after the end of the war, the three allies agreed to exchange medals on a reciprocal basis.

Ar30. La Medalla al Ejército Aliado en Operaciones contra el Gobierno del Paraguay

The Argentine Medal for the Allied Army Operating against the Government of Paraguay was authorized as part of a protocol signed by all three allied powers to exchange campaign medals among themselves.

Instituted: By Law on August 20, 1889

Classes: Chiefs, officers,* enlisted men*

Obverse: Arms of Argentina flanked by scrolls and laurel wreath

Obverse legend: REPUBLICA ARGENTINA | AL EJERCITO ALIADO EN OPERACIONES CONTRA EL GOBIERNO DEL PARAGUAY

Reverse: Sun of May with multiple rays

Reverse legend: AL VALOR Y LA CONSTANCIA | LA NACION AGRADECIDA

Size: 30 mm

Metal: Chiefs: gold; officers: silver; enlisted men: bronze

Ribbon: Light blue, white, light blue

Reference: Argentina 1910, 2:99–100; Gillingham 1932, 35–36; Pratt 2007, 156–58

* * *

In addition to medals issued by the federal government, several Argentine provinces and the city of Buenos Aires issued war medals to provincial National Guard troops.

Ar31. La Medalla de Corrientes a su Guardia Nacional por la Campaña del Paraguay

When the war started, Paraguay seized the city of Corrientes. The National Guard of Corrien-

tes was called on to defend the province and helped retake the city from the Paraguayans. The Province of Corrientes authorized a medal for the officers and men of its National Guard who fought against Paraguay.

Instituted: By Law of Corrientes Province on December 10, 1869

Classes: Chiefs, officers, enlisted men*

Obverse: Arms of the Province of Corrientes within a wreath

Obverse legend: GUARDIA NACIONAL DE CORRIENTES

Reverse legend: CAMPAÑA DEL PARAGUAY 1865 Á 1869

Reverse inscription: AL VALOR | Y LA | CONSTANCIA | LA PROVINCIA | AGRADECIDA

Size: Chiefs and officers: 31 mm; enlisted men: 27 mm

Metal: Chiefs: gold; officers and enlisted men: silver

Engraver: R. Grande

Ribbon: Light blue, white, light blue

Reference: Argentina 1910, 2:85–88; Gillingham 1932, 32–34; Pratt 2007, 134–36

Ar32. La Estrella de Buenos Aires a su Guardia Nacional por la Campaña del Paraguay

The Province of Buenos Aires awarded a star to troops of its National Guard. Recipients, from the rank of sergeant and below, including the widows of deceased recipients, also received land and one thousand pesos.

Instituted: By Law No. 1,264 of Buenos Aires Province on December 16, 1869

Classes: Chiefs, officers, enlisted men*

Obverse: Arms of the Province of Buenos Aires within a laurel and oak wreath

Obverse legend: GUARDIA NACIONAL DE BUENOS AYRES

Ar 30

Ar 30

Ar 31

Ar 32

Reverse legend: CAMPANA DEL PARAGUAY 1865 A 1869

Reverse inscription: AL VALOR | Y A LA | CONSTANCIA | LA | PROVINCIA | AGRADECIDA

Shape: 10-pointed star

Size: Chiefs and officers: 42 mm; enlisted men: 34 mm

Metal: Chiefs: gold; officers and enlisted men: silver

Ribbon: White with 2 narrow, light blue edge stripes displayed on a trapezoidal form

Reference: Argentina 1910, 2:93–95; Gillingham 1932, 35; Pratt 2007, 138–43

* * *

IN THE final peace treaty, Paraguay relinquished its claim to the Chaco south of the Pilcomayo River. This is the same area for which Argentina had awarded the Medal for the Exploration of the Rio Salado in 1856.

INTERNAL STRIFE (1870–1900)

WITH THE end of the Triple Alliance War, Argentina resumed its campaign to expel or kill the Ranquel, Borogas, and Guarani Indians, who continued to resist advances by Argentine ranchers and farmers. Led by General Julio Roca, Argentina repeatedly attacked the Indians. Argentina authorized three medals for a series of campaigns that came to be known collectively as the Campaña del Desierto.

*Ar33. *La Medalla por la Campaña del Rio Negro y Patagonia*

The National Congress authorized the Medal for the Campaign in Rio Negro and Patagonia to dislodge Indians living in what is now the Province of Rio Negro. The Argentine forces used cavalry units and artillery, which were effective against the poorly armed Indians.

Instituted: By Law No. 1,776 on October 27, 1881

Classes: Chiefs,* officers,* enlisted men*

Obverse: Arms of Argentina flanked by branches

Obverse legend: CAMPAÑA DEL RIO NEGRO Y PATAGONIA | 1878

Reverse: sun within rays

Reverse legend: LA NACION AL EJERCITO DEL SUD | 1881

Shape: Oval

Size: 34 × 26 mm

Metal: Chiefs: gold; officers: silver; enlisted men: copper

Ribbon: Light blue, white, light blue

Reference: Argentina 1910, 2:115–23; Gillingham 1932, 37

* * *

IN 1882, now President Julio Roca sent his General Conrado Villegas on a new military campaign against the Indians to the south of the Province of Buenos Aires.

*Ar34. *La Medalla de los Andes*

Argentina divided its army into three divisions covering the entire territory to the Chilean border. As the army marched south, it encountered Tehuelche Indians, who were also killed or expelled. The Indian lands were taken and divided up among the officers and men. According to military reports, not a single Indian was left

alive between the Limary and Neuquen Rivers and the Andes. The army built small, strategically placed forts to prevent the Indians from returning to their lands. The National Congress authorized a medal for the officers and men who fought in the campaign. The award also included two months' pay for all the officers and men.

Instituted: By Law No. 1,942 of the National Congress on July 20, 1885

Classes: Chiefs,* officers, enlisted men*

Obverse: Mountains above wreath flanked by palms

Obverse legend: CAMPAÑA DE LOS ANDES

Obverse inscription: 1882|1883

Reverse: Arms of Argentina flanked by branches

Reverse legend: 2ᴬ DIVISION DEL EJERCITO

Size: 29 mm

Metal: Chiefs: gold; officers: silver; enlisted men: copper

Ribbon: Light blue, white

Reference: Argentina 1910, 2:125–38; Gillingham 1932, 37–38

*Ar35. *La Medalla Conmemorativa a los Sobrevivientes de la Campaña del Desierto*

Some fifty years after the last campaign against the Indians, a semi-official veterans organization authorized a medal sanctioned by the government paying homage to the military killed during the campaign. Presumably, the medals were given mainly to the heirs of those killed.

Instituted: 1929

Obverse: Soldier, farmer, sailor

Obverse inscription: REPUBLICA ARGENTINA | CENTRO MILITAR DE EXPEDICIONARIOS AL DESIERTO DEL EJERCITO Y ARMADA

Reverse inscription: LOS SOBREVIVIENTES | RINDEN JUSTO HOMENAJE | A LOS CAMARADAS CAIDOS | POR LA CIVILIZACION | Y | PROGRESO | 1929

Size: 30 mm

Metal: Silver

Maker: Gotardo y Piena

Ribbon: Light blue with a narrow white center stripe

Ar 35

*Ar36. *La Medalla del Chaco*

The Chaco area between the Pilcomayo, Paraguay, Paraná, and Salado Rivers had been explored, but little settlement took place. Argentina sent armed exploratory missions into the region from 1870 to 1884. A first exploratory expedition commanded by Lieutenant Colonel Napoleón Uriburu left Jujuy in 1870. The following year, a ship explored the Bermejo River up to Salta. In 1875, an expedition explored the Pilcomayo River. In 1878, Uriburu commanded a punitive expedition against the Indians and in 1880, a road was marked from Corrientes to Salta. In 1889, Argentina authorized a medal for its troops as well as those of the National

Ar 35

Guard, who participated in these expeditions. The government approved a silver bar for each campaign to be placed on the ribbon.

Instituted: By Decree No. 718 on August 7, 1888

Classes: Chiefs, officers,* enlisted men*

Obverse: Arms of Argentina

Obverse legend: CAMPAÑA DEL CHACO

Reverse: Laurel wreath

Reverse inscription: LA | NACION | ARGENTINA

Size: 30 mm

Metal: Chiefs: gold; officers: silver; enlisted men: copper; bars: silver

Ribbon: Light blue with narrow white edge stripes

Bars: Expedición 1870, 1876, 1880, 1881, 1882, 1883, 1884

Reference: Argentina 1910, 2:139–58; Gillingham 1932, 36

* * *

IN July 1890, a newly founded political party, Unión Cívica (Civic Union), supported by the Buenos Aires business community and parts of the armed forces rebelled against the government in the center of Buenos Aires, an event known as la Revolución del Parque, or the July Revolution in English. The revolt failed, but it weakened the conservative government of President Miguel Juárez Celman, and he was forced to resign. He was replaced by his vice-president, Carlos Pellegrini. The revolt brought the country's middle class into the political arena.

*Ar37. *La Medalla por la Revolución del Parque*

The government authorized a medal to its loyal forces, including the crew of the USS *Tallapoosa,* an American warship anchored in the harbor, which discouraged rebel warships from bombarding government positions.

Ar 37

Obverse: Figure of Liberty with a sun over mountains edged with laurel branches and surmounted by a radiant sun

Obverse inscription: 26 JULIO | 1890

Reverse inscription: EL | PUEBLO | ARGENTINO | A LOS DEFENSORES | DE LA | LIBERTAD NACIONAL

Shape: Oval

Size: 34 × 25 mm

Metal: Silver, bronze*

Ribbon: Light blue

Reference: Gillingham 1932, 38

Provenance: A. Menke

* * *

THE July Revolution did not resolve the political conflicts inside several provinces, and more fighting broke out involving the Civic Union.

Ar38. *La Medalla de Catamarca*

In June 1891, the Civic Union led a rebellion against the conservative governor of the province of Catamarca, Gustavo Ferrary, who fled. He requested help from the federal government, which sent troops to restore him to the governorship. The same sequence of events was repeated over the next two years. The government authorized a medal for its men who restored order in Catamarca.

Ar 37

Obverse: Arms of Argentina

Reverse inscription: REVOLUCION | DE | CATA MARCA | JUNIO | 23 DE 1891

Shape: Shield-shaped, surrounded by laurel branches and surmounted by a sun with rays

Metal: Bronze

Ribbon: Light blue, white

Reference: Gillingham 1932, 40

Ar 39   Ar 39

*Ar39. *La Medalla de Ringuelet*

In July 1893, another rebellion, led by the Unión Cívica Radical, broke out in the Province of Santa Fe. It initially overcame the provincial authorities but was defeated in August 1893. The rebels rose up again in September but were quickly put down. Argentina authorized a medal to its troops who suppressed the insurrection.

Obverse: Arms of Argentina

Obverse legend: EL GENERAL CAMPOS | Á LOS | VALIENTES EN RINGUELET

Reverse inscription: RECUERDO | AL | 8 AGOSTO | DE | 1893

Shape: Oval with the protruding ends of a Maltese cross

Size: 32 × 29 mm

Metal: Bronze

Ribbon: Light blue, white, light blue

Reference: Gillingham 1932, 39–40

Ar40. *La Medalla de Santa Fe*

The Province of Santa Fe authorized its own medal for its troops who put down the same uprising.

Instituted: By the Province of Santa Fe

Obverse: Arms of the Province of Santa Fe

Obverse legend: REVOLUCION DEL 30 DE JULIO DE 1893

Reverse inscription: VALOR CONSTANCIA PATRIOTISMO

Reverse legend: EL PUEBLO DE LA PROVINCIA A SU DEFENSOR

Size: 32 mm

Metal: Bronze

Reference: Gillingham 1932, 40–41

*Ar41. *La Medalla del Pueblo de Salta a la Brigada San Lorenzo de 1896*

The Medal from the People of Salta to the San Lorenzo Brigade was probably awarded to its National Guard for action against the Indians.

Obverse: 6-pointed star within circle

Obverse legend: EL PUEBLO DE SALTA | Á LOS GUARDIAS NACIONALES | DE LA BRIGADA | SAN LORENZO

Reverse inscription: AL DEBER | CUMPLIDO | SALTA | 15 DE JUNIO 1896 surrounded by a laurel wreath

Size: 30 mm

Metal: Silver

*Ar42. *La Medalla al Ejército del Sud*

Argentina's conflict with the Indians to the south would continue into the twentieth century, when the entire south all the way to the Straits of Magellan would come under army control. Argentina authorized another medal for its ongoing actions against the Indians, this one to the Army of the South.

Obverse: Arms of Argentina

Obverse legend: CAMPAÑA DEL RIO NEGRO Y PATAGONIA | 1884

Reverse: Sun surrounded by rays

Reverse legend: LA NACION AL EJERCITO DEL SUD | 1897

Size: 30 mm

Metal: Silver

Ribbon: Light blue, white, light blue

Provenance: A. Menke

*Ar43. *La Medalla a los Expedicionarios*

Argentina authorized a medal for the conflict with the Indians, this one for the Andes Division, which operated in the west along the border with Chile.

Obverse: Arms of Argentina

Obverse legend: LA NACION A LOS EXPEDICIONARIOS

Reverse: 8 mountains above laurel wreath and palm branches containing the dates 1897 | 1900

Reverse inscription: DIVISION DE LOS ANDES

Size: 30 mm

Metal: Silver

Ribbon: Light blue, white, light blue

Provenance: A. Menke

CAMPAÑA DEL RIO NEGRO Y PATAGONIA

1884

Ar 42

LA NACION AL EJERCITO DEL SUD

1897

Ar 42

LA NACION A LOS EXPEDICIONARIOS

Ar 43

1897 1900

DIVISION DE LOS ANDES

Ar 43

Ar44. *La Medalla de la Provincia de San Luis a los Expedicionarios al Sur, 1878–1926*

The Medal of San Luis Province for the Members of the Expeditionary Force in the South was probably awarded to soldiers from San Luis Province, who participated in the many military expeditions to eradicate the Indians from the southern part of Argentina.

Obverse: Arms of Argentina

Obverse legend: GLORIA AL EJERCITO NACIONAL

Reverse: Arms of the Province of San Luis

Reverse legend: LA PROVINCIA DE SAN LUIS A LOS EXPEDICIONARIOS AL SUR 1878–1926

Ribbon: light blue, white, light blue with bar EXPEDICION 1878

THE TWENTIETH CENTURY:
PEACE, INTERNAL INSURGENCY, AND ONE WAR

THE END OF THE nineteenth century saw Argentina coming onto the world stage with its expanding grain and beef exports. The country became one of the world's most prosperous nations. It attracted millions of European immigrants. Rural landowners prospered from their exports, and the new immigrants changed the nation's political dialogue through the ballot box.

*Ar45. *La Medalla a los Cruzados de la Civilización*

Argentina stayed out of World War I, but it did make a medal for the Crusaders of Civilization that was presumably awarded to Argentine citizens who fought with the Allies against the Central Powers.

Obverse: Hand holding dagger, laurel branch behind

Obverse legend: A LOS CRUZADOS DE LA CIVILIZACIÓN | BUENOS AIRES JULIO 1919

Reverse: Cross surrounded by rays

Size: 30 mm

Metal: Silver

Engraver: J. M. Lubary

Ribbon: Blue, white, blue

Provenance: A. Menke

* * *

IN 1946, Argentina's political dialogue changed forever with the election of Juan Perón to the presidency. A former army officer, Perón had built up a following among labor unions and workers. The alliance gave birth to the Partido Justicialista, which remains today the country's dominant political force. For the next half-century, power alternated between the Peronists and the military. A leftist branch of the Justicialista Party called the Montoneros launched a wave of kidnappings and acts of terrorism. The military defeated them, using repressive measures that came to be known as the Guerra Sucia (Dirty War). No medals are known to have been issued for this period.

In a calculated move to remain in power, the military ordered the invasion of the Falkland

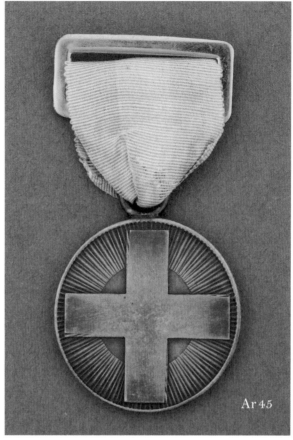

Islands (las Malvinas) in 1982. The Argentine navy attacked East Falkland Island on April 2. Great Britain sent an expeditionary force to retake the Falklands. A British nuclear submarine sank the Argentine cruiser *Belgrano* with significant loss of life. As the British landed their troops at San Carlos Bay, the Argentine air force caused significant casualties to their forces. The Argentine commander surrendered all Argentine forces on the island on June 14, 1982.

The defeat broke the political power of the Argentine military, who were replaced by a democratically elected government in 1983. Argentina instituted an array of military medals for combat operations, which were awarded to the veterans of the Falklands War as well as the families of those killed in action.

*Ar46. *La Medalla por la Campaña de las Malvinas*

The Argentine Congress authorized a medal for the Argentine military who fought on the Falkland, South Georgia, and the South Sandwich Islands from April 2 to June 14, 1982. The medal's design was modified in 1988, creating two variants.

Ar46a. *Variant 1*

Instituted: By Law No. 23,118 on October 31, 1984

Classes: Officers, enlisted men

Obverse: Light blue and white enameled colors superimposed on a raised map of the Falkland Islands surrounded by a broken chain

Obverse legend: RECUPERACION DE LAS ISLAS MALVINAS | 2.4.1982

Reverse: Hand-engraved description of the specific event recognized by each medal

Size: 32 mm

Metal: Officers: silvered; enlisted men: bronze

Ribbon: Light blue, white, light blue

*Ar46b. *Variant 2*

Modified: By Law No. 23,585 on August 17, 1988

Obverse: The Falkland Islands silhouetted against enameled Argentine colors and inscribed above, MALVINAS ARGENTINAS and below, 1986, 1990, or 1991 depending on year of issue

Reverse legend: EL H. CONGRESO DE LA NACION | A LOS COMBATIENTES

Reverse inscription: 2-4-82 and name of the recipient

Size: 31 mm

Metal: Silvered

Ribbon: Light blue, white, light blue

Ribbon bar: The Falkland Islands silhouetted against enameled Argentine colors

Reference: http://www.apos.malvinas.com.ar/medalla.htm, accessed September 15, 2012

*Ar46c. *Air Force*

Obverse: Blue enameled map of the Falkland Islands

Obverse legend: RECUPERACION DE LAS ISLAS MALVINAS | 2 4 1982

Reverse inscription: BAUTISMO | de FUEGO | 1-5-82 | FUERZA | AEREA [in informal font]

Size: 32 mm

Metal: Silvered

Provenance: A. Menke

Ar47. *La Cruz de la Nación "al Heroico Valor en Combate"*

The Cross of the Argentine Nation for Heroic Valor in Combat is awarded to Argentine and foreign military personnel, police, security forces, and civilians for demonstrating heroism

in combat. This cross is the highest award of the Argentine armed forces and the nation's third highest award after the Order of San Martín and the Order of May. It was awarded to combatants of all branches of the armed forces in the Falklands War.

> Instituted: By Law No. 22,607 in 1982
> Obverse disc: Arms of Argentina surrounded by a wreath
> Obverse inscription: LA NACION ARGENTINA | AL | HEROICO | VALOR | EN | COMBATE
> Shape: Cross pattée
> Size: 40 mm
> Metal: Gold, silver
> Ribbon: Light blue, white, light blue
> Reference: Martínez Lamela 1995, 92–93

Ar48. *La Medalla de la Nación "al Valor en Combate"*

The Medal for Valor in Combat was awarded to Argentine and foreign military, police, and security personnel, as well as civilians for demonstrating valor in combat. It is Argentina's second-highest military medal. This medal was awarded to combatants of all branches of the armed forces in the Falklands War.

> Instituted: By Law No. 22,607 in 1982
> Obverse: Arms of Argentina
> Obverse legend: LA NACION ARGENTINA | AL VALOR EN COMBATE
> Reverse: Engraved name of recipient
> Size: 37 mm
> Metal: Silver
> Ribbon: White, with light blue edge stripes
> Reference: Martínez Lamela 1995, 93

Ar49. *La Medalla de la Nación "al Herido en Combate"*

The Medal for Wounded in Combat was awarded to Argentine and foreign military, police, and security personnel, as well as civilians wounded in combat. The medal was awarded to combatants of all branches of the armed forces involved in the Falklands War.

> Instituted: By Law No. 22,607 in 1982
>
> Obverse: Arms of Argentina
>
> Obverse legend: LA NACION ARGENTINA | AL HERIDO EN COMBATE
>
> Reverse: AL [name of the recipient above 2 olive branches]
>
> Size: 37 mm
>
> Metal: Silvered
>
> Ribbon: Light blue, white, light blue with narrow red edge stripes
>
> Reference: http://www.aposmalvinas.com.ar/ medalla.htm, accessed September 15, 2012; http://cgi.ebay.com/ARGENTINA-MEDAL-FALKLANDS-WAR-WOUNDED-IN-COMBAT-1982, accessed June 19, 2010

Ar 50

*Ar50. *La Medalla del Ejército "al Heroico Valor en Combate"*

The Army Medal for Heroic Valor in Combat was awarded to Argentine army veterans for heroism in the Falklands War.

> Obverse inscription: AL | HEROICO | VALOR | EN | COMBATE within laurel branches
>
> Reverse: Star with rays
>
> Reverse legend: EJERCITO ARGENTINO
>
> Reverse inscription: AL [2 bars for engraving]
>
> Shape: Oval
>
> Size: 34 × 25 mm
>
> Metal: Gilt

*Ar51. *La Medalla de la Armada al Muerto Heroico en Combate*

The Navy Medal for Heroic Death in Combat was awarded to Argentine navy personnel killed in combat. The medal has a horizontal black stripe at the top of the ribbon. The larg-

Ar 50

Ar 51

Ar 52

est number of recipients were those who died in the sinking of the cruiser *Belgrano* by a British nuclear submarine.

Instituted: By Law No. 22,607 in 1982
Obverse: Navy emblem
Obverse legend: MURIO HEROICAMENTE EN COMBATE | A.R.A.
Reverse: 2 olive branches
Size: 31 mm
Metal: Gilt
Ribbon: Light blue, white, light blue
Provenance: A. Menke

*Ar 52. *La Medalla de la Armada al Muerto en Combate*

The navy awarded the Medal for Death in Combat to the heirs of those killed in combat dur-

ing the war, particularly the families of those killed in the sinking of the *Belgrano*.

Instituted: By Law No. 22,607 in 1982
Obverse: Navy emblem
Obverse legend: MURIO EN COMBATE | A.R.A.
Reverse: 2 olive branches
Shape: Oblong
Size: 34 × 30 mm
Metal: Silvered
Ribbon: Light blue, white, light blue
Provenance: A. Menke

Ar 53. *La Medalla de la Armada "al Mérito"*

The Medal for Recognition of Merit is awarded to navy personnel for meritorious service over and above the call of duty or for fortitude in combat.

> Obverse: Navy emblem
> Obverse legend: RECONOCIMIENTO AL MERITO | A.R.A.
> Reverse: Two small olive branches
> Shape: Oblong
> Size: 35 × 31 mm
> Metal: Silvered
> Ribbon: Light blue, white, light blue
> Provenance: A. Menke

Ar54. *La Medalla de la Armada al Herido en Combate*

The Medal for Wounded in Combat is awarded to Argentine navy personnel for wounds suffered in combat.

> Obverse: Navy emblem
> Shape: Oblong
> Ribbon: White with 2 blue edges and 1 center red stripe

*Ar55. *La Medalla de la Armada "al Esfuerzo y Abnegación"*

The Medal for Effort and Sacrifice is awarded for outstanding merit to navy personnel.

> Obverse: Navy emblem
> Obverse legend: AL ESFUERZO Y ABNEGACION | A.R.A.
> Reverse: 2 short laurel branches
> Size: 30 mm
> Metal: Silvered
> Ribbon: Light blue, white, light blue
> Provenance: A. Menke

* * *

AFTER the Falklands War, Argentina participated in the American-led war against Iraq's invasion of Kuwait in 1991. The Argentine navy played the most active role. The government authorized a medal for its military personnel who participated in the war.

Ar 55

Ar56. *La Medalla por la Guerra del Golfo*

Argentina sent two navy ships, the missile destroyer *Almirante Brown* and the missile corvette *Spiro*, later replaced by the missile corvette *Rosales* and the transport *Bahia San Blas*. The Argentine warships participated in controlling ship traffic and enforcing the trade embargo against Iraq, as well as in escorting cargo ships in the combat zone.

Obverse: Anchor

Obverse legend: OPERACIONES
INTERNACIONALES | ARA

Metal: Bronze

Ribbon: Blue with 2 light blue and 2 white
side stripes with ribbon bar inscribed
G. PERSICO

Reference: http://www.fuerzas.navales.com/
magazine/makosgolfo.html, accessed February 23, 2013

* * *

ARGENTINA has provided troops for two United Nations peacekeeping operations in Mozambique and in the western Sahara. The government authorized its military personnel participating in these two operations to accept UN medals.

Ar57. *La Medalla por la Misión de las Naciones Unidas para el Referendum en la Sahara Occidental (MINURSO)*

The Medal for the United Nations Mission for the Referendum in the Western Sahara was awarded to Argentine military personnel after the end of their mission. No description is available for this medal.

* * *

ARGENTINE politics sometimes led to violent street demonstrations that required the intervention of local security forces. The government authorized a medal for its security forces that were mobilized on five different occasions over a four-year period.

Ar58. *La Medalla "en Defensa de la Constitución Nacional"*

The Medal for the Defense of the National Constitution was awarded to members of the armed forces and the police who were killed or wounded while putting down internal disturbances during Holy Week in 1987; at Monte Caseros in January 1988; at Villa Martelli in December 1988; and at La Tablada in January 1989, and again on December 3, 1990. Argentina authorizes a monthly payment for life to the families of those killed or seriously wounded.

Instituted: By Law No. 24,973 on May 20, 1998

Obverse: National colors with the cover of the National Constitution and the name of the recipient

Reverse legend: EL HONORABLE CONGRESO
DE LA NACION A LOS CAIDOS EN DEFENSA
DE LA CONSTITUCION

Metal: Steel

Ar 59
Grand Cross

ORDERS

ARGENTINA currently awards two national orders of merit, as well as three military orders, one for each of the three branches of the armed forces. Argentina's orders are awarded only to foreign nationals.

*Ar59. *La Orden del Libertador San Martín*

The Order of the Liberator San Martín is Argentina's highest order. It is awarded only to foreign officials and military personnel. Strict protocol rules, not the importance of the service being recognized, govern which class is awarded. The order is named after General José de San Martín, Argentina's greatest revolutionary hero.

The Collar of the Order of the Liberator San Martín was designed by Ángel Ibarra Garcia, who was reportedly inspired by General San Martín's life. The chain of elliptical laurels on the collar represents the general's military victories. The central link was reproduced from a brooch as a *Divisa al Patriotismo* (Symbol of Patriotism) given by the general in Mendoza to Doña María Josefa Arenales in 1822. The condor hanging from the central link represents San Martín's success in crossing the Andes with his army to liberate Chile, while the sword is a replica of the one he used at the battles of Chacabuco, Maipu, and Lima. The main badge is a stylized sun adapted from republican Argentina's Sun of May.

The Collar of the order is the only grade awarded to heads of state. The government awarded the first Collar of the order to the president of Chile, Juan Antonio Ríos in 1945, two years after the order was authorized. The Collar has also been awarded to HM Queen Elizabeth II; President Rafael Caldera of Venezuela; Ricardo Lagos, president of Chile; and Vicente Fox Quesada, president of Mexico, among others.

Instituted: By Executive Decree No. 5,000 on August 17, 1943

Modified: By Law No. 13,202 on May 21, 1948

Recreated: By Decree Law No. 16,628 on December 17, 1957

Grand Master: President of the Republic

Grades: Collar, Grand Cross,* Grand Officer, Commander, Officer, and Knight*

Obverse disc: Bust of San Martín, ¾ left, encircled by concentric bands of white, light blue, and white enamel

Obverse legend: LIBERTADOR | SAN MARTIN on a blue enameled band

Ar 59
Grand Cross
badge
(reverse)

Ar 59
Knight

Ar 59
Knight

Reverse: Arms of Argentina encircled by concentric bands of light blue and white

Shape: Star with 8 long 3-part rays, with shorter 3-part rays in the angles, separated by wavy rays. Knight's badge is suspended from a laurel wreath. When bestowed on a military recipient, a sword is placed over the wreath

Size: Badge: Grand Cross: 80 mm; Knight: 66 mm. Star: 88 mm

Metal: Grand Cross: gilt; Knight: gilt and blackened

Designer: Ángel E. Ibarra Garcia

Ribbon: Light blue with narrow white edge stripes

Reference: Pardo 1972; Burke's Peerage 2006, 849–52; Werlich 1974, 42

*Ar60. *La Orden de Mayo al Mérito*

The Order of May for Merit is Argentina's second-highest order. It commemorates the May Revolution in 1810, when Buenos Aires deposed the Spanish viceroy and established its own governing authority. The order was originally instituted as the *Orden al Mérito*, with six grades. In 1957, Argentina changed the name to the *Orden de Mayo*, with four divisions: *Al Mérito*, *Al Mérito Militar*, *Al Mérito Naval*, and *Al Mérito Aeronáutico*. The Order of May rec-

Ar 60a1
Grand Cross star

ognizes foreign civilians and military personnel whose efforts promote international understanding to the benefit of Argentina and its armed forces. Like the Order of the Liberator San Martín, the awarding of this order is closely governed by rules of protocol set out by the Ministry of Foreign Affairs.

*Ar60a. *La Orden de Mayo al Mérito*

The Order of May for Merit was instituted as the Order of May by Juan Perón to recognize foreign officials and military personnel who promote progress, well-being, culture, and international understanding of interest to Argentina. The order is awarded according to diplomatic protocol. Its name and design were changed in 1957.

*Ar60a1. *Variant 1*

Instituted: By Presidential Decree No. 8,506 on May 23, 1946

Abolished: By Decree No. 16,629 on December 17, 1957

Grand Master: President of the Republic

Grades: Collar, Grand Cross (star),* Grand Officer, Commander, Officer, Knight

Obverse disc: Torso of worker, right, holding Argentine flag and inscribed AL MERITO above the flag

Shape: Modified Greek cross with 5 flames in the angles

Star shape: 13-pointed star on an 8-pointed sun with 5 rays in each angle

Size: Star: 77 mm

Metal: Gilt bronze

Provenance: A. Menke

*Ar60a2. *Variant 2*

The Order of May for Merit is the civilian version of a family of orders instituted in 1957. The original decree provided for a Collar, but this provision was abolished in 1958, leaving the Order of the Liberator San Martín as the only Argentine Collar awarded to foreign heads of state. The design of the obverse disc was changed from a worker, right, to a female bust symbolizing republicanism, left.

Instituted: By Decree No. 16,629 on December 17, 1957

Regulated: By Decree No. 16,644 on December 18, 1957

Modified: By Decree No. 4,467 on April 10, 1958, abolishing the grade of Collar

Grand Master: President of the Republic

Grades: Grand Cross,* Grand Officer, Commander, Officer, Knight*

Obverse disc: Bust of female wearing Phrygian cap, left

Obverse legend: AL MERITO on a red enameled band

Reverse: Grand Cross badge: enameled arms of Argentina

Shape: 12-pointed star superimposed on a 48-pointed sun; Knight's badge is suspended from a knotwork wreath

Size: Badge: Grand Cross: 78 mm; Knight: 47 mm. Star: 79 mm

Metal: Gilt bronze

Ribbon: Red with narrow white edge stripes

Ar 60a2
Knight

Ar 60a2
Grand Cross badge (reverse)

Ar60a3. *Variant 3*

This variant is the same as variant 2, except for the obverse disc, which was changed back to a worker's torso, right, superimposed on a gilt Argentine flag.

Reference: Argentina 1969, 33–54;
Burke's Peerage 2006, 849–52; Werlich 1974, 42

*Ar60b. *La Orden de Mayo al Mérito Militar*

The Order of May for Military Merit is awarded to foreign civilians and military personnel for meritorious service to the Argentine army. The awarding of this order is governed by diplomatic protocol.

Instituted: By Decree No. 16,629 on December 17, 1957

Regulated: By Decree No. 16,644 on December 18, 1957

Grand Master: President of the Republic

Grades: Grand Cross (star),* Grand Officer (badge),* Commander, Officer, Knight

Obverse disc: Republican Sun of May superimposed on battle symbols surrounded by a wreath

Reverse disc: Enameled arms of Argentina

Reverse legend: REPUBLICA ARGENTINA | AL MERITO MILITAR

Shape: White enameled 2-pointed Maltese cross with 5 rays in the angles

Size: Badge: Grand Officer (with loop and pin back): 68 × 64 mm. Star: Grand Cross: 68 × 64 mm

Metal: Grand Cross star: gilt silver; Grand Officer badge: silver; reverse disc: gilt

Ribbon: Light blue with narrow white edge stripes

Reference: Burke's Peerage 2006, 849–52; Werlich 1974, 44

Ar 60b
Grand Cross star

Ar 60b
Grand Cross star

Ar 60b
Grand Officer
badge

Ar 60b
Grand Officer
badge

*Ar60c. *La Orden de Mayo al Mérito Naval*

The Order of May for Naval Merit is awarded to foreign civilians and military personnel for meritorious service to the Argentine navy. The Grand Cross of the Order is named *Gran Almirante Guillermo Brown,* which is written on the obverse band of the star. Born William Brown (1777–1857) in Ireland, he founded the Argentine navy and led it in many battles during the War of Independence, the Cisplatine War, and a European naval blockade of Buenos Aires.

Instituted: By Decree No. 16,629 on December 17, 1957

Regulated: By Decree No. 16,644 on December 18, 1957

Grand Master: President of the Republic

Grades: Grand Cross,* Grand Officer, Commander,* Officer, Knight

Obverse disc: Sun of May on an anchor on a blue enameled field

Obverse legend: AL MERITO NAVAL on a white enameled band

Reverse disc: Enameled arms of Argentina

Reverse legend: REPUBLICA ARGENTINA | ARMADA DE GUERRA

Shape: Ball-tipped faceted Maltese cross with 5 rays in each angle, joined by concentric rings

Star legend: Obverse: GRAN CRUZ ALMIRANTE BROWN | AL MERITO NAVAL; Reverse: REPUBLICA ARGENTINA | ARMADA NACIONAL

Star shape: Same as badge, but laurel wreath surrounding disc

Size: Badge: 49 × 45 mm. Star: 70 × 65 mm

Ar 60c
Grand Cross

Ar 60c
Grand Cross star (reverse)

Ar 60c
Grand Cross badge (reverse)

Ar 60c
Commander

Ar 60c
Commander

Metal: Grand Cross: gilt; Commander: silver

Ribbon: Blue with 2 narrow white edge stripes and a center white stripe

Reference: Burke's Peerage 2006, 849–52; Werlich 1974, 43

Ar60d. *La Orden de Mayo al Mérito Aeronáutico*

The Order of May for Aeronautical Merit is awarded to foreign civilians and military personnel for meritorious service to the Argentine air force.

Instituted: By Decree No. 16,629 on December 17, 1957

Regulated: By Decree No. 16,644 on December 18, 1957

Grand Master: President of the Republic

Grades: Grand Cross, Grand Officer, Commander, Officer, Knight

Obverse: Winged female figure with gold band, inscribed: AL MERITO

Reverse disc: Air force emblem

Reverse legend: REPUBLICA ARGENTINA | AL MERITO AERONAUTICO

Shape: Cross with a nail head at the end of each arm superimposed on a cross with rectangular ends

Metal: Steel

Ribbon: Blue-green with white stripes of varying width depending on grade

Reference: Burke's Peerage, 2006, 849–52; Werlich 1974, 43–44

BOLIVIA

A CONSTITUTIONAL CONGRESS declared Bolivia's independence from Spain on August 6, 1825, after royalist forces were decisively defeated at the Battle of Ayacucho. The country soon became embroiled in a conflict over whether Peru and Bolivia should be united, as they had been under Spanish colonial rule. A Bolivian general, Andrés de Santa Cruz, became president in 1829. He sought to join the two countries, in alliance with Peruvian politicians. His efforts led to open warfare with Peruvian conservatives. He eventually prevailed by forming the Peru-Bolivian Confederation. This alliance caused Chile to declare war and invade Peru. Chile eventually defeated the Confederation, which was dissolved, and Santa Cruz was forced into exile.

Bolivia's first medals were made to recognize those who fought in these engagements. Most of the battles were waged on Peruvian soil, and many of the recipients were not Bolivian. Almost all of Bolivia's medals were struck at the Potosí mint, inherited from colonial times.

With the departure of Santa Cruz, Bolivia entered into a protracted period of political instability, with thirty-eight governments over the next hundred years. Generals and regional caudillos fought each other for political power. None of them succeeded in establishing a functional government capable of maintaining internal order or defending the country's territorial integrity. Some caudillos made extensive use of the mint to award medals to their supporters.

Bolivia fought more wars with its neighbors than any other Latin American nation and was defeated in all of them. The country lost half of its original territory in the peace negotiations that ended the wars. It lost its access to the sea after the War of the Pacific, making it landlocked.

Bolivia struck medals for its war with Paraguay over the Chaco region in the 1930s. Since then, the country has had no need for military medals in wartime. Instead, it has been instituting orders that promote economic development, education, culture, and sports.

MEDALS

BOLIVIA's mint in Potosí played a significant political role in Bolivia. The mint struck medals supporting its preferred caudillo. Sometimes the mint's employees made medals backing their own candidate. The mint produced hundreds of medals that fall under the category of political propaganda rather than awards for merit, which have not been included in this catalogue.

THE WAR OF INDEPENDENCE

CHARCAS played a relatively unimportant role in achieving its own independence. The decisive battles were fought mainly by forces from other South American nations. Bolivia authorized its first military medal for the Battle of Ayacucho, which enabled it to declare its independence. However, the rebel troops came mainly from Gran Colombia and Peru.

Bo1. *La Medalla por la Batalla de Ayacucho*

Bolivia authorized a medal for the officers of the allied forces who fought at the Battle of Ayacucho on December 9, 1824. The royalist army under Viceroy de la Serna was marching north to block the revolutionary army under Simón Bolívar and General Antonio José Sucre. The revolutionaries took up defensive positions near the town of Ayacucho. The royalists, who outnumbered the revolutionaries, took the offensive. However, the revolutionaries held their positions, inflicting heavy casualties. The revolutionaries defeated de la Serna, capturing most of the royalist officers, including the viceroy himself. Few Bolivian troops are believed to have fought in the battle.

Instituted: By Decree on August 11, 1825

Obverse: A mountain with flags and armaments with a male figure atop the mountain and rays emanating from his body

Obverse inscription: POTOSI

Reverse: Two laurel branches

Reverse inscription: LA | REPUBLICA | BOLIVAR | AGRADECIDA | AL HEROE | CUYO NOMBRE | LLEVA

Shape: Oval

Size: 42 × 36 mm

Metal: Gold, silver

Reference: Gillingham 1932, 44; Barac 2009, 162

* * *

DESPITE the republican victory at Ayacucho, the Spanish commander of the Real Felipe fortress in Callao, Brigadier José Ramón Rodil, refused to capitulate. Bolívar's troops laid siege to the fortress, but its strong fortifications enabled the royalists to hold out for more than a year. An outbreak of disease and a shortage of food finally forced Rodil to surrender on January 11, 1826. His capitulation ended Spanish power in South America, leaving only an isolated garrison in southern Chile, with little military significance.

Bo2. *La Estrella de Callao, 1826*

The Star for Callao was awarded by Antonio José Sucre, the victor at Ayacucho, who had been elected president of Bolivia after he liberated the country. Bolivia authorized a star for the officers laying siege to Real Felipe. Most of the stars were probably awarded to Gran Colombian and Peruvian officers.

Obverse disc: Bust of President Sucre
Obverse legend: BOL A LOS VENC DEL CALLAO
Reverse: Arms of Bolivia
Shape: 6-armed, green-enameled star
Ribbon: Red, blue, white
Reference: Gillingham 1932, 46

Bo3. *La Medalla de Callao, 1826*

Sucre also awarded a medal for the same siege.

Obverse: Tower with a soldier scaling a ladder; inscription on base within laurel wreath
Obverse inscription: RENDIDO | EL CALLAO | AL VALOR | SIN EJEMPLO
Reverse: Tower with flag flying between laurel and palm branches
Reverse legend: TOMA DEL CALLAO | ANO DE 1826
Shape: Oval
Size: 32 × 30 mm
Metal: Silver
Reference: Gillingham 1932, 46

Bo4. *La Estrella de Bolívar*

Bolivia owed its independence to Simón Bolívar and his men, and it issued a star and three medals in Bolívar's name. The star does not appear to be connected to any particular battle.

Obverse disc: Bust of Bolívar, right
Obverse legend: LIBERTADOR SIMON BOLIVAR
Reverse disc: Arms of Bolivia

Reverse legend: REPUBLICA BOLIVIANA
Shape: Star with 2-pointed ends and rays in the angles
Size: 33 mm
Metal: Silver
Reference: Gillingham 1932, 46–47

Bo5. *La Medalla de Bolívar*

This medal is known in three variants.

Bo5a. *Variant 1*

Obverse: Bust of Bolívar, right
Obverse legend: A SU LIBERTADOR SIMON BOLIVAR
Reverse: Arms of Bolivia, 6 stars below
Reverse legend: REPUBLICA BOLIVIANA
Shape: Oval
Size: 33 × 28 mm
Metal: Gold, silver

Bo5b. *Variant 2*

Obverse: Bust of Bolívar, right
Obverse legend: SIMON BOLIVAR LIBERTADOR DE COLOMBIA Y PERU PADRE DE BOLIVIA
Reverse: Arms of Bolivia, 6 stars below
Reverse legend: REPUBLICA BOLIVIANA
Shape: Oval
Size: 33 × 28 mm
Metal: Gold, silver

Bo5c. *Variant 3*

Obverse: Bust of Bolívar, right
Obverse legend: A SU LIBERTADOR SIMON BOLIVAR
Reverse: Arms of Bolivia, 6 stars below
Reverse inscription: EL SENADO RECONOCE LOS GRANDES SERVICIOS DE SU GRAN CIUDADANO
Shape: Oval

Size: 35 × 30 mm

Reference: Gillingham 1932, 47; Barac 2009,
  163

Bo6. *La Medalla "del Valor"*

The circumstances for the issue of this medal
are not known.

Obverse: Bust of uniformed Bolívar, right

Obverse inscription PREMIO DEL | VALOR

Size: 46 mm

Metal: Gold, silver

Reference: Gillingham 1932, 47; Barac 2009,
  163; Salbach 1911, 1555

THE PERU-BOLIVIA CONFEDERATION

BOLIVIA's greatest revolutionary war hero, Marshal Andrés de Santa Cruz, was proclaimed president of Bolivia in 1829. Imbued with Bolívar's dream of politically uniting
Latin America, he sought to unite his country with Peru. For seven years (1828–1835)
Santa Cruz struggled with Peru's conservative two-time president, Agustín Gamarra,
to forge a closer union between their two countries. Santa Cruz pushed for a federal solution with himself at the head. Gamarra favored annexing Bolivia to Peru with himself
as president. In 1835, Gamarra was expelled from Lima and fled to the Peruvian highlands, where he organized an army to depose the incumbent president, Luis José de Orbegoso. As Gamarra gained strength, Orbegoso called on Santa Cruz to help defeat his
rival. On August 13, 1835, Santa Cruz's army crushed Gamarra in the Battle of Yanacocha in the southern Peruvian highlands.

*Bo7. *La Medalla de Yanacocha*

Bolivia awarded medals to the officers in Santa
Cruz's army. At least four different versions
were struck. Some of these are *escudos,* intended
for sewing onto a uniform rather than suspension from a ribbon, but at least one variant
bears a mount for suspension.

Obverse: Palm and laurel wreath
Obverse inscription: VENCEDOR | EN |
  YANACOCHA
Reverse: Combined arms of Peru and Bolivia
Shape: Oval
Size: 35 × 28 mm
Metal: Silver
Ribbon: Blue with narrow red center stripe

Reference: Gillingham 1932, 48; Barac 2009,
  163
Provenance: A. Menke

* * *

SANTA CRUZ's victory at Yanacocha did not
end his differences with the Peruvian conservatives. Conservative General Felipe Santiago de
Salaverry expelled liberal President Orbegoso,
who again asked Santa Cruz for help. Santa
Cruz led his army back into Peru and joined
up with Peruvian forces friendly to Orbegoso.
Salaverry declared war on Bolivia and ordered
a battalion of guardsmen south from Lima to
take the small Bolivian port of Cobija. Salaverry's men under the command of Colonel

José Quiroga took the town on September 24, 1835. Quiroga allowed the garrison's survivors to leave Cobija and rejoin the main Bolivian army, a decision that saved his life when he surrendered after the Battle of Socabaya five months later. Bolivia authorized a medal for its defenders at Cobija.

Bo8. *La Medalla de Cobija*

The medal is known in two variants:

Bo8a. *Variant 1*

Instituted: 1835
Obverse: A mountain with the sun rising behind it; 6 stars beneath
Obverse legend: BOLIVIA A SUS DEFENSORES
Reverse: Sailing ship
Reverse legend: EN COBIJA

Shape: Oval
Size: 34 × 30 mm
Metal: Silver

Bo8b. *Variant 2*

Instituted: 1835
Obverse: A figure of Justice with sword and scales
Reverse: Sailing ship
Reverse legend: EN COBIJA
Shape: Oval
Size: 34 × 30 mm
Metal: Silver
Reference: Gillingham 1932, 44–46; Barac 2009, 162

* * *

SALAVERRY himself led his army to confront Santa Cruz. The two armies fought the Battle of Socabaya on February 7, 1836, near the city of Arequipa. Salaverry's troops took the offensive but were defeated by a combined Bolivian-Peruvian army. Santa Cruz had Salaverry and many of his officers executed. This battle consolidated the creation of the Peru-Bolivian Confederation and the breakup of Peru into two sovereign states.

Bo9. *La Estrella de Socabaya*

Bolivia authorized stars and medals for its officers and men who participated in the battle. The Star of Socabaya is known in two variants:

Bo9a. *Variant 1*

Obverse inscription: 7 DE FEBRERO DE 1836 on a white enameled disc

Obverse legend: VENCEDOR EN SOCABAYA on a red enameled band

Reverse disc: Arms of Bolivia

Shape: White enameled 5-pointed star superimposed on a green enameled oak wreath

Size: 57 mm

Metal: Gold, silver

Ribbon: Green, red, green

Bo9b. *Variant 2*

This medal is known as a round struck piece and as a cutout star from the same dies.

Obverse disc: Flying condor with a laurel wreath in its beak

Obverse legend: DI LA PAZ | AL PERU

Reverse inscription: DE | 1836

Reverse legend: EN SOCABAYA | A 7 DE FEBRERO

Shape: Ball-tipped 5-armed 2-pointed star with a wreath in the angles

Size: 42 mm

Metal: Gold, silver, bronze

Reference: Gillingham 1932, 49–50; Barac

2009, 164; Derman 2007, nos. 482–85; Salbach 1911, 1555a

*Bo10. *La Medalla de Socabaya*

Bolivia struck at least five variants of this medal for the Battle at Socabaya.

*Bo10a. *Variant 1*

Obverse Flying condor with a laurel branch in its beak

Obverse inscription: DÌ LA PAZ | AL | PERÙ.

Reverse: Palm and laurel branches

Reverse inscription: EN | SOCABAYA | A 7. DE | FEBRERO | DE | 1836

Shape: Oval

Size: 30 × 25 mm

Metal: Silver,* bronze

Ribbon: Green, yellow

Provenance: A. Menke

Bo10b. *Variant 2*

Obverse: Arms of Bolivia

Obverse inscription: LA PATRIA PREMIA UN BUEN SERVICIO

Reverse: Palm and laurel branches

Reverse inscription: EN | SOCABAYA | A 7. DE | FEBRERO | DE | 1836

Shape: Oval

Size: 30 × 26 mm

Metal: Silver, bronze

Bo10c. *Variant 3*

Obverse: Arms of Bolivia and Peru combined

Obverse inscription: LA PATRIA PREMIA UN BUEN SERVICIO

Reverse: Palm and laurel branches

Reverse inscription: EN | SOCABAYA | A 7. DE | FEBRERO | DE | 1836

Shape: Oval

Size: 30 × 26 mm

Metal: Silver, bronze

Bo 10d. *Variant 4*

Obverse: Tower with a soldier scaling a
ladder

Obverse inscription: RENDIDO EL CALLAO AL
VALOR SIN EJEMPLO

Reverse Palm and laurel branches

Reverse inscription: EN | SOCABAYA | A 7.
DE | FEBRERO | DE | 1836

Shape: Oval

Size: 30 × 26 mm

Metal: Silver

Bo 10e. *Variant 5*

Obverse disc: Upright condor with displayed
wings

Obverse inscription: HONOR Y PATRIA

Reverse inscription: DE | 1836

Reverse legend: EN SOCABAYA | A 7. DE FEBR

Shape: Octagonal sun

Size: 35 mm

Metal: Silver

Reference: Gillingham 1932, 48–52; Barac
2009, 164; Derman 2007, nos. 474–81, 486

THE WAR OF THE CONFEDERATION (1836–1839)

FOLLOWING the Battle of Socabaya, Santa Cruz was named "Protector" of the new nation. The Confederation was badly received in both Buenos Aires and Santiago, as both felt threatened by its military potential. The United Provinces sent an army north to invade Bolivia.

Bo11. *La Medalla al Ejército del Sud*

In 1838, Santa Cruz defeated the United Provinces forces in southern Bolivia in a series of small engagements. The dictator of the United Provinces, Juan Manuel Rosas, abandoned his invasion. Bolivia authorized a medal to its officers in the Army of the South. This was the only medal authorized by Bolivia during the War of the Confederation.

> Instituted: 1838
> Obverse legend: VALOR LEALTAD | CONSTANCIA
> Obverse inscription: Y
> Reverse legend: HONOR | EJERCITO DEL SUD
> Reverse inscription: AL | 1838
> Shape: Oval
> Size: 30 × 25 mm
> Metal: Gold, silver
> Maker: Casa de Moneda, Potosí
> Reference: Gillingham 1932, 53; Barac 2009, 165; Derman 2007, no. 490

* * *

CHILE took the offensive in the War of the Confederation and twice sent its army north by sea. The first expedition failed, and the Chileans returned home, only to be sent back once more. This time the Chileans, under the command of General Manuel Bulnes, sailed further north to unite with Peruvian allies opposed to Santa Cruz. The Chileans marched east into the highlands and defeated Santa Cruz at Yungay. Santa Cruz left in exile, and the Confederation was dissolved. Agustín Gamarra again became president of Peru. He still hoped to annex Bolivia, and invaded in August 1841, taking advantage of political instability there. However, Bolivian General José Ballivián rallied his forces and defeated Gamarra at the Battle of Ingaví on November 18, an engagement that cost Gamarra his life. Gamarra's death ended the idea of uniting Peru and Bolivia, whose independence was now assured.

Bo12. *La Cruz de Ingaví*

Bolivia authorized crosses and medals to the officers and men in Ballivián's victorious army, each known in several variants.

Bo12a. *Variant 1*

This medal is known as a round struck piece and as a cutout and enameled star from the same dies.

> Instituted: 1841
> Obverse disc: Column of Ingaví surmounted by a radiant sun
> Obverse legend: SALVE LA PATRIA Y SU GLORIA EN INGAVI on a red enameled band
> Reverse disc: 3 mountain peaks
> Reverse legend: 18 DE NOVIEMBRE
> Reverse inscription: DE 1841
> Shape: Red, yellow, and green enameled 6-armed ball-tipped star with a green enameled wreath superimposed on the arms
> Size: 33 mm
> Metal: Gold, silver, brass

Bo12b. *Variant 2*

> Obverse: Same as above
> Reverse: Same as above
> Shape: Black enameled ball-tipped Maltese cross with 3 rays in the angles
> Size: 33 mm
> Metal: Silver

Bo12c. *Variant 3*

> Obverse disc: Column of Ingaví
> Obverse legend: VENCI EN INGAVI on a red enameled band
> Shape: White enameled cross superimposed on a green enameled laurel wreath surmounted by a flat laurel wreath
> Metal: Silver

Bo12d. *Variant 4*

This variant was probably awarded to a combatant who fought at both the Battles of Yanacocha and Ingaví.

> Obverse disc: Arms of Bolivia and Peru
>
> Obverse legend: VENCI EN YANACOCHA AUXILIANDO AL PERU
>
> Reverse disc: Laurel wreath
>
> Reverse inscription: YNGAVI | 18 DE NOVIEMBRE | 1841
>
> Shape: 5-armed star with concave sides and with double concave ends and 4 rays in the angles
>
> Size: 45 mm
>
> Metal: Silver
>
> Reference: Gillingham 1932, 53–54; Barac 2009, 165; Derman 2007, no. 495

*Bo13. *La Medalla de Ingaví*

Bolivia awarded at least three medals for the same battle. No decree authorizing these medals has been found.

Bo13a. *Variant 1*

> Obverse: Arms of Bolivia between furled flags, beneath 8 upright bayonets and a pileus cap and above crossed cannon
>
> Obverse inscription: REPUBLICA BOLIVIANA
>
> Reverse: Wreath
>
> Reverse inscription: YNGAVI | 18 DE NOVIEMBRE | 1841
>
> Shape: Oval
>
> Size: 45 × 40 mm
>
> Metal: Silver

Bo13b. *Variant 2*

> Obverse: SALVE LA PATRIA Y SU GLORIA EN ENGAVI
>
> Reverse: Wreath
>
> Reverse inscription: YNGAVI | 18 DE NOVIEMBRE | 1841

Bo 13c

Bo 13c

> Shape: Round
>
> Size: 43 mm

*Bo13c. *Variant 3*

This medal is known as a round struck piece and as a cutout and enameled star from the same dies.

> Obverse disc: Ingaví column with 10 mountain peaks surmounted by a radiant sun
>
> Obverse legend: PREMIO DE HONOR
>
> Reverse: Laurel wreath

Reverse inscription: YNGAVI | 18 DE
    NOVIEMBRE | 1841
Shape: 7-pointed ball-tipped star with a verti-
    cal bar in place of eighth point
Size: 47 mm,* 44 mm

Metal: Silver
Weight: 41.87 grams
Reference: Gillingham 1932, 55–56; Barac,
    2009, 1:165; Derman 2007, nos. 498–501

INTERNAL INSURGENCIES

BALLIVIÁN's defeat of Gamarra at Ingaví ended Peru's ambitions of annexing Bolivia, but it did not resolve the internal dissension inside Bolivia. In September 1857, Dr. José Maria Linares overthrew the incumbent president, General Jorge Córdova, in a military coup. Linares imposed dictatorial rule, which created many enemies, but his fiscal management was conservative and even-handed.

Bo14. *La Medalla de Potosí, 1857*

The City of Potosí, Linares's hometown, authorized at least three versions of a medal for the troops supporting his revolution. Another medal was made in the name of the Bolivian Council of State, which was created by Linares. These are the first Bolivian military medals awarded in connection with internal insurrections.

Bo14a. *Variant 1*

Obverse: Sun
Obverse legend: LOS HIJOS DE | POTOSI Á
    SUS HERMA | NOS LOS DEFENSORES | DE LA
    CAUSA | NACIONAL EN
Reverse: 3 mountains encircled by a garland
    of flowers below a radiant eye and above
    military trophies and a pileus, 9 stars above
Reverse inscription: 14 DE OCTUBRE DE 1857
Shape: Oval
Size: 36 × 30 mm
Metal: Gold, silver

Bo14b. *Variant 2*

Obverse: Sun
Obverse legend: LOS HIJOS DE | POTOSI Á

SUS HERMA | NOS LOS DEFENSORES | DE LA
    CAUSA | NACIONAL EN
Reverse: 3 mountains encircled by a garland
    of flowers below a radiant eye and above
    military trophies and a pileus, 9 stars
    above
Reverse inscription: 20 DE OCTUBRE DE
    1857
Shape: Oval
Size: 36 × 30 mm
Metal: Gold, silver

Bo14c. *Variant 3*

Obverse: 3 mountains encircled by a garland
    of flowers below a radiant eye and above
    military trophies and a pileus
Obverse legend: DIOS PROTEJE LA CAUSA D
    LOS PUEBLOS with 9 stars beneath (for Bo-
    livia's now 9 departments)
Reverse: Laurel wreath
Reverse inscription: LOS | HIJOS DE | POTOSI
    A SUS | HERMANOS | LOS | DEFENSORES |
    DE LA CAUSA | NACIONAL | EN 20 DE |
    OCTUBRE | 1857
Shape: Oval
Size: 36 × 30 mm
Metal: Gold, silver, gilt

Bo14d. *Variant 4*

This variant appears to have been issued by the Council of State and not the City of Potosí.

> Obverse: 3 mountains encircled by a garland of flowers below a radiant eye and above military trophies and a pileus, 9 stars above
>
> Obverse inscription: 20 DE OCTUBRE DE 1857
>
> Reverse inscription: Radiant sun and surrounded by 2 laurel branches
>
> Reverse inscription: CONSEJO | DE | ESTADO
>
> Shape: Oval
>
> Size: 36 × 28 mm
>
> Metal: Gold, silver
>
> Reference: Gillingham 1932, 56–58; Barac 2009, 166; Derman 2007, nos. 514–19

* * *

LINARES was overthrown in 1861 by General José Maria de Achá, who became president of Bolivia from 1861 to the end of 1864. He in turn was overthrown at the end of 1864 by General Manuel Mariano Melgarejo, who is generally considered the most oppressive of Bolivia's caudillos in the nineteenth century. Melgarejo authorized more medals than all the other nineteenth-century Bolivian presidents combined. He used the Potosí mint to make medals to be awarded to the troops that put down armed insurrections and also to give to his political allies. He ordered from the mint thousands of silver propaganda coins featuring himself, and these were often used as currency. Melgarejo bought new steam-powered machinery for the Potosí mint, enabling it to expand its production at a lower cost. It is sometimes difficult to interpret the meaning of the dates on his medals, which do not always coincide with dates of events according to historians.

*Bo15. *La Medalla de 1865*

Melgarejo authorized a medal for his troops who suppressed several failed insurgencies in 1865. The reference to the month of December is to December 1864, when he seized power and named himself president. January 31, 1865, was the date when Melgarejo defeated an insurgent army commanded by dissident generals. On March 27, 1865, Mariano Belzu was assassinated, presumably on orders from Melgarejo. On September 5, 1865, Melgarejo defeated the combined forces of dissidents from the cities of La Paz, Oruro, Cochabamba, and Sucre at La Cantaria.

> Authorized: 1865
>
> Obverse: Bust of Melgarejo in uniform, left
>
> Obverse legend: EL JENERAL MELGAREJO AL VALOR Y LEALTAD | DE LOS DEFENSORES DE | LA CAUSA DE DICIEMBRE | 1865
>
> Reverse: Radiant eye, with oak and laurel branches beneath
>
> Reverse inscription: DIBRE. 28 | ENERO 31 | MARZO 27 | SETBRE. 5
>
> Shape: Oval
>
> Size: Gilt, silver: 44 × 35mm; white metal: 26 × 21 mm
>
> Metal: Gilt,* silver, white metal
>
> Reference: Gillingham 1932, 58–59; Barac 2009, 167; Derman 2007, nos. 545–48
>
> Provenance: A. Menke

*Bo16. *La Medalla por el Combate de Potosí, 1865*

The city of Potosí authorized a medal for Melgarejo's troops that defeated an insurgent army led by General Nicanor Flores on September 5, 1865, at La Cantería near Potosí. Melgarejo easily defeated Flores, inflicting heavy casualties. He executed many prisoners, including wounded soldiers.

Bo 15

Bo 15

Bo 16

Bo 16

Authorized: 1865

Obverse: Bust of Melgarejo, left, between laurel branches

Obverse legend: SALVADO^R DE LA PATRIA Y SU PACIFICADOR EN 1865

Reverse: Condor holding branches and a cornucopia in its talons

Reverse legend: POTOSI A. S. E. EL JENERAL MARIANO MELGAREJO

Shape: Oval

Size: 33 × 26 mm

Metal: Silver

Reference: Gillingham 1932, 59; Barac 2009, 167; Derman 2007, nos. 531–32

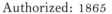

DURING this period in Bolivian history, the mint in Potosí struck hundreds of proclamation and propaganda pieces, some of them with designs nearly identical to those of medals included in this catalogue. Most of these medals had holes drilled in the top so that they could be worn. The known documentation on these coins and medals is minimal, and few, if any, are believed to have been awarded for valor or merit (Bosco 1980; Lill 1986).

*Bo17. *La Medalla a la Juventud*

Melgarejo authorized a medal, bearing the portrait of his chancellor and close political associate Mariano Donato Muñoz alongside his own, to reward his youthful supporters.

Instituted: 1865

Obverse: Jugate busts of Melgarejo and Muñoz, left

Obverse legend: EL GOBIERNO PROVISORIO DE BOLIVIA EN 1865 | MELGAREJO | MUÑOZ | LIBERTAD

Reverse: Arms of Bolivia

Reverse legend: PREMIA A LA JUVENTUD SOBRESALIENTE

Reverse inscription: DE SU | PATRIA

Shape: Oval

Bo 18a

Bo 18a

Size: 37× 30 mm
Metal: Gold, silver, bronze, white metal*
Ribbon: Yellow, red, yellow with white edge stripes
Reference: Barac 2009, 168; Derman 2007, nos. 533–35
Provenance: A. Menke

*Bo18. *La Estrella de Viacha*

Melgarejo won a key battle over his opponents at Las Letanias near Viacha in January 1866. Melgarejo referred to himself and his close associates as the *Pacificadores* of Bolivia, by which he meant to pacify his country by killing his opponents. Some of his *pacificadores* medals were struck bearing the names of Melgarejo's close associates.

*Bo18a. *La Estrella a los Pacificadores*

The Star for the Pacifiers of 1866 was created by Melgarejo at Viacha on January 24, 1866, following his victory over an insurgent army at Las Letanias.

Instituted: By Presidential Decree on February 4, 1866
Obverse disc: Jugate busts of Melgarejo and Muñoz, left
Obverse legend: BOLIVIA A SUS PACIFICADORES
Reverse: Oak wreath
Reverse inscription: VIACHA | 24 DE | ENERO | DE 1866
Shape: Ball-tipped 2-pointed 8-armed star with oak sprigs in the angles suspended from an oval wreath
Size: 38 mm
Metal: Gold, silver,* bronze
Reference: Barac 2009, 169; Derman 2007, no. 551; Bolivia 1866, 4

Bo18b. *La Estrella a Anjel R. Rebollo*

Anjel Rebollo was another of Melgarejo's close supporters. Melgarejo referred to his supporters as pacifiers.

Instituted: By Presidential Decree on February 4, 1866

Obverse disc: Jugate busts of Melgarejo and Muñoz, left

Obverse inscription: BOLIVIA AL ILUSTRISIMO SENOR ANJEL R REBOLLO

Reverse legend: UNO DE LOS PACIFICADORES DE SU PATRIA

Reverse inscription: VIACHA | 24 DE | ENERO | DE 1866

Shape: Ball-tipped 2-pointed 8-armed star with oak sprigs in the angles

Size: 40 mm

Metal: Gold, silver, bronze

Reference: Derman 2007, no. 552

Bo18c. *La Estrella al Dr. José Raimundo Taborga*

Dr. José Taborga was another of Melgarejo's close associates. The medal was probably awarded to troops or followers of Taborga, who helped Melgarejo win the battle at Las Letanias in 1866.

Instituted: By Presidential Decree on February 4, 1866

Obverse disc: Jugate busts of Melgarejo and Muñoz, left

Obverse inscription: BOLIVIA AL DR JOSE RAIMUNDO TABORGA

Reverse legend: UNO DE LOS PACIFICADORES DE SU PATRIA

Reverse inscription: VIACHA | 24 DE | ENERO | DE 1866

Shape: Ball-tipped 2-pointed 8-armed star with oak sprigs in the angles

Size: 40 mm

Metal: Gold, silver, bronze

Reference: Barac 2009, 169; Derman 2007, no. 549; Bolivia 1866, 4

THE CHINCHA ISLANDS WAR (1864–1866)

IN 1864, the Pacific Coast countries of Latin America fought a series of naval engagements with a Spanish fleet. The war is called the Chincha Islands War. A Spanish fleet had arrived on a good will visit to its former colonies. An isolated incident in Peru involving a Spanish citizen was used by the Spanish admiral as a reason to occupy the Chincha Islands, a major source of bird guano for fertilizer, then one of Peru's largest exports. All of the Pacific Coast countries of South America sided with Peru. Bolivia's territory then extended to the Pacific coast, and its government also supported Peru.

Bo19. *La Estrella por el Combate de Papudo*

On November 26, 1865, the Chilean corvette *Esmeralda* captured the Spanish warship *Covadonga* off the Bolivian port of Papudo. Bolivia authorized a medal for the crew of the *Esmeralda* for this action, because Papudo at the time was in Bolivian territory. This medal is known as a round struck piece and as a cutout star from the same dies.

Instituted: 1865

Obverse disc: Bust of Melgarejo, left

Obverse legend: BOLIVIA A LOS VALI[s] DE LA | ESMERALDA

Reverse disc: Arms of Bolivia, wreath around

Reverse inscription: PAPUDO NOVIEMBRE 26 DE | 1865

Shape: Ball-tipped 2-pointed 6-armed star
with a laurel wreath in the angles, suspended from an oval wreath inscribed VIVE
CHILE.

Size: 38 mm

Metal: Gold, silver

Reference: Gillingham 1932, 59 and 112;
Barac 2009, 167; Derman 2007, nos. 536–
38; Brinkmann 2012, 2, 44–45

* * *

SKIRMISHES between the Spanish and allied
fleets continued into 1866. The allied fleet
had anchored in shallow water off Abtao Cove
in southern Chile. On February 7, 1866, two
Spanish steam frigates attacked the Chilean-
Peruvian squadron at Abtao. Both sides suffered damage, and the two Spanish warships
withdrew for tactical reasons. Bolivia authorized two stars and a medal to the crews of the
allied fleet.

*Bo20. *La Estrella por el Combate de Abtao*

Melgarejo awarded two stars for the Battle of
Abtao to the officers of the Chilean and Peruvian warships anchored there. This star is
known in three sizes as a round struck piece and
as a cutout star from the same dies; the uncut
silver pieces seem to correspond in weight to
the debased coinage of the Melgarejo period
(*Standard Catalog of World Coins* 2006, KM Bolivia, no. 146).

Instituted: 1866

Obverse disc: Bust of Melgarejo, left

Obverse inscription: BOLIVIA A LOS
VENCEDˢ DE ABTAO

Reverse disc: Arms of Bolivia

Reverse inscription: EN LA JORNᴬ DEL 7 DE
FEBRᵒ DE | 1866 encircled by a wreath in
some sizes

Shape: Ball-tipped 2-pointed 6-armed star
with a laurel wreath in the angles suspended
from an oval wreath inscribed VIVA CHILE.

Size: 48 mm, 36 mm, 34 mm*

Metal: Gold, silver*

Weight: 19.76 grams

Ribbon: Red, yellow, green

Reference: Gillingham 1932, 60; Barac 2009,
168; Derman 2007, nos. 543–44

Bo21. *La Medalla por el Combate de Abtao*

Instituted: 1866

Obverse: Shield superimposed on the flags of Bolivia, Chile, and Peru and trophies of war

Obverse inscription: A LOS | VENCEDORES | EN | ABTAO

Reverse inscription: 7 DE FEBRERO 1866 | 57 CANONES CONTRA 92

Size: 32 × 26 mm

Metal: Gold, silver, copper

Reference: Medina 1901, 148; Gillingham 1932, 113

*Bo22. *La Estrella por el Combate de Callao, 1866*

On May 2, 1866, following the naval battle at Abtao, the Spanish fleet laid siege to the port of Callao and exchanged fire with the Peruvian shore defenses. Both sides suffered casualties. The Spanish admiral decided he had no possibility of occupying Callao, so he withdrew and the war ended. Although it did not participate in the Battle of Callao, Bolivia struck at least two stars for the Peruvian defenders. This medal is known in two sizes as a round struck piece and as a cutout star from the same dies.

Instituted: 1866

Obverse disc: Head of Melgarejo, left

Obverse inscription: BOLIVIA A LOS VENCEDORES | DEL CALLAO

Reverse: Arms of Bolivia

Reverse legend: EN LA JORNADA DEL 2 DE MAYO | 1866

Shape: Ball-tipped 2-pointed 6-armed star with a laurel wreath in the angles, suspended from a metallic wreath inscribed VIVA EL PERU

Size: 39 mm, 37 mm*

Metal: Gold, gilt silver, silver*

Reference: Gillingham 1932, 60; Barac 2009, 168; Derman 2007, nos. 539–41

Provenance: A. Menke

*Bo23. *La Estrella de Potosí, 1868*

Melgarejo approved a new Bolivian constitution in December 1868, giving him greater

power. He awarded this medal to his supporters in Potosí who backed the new constitution.

Obverse disc: Head of Melgarejo, left, surrounded by 11 stars

Reverse inscription: POTOSI | DIBRE. 24 | DE | 1868 above laurel and palm branches

Shape: Round with ball-tipped star on obverse

Size: 37 mm

Metal: Silver

Reference: Gillingham 1932, 60–62

Provenance: A. Menke

Bo24. *La Estrella de Tarata*

The Star of Tarata is another of the medals authorized by Melgarejo to award his supporters, in this case for Tarata's support of his 1868 constitution. Melgarejo was born in Tarata, which is now part of Peru.

Instituted: 1868

Obverse disc: Bust of Melgarejo surrounded by 11 stars

Reverse: Laurel and palm branches

Reverse inscription: TARATA | DIBRE 25 | DE | 1868

Shape: Ball-tipped star suspended from an oval wreath

Size: 43 mm

Metal: Silver

Reference: Derman 2007, nos. 558–61

Bo25. *La Estrella de 1872*

The Star of 1872 was authorized by the National Assembly, probably in exchange for support from Hilarión Daza, an influential army colonel at the time. Despite the meritorious claim on the medal's reverse, Daza did no more than any other caudillo to create permanent political institutions in Bolivia.

Instituted: 1872

Obverse disc: Figure of Liberty standing holding Bolivian flag in right hand and with left hand atop a book on a pedestal

Obverse legend: LA ASAMBLEA NACIONAL DE 1872 | HILARION DAZA on a blue enameled band

Reverse disc: An open book and an upright sword between a laurel and coffee branch

Reverse legend: AFIANZO LAS INSTITUCIONES DE BOLIVIA on a blue enameled band

Shape: White enameled 9-pointed star with 5 gold rays surmounted by stars in the angles, suspended from a gold eagle with wings displayed

Size: 62.5 × 40 mm

Metal: Gold

Ribbon: Green, yellow, red

Reference: Gillingham 1932, 62; Barac 2009, 169

THE WAR OF THE PACIFIC

IN MAY 1876, Hilarión Daza (1840–94), a career military officer, seized power in La Paz. He is considered the last of the repressive nineteenth-century caudillos. Daza is best known for having revoked the 1874 treaty with Chile extending favorable tax treatment to Chilean miners working in Bolivia. In response to the revocation of the favorable tax treatment, Chile declared war and invaded in 1879. Daza invoked a secret mutual defense treaty signed with Peru in 1873, and that country sided with Bolivia. Chile first gained control of the seas after it captured the flagship of the Peruvian fleet, the ironclad *Huáscar*. It then sent an army north to invade Bolivian territory in Atacama and particularly the key ports of Iquique and Antofagasta. The Chileans first landed at the small port of Pisagua and overwhelmed the town's small Bolivian garrison.

Bolivia and its cities issued at least five medals for its officers and soldiers who fought the Chilean army prior to their withdrawal from the war after the Battle of Tacna.

Bo26. *La Medalla al Batallón Independencia*

The town of Corocoro authorized a medal for its citizens who fought at Pisagua. The town, located relatively near Pisagua, possibly provided much of the manpower for the Independence Battalion, which garrisoned Pisagua at the time of the Chilean attack. The medal was authorized twenty years after the Chilean invasion.

Instituted: 1900

Obverse: LA MUNICIPALIDAD DE COROCORO AL BATALLON INDEPENDENCIA-1900

Reverse: HEROICA ACCION DE PISAGUA NBRE. 2-1879

Shape: Oval

Size: 30 × 23 mm

Metal: Silver

Ribbon: Green, yellow, red

References: Speir 2010, 34–35

Bo27. *La Medalla a los Defensores en Pisagua*

Seven years later, the Bolivian Senate authorized a national medal for Pisagua's defenders.

Instituted: By the National Senate on October 14, 1907

Classes: Chiefs, officers, enlisted men

Obverse: EL SENADO NACIONAL-DE 1907

Reverse: A LOS DEFENSORES DE LA PATRIA EN PISAGUA EN 2. NOVIEMBRE DE 1879

Shape: Oval

Size: 40 × 30 mm

Metal: Chiefs and officers: gold; enlisted men: silver

Ribbon: Green, yellow, red

Reference: Speir 2010

Bo28. *La Medalla por la Batalla de Tarapacá*

Once the Chileans had consolidated their position in Pisagua, they marched south toward the Bolivian port of Iquique. After several skirmishes, the Bolivian troops under the command of President Daza retreated to Bolivia. Daza was forced to resign after his return. The Peruvians alone faced the Chilean army at Tarapacá on November 27, 1879. The Peruvians defeated the Chileans in the battle, but retreated north to Arica, leaving Tarapacá and the Atacama Desert under Chilean control. Bolivia authorized a medal for the Battle of Tarapacá, which was presumably awarded to the Peruvians.

Instituted: By Law of the National Convention on September 8, 1880

Regulated: By Law of the National Convention on December 24, 1880

Classes: Chiefs, officers, enlisted men

Metal: Chiefs and officers: gold; enlisted men: silver

Reference: Banco Central de Bolivia 1999

Bo29. *La Medalla de Tacna*

The Chilean army under the command of General Manuel Baquedano landed in southern Peru and threatened the Peruvian town of Tacna with its rail hub. A joint Bolivian-Peruvian army commanded by General Narciso Campero sought to block the Chilean advance but was defeated on May 26, 1880. The Bolivian troops retreated back to Bolivia following the battle and withdrew from the war. The city of Sucre authorized a medal, apparently for rail-road workers from Sucre, who helped Bolivian troops withdraw after the battle.

Obverse: Mountains with sun above within a wreath

Obverse inscription: LA CAPITAL SUCRE | A SUS DIGNOS HIJOS

Reverse: Bird in flight

Reverse legend: LOS REILEROS LIBRES DEL SUD POR SU | HONROSA COMPORTACION

Reverse inscription: EN EL | SACRIFICIO DEL | 26 DE MAYO DE | 1880 | TACNA

Shape: Oval, suspended from an eagle with displayed wings and laurel and oak branches in its talons

Size: 35 × 26 mm

Reference Derman 2007, nos. 558–61

*Bo30. *La Medalla "al Mérito Sobresaliente"*

The Department of Potosí awarded the Medal for Outstanding Merit to the Bolivian veterans from Potosí in the War of the Pacific.

Obverse: Arms of Potosí

Obverse legend: EL CONSEJO DEPARTAMENTAL | DE POTOSI

Reverse: Laurel and oak branches

Reverse legend: PREMIA AL MERITO SOBRESALIENTE | 1880

Shape: Oval

Size: 30 × 25 mm

Metal: Silver

Ribbon: Green, yellow, red

Reference: Derman 2007, no. 562; Speir 2010

Provenance: A. Menke

* * *

THE TREATY of Ancón between Chile and Peru in 1883, which ended the War of the Pacific, left Chile in physical control of southern Peru, including the cities of Arica and Tacna.

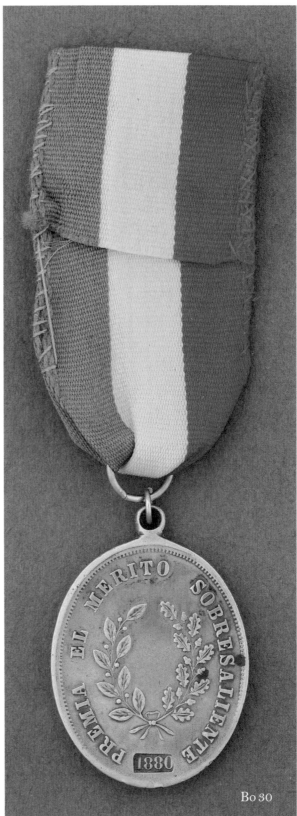

Bo 30

Although Bolivia was not a signatory, its own coastal territories remained occupied by the Chileans. Bolivia and Chile later signed a Treaty of Peace and Friendship in 1904, which permanently transferred all of Bolivia's litoral to Chile, thereby cutting Bolivia off from its access to the sea. Successive Bolivian governments have protested this loss, but there is little prospect of Bolivia ever recovering its coastal territories.

The Acre War

During the War of the Pacific, distant problems were allowed to fester owing to inattention by unstable administrations. One such problem was the region of Acre in northeast Bolivia along its border with Brazil. World demand for rubber put rubber traders and revenue-starved governments into conflict with each other. The Acre region with its natural rubber forests began exporting rubber down the Amazon River to the Atlantic. Both Bolivia and Brazil sought to tax these exports at the port of embarkation. In 1899, Bolivia created Puerto Alonso along the Acre River for the purpose of collecting taxes from the rubber trade. Local rubber exporters opposed the imposition of taxes on their business, and Brazil objected to having Bolivia collect the taxes. The rubber exporters, led by filibusters like Luis Gálvez, demanded political independence. Brazil claimed the territory to be in dispute.

Bolivia sent three military expeditions to fight local secessionists, who were neutralized. Brazil, however, had the stronger military, and Bolivia had to settle the dispute diplomatically. The Treaty of Petrópolis, signed on November 17, 1903, ceded 190,000 square kilometers of Bolivian territory to Brazil in exchange for a payment of two million pounds sterling. The Acre War was a minor conflict from a military perspective, but it caused an important loss of Bolivian territory to Brazil.

*B031. *La Medalla a los Defensores del Acre, 1900*

The Medal for the Defenders of Acre was awarded to the Bolivian officers and men sent to suppress the secessionist rebellion in Acre from 1899 to 1901. The first expedition was led by Bolivian President José Manuel Pando in 1900 and another by Vice-President Lucio Pérez Velasco.

Instituted: By the National Senate in 1901

Classes: 1st,* 2nd, 3rd

Obverse disc: Arms of Bolivia

Obverse legend: bolivia a los defensores del acre en 1900

Reverse inscription: el | senado | nacional | de | 1901

Shape: 1st, 2nd: 9-pointed sun with 5 rays in the angles beneath a flying condor; 3rd: round

Size: 1st: 57 × 44 mm; 2nd: 27 × 23 mm; 3rd: 23 mm

Metal: 1st: gold disc, silver sun; 2nd: silver disc, silver sun; 3rd: silver disc

Ribbon: Red, yellow, green

Reference: A. Menke

*Bo32. *La Medalla a los Defensores del Acre, 1902–1903*

Bolivia authorized another medal for a later military expedition sent in 1902 and 1903. It too was able to contain local secessionists, but it could do nothing against the Brazilian military. The Bolivian Senate approved a medal for its officers and men who were sent to Acre.

Instituted: By the National Senate in 1903

Classes: 1st, 2nd, 3rd*

Obverse disc: Arms of Bolivia

Obverse legend: BOLIVIA A LOS DEFENSORES DEL ACRE EN 1902 Y 1903

Reverse inscription: EL | SENADO | NACIONAL | DE | 1903

Shape: 1st, 2nd: 9-pointed sun with 5 rays in the angles beneath a flying condor; 3rd: round

Size: 1st, 2nd: 27 × 23 mm; 3rd: 23 mm

Metal: 1st: gold disc, silver sun; 2nd: silver disc, silver sun; 3rd: silver disc

Ribbon: Red, yellow, green

Reference: A. Menke

Bo33. *La Medalla de Potosí a los Defensores del Acre*

The City of Potosí awarded its own medal to the members of the first Bolivian expeditionary force sent to Acre.

Obverse: Arms of the city of Potosí

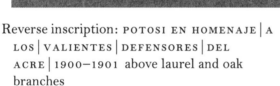

Reverse inscription: POTOSI EN HOMENAJE | A LOS | VALIENTES | DEFENSORES | DEL ACRE | 1900–1901 above laurel and oak branches
Shape: Shield
Size: 25 × 21 mm

Metal: Silver
Maker: Casa de Moneda, Potosí
Ribbon: Red, yellow, green
Reference: http://www.elgrancapitan.org/foro/viewtopic.php?t=17991

THE CHACO WAR (1932–1935)

THE CHACO WAR (*Guerra del Chaco*) pitted Latin America's only two landlocked nations, Bolivia and Paraguay, against each other over the sparsely populated Chaco region. It was the bloodiest war fought in Latin America during the twentieth century. Both sides believed that the Chaco held significant oil deposits. In addition, Bolivia sought better access to the Paraguay River, from which the country could ship its exports down the Paraguay/Paraná Rivers to Buenos Aires.

Bolivia appeared militarily to have the upper hand. Its population exceeded that of Paraguay by three times. It had a much larger air force, more artillery, and a few tanks. However, these advantages were offset by the fact that the Chaco was much further from Bolivia's population centers than from those of Paraguay. It could take Bolivia two weeks to move supplies to the front lines, compared with a few days for Paraguay. Also,

Bolivia had an all-creole officer corps, while the majority of its foot soldiers were Aymara Indians, who spoke little or no Spanish. All of the Paraguayan officers and men could speak Guarani, the native language in the Chaco.

Both countries had been harassing each other for years by attacking isolated military outposts. In June 1932, Bolivian troops attacked and occupied a small Paraguayan fort along Lake Pitiantuta. Both countries mobilized for war. Bolivia followed conventional military strategies, while the Paraguayans resorted to ambushes and guerrilla tactics. Over time, the Paraguayans pushed the Bolivian army ever further northwest. Argentina, Brazil, Chile, Peru, Uruguay and the United States negotiated a ceasefire and later a Treaty of Peace, Friendship, and Boundaries signed in Buenos Aires on July 21, 1938. The peace agreement awarded about one-quarter of the Chaco to Bolivia, which was less than what Bolivia had controlled before the war began. On the other hand, most of the oil and gas deposits remained inside Bolivia. The country suffered about sixty thousand killed, the highest level of war casualties in Bolivia's history. Bolivia awarded two medals to its soldiers for the hardships they endured.

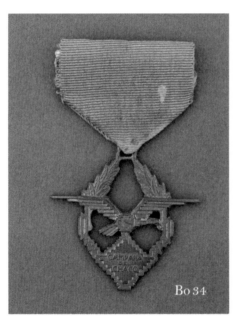 

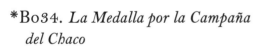

*Bo34. *La Medalla por la Campaña del Chaco*

The Medal for the Chaco Campaign was awarded to members of the Bolivian air force, which controlled the air, but was unable to change the reality on the ground.

Obverse inscription: CAMPAÑA | DEL | CHACO
Reverse inscription: CAMPAÑA | DEL | CHACO
Shape: Flying condor between 2 wreaths
Size: 46 × 40 mm
Metal: Copper
Ribbon: Blue
Reference: Pratt 2007, 224

Bo 35

of those killed in action could request a cross. The award is a bronze cross in a single class, bestowed without regard for rank.

Instituted: By the National Congress

Obverse disc: Arms of Bolivia

Obverse legend: EL HONORABLE CONGRESO NACIONAL | A LOS DEFENSORES DEL CHACO on a red enameled band

Reverse: REPUBLICA DE BOLIVIA [lacking on some examples]

Shape: Red, blue, green, and black enameled gilt-rimmed, 2-pointed Maltese cross with a wreath in the angles, suspended from a condor

Size: 55 mm

Metal: Gilt

Ribbon: Red, yellow, green

* * *

BOLIVIA has remained at peace with its neighbors since the Chaco War. Over the years, Bolivia created an array of merit medals for its military in peacetime.

Bo36. La Cruz "a la Constancia"

Bolivia awards the Cross for Constancy to its army personnel for loyalty and years of service. Medals for various lengths of service differ in the number of wreaths and of stripes in the ribbon. Recipients are expected to have served honorably and loyally during their service. The medal is awarded in three classes.

Instituted: August 24, 1937

Classes: 1st: 25 years;* 2nd: 20 years;* 3rd: 10 years*

Obverse legend: A LA CONSTANCIA

Obverse inscription: 25, 20, or 10 | AÑOS

Reverse inscription EJERCITO DE BOLIVIA

Shape: Cross pattée with convex ends surmounted by crossed swords; 1st: 2 laurel

Bo35. La Cruz a los Defensores del Chaco

The Cross for the "Worthy of the Fatherland" was awarded to all the Bolivian participants in the Chaco War, including noncombatants. Persons wanting to receive the cross had to submit their application to the National Confederation of Ex-Combatants of the Chaco War. The heirs

Bo 36

Bo 36

wreaths in the angles; 2nd: 1 laurel wreath in the angles

Size: 52 × 42 mm

Metal: 1st: gilt; 2nd: silver; 3rd: bronze

Ribbon: 1st: white with 3 green stripes; 2nd: white with 2 green side stripes; 3rd: white with one green center stripe

Bo37. *La Gran Cruz de Boqueron*

The Bolivian army took the Paraguayan fort at Boqueron in 1932 at the outset of the war. Paraguay chose to retake it as the focal point of its first offensive into the Chaco. The Bolivian garrison held out for three weeks but was forced to retreat on September 29, because of a lack of supplies and water. The Bolivian officers demonstrated bravery in defending the fort, for which they were awarded the Grand Cross for Boqueron, for which no information is currently available

Instituted: By Law No. 293 on January 11, 1964

*Bo38. *Las Medallas de la Cruz Roja Boliviana*

The Bolivian army's medical service organized ambulance services under the emblem of a red cross long before the Bolivian Red Cross Society was founded. Officers and nurses with red cross emblems tended to the wounded after the Battle of Tacna on May 26, 1879, during the War of the Pacific. On October 28, 1879, President Hilarión Daza signed the Geneva Convention governing the treatment of the wounded and prisoners of war. In 1880, the National Congress passed a law adhering Bolivia to the principles of the Geneva Convention. Red Cross volunteers worked with the Bolivian army during and after the Acre War. The Bolivian Red Cross Society was officially formed on May 15, 1917; it was recognized by the International Committee of the Red Cross on January 10, 1923, and it joined the League of Red Cross Societies on January 22, 1923. It has created its own medals awarded to those who support its mission, of which a description is available for only one.

*Bo38a. *La Medalla de la Cruz Roja Boliviana*

Obverse: Condor with spread wings below arms of Bolivia, above an enameled Red Cross

Reverse inscription: [Name of recipient]

Size: 35 × 29 mm

Metal: Gilt silver

Recipient: Cnl. Guerino Radillo

Provenance: A. Menke

Bo38b. *La Medalla de Honor de la Cruz Roja Boliviana "Antonia Zalles de Cariaga"*

Bo38c. *La Medalla a la Constancia de la Cruz Roja Boliviana "Francisca Nieto Pando" (1985)*

Reference: http://www.cruzrojaboliviana.org/revista/pdf/Libro.pdf

ORDERS

BOLIVIA created its first order after World War I for meritorious service to the
nation. The decision to create such an order reflected progress in the country's efforts to institutionalize its democracy after more than a century of unstable rule. The
design of Bolivian orders frequently incorporates symbols of the nation, such as the condor, the Huayna Potosí Mountain, the kantuta flower and such pre-Colombian symbols
as the Inca Sun.

*B039. *La Orden Nacional del
Cóndor de los Andes*

The National Order of the Condor of the Andes
was the country's first order of merit and remains today Bolivia's highest official award. It
is given for meritorious service for the devel-

opment and progress of Bolivia. It comes in
six grades and can be awarded to Bolivian or
foreign citizens, civil or military. Like Guatemala, Bolivia honors its most famous bird as
a symbol of the nation. The enameled peak in
the center of the obverse is Huayna Potosí, the
principal source of silver in colonial times. The

Bo 39
Collar

Collar of the order is awarded only to heads of state. Among its recipients have been Argentine President Saúl Menem; Juan Carlos Wasmosy, president of Paraguay; Vicente Fox, president of Mexico; and Haile Selassie I of Ethiopia.

Instituted: By Presidential Decree on April 18, 1925

Regulated: By Law No. 1,762 on March 5, 1997

Grades: Collar,* Grand Cross,* Grand Officer, Commander, Officer, and Knight*

Grand Master: President of the Republic

Obverse disc: Enameled scene: condor flying in front of Mount Potosí with sun to the left

Bo 39
Collar (reverse)

Bo 39
Knight

Bo 39
Grand Cross badge
(reverse)

Bo 39
Knight (reverse)

[condor lacking on Officer and Knight and on some examples of Grand Cross]

Obverse legend: LA VNION ES LA FVERZA | MCMXXV on a white enameled band

Reverse disc: Script RB on enameled field

Shape: Ball-tipped, blue enameled 2-pointed Maltese cross with pink enameled kantuta flowers in the angles, suspended from a flying condor

Collar shape: 5-pointed stars, alternating with enameled kantuta bunches, alternating with 8-pointed suns with RB in the disc

Size: Badge: Collar: 89 mm; Grand Cross: 57 mm; Knight: 47 mm. Star: 79 mm

Metal: Collar, Grand Cross: gilt; Knight: silver

Maker: Collar: Cejalvo, Madrid; Grand Cross: Monnaie de Paris

Ribbon: Green

Reference: Burke's Peerage 2006, 886–88; Gillingham 1932, 63; Barac 2009, 170; Werlich 1974, 58–59

Bo 40
Silver Cross

* * *

Two YEARS later, Bolivia created its first military order for meritorious service to its army.

*Bo40. *La Orden al Mérito Militar*

The Order of Military Merit is awarded to Bolivian and foreign citizens for meritorious service to the Bolivian army. The order exists in seven grades, each with its own design; there is no breast star. The Iron Star is awarded for wounds sustained in combat.

Authorized: By law on January 19, 1927

Modified: July 24, 1935

Grades: 1st: Collar of Honor; 2nd: Gold Star; 3rd: Blue Enameled Silver Cross; 4th: Red Enameled Silver Cross;* 5th: Bronze Cross;* 6th: Bronze Medal;* 7th: Iron Star*

Obverse legend: EJERCITO DE BOLIVIA

Bo 40
Silver Cross

Bo 40
Bronze Cross

Bo 40
Bronze Cross

Bo 40
Bronze Medal

Bo 40
Bronze Medal

Bo 40
Iron Star

Obverse inscription: AL | MERITO; 4th: on stepped cross on red enameled disc; 6th: E DE BE | AL MERITO on white enameled stepped cross

Reverse legend: EJERCITO DE BOLIVIA

Reverse inscription: AL | MERITO; 4th: on stepped cross on red enameled disc; 6th: E DE BE | AL MERITO on white enameled stepped cross

Shape: 3rd: ball-tipped, blue enameled Maltese cross with an Inca motif in the angles attached to a flying condor; 4th: red enameled 2-pointed Maltese cross with an Inca motif in the angles attached to a flying condor; 5th: ball-tipped, bronze Maltese cross with an Inca motif in the angles attached to a flying condor; 6th: Greek cross with Inca motif at each end with laurel leaves in the angles attached to a flying condor; 7th: 6-pointed star, each arm in the shape of a stylized man flanked by animal heads

Size: 3rd: 80 × 68 mm; 4th: 50 × 43 mm; 6th: 79 × 76 mm; 7th: 38 mm

Metal: 1st, 2nd: gold; 3rd, 4th: silver; 5th, 6th: bronze; 7th: iron

Maker: 7th: Loriol Castelli, Milan

Ribbon: 3rd: red, black, red, black; 4th: red, black, red; 6th: black, red

Reference: Burke's Peerage 2006, 888–89; Gillingham 1932, 63–64; Barac, 2009, 169; Werlich 1974, 59

Provenance: 3rd, 5th, 6th: A. Menke

*Bo41. *La Legión de Honor Libertador Simón Bolívar*

The Legion of Honor of the Liberator Simón Bolívar is awarded to Bolivian and foreign citizens, as well as national and international institutions, for providing eminent service to the republic. The order was originally instituted by Marshal Santa Cruz as the Legión de Honor Boliviano.

Instituted: By Presidential Decree on November 17, 1835

Reestablished: By Supreme Decree No. 22,243 on July 11, 1989, changing the name from Legión de Honor Boliviano to Legión de Honor Mariscal Andrés Santa Cruz y Calahumana

Modified: By Supreme Decree No. 27,423 on March 26, 2004, opening membership to foreign citizens as well as national and foreign institutions

Bo41a. *Version 1*

Obverse disc: Female head, right, on a white enameled disc surrounded by a red enameled band

Obverse legend: SIMON BOLIVAR LIBERTADOR on a blue enameled band

Reverse inscription: SIMON BOLIVAR | EN BOUFFET | DE MONTAUBAN | 1822

Shape: 8-pointed 6-part faceted star

Size: 52 mm

Ribbon: Green, yellow, red

Reference: Gillingham 1932, 62; Barac 2009, 170

*Bo41b. *Version 2 (after 1989): Legión de Honor Mariscal Andres Santa Cruz y Calahumana*

Grades: Grand Collar, Grand Cross, Grand Officer, Commander,* Officer, Knight

Grand Master: President of the Republic

Obverse disc: Bust of Santa Cruz

Obverse legend: MINISTERIO DE DEFENSA | MCAL. ANDRES DE SANTA CRUZ on a white enameled band

Shape: Ball-tipped 2-pointed Maltese cross with arms enameled light blue, green, red, yellow with 3 wreaths and crossed sword and kantuta plant in the angles, suspended from a star within laurel branches

Size: Grand Cross, Grand Official: 60 mm; Commander: 55 mm; Officer: 50 mm; Knight 40 mm

Metal: Gilt silver

Ribbon: Blue

Reference: http://www.lexivox.org/norms/ BO-DS-27423.xhtml, accessed September 25, 2012

* * *

Bo41b
Commander

AFTER the Chaco War, Bolivia began instituting orders intended to recognize people who contributed to the social and intellectual life of the nation. Bolivia historically has found it difficult to define its national culture. The early Spanish settlers exploited the country's silver wealth to finance the Spanish crown. The silver miners were provided by Indian communities under the *repartimiento* system, by which the Indians paid their taxes with labor. The nineteenth-century caudillos struggled for personal power but failed to integrate the Indian and creole communities into a single Bolivian national culture. The Bolivian officer corps was recruited from the creole population, whereas the troops were Aymara Indians. None of the officers spoke Aymara, and many Indians could not speak Spanish. This was a major cause of the poor performance by the Bolivian army during the War of the Pacific and the Chaco War.

Bo42. *La Gran Orden Boliviana de la Educación*

The Grand Bolivian Order for Education is awarded to Bolivian and foreign citizens for meritorious service to Bolivian education. It may also be bestowed on academic institutions. This order succeeds the Order of Merit for Teachers instituted on September 17, 1937. The order cites the full name of Bolivia's national liberator Andrés de Santa Cruz y Calahumana, who was half creole and half Aymara. The different grades have been decorated with unique designs, including Bolivian cultural symbols such as the condor, kantuta wreaths, the Inca Sun, and the Tiahuanaco Door of the Sun.

B042a. *La Orden del Mérito del Maestro*

Instituted: By Supreme Decree on September 17, 1937, and January 3, 1940

Grades: Grand Cross, Grand Officer, Commander, Officer, Knight

B042b. *La Gran Orden Boliviana de la Educación*

Instituted: By Decree Law No. 2,783 on October 9, 1951

Modified: By Supreme Decree No. 6,453 on May 3, 1963, allowing the order to be conferred on public and private schools

Grades: Grand Cross, Grand Officer, Commander, Officer, Knight

Obverse: Busts of Grand Marshal Zepita, Andrés de Santa Cruz y Calahumana

Obverse inscription: HONOR A BOLIVIA

Reverse: GRAN ORDEN BOLIVIANA DE LA EDUCACION, LA PATRIA AL MERITO [and the name of the grade]

Metal: Grand Officer: red and green enameled gold and silver; Commander: green and white enameled silver; Officer: green enameled silver; Knight: white enameled bronze

Ribbon: Grand Cross: red, green, red with narrow white edge stripes; Grand Officer: red, green with narrow white edge stripes; Commander: black, green, red with narrow white edge stripes; Officer: green, black, green with narrow white edge stripes; Knight: black, green with narrow white edge stripes

Reference: http://www.lexivox.org/norms/BO-DL-2783.xtml, December 2, 2012

* * *

IN 1965, Bolivia instituted three military orders, one for each of the three branches of the armed forces. They are awarded to military personnel for meritorious service in peacetime.

*B043. *La Orden de José Miguel Lanza*

The Order of José Miguel Lanza is a military order given to military personnel for meritorious service to the army. Lanza was Bolivia's most important guerrilla fighter against the royalists during the War of Independence. He joined the United Provinces' Army of the North, fought in the battles of Tucumán and Salta, and was instrumental in helping it invade Charcas. He fought in the Battle of Ayohuma, an engagement pitting royalist troops against militia from Cochabamba and units of the Army of the North. After the Battle of Ayacucho, Lanza led his men against the royalist garrison in La Paz. Many of its defenders deserted to Lanza's side, and the garrison itself surrendered. Lanza later signed Bolivia's declaration of independence. He died in 1828, trying to suppress an insurrection. Lanza lost most of the engagements that he fought in, but he survived each battle and attacked again.

Instituted: By Decree Law No. 7,256 on July 21, 1965

Regulated: By Supreme Resolution No. 145,550 on May 22, 1968

Grades: Grand Cross, Grand Officer,* Knight*

Obverse disc: Bust of Lanza, ¾ left, on a silver field

Bo 43
Grand Officer

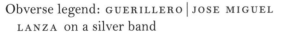

Bo 43
Grand Officer
badge (reverse)

Bo 43
Knight

Bo 43
Knight

Obverse legend: GUERILLERO | JOSE MIGUEL
LANZA on a silver band

Reverse disc: Grade of order

Reverse legend: EJERCITO NACIONAL |
BOLIVIA

Shape: Green and red enameled Maltese cross
with double concave ends, with a crossed
sword and lance and 3 parallel metallic
wreaths in the angles

Size: Badge: Grand Officer: 61 mm; Knight:
50 mm. Star: 68 mm

Metal: Gilt

Ribbon: Green, red

Reference: http://www.derechoteca.com/
gacetabolivia/decreto-ley-7256-del-21-julio-
1965.htm, accessed September 23, 2012

*Bo44. *La Orden al Mérito Naval*

Bolivia lost its territorial access to the Pacific Ocean to Chile during the War of the Pacific. The Bolivian navy patrols Lake Titicaca, the world's highest freshwater body, which it shares with Peru, as well as a network of navigable rivers in the lowlands, some of which act as borders with Brazil and Peru. Bolivia's only navigable waterway to the Atlantic Ocean is from Puerto Suárez down the Paraguay River to the River Plate. The Order of Naval Merit is awarded to Bolivian and foreign nationals for meritorious service to the Bolivian navy in peacetime.

Bo44
Knight

Instituted: By Decree Law No. 7,256 on July 21, 1965

Regulated: By Supreme Resolution No. 145,550 on May 22, 1968

Grades: Grand Cross,* Grand Officer, Knight*

Obverse disc: Blue enameled anchor superimposed on a red edged, white enameled Latin cross on a silver field

Obverse legend: AL MERITO NAVAL | BOLIVIA on a silver band

Reverse legend: Knight: FUERZA FLUVIAL Y LACUSTRE

Reverse inscription: [Grade of the order]

Shape: Blue enameled Maltese cross with double concave ends with gilt Incan design on each arm; Grand Cross: 3 wreaths in the angles; Knight: wreath in the angles

Size: Badge: Grand Cross: 62 mm; Knight: 49 mm. star: 70 mm

Metal: Gilt

Ribbon: Blue, white

Bo44
Knight

Bo 44
Grand Cross

*Bo45. *La Orden al Mérito Aeronáutico*

The Order of Aeronautical Merit is awarded to Bolivian and foreign nationals for meritorious service to the Bolivian Air Force.

> Instituted: By Decree Law No. 7,256 on July 21, 1965
>
> Regulated: By Supreme Resolution No. 145,550 on May 22, 1968
>
> Grade: Grand Cross,* Grand Officer, Officer,* Knight
>
> Obverse disc: Snow-capped peak against a blue enameled sky behind a flying gilt condor with the arms of Bolivia in its talons
>
> Obverse legend: AL MERITO | AERONAUTICO on a silver band
>
> Reverse legend: FUERZA AEREA | BOLIVIA
>
> Reverse inscription: [Grade of the order]
>
> Shape: Ball-tipped, light blue enameled, gilt-rimmed 2-pointed Maltese cross with wings in the angles
>
> Size: Badge: Grand Cross: 68 mm; Official: 56 mm. Star: 78 mm
>
> Metal: Gilt
>
> Maker: Esmaltarte, Brazil
>
> Ribbon: Light blue with narrow yellow edge stripes

Bo46. *La Orden al Mérito Civil del Libertador Simón Bolívar*

The Order of Civil Merit of the Liberator Simón Bolívar recognizes merit in the field of diplomacy and international relations.

> Instituted: July 24, 1986
>
> Grades: Grand Cross, Commander, Officer.
>
> Obverse disc: Silver bust of Bolívar, left, on gilt disc
>
> Shape: Grand Cross: ball-tipped, red enameled, 5-armed, 2-pointed star with a green enameled laurel wreath in the angles suspended from an oval green laurel wreath;

Bo 45
Officer

Bo 45
Officer

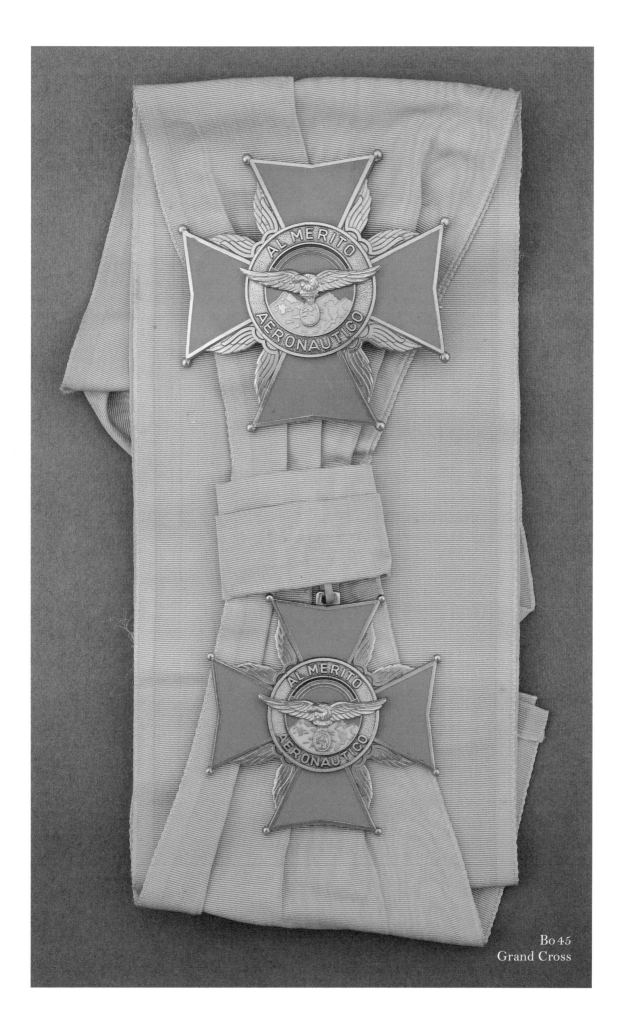

Bo 45
Grand Cross

Officer: the same, but star is 4-armed Maltese cross

Star shape: Oval disc as for the badge, surrounded by a 24-pointed red enameled gilt-edged star

Metal: Gilt

Ribbon: Red

Reference: Burke's Peerage 2006, 1:886–88; http://www.docelinajes.blogspot.com/2010/08/derecho-premial-de-Bolivia.html, accessed September 23, 2012

B047. *La Orden de la Policía Boliviana*

The Order of the Bolivian Police is awarded to police and military personnel, foreign diplomats, and also to national and foreign citizens for outstanding service to the police force. This order has three divisions: Al Mérito, A la Constancia, and Al Valor. The three divisions are regulated differently.

Instituted: By Supreme Decree No. 6,129 on June 8, 1962

Regulated: By Administrative Resolution No. 91,350/91 on December 23, 1991

Modified: By Administrative Resolution No. 0564/10 of the General Staff of the Bolivian Police on May 24, 2010

Grand Master: Commanding General of the National Police

B047a. *Al Mérito*

Grades: Grand Cross, Grand Officer, Commander, Officer, Knight, Merit Cord

Obverse disc: Grand Cross: arms of Bolivia; Grand Officer, Commander, Officer, Knight: emblem of the National Police

Obverse legend: Commander, Officer, Knight: POLICIA NACIONAL | BOLIVIA on a white enameled band

Shape: Grand Cross and Grand Officer: olive green enameled, gilt-edged Maltese cross

between 2 olive and laurel wreaths, surmounted by crossed carbines beneath a blue ribbon inscribed CONTRA EL MAL POR EL BIEN DE TODOS; Commander, Officer, Knight: olive green enameled Maltese cross surmounted by crossed carbines

Size: Badge: 40 × 40 mm. Star: 50 × 50 mm

Metal: Grand Cross, Grand Officer, Commander: gilt; Officer: silver; Knight: copper

Ribbon: Grand Cross: olive green sash; Grand Officer: no ribbon; Commander: olive green with 3 white stripes; Officer: olive green with 2 white stripes; Knight: olive green

B047b. *La Estrella "a la Constancia"*

The Star for Loyalty is awarded to police personnel for length of service with an unbroken record of moral fortitude and exemplary service.

Obverse inscription: A LA | CONSTANCIA | 10 [20, 25, and 30 years]

Shape: Green enameled 6-pointed star surrounded by a metallic wreath beneath crossed carbines

Ribbon: Olive green with 1 white stripe for 10 years (2 for 20 years; red, yellow, and green center stripes for 25 years; and 3 white stripes for 30 years)

B047c. *La Cruz al Valor*

The Cross for Valor is bestowed on police personnel for personal bravery and valor.

Shape: Ball-tipped, gray enameled Maltese cross with a metallic wreath in the angles surmounted by crossed carbines

Ribbon: Red

Reference: http://www.slideshare.net/wllanos/reglamento-de-condecoraciones-de-la-policia-boliviana, accessed September 24, 2012; http://www.policia.bo/REGLAMENTODECONDECORACIONES.pdf,

Bo 48

accessed September 24, 2012; http://www.
gacetaoficialdebolivia/gob/bno/normas/
buscar/page.29, accessed September 23,
2012

*Bo48. *La Orden Deportiva Bolivariana*

This order is given for contributions in the field
of sports.

> Shape: Crowned condor with displayed wings
> and kantuta plants in its talons, 5 linked,
> enameled circles beneath
>
> Size: 40 × 34 mm
>
> Metal: Gilt silver
>
> Maker: Huguenin, Le Locle
>
> Ribbon: White with yellow, blue, white, red,
> green edge stripes
>
> Provenance: A. Menke

Bo49. *La Orden Boliviana del Trabajo*

The Bolivian Order of Labor is awarded to
workers, technicians, and labor organizations
for contributing responsibly to the economic
development of Bolivia.

> Instituted: By Supreme Decree No. 9,305 on
> July 9, 1970

Grand Master: President of the Republic
Grades: 1st, 2nd, 3rd
Reference: Bolivia 1970, No. 9,305

Bo50. *La Gran Orden Boliviana de la Alfabetización y Educación de Adultos*

The Grand Bolivian Order of Literacy and
Adult Education is awarded to Bolivian and
foreign nationals for contributing morally, in-
tellectually, materially, or economically to the
literacy campaign.

> Instituted: By Supreme Decree No. 9,299 on
> July 9, 1970
>
> Grades: Grand Benefactor of Literacy, Com-
> mander, Officer, Knight
>
> Obverse: Map of Bolivia with a large letter A
> in the center
>
> Reverse inscription: GRAN ORDEN
> BOLIVIANA DE LA ALFABETIZACION Y
> EDUCACION DE ADULTOS
>
> Ribbon: Grand Benefactor: red, yellow, green;
> Commander: yellow; Officer: red; Knight:
> green
>
> Reference: Bolivia 1970, No. 9,299

BRAZIL

A S FRENCH TROOPS neared Lisbon during the Napoleonic Wars, Portugal's King João VI and his court sailed off in voluntary exile to Brazil. João ruled his empire from Rio de Janeiro for fourteen years. When summoned back to Portugal by the Cortes in 1821, he left his son Pedro to rule Brazil in his stead. Pedro took the title of emperor and went on to create his own imperial court in Brazil. When the Cortes ordered him to return, he refused and declared Brazil's independence from Portugal in 1822.

Pedro I instituted Brazilian branches of the three great Portuguese ancient military orders and named himself Grand Master. He also founded two entirely new Brazilian orders. He authorized Brazil's first military medals for those who fought for Brazil's independence and remained loyal to him. He also awarded medals for the second military campaign against Uruguay from 1816 to 1822.

When João VI died in 1826, Pedro I returned to Portugal and designated his minor son, Pedro II, as regent. The Brazilian parliament named him emperor in 1840 at the age of fourteen, and he ruled until 1889. Although Pedro II did not institute any new monarchical orders, he continued to award those founded by his father. He authorized his first military medal in 1837 for suppressing an internal revolt. Pedro II fought two wars during his reign, the first against Argentina during the dictatorship of Manuel Rosas and the second against Paraguay under President Solano López. He awarded medals for the major battles of both wars.

Brazil became a constitutional republic in 1891 following a bloodless military coup against Pedro II in 1889. The nation has remained at peace with its neighbors since then. Brazil issued medals for its token participation in World War I and its involvement in the Italian Campaign during World War II.

After World War II, the Brazilian government took an increasingly proactive role in developing the national economy and has instituted new orders recognizing individual contributions to its economy, culture, and justice system. The country has created an array of military medals for its armed forces in peacetime.

MEDALS

IMPERIAL RULE AS A PORTUGUESE COLONY (1807–1822)

JOÃO VI authorized Brazil's first military medal after capturing the French fort at Cayenne in French Guiana during the Napoleonic Wars. João's marines were mainly Brazilian, and his ships embarked from Brazilian territory.

Br1. *A Medalha da Tomada de Cayenna*

When Britain decided to attack Cayenne, the fortified capital of French Guiana, the bulk of its navy and army was engaged in fighting Napoleon's forces in Europe. The English king asked João VI to send an expeditionary force from Brazil. João sent some five hundred Brazilian colonial marines in Portuguese warships, which rendezvoused with a small British warship off the Guianese coast. The combined British-Portuguese-Brazilian force under the command of Manuel Marques de Elva Portugal laid siege to the Cayenne fortress by attacking satellite forts with their own superior forces. On January 14, 1809, the French garrison sur-

rendered. The battle marked the first time that native Brazilian soldiers fought an engagement outside of their country. João VI created the Medal for Capturing Cayenne, Brazil's first military medal

Instituted: 1809

Obverse: Bust of Prince Regent, left

Obverse legend: D. JOAM P:G: D: PRINC: REGENT: DE PORTUGAL & | 1809

Reverse inscription: 14.JAN | 1809. surrounded by crossed wreathes

Reverse legend: CAYENNA TOMADA A: OS FRANCEZES.

Metal: Gold, silver-gilt, silver, bronze

Reference: Gillingham 1932, 76; Barac 2009, 171

EMPIRE OF BRAZIL (1822–1889)

AFTER NAPOLEON'S defeat, the reconstituted Portuguese Cortes pressured João VI to return to Portugal. Before leaving in 1821, he appointed his son Pedro to rule Brazil in his stead. When the Cortes later demanded that Pedro also return, he refused and declared Brazil independent on September 7, 1822. Pedro named himself emperor as Pedro I. Some Portuguese officers in Brazil remained loyal to the Portuguese crown. At the time of independence, Brazil was occupying Uruguay, and Pedro I relied on his loyal military there to neutralize those still loyal to Portugal and return them to Lisbon. Pedro I instituted several military medals for those who defended his throne.

Br2. *A Cruz do Uruguai*

Pedro I created the Cross for Uruguay just two weeks after proclaiming himself emperor; this

is the first medal that he authorized. He permitted the recipients of the *escudo* given by João VI in the first Cisplatine Campaign in 1811 to attach a yellow ribbon to it and wear it on the left chest. He instituted this cross for those who participated in both campaigns.

Instituted: By Imperial Decree on September 25, 1822

Obverse disc: A crowned laurel wreath and a dove of peace; inscribed at the bottom URUGUAI

Reverse disc: Same as obverse

Shape: Ball-tipped Maltese cross surmounted by an imperial crown suspended from a ribbon bar

Size: 27 mm

Metal: Silver

Ribbon: Yellow

Reference: Gillingham 1932, 76; Barac 2009, 171; Schulman 1970, no. 426

Br3. *A Cruz de Distinção para as Forças da Cisplatina*

João VI felt threatened by republican influence in Uruguay and had invaded in the second Cisplatine campaign, which lasted from 1816 to 1820. He later annexed Uruguay to colonial Brazil in July 1821, calling it the Cisplatine Province. His son, Emperor Pedro I, authorized a cross for the army and navy officers and men who participated in this invasion.

Portuguese troops still occupied Montevideo when Pedro I declared Brazil independent in 1822. Many of them pledged their allegiance to the new Brazilian emperor, but some remained loyal to the Portuguese crown. The loyalists returned home, while the new Brazilians remained in the Cisplatine Province in the name of Pedro I. He created a cross for his loyal officers and men, who fought in both Cisplatine campaigns. The olive tree on the medal represents Cisplatina, and the griffon is the symbol of the House of Braganza—the then reigning family of Portugal and Brazil.

Instituted: By Imperial Decree on January 31, 1823

Classes: Generals, other officers, enlisted men, civilians

Obverse disc: Olive branch over Montevideo Hill on a blue enameled field

Obverse legend: MONTEVIDEO on a green enameled band

Reverse: PETRUS I B.I.D. on a green enameled field and surrounded by a laurel wreath

Shape: Cross pattée with double concave ends surmounted by a griffon. The arms bear the year of the recipient's tour of duty in Cisplatina and, if less than four years, rosettes.

Size: 45 × 30 mm

Metal: Generals: gold, gilt; other officers: gold, silver; enlisted men and civilians: white metal

Ribbon: Green with yellow edge stripes with a metal bar: MDCCCXXII

Br3a. *Variant*

Obverse disc: URUGUAI with an olive branch interlaced with the griffon

Reverse: Same as obverse

Shape: Ball-tipped Maltese cross suspended from an imperial crown

Size: 27 mm

Metal: Gold, silver, white metal

Reference: Gillingham 1932, 77–78; Barac 2009, 172; Schulman 1970, no. 427; Brazil 1983, 1–4

Br4. *A Cruz dos Voluntarios Reais de el Rei, 1822–1823*

The Cross for the King's Royal Volunteers was given to the officers and men who took part in the first Cisplatine War and remained loyal to Pedro I following his declaration of independence.

Instituted: By Imperial Decree on July 25, 1824

Classes: Officers, enlisted men

Obverse disc: Bust of Pedro I, right

Obverse legend: VOLUNTARIOS REAIS DE EL REY

Reverse disc: MONTEVIDEO 1822 E 1823

Shape: Maltese cross with gold globules in the angles, linked by a laurel wreath suspended from a brooch

Size: 27 mm

Metal: Officers: silver; enlisted men: bronze

Ribbon: Green edged in yellow

Reference: Gillingham 1932, 76–77; Barac 2009, 171; Schulman 1970, no. 425; Musso Ambrosi 1976, 140–41

Br5. *A Medalha da Restauração de Bahia* (*Medalha da Independência do Brasil*)

On February 19, 1822, units of the Portuguese army in Bahia rebelled against Pedro I, and the rebellion soon spread to other parts of the northeast. Pedro I sent a fleet under Lord Cochrane to blockade Salvador and to land Brazilian soldiers. The two sides fought for a year, when the Portuguese troops finally sailed for home in July 1823. Their departure consolidated Brazil's independence, and Pedro I authorized a medal for his officers and men who forced them to leave. This medal is also known as the Medal of Independence of Brazil.

Instituted: By Pedro I on July 2, 1825, for the army; on August 17, 1825, for the navy

Classes: Generals, other officers, enlisted men

Obverse disc: Crossed enameled laurel branch (laurel crown for medals made in Bahia) and a sword surmounted by the initials P.I. and the imperial crown

Obverse legend: RESTAURACAO DE BAHIA | 1823 on a black enameled band

Reverse disc: Bust of Dom Pedro I (medals struck in Rio de Janeiro are uniface)

Shape: Oval sun with 32 rays suspended from an imperial crown

Size: 95 × 50 mm

Metal: Generals: gold; other officers: silver; enlisted men: copper

Maker: Casa de Moeda, Rio de Janeiro; Casa de Moeda, Bahia

Ribbon: 5 equal stripes—2 yellow and 3 green

Reference: Gillingham 1932, 79; Barac 2009, 172; Schulman 1970, no. 428; Brazil 1983, 1–4

Br6. *A Primeira Medalha de Distinção*

Some Brazilian provinces wanted to create a separate republic instead of pledging loyalty to Pedro I. Pernambuco, in particular, harbored strong anti-imperial feelings, partly because of the severe repression a few years earlier in Bahia. In 1824, Pernambuco tried to create the Confederation of the Equator by uniting rebellious provinces. Republican rebels took control of Recife. The emperor responded once again by sending Lord Cochrane with his fleet to blockade the city and attack it by land. The rebellion was suppressed, and Pedro I authorized two medals for the officers and men who fought under Lord Cochrane. This medal is better known in English as the Cross for Pernambuco. A variant of this medal has CONSTANCIA E BRAVURA inscribed on the reverse, when awarded for at least six months' service. There are also three types of imperial crowns with minor differences and two ribbon designs.

Instituted: By Imperial Decree on October 20, 1824, for the army; on February 7, 1825, for the navy

Classes: Generals, officers, enlisted men

Obverse disc: Bust of Pedro I, left

Reverse disc: Same as obverse in most cases; sometimes uniface

Shape: Ball-tipped Maltese cross suspended from an imperial crown. "17" and "9" on the upper and lower arms; "18" and "24" on the left and right arms

Size: 36 mm

Metal: Generals: gold; other officers: silver; enlisted men: copper

Ribbon: Yellow with narrow green edge stripes with a metal bar inscribed CONSTANCIA

Reference: Gillingham 1932, 78; Barac 2009, 172; Schulman 1970, no. 428; Brazil 1983, 4–6

Br7. *A Segunda Medalha de Distinção "Aos Mais Bravos" (A Insignia de Ouro de Distinção em Combate)*

The second medal for this conflict is round, made of gold, and quite rare. The medal was struck simultaneously in Rio de Janeiro and in Recife. Some examples are uniface.

Instituted: By Imperial Decree on October 20, 1824, for army personnel; on January 22, 1825, for navy personnel

Obverse: Bust of emperor

Obverse legend: PETRUS I. D. G. CONST. IMP. ET. PERP. BRAS. DEF. | 1824 (medals struck in Rio de Janeiro); PEDRO I. IMP. CONST. DO BRAZ. (medals struck in Recife)

Reverse inscription: PELO | IMPERADOR | AOS MAIS | BRAVOS | 1824 in blue enamel (medals struck in Rio de Janeiro); PELO | I. | AOS MAIS | BRAVOS | 1824 in blue enamel (medals struck in Recife)

Shape: Round with the ends of crossed swords extending from the rim, suspended from an imperial crown

Metal: Gold

Ribbon: Green, yellow

Reference: Gillingham 1932, 78; Barac 2009, 172; Brazil 1983, 4–7

*Br8. *A Medalha da Revolução da Pará*

The Medal for the Pará Revolution was awarded to the imperial officers and men who suppressed a rebellion in Grão-Pará Province.

In 1831, when Pedro I abdicated in favor of his infant son, the event caused political discord in Pará and Rio Grande Provinces. By 1837, both provinces were in open rebellion against the Regency. The insurrection lasted for five years (1835–40). The Regency sent a fleet to blockade Belem, the provincial capital, and the revolt finally ended when the insurgents accepted an amnesty.

> Instituted: 1837
>
> Obverse: Bust of Pedro II as a boy, right
>
> Obverse legend: PETRUS. II. D.G.C. IMP. ET. PERP. BRAS. DEF. | 1837

Reverse: Arms of imperial Brazil bracketed by coffee and tobacco branches

Reverse legend: IN HOCS. VINCES.

Shape: Gilt: round surrounded by 2 female figures and coffee and tobacco branches surmounted by an imperial crown; silver, bronze: round with no crown in the suspension

Size: 34 mm

Metal: Gilt, silver, bronze*

Ribbon: Green

Reference: Gillingham 1932, 79–80; Barac 2009, 173

THE SECOND CISPLATINE WAR

IN 1851, the Argentine dictator Juan Manuel Rosas declared war on Brazil over control of Uruguay. Pedro II allied himself with Uruguay and the Argentine provinces of Entre Rios and Corrientes. On February 3, 1852, both sides fought the Battle of Monte Caseros in Buenos Aires Province. Rosas's army faced the combined forces of Brazil, Uruguay, and an Argentine army commanded by the governor of Entre Rios, Justo José de Urquiza. The allied forces defeated Rosas, who fled Argentina. The battle ended the twenty-year reign of Rosas.

*Br9. *A Medalha de Campanha do Uruguai, 1852*

The Brazilian troops were the only professional soldiers in Urquiza's army and probably proved decisive in defeating Rosas. Pedro II awarded the Medal for the Uruguay Campaign to the officers and men of the 3,500-man Brazilian expeditionary force. There are at least four variants of this medal.

> Instituted: By Imperial Decree No. 932 on March 14, 1852, for the army; by No. 947 on April 1, 1852, for the navy
>
> Classes: Generals, other officers,* enlisted men*

Obverse: Bust of Pedro II, left

Obverse legend: D. PEDRO SEGUNDO. IMPERADOR DO BRAZIL

Reverse: 1852 surrounded by a wreath (variant has 1851 | 1852 and no loop for suspension)

Reverse legend: CAMPANHA DO URUGUAY

Shape: Round, suspended by a hinge from an imperial crown

Size: 30 mm

Metal: Generals: gold; other officers: silver; enlisted men: white metal

Ribbon: Green with red edge stripes

Reference: Gillingham 1932, 82; Barac 2009, 173; Brazil 1983, 9–10; Musso Ambrosi

Br 9

Br 9

1976, 146–48; Schulman 1970, nos. 439–44; de Urquiza 1928, 92–93

Provenance: Other officers: A. Menke

*Br10. *A Medalha de Campanha Naval do Rio da Prata, 1852*

This is the navy version for the same campaign as above. The Brazilian navy carried its land forces up the Paraná River to link up with Urquiza's men before advancing against Rosas.

Instituted: By Imperial Decree No. 947 on April 1, 1852

Classes: Generals, other officers, enlisted men*

Obverse: Bust of Pedro II, left

Obverse legend: D. PEDRO II. IMPERADOR DO BRAZIL

Reverse: 1851 | 1852 surrounded by a wreath

Reverse legend: CAMPANHA NAVAL DO RIO DA PRATA

Shape: Round, suspended from an imperial crown

Size: 30 mm

Metal: Generals: gold; other officers: silver; enlisted men: white metal

Ribbon: Green

Reference: Gillingham 1932, 82; Barac 2009, 173; Brazil 1983, 9–10

Provenance: A. Menke

Br11. *A Medalha de Campanha Naval do Rio da Prata e Batalha da Passagem de Tonelero*

The Medal for Passing the Tonelero Narrows was bestowed on the navy officers and men who crewed the seven Brazilian warships that forced their way past the Argentine batteries at the Tonelero narrows on the River Plate. The Brazilian fleet filed past the Argentine batteries and suffered only light casualties. None of the

Brazilian ships were sunk. This medal has at least four variants.

Instituted: By Imperial Decree No. 947 on April 1, 1852

Classes: Senior officers, other officers, enlisted men

Obverse: Bust of Pedro II, left

Obverse legend: D. PEDRO II. IMPERADOR DO BRAZIL

Reverse inscription: 17 | 1851 | 12 surrounded by a wreath

Reverse legend: CAMPANHA NAVAL DO RIO DA PRATA.E.C. DO TONELERO

Shape: Round, suspended from an imperial crown

Size: 31 mm; also known as a 60 mm copper medal

Metal: Senior officers: gold; other officers: silver; enlisted men: white metal

Ribbon: Light blue; the ribbon for the gold medal was hung around the neck

Reference: Gillingham 1932, 80; Barac 2009, 173; Brazil 1983, 10; Schulman 1970, no. 432a; de Urquiza 1928, 103–4

Br 12

*Br 12. *A Medalha do Uruguai e de Buenos Ayres, 1852*

The Medal for the Uruguay and Buenos Aires Campaign was awarded to the troops who participated in the same campaign as the preceding medal. It has no ribbon or other means of suspension.

Instituted: By Imperial Decree No. 947 on April 1, 1852

Obverse: Bust of Pedro II, left

Obverse legend: D. PEDRO SEGUNDO IMPER. DO BRAZIL

Reverse inscription: 3 | 1852 | 2 surrounded by a wreath

Reverse legend: CAMPANHA DO URUGUAY E DE BUENOS AYRES

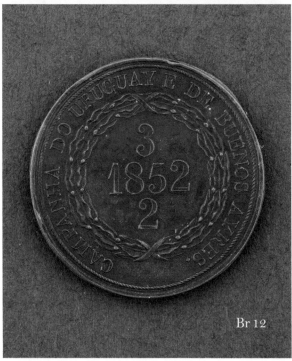

Br 12

Size: 30 mm

Metal: Gold, silver, bronze,* zinc

Reference: Gillingham 1932, 82–85; Barac 2009, 174; de Urquiza 1928, 96–97

The Triple Alliance War (1865–1869)

PEDRO II acted to reestablish Brazilian influence in Uruguay by sending his fleet and army to support his Colorado allies. The Uruguayan Blancos turned to Paraguay for support. In November 1864, Paraguay responded by capturing a Brazilian ship in the Paraná River and declared war on Brazil. Paraguayan forces moved up the Paraguay River and overwhelmed the Brazilian fort at Coimbra on December 28, 1864. The Brazilians troops at Coimbra fought bravely, but they were outnumbered and withdrew. Brazil authorized a medal for the defenders of Coimbra Fort.

*Br 13. *A Medalha do Forte de Coimbra*

The Medal for Coimbra Fort was awarded to the 120 defenders under the command of Colonel Porto Carreira. Coimbra controlled the Paraguay River upstream, and its loss allowed the Paraguayans to advance further into Matto Grosso. However, there were few stra-tegic objectives in that isolated state, and the Paraguayan invasion had little impact on the war.

Instituted: By Imperial Decree No. 3,492 on July 8, 1865 (army); by Imperial Decree No. 4,158 on April 21, 1868 (navy) for the crews of the Matto Grosso flotilla

Classes: Senior officers, other officers, enlisted men*

Br 13

Br 13

Obverse inscription: VALOR | E | LEALDADE
between 2 laurel branches

Reverse inscription: 26.27.28 | DE | DEZEMBRO
| FORTE | DE | COIMBRA | 1864

Shape: Oval

Size: Senior officers: 35 × 23 mm; other officers and enlisted men: 28 × 20 mm

Metal: Senior officers: gilt; other officers: silver; enlisted men: bronze

Engraver: Victor Resse

Maker: Casa de Moeda, Rio de Janeiro; Victor
Resse, Rio de Janeiro

Ribbon: Red, black, red

Reference: Dos Santos 1937, 19–22; Gillingham 1932, 83; Brazil 1983, 13–14; Barac
2009, 174

Provenance: A. Menke

*Br 14. *A Medalha da Campanha do
Uruguai*

Brazil invaded Uruguay in October 1864 and
sent its fleet to the River Plate. The fleet supported the capture of the Blanco-controlled
port of Paysandú by Brazilian and Uruguayan
Colorado troops. The allies then took Montevideo in February of 1865. With the Colorados controlling Montevideo, Uruguay declared
war on Paraguay. Pedro I instituted the Medal
for the Uruguayan Campaign in the following
year. The medal was awarded to members of
the Brazilian army and the navy.

Instituted: By Imperial Decree No. 3,468 on
May 8, 1865 (army); by Imperial Decree No.
3,488 on June 28, 1865 (navy)

Classes: Generals, other officers, enlisted
men*

Obverse: Bust of Pedro II, left

Reverse: CAMPANHA | DO | URUGUAY | 1865
within a laurel wreath

Shape: Oval

Size: 25 × 20 mm

Metal: Generals: gold; other officers: silver;
enlisted men: bronze

Ribbon: Red, blue

Reference: Gillingham 1932, 83–84; Barac
2009, 174; Brazil 1983, 12; Musso Ambrosi
1976, 154

* * *

THE PARAGUAYANS advanced south, capturing the Argentine city of Corrientes on the
Paraná River and then continuing east down
both sides of the Uruguay River. Brazil countered by sending its fleet of steam-powered warships up the Paraná River. Paraguayan President Francisco Solano López sent his own
steamboats south to attack the Brazilian fleet
at Riachuelo. The two fleets met on June 11,
1865. The Brazilians prevailed with difficulty,
and the Paraguayans withdrew their surviving ships north. The battle was the largest
single naval engagement in Latin American
history.

*Br 15. *A Medalha do Combate Naval do Riachuelo*

Brazil awarded the Medal for the Naval Engagement at Riachuelo to its navy officers and
crew present at the battle.

Instituted: By Imperial Decree No. 3,529 on
November 18, 1865

Classes: 1st: chiefs; 2nd: officers; 3rd: enlisted
men*

Obverse: Bust of Pedro II, left, between tobacco and coffee branches

Br 15   Br 15

Obverse legend: PETRUS II D.G. CONST. IMP.
ET PERP. BRAS. DEF.1865

Reverse: Crossed anchor and cannon under a
shield inscribed: 11 | DE JUNHO | DE | 1865

Reverse legend: COMBATE NAVAL DO
RIACHUELO

Shape: Round, suspended from an imperial
crown

Size: 1st: 37 mm; 2nd, 3rd: 26 mm

Metal: 1st: gold; 2nd: silver; 3rd: bronze

Maker: Casa de Moeda, Rio de Janeiro; Victor
Resse, Rio de Janeiro

Ribbon: White with green side stripes

Reference: Gillingham 1932, 86; Barac 2009, 175; Brazil 1983, 15–18; Dos Santos 1937, 32–35; Pratt 2007, 84–89

*Br16. *A Medalha do Combate Naval do Riachuelo (Exército)*

The army version of the Medal for the Naval Engagement at Riachuelo was authorized eleven days after the navy version.

Instituted: By Imperial Decree No. 3,548 on November 29, 1865

Classes: Senior officers, general officers,* enlisted men

Obverse: Bust of Pedro II, left, between tobacco and coffee branches

Obverse legend: PETRUS II D.G. CONST. IMP. ET PERP. BRAS. DEF. 1865

Reverse: Crossed anchor and cannon beneath a shield inscribed 11 DE JUNHO DE 1865

Reverse legend: COMBATE NAVAL DO RIACHUELO

Shape: Round, suspended from an imperial crown

Size: Gilt: 37 mm; other metals: 25 mm

Metal: Generals: gilt silver; other officers: silver; enlisted men: bronze

Maker: Casa de Moeda, Rio de Janeiro; Joalheria do Barão de São Victor, Rio de Janeiro

Ribbon: White with green edge stripes

Reference: Dos Santos 1937, 35; Brazil 1983, 18; Pratt 2007, 85

Provenance: A. Menke

*Br17. *A Medalha da Rendição de Uruguayana*

Solano López sent his army down both sides of the Uruguay River under the command of Colonel Antonio de la Cruz Estigarribia. His objective was to join his Blanco allies in Uruguay. Pedro II led his army by forced march south to block the Paraguayan advance. The Paraguayans occupied the Brazilian town of Uruguayana along the Uruguay River and fortified it. The Brazilians laid siege to the city. Estigarribia surrendered his forces without a fight on September 18, 1865. Pedro II awarded the Medal for the Surrender of Uruguayana to his officers and men who laid siege to the city. The medals of chiefs and officers were worn on the right breast, while those of enlisted men were worn on the left breast.

> Instituted: By Imperial Decree No. 3,515 on September 20, 1865
>
> Classes: Chiefs, officers,* enlisted men*
>
> Obverse inscription: URUGUAYANA between tobacco and coffee branches
>
> Reverse inscription: 18 | DE SEPTEMBRO | DE 1865 between laurel branches
>
> Size: 20 mm
>
> Metal: Chiefs: gold; officers: silver; enlisted men: white metal
>
> Maker: Casa de Moeda, Rio de Janeiro; Victor Resse, Rio de Janeiro
>
> Ribbon: Blue, green, blue
>
> Reference: Gillingham 1932, 84; Barac 2009, 174; Dos Santos 1937, 23–31; Pratt 2007, 96–99; Brazil 1983, 14–15

*Br18. *A Medalha "Aos Mais Bravos"*

For outstanding military merit, Pedro II bestowed upon his officers and men his most important orders: those of Christ, the Rose, Avis, and the Cross. However, these orders were not usually given for bravery in the field. The Medal for the Bravest was intended for members of the military physically present on the battlefield.

> Instituted: By Imperial Decrees No. 3,853 (army) and 3,854 (navy) on May 1, 1867
>
> Classes: Officers, enlisted men*
>
> Obverse: Bust of Pedro II, left, between 2 laurel branches with the initials RD
>
> Reverse inscription: AOS | MAIS | BRAVOS between 2 laurel branches

Reverse legend: CAMPANHA DO PARAGUAY | 1867

Shape: Oval

Size: 25 × 20 mm

Metal: Officers: gold; enlisted men: silver; also known in bronze

Designer: Roberto Depaux

Maker: Casa de Moeda, Rio de Janeiro

Ribbon: Red with narrow green edge stripes

Reference: Gillingham 1932, 87; Barac 2009, 175; Dos Santos 1937, 36–39; Pratt 2007, 130–32; Brazil 1983, 18

Br19. *A Medalha da Passagem de Humaitá*

The allied forces advanced slowly up the Paraná River and crossed into Paraguayan territory. One allied column marched through Paraguay, flanking the major Paraguayan fortress at Humaitá on the Paraguay River. A second allied army was slowly making its way up the west bank of the Paraguay River. The Brazilian navy forced its way past the Paraguayan guns at Humaitá on February 19, 1868, thereby threatening Asunción. The Paraguayans retreated upstream to protect their capital. Brazil awarded the Medal for the Passage of Humaitá to its navy officers and men who broke through the Paraguayan defenses.

Instituted: By Imperial Decree No. 4,118 on March 14, 1868

Classes: Generals, other officers, enlisted men

Obverse: View of Paraguay River and the Humaitá Fortress with Brazilian steam warships in the river

Obverse legend: A ESQUADRA BRASILEIRA FORÇA O PASSO DE HUMAITÁ

Obverse exergue: XIX DE FEVEREIRO DE | MDCCCLXVIII

Reverse: AOS | DA | PASSAGEM | DE | HUMAYTA between laurel branches

Shape: Round, suspended from a bar with an imperial crown on top

Size: 34 mm

Metal: Generals: gold; other officers: silver; enlisted men: bronze

Designer: Roberto Depaux; Casa Luiz de Razende

Maker: Casa de Moeda, Rio de Janeiro

Ribbon: Red, light blue, red

Reference: Gillingham 1932, 88; Barac 2009, 176; Dos Santos 1937, 42–44; Pratt 2007, 170–71; Brazil 1983, 20–22; Meili 1890, 14

* * *

THE BATTLE of Humaitá was the last major engagement of the war. The Paraguayans fought tenaciously on their home territory, resorting to guerrilla tactics, which slowed the allied advance. This was also true in Matto Grosso, where the Brazilians were finally able to advance down the Paraguay River into Paraguayan territory. The emperor authorized three military medals for the officers and men who fought on the various fronts inside Paraguay.

*Br20. *A Medalha de Matto Grosso*

Also known as the Medal for Loyalty and Valor, the Medal for Matto Grosso was awarded to the officers and men who fought an extended campaign against the Paraguayans in southern Matto Grosso along the Paraguayan border. The medal was also given to the men who recaptured the town of Corumba, which the Paraguayans occupied for two years. Military operations in Matto Grosso required great personal sacrifice, owing to the heat and thick vegetation.

Instituted: By Imperial Decree No. 3,926 on August 7, 1867, for military operating in the Apa Campaign

Modified: By Imperial Decree No. 4,201 on June 6, 1868, for military operating in the Corumba Campaign

Br 20

Classes: Chiefs, officers,* enlisted men

Obverse: Bust of Pedro II, left

Reverse: Inscribed around a wreath: CONSTANCIA E VALOR and below the wreath MATTO | GROSSO | 1867

Shape: Oval

Size: 25 × 20 mm

Metal: Chiefs: gold; officers: silver; enlisted men: white metal

Maker: Casa de Moeda, Rio de Janeiro; Victor Resse, Rio de Janeiro. The design differs slightly between the 2 makers

Ribbon: Yellow, green, with 2 light blue edge stripes

Reference: Gillingham 1932, 86; Barac 2009, 175; Dos Santos 1937, 39–42; Pratt 2007, 162–67; Brazil 1983, 20–22

*Br21. *A Medalha "a Bravura Militar"*

Pedro II authorized a medal for bravery, which was awarded without regard for rank. The medal was made in one grade out of bronze. A bar was placed on the ribbon with the year inscribed for each act of bravery during operations against Paraguay.

Instituted: By Imperial Decree No. 4,131 on March 28, 1868 (army) and by Imperial Decree No. 4,143 on April 5, 1868 (navy)

Obverse: Military objects

Obverse legend: EXERCITO EM OPERAÇÕES CONTRA O GOVERNO DO PARAGUAY

Reverse inscription: RECOMPENSA | A BRAVURA | MILITAR

Reverse legend: DECRETO DE 28 DE MARÇO DE 1868

Shape: Oval

Size: 35 × 25 mm

Metal: Bronze

Maker: Casa de Moeda, Rio de Janeiro

Ribbon: Green, red, green

Ribbon bars: Bars were issued for specific days in combat. The medal in the collection has five bars with the dates 6, 11, 21, 25, AND 27 DE DEZEMBRO DE 1868. Other bars specify battles: Curupaity, Curuzu, Humayta, Itapiru, Paso de la Patria, Timbo, and Tagy.

Reference: Gillingham 1932, 87; Barac 2009, 176; Dos Santos 1937, 35–48; Pratt 2007, 110–13; Brazil 1983, 22–24

*Br22. *A Medalha Geral de Campanha do Paraguai*

Pedro II authorized a general campaign medal for his army a year after the war ended. The medals were made from captured Paraguayan cannon. The medal was not given for merit, per se, but rather for the number of years that the recipient was present on the field of battle. The

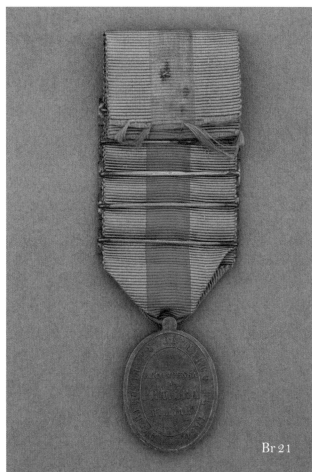

Br 21

Br 21

Br 22

Br 22

ribbon bar denotes the number of years in the field, which varies from one to five.

Instituted: By Imperial Decree No. 4,560 on August 6, 1870 (army); by Imperial Decree No. 4,573 on August 20, 1870 (navy)

Classes: Senior officers, other officers, enlisted men*

Obverse disc: CAMPANHA | DO | PARAGUAY surrounded by a wreath

Reverse disc: 6 | 18-70 | 8 surrounded by a wreath

Shape: Maltese cross with 2-pointed ends

Size: 28 mm

Metal: Senior officers: gold; other officers: silver; enlisted men: bronze

Ribbon: Green, white, blue, white, and yellow (the colors of the flags of Argentina, Brazil, and Uruguay)

Reference: Gillingham 1932, 88–90; Barac 2009, 176; Pratt 2007, 146–53; Brazil 1983, 24–25; Musso Ambrosi 1976, 169

Republican Medals

THE EMPIRE OF BRAZIL ended on November 15, 1889, when General Deodoro da Fonseca overthrew Emperor Pedro II in a bloodless coup. Fonseca named himself de facto president and changed the country's name to the Republic of the United States of Brazil. Prior to World War I, Brazil instituted one new military medal for length of service, but none for the many internal insurgencies that challenged constitutional rule. Brazil did authorize two medals for its military and civilian personnel involved with Brazil's token participation in World War I.

World War I

BRAZIL maintained its neutrality in the beginning of the war. However, German submarines began sinking Brazilian merchant ships. In response, Brazil broke diplomatic relations with Germany on April 11, 1917. German U-boats continued their attacks, causing Brazil to declare war on October 26. Brazil was not prepared for war in Europe, and it was many months before the country was able send military forces across the Atlantic. The Brazilian fleet was used to patrol the waters between Dakar and the entrance to the Mediterranean, but it did not become active until shortly before the war ended. Brazil did send a medical unit with surgeons, which arrived at the front only shortly before the armistice was announced. The government authorized two medals to award both military and civilian personnel.

*Br23. *A Cruz de Campanha de 1917 a 1918*

Brazil awarded the Campaign Cross of 1917–18 to reward both military and civilian personnel who participated in the war. Two versions of the combatant medal were struck with the same inscriptions and ribbon, but the width of the medal differs.

Instituted: By Legislative Decree No. 4,386
on December 10, 1921

Classes: Combatants,* noncombatants*

Obverse disc: Constellation of the Southern
Cross

Obverse legend: PELA JUSTICA E PELA
CIVILISAÇÃO

Reverse inscription: 1917|–|1918

Reverse legend: GRANDE-GUERRA | BRASIL

Shape: Maltese cross with convex ends with
roman numerals at the top of the upper
arms representing the number of semesters
the recipient spent on duty outside of the
country

Size: 42 mm

Metal: Bronze

Ribbon: Combatants: orange with 1 central
black stripe and edged in black; noncombatants: orange with 1 central white stripe and
edged in white

Reference: Gillingham 1932, 91; Barac 2009,
177; Brazil 1983, 26–28; Floyd 2004, 2

Provenance: Noncombatants: American Numismatic Society, A. Menke

Br24. *A Medalha da Vitoria*

Brazil's version of the standard World War I
allied victory medal was intended to recognize
its combatants, both military and civilian, who
had served for at least three months in direct
support of the war effort.

Instituted: By Decree No. 16,074 on June 23,
1923

Obverse: Symbolic figure of victory

Reverse: The coats of arms of the allied nations surrounded by GRANDE GUERRA
PELA CIVILISAÇÃO

Size: 34 mm

Metal: Bronze

Maker: Casa de Moeda, Rio de Janeiro (early
strikes only)

Ribbon: Allied rainbow colors

Reference: Barac 2009, 177; Brazil 1983, 27–
28; Floyd 2004, 3

World War II

A military junta ruled Brazil from 1930 until 1945. The Brazilian military tended to side with the Axis but followed a cautious policy of wait and see. Brazil was pushed into the Second World War once again by German and Italian submarines, which attacked Brazilian merchant vessels. Brazil broke diplomatic relations with Germany and Italy early in 1942, but the submarine attacks continued. Brazil lost thirty-eight ships, with some 1,600 passengers and crew killed. Eventually, public opinion forced the government to end its neutrality. Brazil declared war on August 22, 1942. As an Atlantic power, Brazil fought only in the European theater, where it played a direct, albeit minor, role during the long Allied march up through Italy.

The Brazilian forces all fought under a unified Allied command. Brazil sent one infantry division with some twenty thousand troops, beginning in the summer of 1944. Its air force sent a squadron of P47 Thunderbolts. The Brazilian division was credited with capturing more than twenty thousand enemy prisoners, and it suffered some one thousand killed in action.

The Brazilian navy assumed responsibility for defending its convoys of supplies to the Mediterranean; it patrolled the South Atlantic as well as the sea routes to the Straits of Gibraltar. Brazil awarded at least twenty-three medals to members of its army, navy and air force for their participation in the war.

ARMY

*Br25. *A Cruz de Combate*

The Combat Cross was awarded to Brazilian soldiers in two classes. The first class was awarded for individual or unit acts of heroism and personal sacrifice. Units were awarded the cross for significant victories. The second class was given collectively to units for exceptional service.

>   Instituted: By Decree Law No. 6,795 on August 17, 1944
>   Regulated: By Decree No. 16,821 on October 13, 1944
>   Classes: 1st,* 2nd*
>   Obverse disc: Stars of the Southern Cross surrounded by a laurel wreath

>   Reverse disc: 1st: ESTADOS UNIDOS DO BRASIL-CRUZ DE COMBATE 1ᴬ CLASSE; 2nd: ESTADOS UNIDOS DO BRASIL-CRUZ DE COMBATE 2ᴬ CLASSE
>   Shape: Ball-tipped Maltese cross with 2-pointed ends and 7 rays in each angle, suspended from a globe with banners superimposed on an anchor and a cannon
>   Size: 40 mm
>   Metal: 1st: gilt; 2nd: silvered white metal
>   Ribbon: Red with narrow green edge stripes
>   Reference: Brazil, 1968, no. 51

*Br26. *A Medalha de Guerra*

Brazil's War Medal was awarded to army personnel on active duty or in the reserves and also to civilians who volunteered their services

Br 25

Br 25

Br 26

Br 26

of any kind in support of the war effort, both inside and outside Brazil. The medal was also awarded to Allied army personnel.

> Instituted: By Decree Law No. 6,795 on August 17, 1944
>
> Regulated: By Decree No. 16,821 on October 13, 1944
>
> Obverse disc: Stars of the Southern Cross on a blue enameled field
>
> Obverse legend: ESTADOS UNIDOS DO BRASIL
>
> Reverse inscription: MEDALHA | DE | GUERRA | 22-VIII | 1942 (the day Brazil declared war)
>
> Shape: Green and yellow enameled cross pattée with convex ends and a laurel and oak wreath in the angles
>
> Size: 38 mm
>
> Metal: Gilt
>
> Ribbon: Yellow with narrow green edge stripes
>
> Reference: Brazil 1968, no. 12; Brazil 1952, 5, 8–14; Floyd 2004, 8

*Br27. *A Medalha "Sangue do Brasil"*

The Blood of Brazil medal was given to both army personnel and civilians wounded in action. The three stars on the obverse symbolize the three wounds received by General Sampaio, a Brazilian military hero, at the Battle of Tuiuti in 1866 during the Triple Alliance War.

> Instituted: By Decree Law No. 7,709 on July 5, 1945
>
> Obverse: Vertical sword and 3 red enameled stars over rays and behind a ribbon inscribed SANGUE DO BRASIL and surrounded by a wreath. 2 branches of brazilwood rim the medal.
>
> Reverse: Globe with 21 stars and band reading ORDEM E PROGRESSO
>
> Shape: Oval
>
> Size: 45 × 35 mm

Br 27

Br 27

Metal: Bronze

Ribbon: Orange with a narrow green center
stripe edged in yellow

Reference: Brazil 1968, no. 10; Brazil 1952, 7,
14–15

*Br28. *A Medalha de Campanha-Força Expedicionaria Brasileira*

Brazil's sole participation in the land war in
the European theater took place in Italy. The
Campaign Medal was awarded to active and
reserve troops who fought in this campaign. It
was also given to Allied soldiers who fought in
Brazilian units. The date on the obverse is when
the Brazilian Expeditionary Force arrived in
Europe.

Instituted: By Decree Law No. 6,795 on August 17, 1944

Regulated: By Decree No. 16,821 on October
13, 1944

Obverse disc: FEB surrounded by a laurel
wreath

Obverse arms: BRASIL on the upper arm, "16"
on the left arm, "VII" on the right arm, and
"1944" on the lower arm

Reverse
inscription: MEDALHA│DE│CAMPANHA

Reverse legend: FORÇA EXPEDICIONARIA
BRASILEIRA

Shape: Maltese cross with 2-pointed ends

Size: 32 mm

Metal: Bronze

Ribbon: Green, red, green. A bar reads FEB

NAVY

Br29. *A Cruz Naval*

The Navy Cross was awarded to active and
reserve navy personnel for acts of bravery or
above and beyond the call of duty during World
War II.

Br 28

Br 28

Br 30   Br 30

Instituted: By Decree No. 6,095 on December 13, 1945, and Decree No. 6,774 on August 7, 1944

Regulated: By Decree No. 16,368 on August 16, 1944

Obverse disc: Anchor

Obverse legend: BRAZIL

Reverse: 3 torpedo boats

Reverse legend: 21 stars

Shape: Cross pattée

Size: 35 mm

Metal: Bronze

Ribbon: Red with an orange center stripe and 2 narrow white side stripes

Reference: Brazil 1968, no. 24; Brazil 1952, 21

*Br30. *A Medalha de Serviços Relevantes*

The Medal for Relevant Services was awarded to Brazilian navy personnel both on active duty and in the reserves for outstanding service in support of the war effort. This service could be rendered inside or outside Brazil. Sea duty for more than three hundred days qualified a recipient for this medal.

Instituted: By Decree No. 6,095 on December 13, 1943, and Decree No. 6.774 on August 7, 1944

Regulated: By Decree No. 16.368 on August 16, 1944

Obverse: Anchor

Obverse inscription: SERVIÇOS RELEVANTES —BRAZIL

Reverse: 3 torpedo boats

Size: 34 mm

Metal: Silver

Ribbon: Yellow with a black center stripe edged in white and 2 narrow green side stripes

Reference: Brazil 1968, no. 23; Brazil 1952, 21–22; Floyd 2004, 9, 12

Provenance: A. Menke

*Br31. *A Medalha de Serviços de Guerra*

The Navy Medal for War Service was conferred on Brazilian and Allied navy personnel on active duty or in the reserves, as well as the Brazilian and Allied merchant marine, for valorous service at sea or on land.

> Instituted: By Decree Law No. 6,095 on December 13, 1943, and No. 6,774 on August 7, 1944
>
> Regulated: By Decree No. 16,368 on August 16, 1944
>
> Obverse: Anchor
>
> Obverse legend: SERVIÇOS DE GUERRA | BRAZIL
>
> Reverse: 3 torpedo boats
>
> Size: 34 mm
>
> Metal: Bronze
>
> Ribbon: Blue with a center white stripe and 2 white aquamarine side stripes

Reference: Brazil 1968, no. 25; Brazil 1952, 22; Floyd 2004, 13

Br32. *A Medalha da Força Naval do Sul*

The Medal for the Southern Naval Force recognized the officers and men engaged in patrolling the South Atlantic. Ships in this force guarded Brazil's southern coast for the entire war, primarily in defense against enemy submarines. Brazilian warships were engaged in protecting commercial shipping well before the government declared war. The government authorized this medal ten years after the end of World War II in three classes.

> Instituted: By Decree No. 35,586 on June 2, 1954
>
> Classes: Commanding officers, ships' captains and other officers at sea, petty officers and seamen
>
> Obverse: Sea lion

Reverse: Anchor

Reverse inscription: FORÇA NAVAL DO SUL 1942–1945

Metal: Commanding officers: gold; ships' captains and other officers at sea: silver; petty officers and seamen: bronze

Ribbon: Blue, white, blue with 2 green stripes on the white stripe

Reference: Brazil 1968, no. 27; Floyd 2004, 15

*Br33. *A Medalha da Força Naval do Nordeste*

The government awarded a medal for navy officers and men serving in the Naval Force of the Northeast. This force protected Brazilian ships heading into the Mediterranean.

Br 33

Instituted: By Executive Order No. 35,587 on June 2, 1954

Classes: Commanding officers, ships' captains and other officers; petty officers and seamen at sea*

Obverse: Sea lion

Reverse: Anchor

Reverse legend: FORÇA NAVAL DO NORDESTE

Reverse inscription: 1942 | 1945

Shape: Round, with an anchor protruding below the bottom, attached to a suspension bar

Size: 41 × 35 mm

Metal: Commanding officers: gold; ships' captains and other officers: silver; petty officers and seamen at sea: bronze

Ribbon: White with 2 green side stripes; commanding officers, worn around the neck

Reference: Brazil 1968, no. 26; Floyd 2004, 14

Br 33

*Br34. *A Cruz do Merito Naval*

It is believed that the Cross for Naval Merit was awarded for naval merit to officers of Brazilian merchant marine ships sailing in the South

Atlantic. German and Italian submarines sank a number of Brazilian merchant vessels, with considerable loss of life.

Obverse disc: Arms of Brazil on a silver field

Obverse legend: REPUBLICA DOS ESTADOS UNIDOS DO BRASIL on a silver band

Reverse disc: Female head, right, with a laurel wreath on her head

Reverse legend: MERITO NAVAL

Shape: Red enameled cross pattée with pointed ends and anchors in the angles

Size: 26 mm

Metal: Silver

Ribbon: Red, white, blue

Provenance: A. Menke

AIR FORCE

*Br35. *A Cruz de Bravura*

Brazil awarded the Cross for Bravery to active and reserve air force personnel for exceptional acts of courage. Additional exceptional acts were awarded by adding a palm branch to the ribbon. The cross could be awarded to flight crews as well as ground personnel. It reportedly has only been awarded to five air force officers, who flew combat missions in the Italian Campaign, all posthumously.

Instituted: By Decree Law No. 7,454 on April 10, 1945

Regulated: By Decree Law No. 20,497 on January 24, 1946

Regulated: By Ministerial Directive No. 13 on January 11, 2001

Obverse disc: Emblem of the Brazilian air force

Reverse legend: BRAVURA | FAB

Shape: Maltese cross with pointed convex ends with a wreath in angles suspended from a ribbon bar of extended wings

Size: 40 mm

Metal: Oxidized bronze

Ribbon: Blue with 2 side red stripes edged in white

Reference: Brazil 1968, no. 41; Brazil 1952, 34–42; Floyd 2004, 18

Br36. *A Cruz de Serviços Relevantes*

The Cross for Relevant Services was awarded to active and reserve air force officers who performed a service of any kind related to the war effort or for specific missions ordered by the government inside or outside Brazil.

Instituted: By Decree Law No. 7,454 on April 10, 1945

Regulated: By Decree Law No. 20,497 on January 24, 1946

Modified: By Decree Law No. 8,901 on January 24, 1946

Modified: By Decree Law No. 9,211 on April 29, 1946

Obverse disc: Emblem of the Brazilian air force

Reverse legend: SERVIÇOS RELEVANTES FAB

Shape: Cross pattée with convex ends and a laurel wreath in the angles, suspended from a ribbon bar with extended wings

Size: 40 mm

Metal: Oxidized bronze

Ribbon: Blue with a red center stripe edged in white and 2 white edge stripes

Reference: Brazil 1968, no. 45; Brazil 1952, 36–42; Floyd 2004, 22

Br37. *A Cruz de Sangue*

The Cross of Blood was awarded to air force servicemen wounded in combat during the Italian Campaign. The medal could also be conferred on air force units. More recently, the medal has been conferred on Brazilians serving with the United Nations, such as in Katanga in 1961.

> Instituted: By Decree Law No. 7,454 on April 10, 1945
>
> Regulated: By Decree Law No. 20,497 on January 24, 1946
>
> Modified: By Decree Law No. 8,901 on January 24, 1946
>
> Obverse disc: Emblem of the Brazilian air force
>
> Reverse disc: CRUZ DE SANGUE | FAB
>
> Shape: Cross with trilobe ends
>
> Size: 40 mm
>
> Metal: Oxidized bronze
>
> Ribbon: Red with 2 side blue stripes edged in white
>
> Reference: Brazil 1968, no. 45; Brazil 1952, 34–42; Floyd 2004, 19

Br38. *A Cruz de Aviação*

This medal was awarded with two different ribbons.

Br38a. *Fita A*

The Aviation Cross with an "A" ribbon was awarded to active Brazilian and Allied air force officers who flew missions with the Brazilian air force during the Italian Campaign. The medal could also be conferred on air force units. A star was added to the ribbon for each twenty missions flown. Multiple awards were denoted by a palm on the ribbon for each five stars awarded.

> Instituted: By Decree Law No. 7,454 on April 10, 1945

> Regulated: By Decree Law No. 20,497 on January 24, 1946
>
> Modified: By Decree Law. No. 8,901 on January 24, 1946
>
> Obverse: Emblem of the Brazilian Air Force
>
> Reverse disc: CRUZ DE AVIAÇÃO FAB
>
> Shape: Cross pattée with pointed ends suspended from a ribbon bar of extended wings
>
> Size: 40 mm
>
> Metal: Oxidized bronze
>
> Ribbon: For missions flown in Italy: white with 2 blue side stripes and 2 blue edge stripes; for missions in and around Brazil: red, yellow, red

Br38b. *Fita B*

The Aviation Cross with a "B" ribbon was awarded to active air force officers who flew patrols in the South Atlantic to defend against submarine attacks near its ports.

> Ribbon: Yellow with 2 red stripes on each side, separated by a narrow yellow and green stripe; for every 20 missions flown, the recipient had the right to receive a star on the ribbon
>
> Reference: Brazil 1968, no. 43; Brazil, 1952, 34–42; Floyd 2004, 20

*Br39. *A Medalha de Campanha do Atlântico Sul*

The Medal for the South Atlantic Campaign was awarded to active and reserve air force personnel and civilians who participated in patrolling the coastal areas of Brazil between 1942 and 1945.

> Instituted: By Law No. 497 on November 28, 1948
>
> Regulated: By Decree Law No. 26,550 on April 4, 1969
>
> Obverse: Airplane flying over warship

Obverse legend: CAMPANHA NO ATLANTICO SUL

Reverse: Emblem of the Brazilian air force

Reverse legend: F.A.B. | 1942 1945

Shape: Round, suspended from a ribbon bar of extended wings

Size: 31 mm

Metal: Oxidized bronze

Ribbon: Blue with 5 narrow yellow stripes

Reference: Brazil 1968, no. 46; Brazil 1952, 42–45; Floyd 2004, 34

*Br40. *A Medalha de Campanha de Italia*

Brazil awarded the Medal for the Italian Campaign to active and reserve air force personnel who participated in the Italian Campaign in 1944–1945. The medal was also awarded to individual units for outstanding service.

Instituted: By Decree Law No. 7,454 on April 10, 1945

Obverse: Emblem of the Brazilian air force

Reverse: CAMPANHA | NA ITALIA | FAB

Shape: Round, surrounded by a laurel wreath, suspended from a ribbon bar of extended wings

Size: 35 mm; Miniature: 17 mm*

Metal: Oxidized bronze

Ribbon: Purple with narrow red, white, and green center stripes

Reference: Brazil 1968, no. 44; Brazil 1952, 34–42; Floyd 2004, 21

MEDALS OF THE EXPEDITIONARY FORCES

Some of these medals, which are for the most part not listed in the standard catalogues, are for service in specific units during World War II.

*Br41. *A Medalha da Força Expedicionaria Brasileira na Italia*

The Medal for the Brazilian Expeditionary Force was awarded to Brazilian army officers and men who fought with the 5th United States Army in the Italian Campaign.

Obverse: Brazilian flag

Obverse inscription: 5º | EXERCITO AMERICANO FORÇA | EXPEDICIONARIA | BRASILEIRA NA | ITALIA

Reverse: Vertical sword held in hand superimposed on a map of Italy and the central Mediterranean

Reverse inscription: 1944–1945 | PELA | LIBERDADE DO MUNDO

Size: 32 mm

Metal: Bronze

Maker: S. Vatteroni, Carrara, Italy

Provenance: A. Menke

Br 41

Br 41

Br42. *A Medalha Castello Branco da Força Expedicionaria Brasileira*

Obverse: Bust of Castello Branco, facing

Obverse legend: MEDALHA DE MERITO MARECHAL CASTELLO BRANCO

Shape: Round, attached to a medieval helmet with crossed rifles

Metal: White metal

Ribbon: Light blue with white stars, with red and blue center stripes and yellow and green edge stripes

Reference: http://www.omsa.org/photopost/showphoto.php?photo=4512, accessed January 26, 2013

Br43. *A Cruz do Mérito "Legionnaire" da Força Expedicionaria Brasileira*

Obverse: Shield inscribed "BRASIL" above serpent on a yellow enameled field

Shape: Cross with floriated ends suspended from ribbon bar of extended wings

Metal: Bronze

Ribbon: Light blue and yellow edged in white with light blue, red, and blue edge stripes

Reference: http://www.omsa.org/photopost/showpost/showphoto.php?.photo=4517 size=bnis, accessed January 25, 2013

Br44. *A Medalha do Mérito da Força Expedicionaria Brasileira*

Obverse disc: Symbols of army, navy and air force on a white enameled field

Obverse legend: MÉRITO EX COMBATE DO BRAZIL | CONSELHO NACIONAL on a red enameled band

Shape: Ball-tipped white enameled star

Metal: Gilt

Ribbon: Green, red

Reference: http://www.omsa.org/photopost/showphoto.php?photo=2939&size=big&cat, accessed January 26, 2013

Br45. *A Medalha Paladins de Libertade da Força Expedicionaria Brasileira—*

Obverse: Soldier with rifle planting flag in ground. Army symbol between words "VALOR" and "HONOR"

Shape: Shield suspended from a small star

Metal: Gilt

Ribbon: Blue with large burgundy center stripe edged in yellow

Reference: http://www.omsa.org/photopost/showphoto.php?photo=4518&size=-big, accessed January 26, 2013

Br46. *A Cruz de Paz d Força Expedicionaria Brasileira*

Obverse: 3 walking soldiers on a white enameled field

Obverse exergue: 1945 on green, white, and red enameled ribbon

Shape: White enameled Latin Maltese cross

Ribbon: White with narrow red center stripe and narrow yellow and red side stripes on the right

Reference: http://www.omsa.org/photopost/showphoto.php?photo=4510&size-big, accessed January 26, 2013

Br47. *A Estrela à União de Heroes da Força Expedicionaria Brasileira*

Classes: Gold, silver, bronze

Obverse disc: Southern Cross on an enameled field

Reverse: Symbols of army, navy, air force on each arm

Shape: 6-pointed star with 3 rays in each angle

Metal: Gilt, silvered, bronze

Ribbon: White, black, yellow, green, white, red, blue, white, blue

Reference: http://www.omsa.org/photopost/showphoto.php?photo-85108&size=big, accessed January 26, 2013

MEDALS FOR MERIT IN PEACETIME

BRAZIL's constitution proscribes wars of conquest by its armed forces. The country has an unbroken history of peaceful relations with its neighbors since Brazil became an independent republic in 1889. Brazil has authorized at least six military medals to reward meritorious service in its armed forces during peacetime.

*Br48. *A Medalha Naval de Serviços Distintos*

The Navy Medal for Distinguished Service is awarded to military and civilian personnel, Brazilian or foreigners, for meritorious service to the navy.

    Instituted: By Law No. 2,225 on June 12, 1954

    Obverse disc: A dolphin coiled around an anchor surrounded by a rope

    Reverse inscription: SERVIÇOS | DISTINTOS surrounded by a rope

    Shape: Cross pattée with floriated ends

    Size: 43 mm

    Metal: Silver

    Ribbon: Blue with gray center stripe edged in red

    Reference: Brazil 1968, no. 28; Brazil 1983, 36; Floyd 2004, 16

*Br49. *A Medalha do Mérito Tamandaré*

The Medal for Naval Merit Tamandaré is awarded to military personnel and civilians, both Brazilian and foreign, as well as institutions that have strengthened the traditions of the Brazilian navy. It is named for Joaquim Marques Lisboa (1807–97), better known as Admiral Tamandaré, Brazil's most celebrated

Br 49

Br 49

naval officer. He volunteered in the navy as a seaman and fought under Lord Cochrane at the blockade of Bahia. He was promoted to officer for his leadership and fought in the Farrapos War and the Praieira Revolt in Pernambuco, and he commanded the Brazilian fleet during the Triple Alliance War. He was made Patron of the Navy.

Instituted: By Decree No. 42,112 of August 20, 1957

Obverse: Bust of Tamandaré, ¾ right

Obverse legend: ALMIRANTE TAMANDARÉ

Reverse inscription: A | MARINHA | BRASILEIRA | AO SEU | GLORIOSO | PATRONO | 1957

Shape: Round, with 2 crossed anchors extending above & below, attached to a ribbon bar

Size: 37 × 32 mm

Metal: Bronze

Ribbon: 3 green and 2 yellow stripes

Reference: Brazil 1968, no. 14; Brazil 1983, 38; Floyd 2004, 17

*Br 50. *A Medalha do Mérito Marinheiro*

The Medal for Naval Merit is awarded to encourage navy personnel to serve on board ship at sea. There is no requirement for outstanding service.

Instituted: By Decree No. 83,805 on August 1, 1975

Br 50

Br 50

Obverse: A modern warship, the frigate *Niterói*, and a sailing vessel

Reverse inscription: A | BRAZIL | A | UM MARINHEIRO

Shape: Pentagon surmounted by crown

Size: 55 × 41 mm

Metal: Bronze; anchors on bar are of white metal

Ribbon: Blue with a central green stripe edged in narrow white stripes. Small anchors are added to the ribbon depending on how many days the recipient has spent at sea. The number of anchors varies from one (500 days at sea) to four (1,500 days at sea).

Reference: Brazil 1983, 40

*Br51. *A Medalha do Pacificador Duque de Caxias*

The Medal of the Pacifier Duke of Caxias is awarded to military personnel and civilians, both national and foreign citizens, for meritorious service to the army. The medal recognizes efforts to raise the prestige of the army as well as to improve relationships with armies of other nations. It is sometimes awarded with a palm on the ribbon, when the recipient's life was at risk in the performance of the service. The medal is named after Luis Alves de Lima e Silva (1803–80), who was given the title Duke of Caxias after he suppressed an insurrection in the city of Caxias. The duke was born in

colonial Brazil and served as an officer in the imperial army for all of his life. He successfully fought Portuguese forces in Bahia in the name of Pedro I. He went on to command troops and suppressed a number of local uprisings in Brazil. He fought in the Uruguayan campaign in 1851–52 and commanded the Brazilian forces in the Triple Alliance War against Paraguay. The duke was Brazil's most recognized military leader and is still considered the patriotic ideal and defender of the nation's unity. He was posthumously awarded the title of Patron of the Army.

> Instituted: By Ministerial Directive No. 345 on August 25, 1953
>
> Ratified: By Decree No. 39,745 on August 17, 1955
>
> Modified: By Decree No. 1,884 on December 17, 1962, which authorized a palm leaf

on the ribbon in recognition of bravery and personal risk

> Obverse: Arms of the Duke of Caxias
>
> Reverse legend: DUQUE DE CAXIAS above
>
> Reverse inscription: MEDALHA | DO | PACIFICADOR in a frame
>
> Shape: Shield surmounted by crown
>
> Size: 45× 28 mm
>
> Metal: Bronze
>
> Ribbon: 3 blue and 2 red stripes
>
> Reference: Brazil 1968, no. 17; Floyd 2004, 9

*Br 52. *A Medalha do Mérito "Santos Dumont"*

The Medal for Merit "Santos Dumont" is awarded to military personnel and civilians, both Brazilian and foreign, for outstanding service to the Brazilian air force. It is named after

Alberto Santos Dumont (1873–1932), a pioneer in civil aviation. He studied and spent most of his adult life in Paris, where he flew the world's first practical dirigible at the turn of the past century.

Instituted: By Decree No. 39,905 on September 5, 1956

Modified: By Decree No. 66,815 on June 30, 1970

Regulated: By Portaria No. 106/scc on February 20, 1998

Modified: By Decree No. 4,209 on April 23, 2002, revoking Decree No. 39,905 and Decree No. 66,815

Obverse: Bust of Santos Dumont, left

Obverse inscription: SANTOS DUMONT | MERITO

Reverse: Emblem of the Brazilian air force

Reverse legend: MINISTERIO DE AERONAUTICA | FORCA AEREA BRASILEIRA

Shape: Round, suspended from a wreath with wings behind

Size: 35 mm

Metal: Silver

Ribbon: Blue with yellow edge stripes

Reference: Brazil 1968, no. 47; Floyd 2004, 24

Br 53. *A Medalha Serviço Amazônico*

The Medal for Service in the Amazon is awarded to army personnel for sacrifice, dedication, professionalism, and years of military service in the Amazon region. The Amazon is considered a hardship post by the army.

Instituted: By Decree No. 93,209 on September 3, 1986

Modified: By Decree No. 97,662 on April 14, 1989

Modified: By Decree No. 4,622 on March 21, 2003

Obverse disc: Image of entrance to fort at São José de Macapá Amazônica

Obverse legend: AMAZONIA

Reverse disc: Shield of the Brazilian army and inscribed

Reverse legend: SERVICO AMAZONICO

Size: 36 mm

Metal: Silver

Ribbon: Light blue, yellow, green, yellow, light blue. For 2 years continuous service in the Amazon, the recipient receives one chestnut on a ribbon bar; for 5 years, 2 chestnuts; and for 10 years, 3 chestnuts.

Reference: http://www.ahimtb.org.br/ medcpaz.htm, accessed August 22, 2012; http://www.omsa.org/photopost/showpost/ php?photo=4649, accessed January 26, 2013

*Br54. *A Medalha da Cruz Vermelha Brasileira*

By Presidential Decree No. 7,928 on September 3, 1945, President Getulio Vargas instituted and regulated eight medals and crosses for the Brazilian Red Cross Society. These decorations are semiofficial, as they were authorized by the president. The Brazilian Red Cross decorations may be awarded to Brazilian and foreign nationals, to civilians and military personnel, and in exceptional cases to institutions. The awards are intended to reward services to humanity through the Brazilian Red Cross Society. The eight decorations are designed to recognize different degrees and relevance of service. Some of the designs of the decorations are similar.

*Br54a. *A Cruz de Honra*

The Honor Cross is awarded to honorary presidents of the Brazilian Red Cross Society or, exceptionally, to organizations that have made an outstanding contribution to humanity.

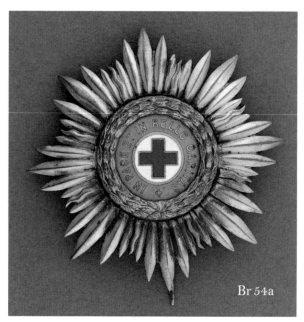

Br 54a

Obverse disc: Red enameled cross on a white enameled field

Obverse legend: IN PACE ET IN BELLO CARITAS on a green enameled band

Reverse inscription: 1945

Reverse legend: CRUZ VERMELHA BRASILEIRA

Shape: Cross pattée

Star shape: 8-pointed silver star with 1 wavy and 4 pointed rays in each angle; disc within gilt wreath in the center

Size: Star*: 72 mm

Metal: Silver

Ribbon: Red with 1 white center stripe and 2 white edge stripes, neck ribbon

Br54b. *A Cruz de Benemerência*

The Cross for Worthy Merit is awarded to persons or institutions that provide meritorious services to the Brazilian Red Cross Society. This medal is identical to the Honor Cross, but without the silver star. The Honor Cross and the Cross for Worthy Merit are authorized by presidential decree on recommendation from the Brazilian Red Cross Society.

Br54c. *A Cruz de Distinçao*

The Cross of Distinction is awarded to persons or organizations that have collabrated with the Brazilian Red Cross. It has the same design as the Honor Cross, but is smaller.

Br54d. *A Cruz de Mérito*

The Cross for Merit is awarded to persons or institutions for outstanding and continuous service to the Brazilian Red Cross. The Cross for Merit is identical to the Cross of Distinction.

Br54e. *A Cruz de Serviços Distintos*

The Cross for Distinguished Services is awarded only to members of the Brazilian Red Cross for heroism and self-sacrifice. The design of the cross is identical to that of the Cross of Distinction. The cross is silver when the recipient's life was at risk in performing the service, and bronze when the circumstances were less dangerous.

Br54f. *A Medalha de Bons Serviços*

The Medal for Good Services is awarded for treating wounded in wartime.

> Obverse: Nurse attending a wounded man on a battlefield
> Obverse legend: IN PACE ET IN BELLO CARITAS above a Greek cross
> Reverse legend: CRUZ VERMELHA BRASILEIRA bracketed by a laurel wreath
> Shape: Round
> Metal: Silver, bronze

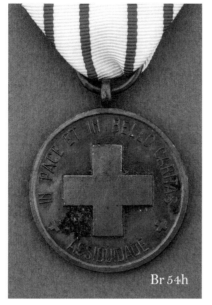

Br 54h

Br 54h

> Ribbon: White with 2 narrow red center stripes

Br54g. *A Medalha de Conduta Exemplar*

The Medal for Exemplary Conduct is given for various services provided by Red Cross personnel in treating the wounded and collaborating in the Red Cross's humanitarian mission.

> Obverse: Greek cross in relief
> Reverse legend: CRUZ VERMELHA BRASILEIRA bracketed by a laurel wreath
> Shape: Round
> Metal: Bronze
> Ribbon: White with 3 narrow red stripes

*Br54h. *A Medalha de Assiduidade*

The Medal for Perseverance is awarded exclusively to members of the Brazilian Red Cross Society for a minimum of five years uninterrupted service.

> Obverse: Greek cross
> Obverse legend: IN PACE IN BELLO CARITAS | ASSIDUIDADE

Reverse inscription: CRUZ | VERMELHA |
BRASILEIRA beneath a cross, flanked by
branches
Size: 32 mm

Metal: Copper
Ribbon: White with 4 narrow red side stripes
Reference: Brazil 1968, no. 56

LA RÉPUBLIQUE DU COUNANI

FOR TWO hundred years, France and Brazil tried to resolve sovereignty over a piece
of territory in northeast Brazil bordering on French Guiana between the mouth of the
Amazon and the Oyapock Rivers. The Treaty of Utrecht in 1713 placed Brazil's border
with Guiana along the Oyapock River. However the Treaty of Badajoz (1801) fixed the
border further south along the Araguaia River. The Congress of Vienna in 1815 moved
the border back once again to the Oyapock River. In 1883, the French government appointed a French journalist, Jules Gros, to develop the economy of French Guiana. In
1886, Gros entered into partnership with a Swiss friend, Paul Quartier, to create the
Republic of Counani inside Brazil and put it under French protection. From then until
1912, Gros and other French filibusters ran an ephemeral Republic of Counani that no
one recognized, including France or Brazil. The discovery of gold in this territory attracted the attention of other potential filibusters. In 1904, a French adventurer, Adolphe
Brezet, proclaimed himself president of the État Libre de Counani, which claimed sovereignty until 1912.

Meanwhile, France and Brazil requested Swiss arbitration in 1895. Five years later the
Swiss commission ruled that the Oyapock River was the border between French Guiana and Brazil. The territory was formally annexed to Brazil as the state of Amapá, and
Brazilian soldiers gradually occupied the territory by establishing guard posts. During
this twenty-six year period, the reigning filibusters created their own flags, currency,
stamps, and medals, which they awarded to their supporters. At least two of the medals are known to exist.

*Br55. *La Médaille de Bons Services*

The Medal for Good Services was awarded
to allies and friends of the filibusters for their
support.

Classes: Silver, bronze*
Obverse: Star surrounded by floral and corn
  branches

Reverse inscription: BONS SERVICES
Reverse legend: ETAT LIBRE DU COUNANI
Shape: Round, attached to an oval oak
  wreath
Size: 37 × 30 mm
Metal: Silver, bronze
Ribbon: Red
Provenance: A. Menke

Br 55

Br 55

Br 56

Br 56

*Br 56. *La Médaille aux Organisateurs de la Patrie*

The Medal to the Organizers of the Fatherland was awarded to those willing to help the filibusters run Counani and raise money to keep it viable.

Obverse: Arms of Counani beneath 7-pointed sun rays inscribed LIBERTE | JUSTICE

Obverse inscription: JE MAINTIENDRAI | PAR LA RAISON OU | PAR LA FORCE on a ribbon

Reverse legend: AUX ORGANISATEURS

Reverse inscription: DE LA | PATRIE

Shape: Round, suspended from a laurel wreath

Size: 30 mm

Metal: Silver

Provenance: A. Menke

Br 57
Grand Cross
badge

Br 57
Grand Cross
badge

Br 57
Commander
badge

Br 57
Commander
badge

ORDERS

IMPERIAL ORDERS OF BRAZIL

WHEN KING JOÃO VI crossed the Atlantic to Brazil in 1807, he was the Grand Master of three religious-military orders that traced their origins to the Middle Ages. While ruling from Rio de Janeiro, he continued to create knights of the three orders: the Order of Christ, the Military Order of Avis, and the Order of Santiago of the Sword. The most influential of these was the Order of Christ.

*Br57. *A Ordem Imperial de Cristo*

Br 57
Commander star

The Imperial Order of Our Savior Jesus Christ was founded in 1319 by Portugal's King Dinis. The king created the Real Ordem dos Cavaleiros de Nosso Senhor de Jesus Cristo to inherit the assets and retain the knights of the recently dissolved Order of the Templar Knights. King Dinis drew upon the Templar Knights' structure to build a new Military Order of Christ to help him expel the Moors from Portugal. Prince Henry the Navigator, himself a Grand Master of the order, used it to expand Portugal's trade through long-distance exploration. He created the world's first School for Navigators in Sagres, paid for with money from the Order of Christ. Portugal's greatest explorers were all knights of the order, including Pedro Álvares Cabral, who first discovered Brazil. The sails of Cabral's ships when he discovered Brazil were emblazoned with the cross of the order. The full extent of the order's impact in Brazil has yet to be fully studied.

When João VI arrived in the New World in 1807, the Order of Christ became the social pinnacle of royal society in Brazil, and its knights were placed in privileged positions in commerce and the militia. Following independence, Pedro I bestowed the order, but he was never formally made its Grand Master, and there is some legal controversy over his powers. Pedro II revised the order in 1843 as a Brazilian order awarded for exceptional service to the state. Brazilian knights became part of the untitled nobility and received certain military honors, depending on rank. The Order of Christ was made the nation's highest order during the Brazilian Empire of Pedro II. The cross of the order was incorporated into the design of the imperial flag.

The Grand Cross of the order was limited to twelve recipients, other than the royal family and foreign citizens. There were no limits on the number of recipients of the other grades. Pedro II awarded some two thousand orders, mainly knights, during his rule, making this the

Br 57
Knight

Br 57
Knight

Br 57
Knight
miniature

Br 57
Knight
miniature

most popular of the three military orders. It was rescinded in 1890 by the interim government of the United States of Brazil. As this order was awarded from the Middle Ages through the nineteenth century, and in Portugal as well as Brazil, it exists in many forms; the version described below is that in the Ross Collection.

Instituted: 1319

Reformed: By Imperial Decree 321 on September 9, 1843, creating a Brazilian Order of Christ and naming Pedro II as the Grand Master. The Brazilian crown was substituted for the Portuguese crown. The ribbon was edged in blue.

Reformed: Imperial Decree 2,853 on December 7, 1861

Rescinded: By decree on March 22, 1890

Grand Master: Emperor of Brazil

Grades: Grand Cross,* Commander,* Knight* (miniature)*

Obverse disc: Commander: red enameled Sacred Heart; Knight: red enameled Latin cross with expanding ends with a white enameled Latin cross within

Reverse disc: Knight (on miniature): Bust of the emperor, left, on a gilt field

Reverse legend: Knight (on miniature): PETRUS I BRASILIAE IMPERATOR D on a blue enameled band

Shape: Grand Cross: Latin cross with expanding ends of red semiprecious stones with a cross of [paste] diamonds within; Commander: disc on a white enameled 8-pointed star with 4 rays in the angles, from which is suspended a red enameled Latin cross with expanding ends with a white enameled Latin cross within; Knight: white enameled ball-tipped 2-pointed star with green enameled wreath in the angles, suspended from an imperial crown

Star shape: Commander: disc with a red enameled Latin cross with expanding ends with a white enameled Latin cross within

on a ball-tipped, faceted 8-pointed star with convex ends with 5 rays in each angle

Size: Badge: Grand Cross: 63 × 47 mm; Commander: 50 × 36 mm; Knight: 24 mm; miniature: 18 mm. Star: 30, 60 mm

Metal: Grand Cross, Commander star, Knight: silver; Commander badge: gilt; Knight miniature: gold

Ribbon: Red with light blue borders

Reference: Gillingham 1932, 66; Barac 2009, 188–89; Fonseca and Chaves 1945, 11–12

*Br58. *A Ordem Imperial de São Bento de Avis*

The original Order of Avis was founded in 1162 by King Ãfonso Henriques in Coimbra. It evolved out of the Spanish religious-military Order of Calatrava. The order adopted a green cross in the form of a fleur-de-lys as its symbol in 1352. King João VI reformed the order on July 5, 1809. Pedro II nationalized the order and named himself Grand Master in 1843. This was the Brazilian order of second most importance after the Order of Christ. It was dissolved in Brazil by the 1891 constitution.

Instituted: August 13, 1162

Reformed: By Imperial Decree No. 321 on September 9, 1843, creating a Brazilian Order of Avis, but changing its religious character to an honorific one. Pedro II was named Grand Master. The Brazilian crown was substituted for the Portuguese one. The ribbon was edged in red.

Reformed: By Decree No. 227 on March 22, 1890, converting the order into a military one for the army

Rescinded: February 24, 1891, by the constitution

Grades: Grand Cross, Commander (star*), Knight (miniature*)

Shape: Green enameled Latin cross with floriate ends, suspended from an imperial crown

Br 58
Commander

Br 58
Knight

Star shape: Green enameled Latin cross with floriated ends on a white enameled field surrounded by silver bands surrounded by eleven 2-pointed faceted rays of alternating length surmounted by a red enameled heart topped by a black enameled cross

Size: Badge miniature: 30 × 14 mm. Star: 60 × 55 mm

Metal: Silver

Ribbon: Green with red edge stripes

Reference: Gillingham 1932, 66; Barac 2009, 188; Fonseca and Chaves 1945, 15–16

Br 59. *A Ordem Imperial de Santiago da Espada*

This is hierarchically the lowest of the three ancient military orders in Brazil. The order had played a leading role in Portugal's first expeditions to India. Originally a religious-military order, Pedro II removed its religious character in 1843 and named himself Grand Master. The Imperial Order of Santiago of the Sword was rarely awarded in the Brazilian Empire.

Instituted: Circa 1210

Rescinded: February 24, 1861

Grades: Grand Collar, Grand Cross, Grand Officer, Commander, Officer, Knight

Obverse disc: Red enameled cross with floriated ends with a sword as the lower arm; second class surmounted by a star bearing a flaming heart

Ribbon: Dark purple edged with light blue

Reference: Gillingham 1932, 67

*Br60. *A Ordem Imperial do Cruzeiro*

Br 60
Grand Cross

Emperor Pedro I founded the Imperial Order of the Cross in 1822 on the occasion of his coronation, and the first knights were accepted into the order on that same day. The order was designed to commemorate Brazil's independence as well as his own coronation. The Imperial Order of the Cross was Brazil's first entirely indigenous order. In terms of precedence, it ranked below the three ancient military orders, but ahead of all the purely Brazilian imperial orders founded subsequently. The higher grades of the order were subject to numerical restrictions. The order was abolished by the 1891 constitution. A republican order with a similar name, the *Ordem Nacional do Cruzeiro do Sul*, was created in 1932 (Br63, below).

Instituted: December 1, 1822

Rescinded: By Decree on March 22, 1890

Grades: Grand Cross* (12), Dignitary (45), Officer (320), Knight* (unlimited)

Obverse disc: Constellation of the Southern Cross on a white enameled field

Obverse legend: BENEMERENTIUM PRAEMIUM on a blue enameled band

Reverse disc: Bust of the emperor, left, on a gilt field

Reverse legend: PETRUS I BRASILIAE IMPERATOR D on a blue enameled band

Shape: White enameled, gold-edged, ball-tipped, 5-armed 2-pointed star with wreaths of tobacco and coffee in the angles, surmounted by an imperial crown

Star shape: White enameled, gold edged, ball-tipped, 5-armed 2-pointed star with five 2-pointed rays in each angle surmounted by an imperial crown

Size: Badge: Grand Cross: 70 mm; Knight: 29 mm. Star: 85 × 72 mm

Metal: Gilt

Ribbon: Light blue

Br 60
Grand Cross
badge (reverse)

Reference: Gillingham 1932, 68–69; Barac 2009, 180

Provenance: Grand Cross: American Numismatic Society, A. Menke

* * *

PEDRO I later created two more Brazilian orders, one bearing his name and the other commemorating his second marriage.

Br 61. *A Ordem Imperial de Dom Pedro Primeiro*

Pedro I founded the Imperial Order of Dom Pedro I in 1826, shortly before he abdicated. The order's statutes limited the number of recipients for each grade. The order was awarded to Brazilian and foreign citizens for exceptional civil or military merit.

Instituted: By Dom Pedro I on April 16, 1826

Regulated: By Dom Pedro II on October 19, 1842, dividing the order into 3 grades

Br 60
Knight

Br 60
Knight

Rescinded: By Decree of General Manuel
    Deodora de Fonseca on March 22, 1890

Grand Master: Emperor of Brazil

Grades: Grand Cross (12), Commander (50),
    Knight (100)

Shape: Displayed griffin facing right, green
    enameled shield with PI on the breast and
    ribbon to left and right with FUNDADOR
    DO IMPERIO DO BRASIL, ball-tipped, white
    enameled crown beneath, imperial crown
    above

Badge reverse: Shield reads 16 | 18–26 | 4;
    ribbon reads AO RECONHECIMENTO DO
    IMPERIO DO BRAZIL

Star shape: White enameled, ball-tipped
    5-armed star with 9 rays in each angle, sur-
    mounted by an imperial crown

Ribbon: Dark green with narrow white edge
    stripes

Reference: Gillingham 1932, 70; Barac 2009,
    184

Br 62
Knight

*Br62. *A Ordem Imperial da Rosa*

Dom Pedro created the Imperial Order of the
Rose to commemorate his second marriage
on August 2, 1829, to the Princess Amalie-
Augusta-Eugenie-Napoleon of Leuchtenberg
and Eichstadt. The order was awarded for both
civil and military merit. Limits were placed on
the number of recipients in some grades. This
became the most popular of Pedro I's orders.

Instituted: By Pedro I on October 17, 1829

Rescinded: By Decree of General Manuel
    Deodora de Fonseca on March 22, 1890

Grand Master: Emperor of Brazil

Grades: Collar, Grand Cross* (16), Grand
    Dignitary (16), Dignitary (32), Commander,
    Officer, Knight,* Member*

Obverse disc: Intertwined elaborate initials
    PA on a gold field

Obverse legend: AMOR E FIDELIDADE on a
    blue enameled band

Br 62
Knight

Br 62
Grand Cross

Br 62
Knight variant

Br 62
Knight variant

Br 62
Grand Cross
badge
(reverse)

Br 62
Grand Cross star variant

Br 62
Member

Reverse disc: Knight: 2 | 18–29 | 8 on a gold field

Reverse legend: Knight: PEDRO E AMELIA on a blue enameled band

Shape: White enameled, ball-tipped 6-pointed star with a rose wreath in the angles, enameled pink except for Member

Star shape: White enameled, ball-tipped 6-pointed star with a rose wreath and 5 rays in the angles, surmounted by an imperial crown (some examples)

Size: Badge: Grand Cross: 57 mm; Knight: 30 mm; Member: 44 mm. Star: 64 mm (uncrowned), 65 × 54 mm (crowned bronze)

Metal: Gold, bronze

Ribbon: Light pink with narrow white side stripes

Reference: Gillingham 1932, 71–73; Barac 2009, 185–87; Werlich 1974, 44–45

Provenance: Grand Cross: A. Menke

REPUBLICAN ORDERS

IN 1889, the Brazilian military overthrew Pedro II and established the Republic of the United States of Brazil. By decree on March 22, 1890, the government rescinded all of Brazil's orders of chivalry, except for the Order of Avis and the Order of the Cross. Within a few months, Brazil created the Order of Christopher Columbus, but abolished it eight months later. Since then Brazil has created at least twenty-two orders for merit, covering a wide range of fields from politics, the military, and diplomacy to culture, science, the economy, and sports. Brazil's first orders were instituted as military and diplomatic awards of merit. The nation's new political imperative has sought to promote a distinctly Brazilian national culture tied to a vibrant economy. Brazil continues to create new orders to recognize and encourage individual achievements in support of these goals.

*Br63. *A Ordem Nacional do Cruzeiro do Sul*

In 1930, the military overthrew the democratically elected government and installed a new president, Getulio Vargas. He was the first president to institute orders of merit since the creation of the republic. He created the National Order of the Southern Cross by drawing on the design of the Imperial Order of the Cross. The National Order of the Southern Cross is awarded for distinguished service to foreign

Br 63
Collar

Br 63
Collar
(reverse)

Br 63
Grand Cross
badge
(reverse)

Regulated: By Decree No. 22,610 on April 4, 1933

Modified: By Decree No.1,424 on July 17, 1939, creating the collar

Reregulated: By Decree No. 14,265 on December 14, 1943

Grand Master: President of the Republic

Grades: Grand Cordon, Collar,* Grand Cross,* Grand Officer, Commander, Officer, Knight

civilians and military personnel. The Ministry of Foreign Affairs administers the order. It has never been ranked by precedence among the Brazilian orders. There are no restrictions on the number of recipients in any grade. Eligibility is determined by one's position in society.

Instituted: By Presidential Decree No. 22,166 on December 5, 1932

Obverse disc: Constellation of the Southern Cross on a light blue enameled field Obverse legend: BENEMERENTIUM PRAEMIUM on a blue enameled field

Reverse disc: Bust of woman wearing a Phrygian cap, left, on a gold field

Reverse legend: REPUBLICA DOS ESTADOS UNIDOS DO BRASIL (prior to 1968);

Br 63
Grand
Cross

REPUBLICA FEDERATIVA DO BRASIL (after 1968) in a blue enameled wreath

Shape: Ball-tipped, white enameled 5-armed star with 2-pointed ends edged in gold with an enameled laurel and a coffee wreath in the angles, suspended from an enameled laurel and coffee wreath

Star shape: Ball-tipped, white enameled 5-armed star with 2-pointed ends edged in gold with 7 rays in each angle

Collar: White enameled 5-pointed stars alternating with laurel leaves and coffee branches

Size: Badge: Collar: 63 mm; Grand Cross: 71 mm. Star, 76 mm

Metal: Grand Cross: gilt; Knight and Officer: silver

Maker: La Royale, Rio de Janeiro

Ribbon: Sky blue

Reference: Brazil 1968, no. 1; Gillingham 1932, 68; Barac 2009, 181–83; Burke's Peerage 2006, 916–18; Floyd 2004, 2

*Br64. *A Ordem do Mérito Militar*

The Order of Military Merit is awarded to military personnel and civilians, both foreign and national, for distinguished service to the army. It is consists of two divisions: ordinary and supplementary. Ordinary membership is restricted to members of the army on active service. All others, including foreigners, are eligible to receive the supplementary order. This is the fourth-highest of the Brazilian orders. Ordinary membership is limited in number, while the supplementary membership has no numerical restrictions. Awards to an institution or a banner are given without any grade.

Instituted: By Presidential Decree No. 24,660 on June 11, 1934

Regulated: By Decree No. 48,461 on July 5, 1960

Modified: By Decree No. 1,438 on October 8, 1962

Br 64
Grand Cross badge (reverse)

Modified: By Decree No. 59,476 on November 8, 1966

Modified: By Decree No. 60,895 on June 23, 1967

Grand Master: President of the Republic

Grades: Grand Cross,* Grand Officer, Commander, Officer, Knight*

Obverse disc: Woman's head, left, on a gilt field

Obverse legend: MERITO MILITAR on a green enameled band

Reverse disc: Concentric circles of blue, yellow, and green enamel

Reverse legend: REPUBLICA DOS ESTADOS UNIDOS DO BRASIL | 1934 (until 1968); BRASIL (after 1968) on a gilt band

Shape: White enameled cross with floriated ends

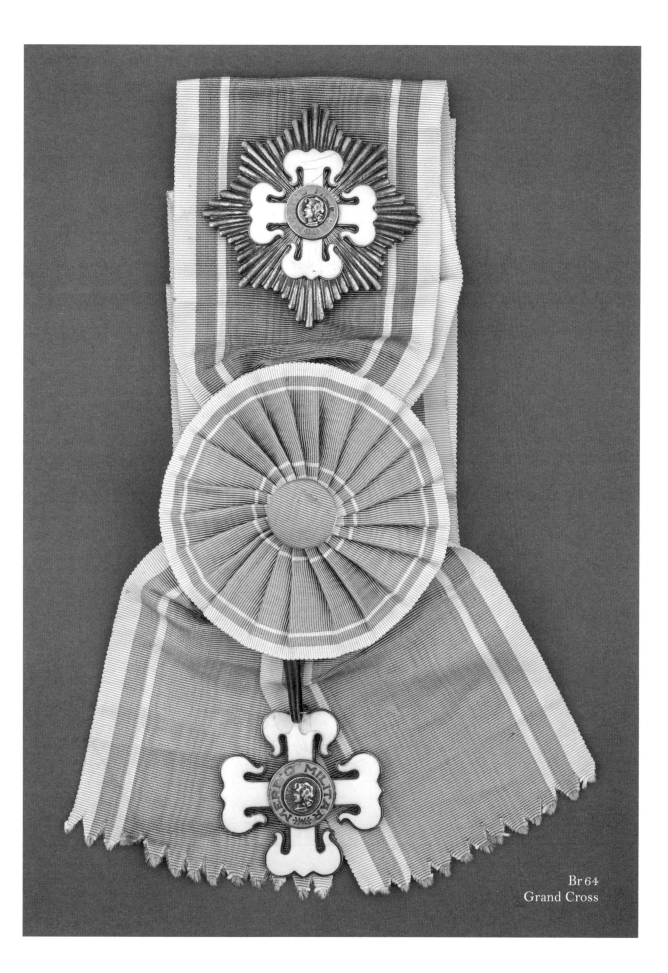

Br 64
Grand Cross

Br 64
Knight

Br 64
Knight

Star shape: Badge on an 8-pointed star, with 6 rays in each angle

Size: Badge: Grand Cross: 55 mm; Knight: 40 mm. Star: 75 mm

Metal: Badge: gilt; star: silver

Maker: Randal, Rio de Janeiro

Ribbon: Green with narrow white edge stripes and narrower white side stripes

Reference: Burke's Peerage 2006, 901–4; Brazil 1968, no. 4; Barac 2009, 190–91; Werlich 1974, 61; Floyd 2004, 1–5

*Br65. *A Ordem do Mérito Naval*

The Order of Naval Merit was created on the same day as the Order of Military Merit. It is ranked third in the Brazilian order of precedence. It is awarded to navy personnel for distinguished service and to foreign and Brazilian citizens as well as to institutions for exceptional service to the navy. When awarded to organizations, the order comes in one grade. Like the Order of Military Merit, this order is divided

Br 65
Grand Officer
badge

Br 65
Grand Officer
badge

into ordinary and supplementary members. Ordinary membership is restricted to navy officers
on active duty above the rank of warrant officer.
Supplementary membership has no numerical
restrictions and is open to most persons who
have provided a relevant service to the navy.
Restrictions on ordinary membership are listed
below by grade.

Instituted: By Presidential Decree No. 24,659
on July 4, 1934

Regulated: By Decree No. 21 on August 23,
1934

Modified: By Decree No. 60,188 on February
8, 1967

Modified: By Decree No. 3,400 on April 3,
2000

Grand Master: President of the Republic

Grades: Grand Cross (8), Grand Officer*
(18), Commander (50), Officer (100), Knight
(150)

Obverse disc: Woman's head, right

Obverse legend: MERITO NAVAL on a blue
enameled band

Reverse disc: Arms of Brazil

Reverse legend: REPUBLICA DOS ESTADOS
UNIDOS DO BRASIL (until 1968); BRASIL on
a blue enameled band (after 1968)

Shape: White enameled cross pattée with
pointed slightly concave ends with a gilt anchor in each angle surmounted by a florette

Star shape: Badge on an 8-pointed star with 8
rays in each angle

Br 65
Grand Officer srar

Br 66
Officer

Size: Badge: Grand Officer: 75 × 62 mm;
   Officer miniature: 26 mm. Star: 78 mm
Metal: Badge: gilt; star: silver
Ribbon: Red with a blue center stripe
Reference: Burke's Peerage 2006, 901; Brazil
   1968, no. 3; Barac, 2009, 192; Werlich 1974,
   62; Floyd 2004, 4

*Br66. *A Ordem do Mérito Aeronáutico*

The Order of Aeronautical Merit is awarded to
air force personnel for exceptional service. It is
also awarded to national and foreign civilians,
to members of another air force, and to national
and foreign institutions. It is the fifth-highest
order among the Brazilian orders. Members
may be admitted to one of three divisions: ordinary, for active air force officers above the
rank of warrant officer; supplementary, for air
force officers of lower rank or those on inac-
tive duty; and special, for all others, including
foreign citizens.

Instituted: By Presidential Decree No. 5,961
   on November 1, 1943
Grand Master: President of the Republic

Br 66
Officer

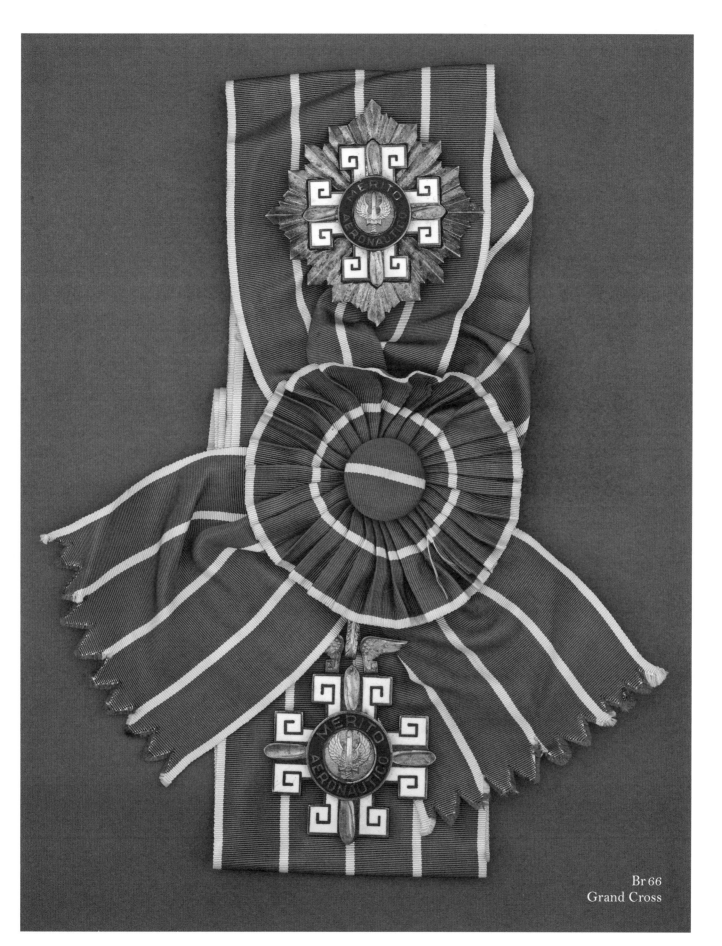

Br 66
Grand Cross

Br 66
Grand Cross badge (reverse)

Grades: Grand Cross* (unlimited), Grand
Officer (35), Commander (50), Officer*
(125), Knight (185)

Obverse disc: Air force emblem on a gilt field

Obverse legend: MERITO AERONAUTICO on a
blue enameled band

Reverse disc: Green and yellow enameled star
with blue center on a gilt field

Reverse legend: REPUBLICA DOS ESTADOS
UNIDOS DO BRASIL on a blue enameled
band

Shape: White enameled cross with rectangular ends with a key pattern with a gilt propeller down the center of each arm attached
to two displayed wings; knight's badge suspended from two displayed wings

Star shape: Badge on an 8-pointed star with 3
rays in each angle

Size: Badge: Grand Cross: 73 × 62 mm;
Knight: 45 × 40 mm. Star: 79 mm

Metal: Grand Cross: gilt silver; Officer: gilt

Maker: Condal, Randal and La Royale, Rio de
Janeiro

Ribbon: Blue with 5 narrow white stripes

Reference: Burke's Peerage 2006, 904; Brazil
1968, no. 5; Barac 2009, 193; Werlich 1974,
62–63; Floyd 2004, 6

*Br67. *A Ordem Nacional do Mérito*

The National Order of Merit is awarded to Brazilian and foreign citizens for extraordinary civilian and military merit of interest to Brazil.
It is the highest Brazilian award in order of
precedence. The order is divided into ordinary
and supplementary divisions, with numerical
restrictions applying to ordinary recipients. A
silver merit medal is awarded to civil servants
whose grades do not qualify for knight. The
order is administered in the Presidential Palace. The form of the globe was borrowed from
the imperial flag.

Instituted: By Presidential Decree No. 9,732
on September 4, 1946

Regulated: By Decree No. 21,854 on September 26, 1946

Grand Master: President of the Republic

Grades: Grand Cordon, Grand Cross* (45),
Grand Officer (150), Commander (350),
Officer (650), Knight (unlimited)

Obverse disc: Gilt globe of the world atop a
blue enamel background beneath a diagonal
metallic strip and 5 rays in the angles

Reverse inscription: ORDEM | NACIONAL | DO
| MERITO

Shape: Ball-tipped, white enameled 6-pointed
star edged in gilt with a wreath of roses in
the angles

Star shape: White enameled, 6-pointed star
edged in gilt with a wreath of roses in the
angles, on a 6-pointed star with a ball and
4 rays in each angle

Size: Badge: 59 mm. Star: 77 mm

Br 67
Grand
Cross

Br 67
Grand Cross badge (reverse)

Metal: Badge: silver gilt; star; bronze
Maker: La Royale, Rio de Janeiro
Ribbon: Red with white side stripes
Reference: Burke's Peerage 2006, 898–99;
    Brazil 1968, no. 2; Werlich 1974, 61
Provenance: A. Menke

Br68. *A Ordem do Mérito Médico*

The Order of Medical Merit recognizes Brazilian and foreign medical doctors who have provided noteworthy service to the country or have carried out important medical research or published important books on medical subjects. The order is ranked eighth in the Brazilian hierarchy of orders. The three highest grades have limitations on the number of members.

Instituted: By Law No. 1,074 on March 24, 1950
Regulated: By Decree No. 29,198 on January 24, 1951
Amended: Frequently, but Law No. 66,981 on July 29, 1970, revoked all former legislation
Grades: Grand Cross (70), Grand Officer (90), Commander (130), Officer, Knight
Obverse disc: Caduceus on a gold field
Obverse legend: SALUS POPULI on a green enameled band
Reverse disc: ORDEM DO MERITO MEDICO on a gold field
Reverse legend: REPUBLICA FEDERATIVA DO BRASIL on a green enameled band
Shape: White enameled 6-pointed star with a laurel wreath in the angles, suspended from a green enameled wreath
Ribbon: Dark green with 2 narrow yellow side stripes
Reference: Burke's Peerage 2006, 907–8; Brazil 1968, no. 8; Floyd 2004, 9

Br69. *A Ordem do Mérito do Trabalho*

The Order of Labor Merit recognizes exceptional service in the professions related to labor. It recognizes improvements in labor productivity, union organization, job creation, professional training, job safety, and social security, among others. It is the ninth order by rank. Membership is restricted according to grade.

Instituted: By Presidential Decree No. 28,527 on August 22, 1950
Modified: By Decree No. 57,278 on November 17, 1965
Modified: By Decree No. 62,682 on March 10, 1968
Grand Master: President of the Republic
Grades: Grand Cross (50), Grand Officer (75), Commander (100), Officer (150), Knight (250)
Obverse disc: Image of a worker wearing a winged helmet

Br 71
Commander

Obverse legend: ORDEM DO MERITO DO TRABALHO on a green enameled field

Reverse disc: Same as obverse

Reverse legend: MINISTERIO DO TRABALHO E DA PREVIDENCIA SOCIAL

Shape: Red enameled Maltese cross with 2-pointed ends

Ribbon: Gray with a center red stripe edged in yellow

Reference: Burke's Peerage 2006, 908–9

Br70. *A Ordem do Mérito Deportivo*

The Order of Merit for Sport is given for outstanding achievement in encouraging sports in Brazil. It has no numerical restrictions. This is the lowest order in the Brazilian hierarchy. It lacks official statutes.

Instituted: By Presidential Decree No. 36,328 on October 15, 1954

Grades: Medal, Cross

Obverse: Hand holding torch

Medal legend: MENS SANA IN CORPORE SANO

Cross shape: Maltese cross superimposed on shorter, broader Maltese cross, laurel wreath in the angles

Ribbon: Green with central yellow stripe

Reference: Burke's Peerage 2006, 916–17

*Br71. *A Ordem Nacional do Mérito Educativo*

The National Order of Educational Merit recognizes distinguished service in the field of education. The order is eleventh in the Brazilian ranking, and it has been reorganized several times. It has two divisions: ordinary and supplementary. Ordinary membership is restricted to Brazilian citizens, and each grade has its own numerical limits. Foreigners are eligible for supplementary membership, for which there are no numerical restrictions.

Instituted: By Presidential Decree No. 38,162 on October 28, 1955

Modified: By Decree No. 65,495 on November 5, 1971

Grand Master: President of the Republic

Grades: Grand Cross (80), Grand Officer (160), Commander* (200), Officer (240), Knight (800)

Obverse disc: An open book on a red enameled oval disc

Obverse legend: MERITO EDUCATIVO | BRASIL on a white enameled band surrounded by a green enameled wreath

Shape: 8-pointed faceted star with 5 rays in each angle

Size: 53 mm

Metal: Commander: silver

Ribbon: Purple with narrow white edge stripes

Reference: Burke's Peerage 2006, 910

Provenance: A. Menke

*Br72. *A Ordem do Mérito Judiciário Militar*

The Order of Judicial Military Merit is awarded to military judges for merit or to other persons who have performed a service the military court wishes to recognize. It is ranked seventh in the order of precedence. It consists of three divisions: ordinary, supplemental, and special. Ordinary members must be employees of the Higher Military Court; supplementary members must be retired from the Court; while special members covers everyone else. The order has no limitations on the number of recipients.

Instituted: By Presidential Decree No. 772 on June 12, 1957

Modified: By Presidential Decree No. 43,195 on February 20, 1958

Modified: August 16, 1968, changing name from "Jurídico" to "Judiciário"

Regulated: By Decree on August 7, 1991

Amended: By Decree on November 8, 1995; November 5, 1997; and October 15, 1999

Grand Master: President Minister of the Higher Military Court

Grades: Grand Cross,* High Distinction, Distinction, and Good Service

Obverse disc: The scales of justice surrounded by symbols of the 3 military branches

Obverse inscription: MARINHA EXERCITO AERONAUTICA on a ribbon below scales

Shape: Red enameled Maltese cross with 2-pointed ends surmounted by a suspension device with 2 oak leaves

Star shape: Badge on 8-pointed star with 5 rays in each angle

Size: Grand Cross badge: 60 mm. Star: 82 mm

Metal: Gilt

Maker: Randal, Rio de Janeiro

Ribbon: 3 stripes of yellow, red, and white, each bisected by a thin blue stripe

Reference: Burke's Peerage 2006, 906–7; Brazil 1968, no. 7; Floyd 2004, 8

Provenance: A. Menke

*Br73. *A Ordem de Rio Branco*

The Order of Rio Branco recognizes those who have given distinguished service to Brazil in the field of international diplomacy; it is ranked sixth in the Brazilian hierarchy. The order has two divisions: ordinary and supplementary. Ordinary members must be diplomats in active service, whose numbers are generally limited according to grade. All others, including foreigners, are eligible for supplementary membership. A silver merit medal may be awarded to persons whose rank does not qualify for knight.

The order is named after José Maria de Silva Paranhoa, the Baron of Rio Branco (1845–1912). Rio Branco became a politician, monarchist, diplomat, teacher, and journalist under Pedro II. He negotiated peace with Uruguay

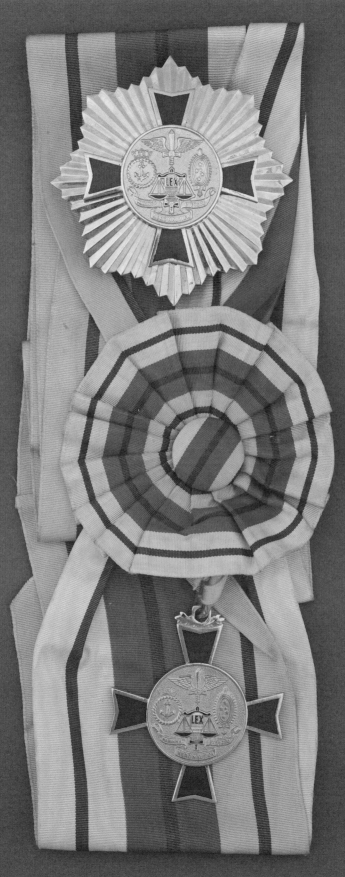

Br 72
Grand Cross

Br 73
Grand Cross star

and later with Paraguay at the end of the Triple Alliance War. As foreign minister, he negotiated the Treaty of Persepolis, whereby Bolivia ceded 190,000 square kilometers in the region of Acre to Brazil for two million pounds sterling. He joined the Conservative Party and was appointed president of the Council of Ministers, becoming its longest serving president.

Instituted: By Law No. 51,410 on February 14, 1962

Regulated: By Decree No. 834 on April 3, 1962

Modified: By Decree No. 61,295 on September 6, 1967, authorizing the order to be worn on military uniforms

Grand Master: President of the Republic

Grades: Grand Cross,* Grand Officer (60), Commander, (50), Officer* (40), Knight (30)

Obverse disc: World globe

Obverse legend: VBIQVE PATRIAE MEMOR on a blue enameled band

Br 73
Grand Cross badge

Br 73
Grand Cross badge (reverse)

Br 73
Officer

Br 74
Collar

Br 73
Officer

Reverse inscription: 1845 | 1912

Shape: White enameled Maltese cross with 2-pointed ends

Star shape: Badge on an 8-pointed star with 8 rays in each angle

Size: Badge: Grand Cross: 73 × 65 mm; Officer: 49 × 45 mm. star: 81 mm

Metal: Grand Cross: gilt silver; Officer: gilt

Maker: H. Stern, Rio de Janeiro

Ribbon: Dark blue with white edge stripes

Reference: Burke's Peerage 2006, 905–6; Brazil 1968, no. 6; Werlich 1974, 63; Floyd 2004, 7

*Br74. *A Ordem do Congresso Nacional*

The Order of the National Congress is awarded to persons for merit considered worthy of recognition by the National Congress. It is open to both Brazilian citizens and foreigners with no numerical restrictions. The order is not ranked.

Br 74
Collar (reverse)

Br 74
Collar star

Instituted: By Law Decree No. 70 of the National Congress on November 28, 1972

Grades: Collar,* Grand Cross, Grand Officer, Commander, Officer, Knight

Obverse disc: Constellation of the Southern Cross on a light blue field

Obverse legend: ORDEM DO CONGRESSO | NACIONAL on a white enameled band

Reverse disc: Silhouette of the Congress buildings in front of white enameled map of Brazil on light blue field

Reverse legend: REPUBLICA FEDERATIVA | DO BRASIL on a white enameled band

Shape: Ball-tipped green and yellow enameled cross pattée with concave pointed ends with light blue enameled squinches and a gilt wreath in the angles

Star shape: Ball-tipped green and yellow enameled cross pattée with concave pointed ends on an 8-pointed star with 7 rays in each angle

Collar: Alternating bronze horseshoe-shaped wreaths and ball-tipped green and yellow enameled crosses pattée with concave pointed ends

Size: Badge and star: 85 mm

Metal: Gilt

Ribbon: Green, yellow

Reference: Burke's Peerage 2006, 918

*Br75. *A Ordem do Mérito das Comunicações*

The Order of Merit for Communications is awarded for outstanding achievement in the field of communications; it is the twelfth-highest in the Brazilian hierarchy. At the time the order was promulgated, the major telephone companies still belonged to the government. Most of them have since been privatized. The order has two divisions: ordinary and supplementary. Ordinary membership is restricted to Brazilian citizens, while foreigners are eli-

Br 75
Grand Officer
badge

Br 75
Grand Officer
badge

Br 75
Grand Officer star

Br 75
Grand Officer star

gible for supplementary membership. Ordinary membership is restricted numerically, while supplementary membership is not.

Instituted: By Presidential Decree No. 87,009 on March 15, 1982

Modified: By Decree No. 3,519 on August 20, 2000

Modified: By Law No. 11,655 on April 15, 2008, changing the name of the Order to Ordem do Mérito das Comunicações Jornalista Roberto Marinha

Grand Master: President of the Republic

Grades: Grand Cross (50), Grand Officer* (70), Commander (150), Officer (200), Knight (300)

Obverse disc: Image of satellite disc

Obverse legend: MÉRITO DAS COMUNICAÇÕES

Reverse disc: Bust of Dom Pedro II, left

Reverse legend: D. PEDRO II O PRECURSOR

Shape: Black enameled star with radio waves in the angles surmounted by a laurel wreath

Star shape: Badge on a round silvered disc with concentric circles

Size: Badge: 81 × 60 mm. Star: 60 mm

Metal: Brass

Ribbon: Blue with 2 narrow white side stripes

Reference: Burke's Peerage 2006, 911

Br76. *A Ordem Nacional do Mérito da Justiça*

The National Order of Juridical Merit recognizes outstanding performance in the judicial field. It ranks thirteenth in the Brazilian hierarchy of orders. The order has two divisions: ordinary and supplementary. Ordinary membership is restricted to Brazilian citizens, while foreigners are eligible to receive the supplementary order. It is not certain whether this order has been activated.

Instituted: By Presidential Decree No. 90,040 on August 11, 1984

Regulated: By Ministerial Directive No. 66 on February 15, 1985

Amended: By Ministerial Directive No. 1,048 on July 7, 2006

Grand Master: President of the Republic

Grades: Grand Cross, Grand Officer, Commander, Officer, Knight

Obverse disc: JUSTITIA on a red enam-

eled field surrounded by a green enameled wreath

Reverse disc: MINISTERIO DE JUSTICA

Shape: Cross superimposed on a light blue enameled circle and attached to a white enameled crown at the top

Ribbon: Orange-red with 4 narrow stripes of brown and yellow

Reference: Burke's Peerage 2006, 912–13

*Br77. *A Ordem das Forças Armadas*

The Order of the Armed Forces was awarded to members of the army, navy, and air force for service to the armed forces. Membership was extended to Brazilian and foreign nationals, civilian and military, as well as foreign organizations for meritorious service to Brazil's armed forces. The order was ranked fifth in the national ranking until it was dissolved in 2002 and replaced by the Order of Merit of Defense.

Instituted: By Presidential Decree No. 91,343 on June 18, 1985

Rescinded: By Presidential Decree No. 4,263 on June 11, 2002

Grades: Grand Cross,* Grand Officer, Commander, Officer and Knight (Ladies)*

Obverse disc: Emblem combining the symbols of the army, navy, and air force

Obverse legend: MERITO | FORÇAS ARMADAS on a blue enameled band

Reverse disc: Arms of Brazil

Reverse legend: BRASIL | EMFA on a blue enameled band

Shape: White enameled cross pattée with slightly concave ends edged in gold or silver

Star shape: Badge on 8-pointed star with 8 rays in each angle

Size: Badge: Grand Cross: 72 mm; Knight: 52 mm. Star: 89 mm

Br 77
Grand Cross

Br 77
Grand Cross star
(reverse)

Br 77
Grand Cross badge
(reverse)

Br 77
Knight

Br 77
Knight

Metal: Gold, silver

Ribbon: Green, white, blue

Reference: http://www.pt.wikipedi.org/wiki/
Ordem_do_Merito_das_Forcas_Armadas,
accessed August 26, 2012

Br78. *A Ordem do Mérito Cultural*

The Order of Cultural Merit is awarded to Brazilians and foreigners for their contribution to culture. The order has no numerical restrictions for foreigners. Ordinary membership is limited to Brazilians and is subject to numerical restrictions.

Instituted: By Law No. 8,313 on December 23, 1991

Regulated: By Decree No. 1,711 on November 22, 1995

Grand Master: President of the Republic

Grades: Grand Cross (50), Commander (150), Knight (200)

Obverse disc: Open book surrounded by a laurel wreath

Obverse legend: ORDEM DO MÉRITO CULTURAL on a purple enameled band

Shape: Gold-rimmed, white enameled cross with spiked bottom and other 3 ends floriate

Ribbon: Red

Reference: Brazil 1995; Burke's Peerage 2006, 915–16

Br79. *A Ordem Nacional do Mérito Científico*

The National Order for Scientific Merit is awarded for outstanding scientific achievement. It has two divisions: ordinary and supplementary. Ordinary members must be Brazilian citizens, and restrictions are placed on their numbers. Foreigners may become supplementary members, and there are no numerical restrictions on them. The statutes of the order have been modified at least four times since its foundation.

The order recognizes the work of José Bonifácio de Andrada e Silva (1763–1838), a naturalist, professor of geology, poet, and statesman. Following Brazil's declaration of independence, he was appointed minister of foreign affairs. He later fell out of favor with Pedro I.

Instituted: By Presidential Decree No. 772 on March 16, 1993, and Decree No. 4,115 on February 6, 2002

Grand Master: President of the Republic

Grades: Grand Cross (200), Commander (500), Silver Medal (for institutions)

Obverse disc: Bust of José Bonifácio de Andrada e Silva, facing, on a metallic field

Obverse legend: ORDEM DO MERITO CIENTIFICO on a light blue band

Reverse disc: Arms of Brazil

Reverse legend: The grade of the order on a light blue enameled band

Shape: Red enameled cross

Size: Badge: Grand Cross: 120 × 100 mm; Commander: 60 × 40 mm; Knight: 30 × 20 mm. Star: 100 mm

Ribbon: Red with narrow white edge stripes

Reference: Burke's Peerage 2006, 913–15

Br80. *A Ordem do Mérito do Ministério Público Militar*

The Order of Merit for Public Military Administration is awarded mainly to current and former employees. It is the tenth-highest of the Brazilian orders. Ordinary membership is restricted to current employees of the Public Military Administration, while retired officials are eligible for supplementary membership. Other candidates may become special members. There are no restrictions on the number of recipients, but there are limits on how many may be awarded in one year. The order has elaborate eligibility requirements for each grade.

Instituted: By Decree No. 29/CSMPM of the Superior Council of the Public Military Ministry on March 26, 1999

Modified: By Resolution No. 32/CSMPM on August 18, 2000, and Resolution No. 36/CSMPM on May 30, 2001

Grades: Grand Cross, High Distinction, Distinction, Good Service

Obverse disc: MÉRITO MINISTÉRIO PÚBLICO MILITAR on a light blue enameled band

Shape: Red enameled Maltese cross with slightly concave ends

Ribbon: Red, light blue, and red stripes each bisected by a gray strip

Reference: Burke's Peerage 2006, 909

Br81. *A Ordem do Mérito da Defesa*

The Order of Merit for Defense is awarded for service to the armed forces or in defense of the nation. This order replaced the Order of Merit for the Armed Forces as the country's second-most important order. It is awarded to military personnel and civilians, Brazilian and foreigners, who perform valuable services to the Brazilian armed forces. Membership is also extended to organizations, both civilian and military, foreign and national. It has two levels of membership: ordinary and supplementary. Ordinary members must be Brazilian nationals, and numerical restrictions apply. There are no numerical or nationality requirements for supplementary membership.

Instituted: By Presidential Decree No. 4,263 on June 11, 2002

Amended: By Presidential Decree No. 4,424 on October 14, 2002, making the order the second-highest in the national ranking

Grand Master: President of the Republic

Grades: Grand Cross (20), Grand Officer (90), Commander (170), Officer (190), Knight (280)

Obverse disc: Woman's head, right

Obverse legend: MERITO | DA DEFESA on a blue enameled band

Reverse disc: Arms of Brazil

Reverse legend: BRASIL | MINISTERIO DA DEFESA on a blue enameled band

Shape: White enameled cross pattée with gold edges

Metal: Gold

Ribbon: Green, white, blue

Reference: Burke's Peerage 2006, 898–900

Br82. *A Ordem do Merito Cívico e Cultural*

The Order of Civic and Cultural Merit is awarded for outstanding contributions to society and the arts.

Obverse disc: Map of Brazil with a star in the center

Obverse legend: MERITO CIVICO E CULTURAL | BRASIL on a white enameled band

Shape: Green and white enameled, ball-tipped Maltese cross with a gilt wreath in the angles

Ribbon: Yellow with green side stripes with a narrow white stripe edged in blue

Reference: http://www.omsa.org/photopost/showphoto.php?photo=big&cat, accessed January 25, 2013

Br83. *A Ordem do Visconde de Mauá*

The Order of the Viscount of Mauá is given for entrepreneurial effort of importance to the economic development of Brazil.

Grades: Grand Cross, Grand Officer, Commander

Obverse: Bust of Mauá, ¾ left

Shape: Blue enameled cross with white enameled Greek cross in the center and 5 rays in the angles

Metal: Gilt

Ribbon: Blue

CHILE

CHILE dates its independence back to September 18, 1810, when local notables in Santiago formed a junta to run the country in the name of Ferdinand VII after Napoleon exiled him to France. The junta members plotted against each other as they competed for power. Six separate juntas ruled Chile until Spain regained control in 1814, following Ferdinand VII's reinstatement as king. During this time, no medals or orders are known to have been instituted.

Chile proclaimed its independence from Spain on February 12, 1818, one year after José de San Martín and Bernardo O'Higgins defeated the royalist army at Chacabuco on February 17, 1817. The royalists regrouped but were defeated decisively at the Battle of Maipú on April 5, 1818. Chile authorized its first medals for the Chilean and Argentine troops that participated in the two battles. Chilean forces later fought royalist holdouts at Valdivia and the island of Chiloé, for which medals were also struck.

Politically, Chileans were more successful at creating a unified central government, although many of them still supported Spanish rule. Occasional revolts against the government were suppressed, and medals were awarded to the country's military. With these few exceptions, all of Chile's military medals during the nineteenth century were awarded for military action abroad.

San Martín followed up his victories in Chile by sending his army to expel the Spanish viceroy in Lima. The Chilean navy transported his army by sea and helped him occupy Lima. Chile became militarily involved with Peru three more times during the nineteenth century; twice as enemies, during the War of the Confederation and the War of the Pacific, and once as allies, during the Chincha Islands War against Spain. Chile authorized many medals for its involvement in these three wars. The War of the Pacific marked the end of Chile's military operations on foreign soil. The country later instituted a large array of medals for its military in peacetime. Most of these reward years of service, academic achievements, and promotions in rank.

Chile did not create its first order of merit until 1929, when it restructured the Legion of Merit founded by Bernardo O'Higgins for the victors at Chacabuco. The new order was awarded only to foreign nationals. After World War II, Chile instituted a second order for foreign nationals, the Order of Bernardo O'Higgins. It was not until 1977, under General Augusto Pinochet, that Chile created its first orders of merit for its own citizens as well as foreign nationals. The new orders recognize cultural and educational accomplishments.

MEDALS

MOST OF CHILE's military medals were created to recognize members of its armed forces, first in the War of Independence, then for action abroad in wartime: the War of the Confederation, the Chincha Islands War, and finally the Triple Alliance War. Chile has not gone to war in a foreign country since 1883. It remained neutral in the two world wars. Chile later created military medals for bravery, merit, and distinguished service.

WAR OF INDEPENDENCE (1817–1820)

IN JANUARY 1817, Argentine General San Martín and Bernardo O'Higgins, Chile's revolutionary hero, crossed the Andes from Mendoza into Chile with their army. San Martín took the bulk of his forces through the Los Patos Pass down into the Aconcagua Valley. A Spanish force under the command of Brigadier Rafael Maroto had marched north from Santiago to block his passage. The combined Chilean-Argentine force attacked the royalists at Chacabuco in a two-pronged front on February 12, 1817. The bulk of the royalist troops were either killed or captured, although their commander escaped. The royalist defeat forced them to abandon Santiago. O'Higgins was appointed director general of Chile and held that office for six years.

Ch1. *La Medalla por la Batalla de Chacabuco*

Two months after the battle, Chile authorized three versions of a medal for the Battle of Chacabuco. The first two were pentagonal, struck in London. The medal was awarded to all of the officers and men who fought at Chacabuco. It is probable that the first version was awarded to officers and the second one to the troops. The sun with rays above the pentagon represents the Sun of May, one of the republican symbols of the United Provinces of the River Plate (today's Argentina).

Ch1a. *Variant 1*

Instituted: By decree on April 15, 1817
Obverse: Arms of the United Provinces between laurel branches

Obverse inscription: 12 DE FEBº DE 1817
Reverse inscription: LA | PATRIA | A LOS | VENCEDORES | DE LOS | ANDES within a laurel wreath
Obverse legend: CHILE RESTAURADº POR EL VALOR EN CHACABUCO
Shape: Pentagon surmounted by a Sun of May
Metal: Gold, silver
Ribbon: White, light blue, gold

Ch1b. *Variant 2*

Obverse: Arms of the United Provinces between laurel branches
Reverse inscription: LA | PATRIA | A LOS | VENCEDORES | DE LOS | ANDES within a laurel wreath
Reverse legend: CHILE RESTAURº Pᴿ EL VALOR EN CHACABᶜᴼ

Shape: Pentagon surmounted by a Sun of May and attached to a suspension bar

Metal: Gold, silver

Ribbon: White, light blue, gold

Ch1c. *Variant 3*

The third version was struck in Chile, probably at the Santiago mint.

Obverse: Arms of the United Provinces superimposed on mountain peaks and a Sun of May and encircled by 2 laurel branches

Reverse inscription: LA | PATRIA | A LOS VENCED | DE LOS | ANDES within a laurel wreath

Reverse legend: CHILE RESTAURADO POR EL VALOR EN CHACABUCO

Shape: Oval

Size: 41 × 34 mm

Metal: Gold, silver

Ribbon: White, light blue, gold

Reference: Argentina 1910, 266–72; Gillingham 1932, 94–96; Brinkmann 2012, 1, 4–6; Barac 2009, 234

* * *

THE ROYALIST survivors from Chacabuco withdrew by sea to Lima but were ordered back to Talcahuano, where Spain maintained a strong garrison. They regrouped and took the offensive in the following year under the command of Mariano Osorio. San Martín put his own forces in a blocking position south of Santiago. The two sides met at Maipú on April 5, 1818. They were numerically equally matched, but the Chilean-Argentine forces again proved victorious. Both sides reported one thousand men killed. Nearly half of the royalist army surrendered along with its officers. The Spanish commander escaped with a few survivors. The battle consolidated Chile's independence and ended Spain's hope of regaining control over the country.

Ch 2

Ch 2

Ch2. La Medalla por la Batalla de Maypo

Chile authorized its second military medal shortly after the Battle of Maypo (Maipú). It was awarded to both Chilean and Argentine officers and men.

Instituted: May 10, 1818

Obverse: Star within 2 laurel branches

Obverse legend: CHILE RECONOCIDO AL VALOR Y CONSTANCIA

Reverse inscription: DE LOS | VENCEDORES | DE MAYPO | AB. 5 1818 within 2 laurel branches; on some gold examples: LA PATRIA A LOS VENCEDORES DE MAYPO ABRIL 5 DE 1818

Shape: Oval (some examples suspended from a bronze ribbon bow)

Size: 30 × 27 mm

Metal: Gold, silver,* copper*

Maker: Casa de Moneda, Santiago

Ribbon: Red

Reference: Gillingham 1932, 98–101; Brinkmann 2012, 1, 8–12

Provenance: Silver: A. Menke

*Ch3. *La Estrella por la Batalla de Maypo*

An octagonal star for the same battle was issued to Chilean and Argentine troops.

Obverse: Star within 2 laurel branches

Obverse inscription: CHILE RECONOCIDO AL VALOR Y CONSTANCIA

Reverse inscription: DE LOS | VENCEDORES | DE MAYPO | A B.5-1818

Shape: Ball-tipped octagon with concave sides

Metal: Gold, silver,* copper

Size: 29 mm

Ribbon: Red

Reference: Gillingham 1932, 100; Barac 2009, 235; Brinkmann 2012, 1, 16–17; Medina 1901, 34

Provenance: A. Menke

*Ch4. *La Medalla por la Batalla de Valdivia*

Although the royalist defeats at Chacabuco and Maipú effectively ended Spanish rule in Chile, more than a dozen less significant battles and skirmishes were fought on Chilean soil. The most important of these was the capture of the key Spanish stronghold of Valdivia in February 1820 following a three-day siege by Chilean forces under the command of Lord Cochrane.

*Ch4a. *Variant 1*

Obverse: Walls of Valdivia fortress, an arm holding a sword and an inkwell on a book within a 6-pointed star

Obverse legend: RESTAURADOR DE LA PATRIA on a white enameled band

Shape: Gold: 6-pointed star surrounded by a green enameled laurel wreath suspended from an oval laurel ribbon bar; silver: same but ball-tipped and not enameled, superimposed on a hexagon with radiating lines

Size: 40 mm

Metal: Gold, silver*

Provenance: A. Menke

Ch 4a

Ch4b. *Variant 2*

Instituted: April 24, 1821

Obverse: Fort with a flag flying

Obverse legend: LA PAT A LOS HERO Y RESTAUR° DE VALD^A

Reverse inscription: EL | DIA 2 FEB° | DE | 1820 within a circle

Shape: Hexagon with concave sides within a laurel wreath; also known as an uncut struck disc

Size: 28 mm

Metal: Gold, silver

Ribbon: White, blue, red

Reference: Gillingham 1932, 100–103; Barac 2009, 235–36

* * *

WITH THE Spanish threat inside Chile eliminated, San Martín turned his attention to the Spanish Viceroyalty in Lima. With the help of the British mercenary Lord Cochrane, he sailed north in August 1820 with his army to Peru. He landed his forces in Paracas, causing the royalists to withdraw from Lima. San Martín declared Peru to be an independent nation on July 28, 1821, and the Peruvians appointed him Protector of Peru.

Ch5. *La Medalla al Ejército la Escuadra Libertadora del Perú*

San Martín authorized a medal for the Chilean army and navy officers and men who accompanied him to Peru. There are a number of variants, with only minor differences in design and inscription.

Instituted: By Decree of San Martín on August 15, 1821

Obverse: Shield beneath a Sun of May, between flags, and above military trophies and all surrounded by a laurel wreath

Obverse inscription: Army version: YO FUI | DEL EXTO | LIBERTA | DOR; navy version: YO FUI DE LA ESCUADRA LIBERTADORA

Reverse: Sun

Shape: Oval suspended from a ribbon ring with laurel branches

Size: 30 × 25 mm

Metal: Gold, silver

Reference: Medina 1901, 129; Argentina 1910, 49–52; Gillingham 1932, 103

* * *

ALTHOUGH San Martín successfully occupied Lima, he remained outnumbered by royalist forces in the interior and avoided a direct confrontation with them. Instead, he encouraged Peruvian revolutionaries to harass the Spanish forces using guerrilla tactics. He authorized a medal for these guerrillas, which is included under Peru (see below, Pe4).

Domestic Instability

THE FIRST internal threat to political stability in Chile came from General José Miguel Carrera Verdugo (1785–1821), one of the country's founders. Carrera came from a well-connected family in Santiago. He was a rising officer in the Spanish army when O'Higgins began advocating independence. He returned to Chile from Spain and briefly served in one of the juntas ruling in the name of the exiled King Ferdinand VII. When Ferdinand returned to Madrid, he sent an army to reassume control over Chile. Carrera was defeated and taken prisoner. He tried to join San Martín in Mendoza, but Carrera did not get along with either San Martín or O'Higgins. He stayed in the United Provinces and allied himself with the federalists against Buenos Aires. He tried to return to Chile at the head of a small army, but the Argentine Province of Cuyo defeated Carrera at the Battle of Punta del Medano. The medal issued for this battle is listed under Argentina (see above, Ar12).

Spain still kept a small garrison on the southern Chilean island of Chiloé, where it survived thanks to support from the local Araucano Indians. Chile made the first of several unsuccessful attempts to defeat the royalists commanded by the Spanish governor of Chiloé, Antonio Quintanilla. In 1826, a larger Chilean force commanded by Ramón Freire landed in Chiloé. After several days of fighting, the royalists surrendered. Quintanilla, as the Spanish governor, signed the Treaty of Tantauco on January 15, 1826, which ended Chile's War of Independence.

Ch6. *La Medalla de Chiloé*

Chile authorized a medal for its officers and men in Chiloé. Although the war with Spain had ended, royalist irregulars and allied Indians periodically engaged in guerrilla warfare against Chile.

Instituted: By decree on February 18, 1826
Classes: Officers, enlisted men

Obverse inscription: Army: COLMO SU GLORIA EN CHILOE LA MILITAR DE CHILE; NAVY: LA MARINA DE CHILE
Reverse inscription: CAMPANA DE 1826
Metal: Officers: gold; enlisted men: silver
Reference: Medina 1901, 126; Gillingham 1932, 104; Brinkmann 2012, 1, 32

War of the Confederation (1836–1839)

IN 1836, Bolivian President Andrés de Santa Cruz formed the Peru-Bolivian Confederation with himself as the Supreme Protector. Chile considered the Confederation to be a security threat and sent a warship, purportedly on a courtesy call, to Callao. In fact, its crew boarded and captured three Peruvian warships in the harbor. Santa Cruz tried to negotiate a settlement with Chile, but was unwilling to dismantle the Confederation. Chile declared war in December 1836.

Ch7. *La Medalla por la Tripulación de la Fragata Monteagudo*

Chile's first medal for this conflict was awarded to sailors for a relatively insignificant event. A group of Chilean exiles led by former President Ramón Freire was given an unused Peruvian warship, the *Monteagudo*. They sailed south from Callao to attack the Chilean fleet. However, the crew switched sides en route. Chile awarded a medal to at least the two leaders of the defection, Manuel Zapata and José Rojas.

Instituted: By Decree of the National Congress on September 6, 1836

Obverse inscription: FIEL A LA PATRIA EN 10 DE AGOSTO DE 1836 within laurel branches

Reverse inscription: LA LEALTAD MANIFESTADA EN LA FRAGATA MONTEAGUDO

Reference: Medina 1901, 137; Gillingham 1932, 108

* * *

CHILE was going through a period of internal turmoil even as tension with the Confederation was rising.

Ch8. *La Estrella a los Vencedores del Baron*

Chile's dictator, Diego Portales, was arrested by a disaffected Chilean officer, Colonel José Antonio Vidaure. Colonel Vidaure then attacked the port of Valparaiso. The port was defended by Admiral Manuel Blanco Encalada, who defeated Vidaure in the Battle of the Baron Heights. However, Portales's captors executed him, an act that Chilean public opinion blamed on the Confederation. Chile authorized a medal for its officers and men, who defeated Vidaure.

Instituted: By decree on June 16, 1837

Classes: Generals, officers, enlisted men

Obverse disc: Shield with star

Obverse legend: A LOS FIELES DEFENSORES D LA LEI

Reverse disc: Star with 5 rays projecting out from the right arm points

Reverse legend: ALTURAS DEL BARON JUN. 6 DE | 1837

Shape: Ball-tipped star

Size: 38 mm

Metal: Generals and officers: gold; enlisted men: silver

Ribbon: Red, black, red

Reference: Gillingham 1932, 108–9; Barac 2009, 236; Brinkmann 2012, 1:34–35

* * *

IN 1837, Chile landed an expeditionary force in southern Peru, which marched inland to occupy the southern Peruvian city of Arequipa. The Confederation countered by sending a naval squadron to attack Chilean ports, while Santa Cruz's army surrounded the Chileans in Arequipa. On November 17, the Chileans signed the Peace Treaty of Pancarpeta, whereby they left Peru. However, the Chilean parliament repudiated the treaty.

In January 1838, the Chileans sent General Manuel Bulnes at the head of a second expedition, which landed north of Lima and marched inland to confront Santa Cruz. The two armies met at Yungay in the Callejón de Huaylas.

Ch 9　　　　　　Ch 9

Obverse: Shield surrounded by a laurel wreath beneath a radiant star

Obverse inscription: YO FUI DEL | EJERCITO | RESTAURAD[R]

Reverse inscription: VENCEDOR | EN YUNGAY | EL 20 | DE ENERO | DE 1839 within a wreath

Shape: Oval

Width: 38 × 31 mm

Metal: Officers: gold; enlisted men: silver

Ribbon: Red, white, blue

Reference: Gillingham 1932, 110; Barac 2009, 237; Brinkmann 2012, 1:38–40

* * *

IN ADDITION to the medal, Chile authorized two stars for the same battle.

Ch 10. *La Estrella por la Batalla de Yungay*

Instituted: By decree on March 25, 1839

Classes: Officers, enlisted men

Obverse disc: Volcano with buildings below and laurel wreath above

Obverse inscription: PAN DE AZUCAR

Obverse legend: EL GOB[o] DE CHILE A LOS VENC[s] EN YUNGAY on a red enameled band

Reverse inscription: EL 20 | DE | ENERO DE | 1839

Shape: Ball-tipped, white enameled star with 3 rays in each angle, suspended from an oval green enameled wreath

Size: 39 mm

Metal: Officers: gold; enlisted men: silver

Ribbon: Red, white, blue

Reference: Gillingham 1932, 107–10; Barac 2009, 237; Brinkmann 2012, 1:38–39

*Ch 9. *La Medalla por la Batalla de Yungay*

On January 20, 1839, Bulnes attacked Santa Cruz, whose troops were more numerous and enjoyed a strong defensive position. Despite these disadvantages, Bulnes defeated Santa Cruz at the Battle of Yungay. Santa Cruz fled the country, and Bulnes went on to reoccupy Lima. General Augstín Gamarra assumed the presidency of Peru and dissolved the Peru-Bolivian Confederation. With the war over, the Chilean army returned home. Chile authorized a medal and a star for its officers and men who fought at Yungay. Variants exist for both the medal and the star.

Instituted: December 21, 1839

Classes: Officers, enlisted men*

Ch 11   Ch 11

Metal: Gold, silver*

Ribbon: Red, white, red

Reference: Gillingham 1932, 106–8; Barac 2009, 236, Brinkmann 2012, 1:36–37

Provenance: American Numismatic Society, A. Menke

* * *

As the two sides were maneuvering in Ancash, Chilean and Peruvian warships were seeking each other to do battle. A Chilean squadron was cutting firewood in the Peruvian port of Casma when Peruvian ships attacked them.

Ch 12. *La Estrella por el Combate Naval de Casma*

The naval battle at Casma was intense, with both sides ramming the other, firing at point-blank range, and attempting to board each other. The battle was inconclusive. The Peruvian squadron withdrew under cover of night and sought refuge under the guns of the Callao fortress, thereby enabling the Chileans to control the sea routes to Peru. Chile awarded a cross for the engagement. The Casma Cross has a similar design to the Yungay Cross described above.

Instituted: By decree on March 28, 1839

Obverse disc: A crown above 2 laurel branches on a white-enameled field

Obverse legend: EL GOB⁰ DE CHILE A LOS VENC^S EN CASMA on a red enameled band

Reverse inscription: EL 13 DE ENERO DE 1839

Shape: Ball-tipped, white enameled star with 3 rays in the angles, surmounted by a wreath and a suspension bar

Ch 11. La Estrella de Ancash

The Battle of Yungay was fought along the Ancash River in the Department of Ancash. A number of variants of this star were made.

Instituted: March 28, 1839

Obverse disc: White enameled star on a red enameled field

Obverse legend: AL VALOR INVENCIBLE EN ANCACHS on a white enameled band surrounded by a green enameled wreath

Reverse inscription: 20 | ENERO | DE | 1839 on a band surrounded by a green enameled wreath

Shape: 8-pointed star with 5 rays in the angles; on some examples surmounted by an oval green enameled wreath and a suspension bar

Size: Gold: 36 mm; silver: 45 mm

Size: Gold: 36 mm; silver: 43 mm
Metal: Gold, silver
Ribbon: Red, white, blue

Reference: Gillingham 1932, 110–11; Barac 2009, 237; Brinkmann 2012, 1:41

Civil War (1851)

CHILE SUFFERED from political instability during much of the nineteenth century but rarely authorized medals for its security forces. However, after liberal politicians rebelled against their loss in a contested election in 1851, the government authorized a medal for the members of the security forces who suppressed the uprising.

Ch13. *La Medalla a los Defensores de las Leyes*

On April 20, 1851, Colonel Pedro Urriola Balbontín led a coup d'état against President Manuel Montt and the constitution of 1833. The coup failed, but fighting continued for the rest of the year, inflicting heavy casualties on both sides. General Bulnes defeated the rebels at the Battle of Loncomilla in December. The Medal for the Defense of the Laws was awarded to members of the Santiago National Guard.

Instituted: By decree on April 23, 1851
Classes: Officers, enlisted men
Obverse: Open book with a radiant star above
Obverse legend: DEFENSOR DE LAS LEYES
Reverse inscription: 20 | DE ABRIL | DE | 1851 within laurel branches
Shape: Oval
Size: 35 × 28 mm
Metal: Officers: gold; enlisted men: silver
Ribbon: Red, white, blue
Reference: Gillingham 1932, 112; Barac 2009, 237; Brinkmann 2012, 1:42–43

The Chincha Islands War (1864–1866): "La Guerra contra España"

THE CHINCHA ISLANDS WAR pitted Spain primarily against Chile and Peru. Spain had sent a fleet on a good will visit to the West Coast of Latin America in 1863. During this visit, a minor incident in northern Peru involving the death of a Spanish citizen led to an armed conflict first with Peru and later with Chile.

The Spanish fleet sought logistical support in the Chilean port of Valparaiso, which Chile denied. Tensions grew, and Chile declared war on Spain. The Spanish squadron then blockaded all of Chile's ports. The Spanish and Chilean navies fought several engagements, for which Chile authorized a cross and a medal.

Ch 14. *La Estrella por el Combate Naval de Abtao*

When the Spanish fleet arrived off Abtao, its commander demanded that the *Covadonga* be returned, but he was rebuffed. On February 7, 1866, the Spanish ships opened fire on the Chilean-Peruvian fleet. Both sides exchanged fire, but no ships were sunk. The Spanish ships could not approach the Chilean ships, which were in shallow water. The Spanish commander finally withdrew to the north, and the battle ended inconclusively. Chile authorized a star for the officers participating in the battle. Bolivia also authorized a medal for the Chilean sailors in the battle (see above, Bo20).

Obverse inscription: ABTAO | 7 DE FEBRERO | 1866 on a white enameled field

Reverse inscription: LA PATRIA RECONOCIDA

Shape: 6-armed white enameled star with 2-pointed ends and 3 rays in the angles, attached to a suspension bar

Size: 38 mm

Metal: Gold, silver

Ribbon: Red, white

Reference: Gillingham 1932, 11–13; Brinkmann 2012, 1:46–47

THE WAR OF THE PACIFIC (1879–1883)

THE WAR OF THE PACIFIC pitted Chile against the combined forces of Bolivia and Peru. The discovery of large deposits of nitrate in Atacama in the middle of the nineteenth century attracted British and Chilean investors. The Chilean government negotiated a favorable tax treaty with Bolivia covering its mine owners in Antofagasta. In 1878, the Bolivian Congress voted to impose a tax on nitrate shipments. The two countries failed to negotiate a settlement, and Chile took the military initiative. Chile occupied the Bolivian port of Antofagasta on February 14, 1879, the same day that Bolivia expropriated the Antofagasta Nitrate and Railway Company. The two countries did not actually declare war on each other until April 5, shortly after Peru acknowledged having signed a secret military alliance with Bolivia. Chile then declared war on Peru. Chile needed to control the seas if it was to send its army north as it did in the War of the Confederation. As Bolivia had no navy, Peru faced the Chilean navy alone.

Ch 15. *La Medalla por el Combate Naval de Iquique*

The Chilean navy sent the *Esmeralda* and the *Covadonga* to blockade the Peruvian port of Iquique. Peru countered by sending its two ironclads, the *Huáscar* and the *Independencia* to lift the blockade. On May 21, 1879, the *Huáscar* engaged and sank the *Esmeralda* at the Battle of Iquique, the war's most celebrated naval engagement. Chile awarded medals to the survivors of the battle and declared a national holiday on May 21. At least one variant of this medal was produced.

Instituted: By decree on September 12, 1879

Obverse: Warship under sail within a shield

Reverse inscription: IQUIQUE | 21 DE MAYO | DE 1879

Shape: Shield superimposed on an anchor and flags framed by green enameled laurel branches

Size: 46 mm

Metal: Gold, silver

Ribbon: Dark blue

Reference: Gillingham 2009, 114–15; Barac 2009, 237

*Ch16. *La Medalla a la Marina Chilena*

Obverse: Figure of winged victory

Obverse inscription: GLORIA on a ribbon at top, and on either side A LA | MARINA CHILENA

Reverse: Image of the *Esmeralda* sinking in front of the *Huáscar*

Reverse inscription: XXI–V | MDCCCLXXIX | COMBATE NAVAL | DE IQUIQUE

Size: 39 × 35 mm

Metal: Silver, bronze*

Ribbon: Red, white, blue

Provenance: A. Menke

Ch17. *La Medalla de Santiago por el Combate de Iquique*

The City of Santiago issued its own medal for the crew of the *Esmeralda*.

Obverse: The *Esmeralda* and *Huáscar* in combat

Obverse legend: EL PUEBLO DE SANTIAGO A LOS HEROES DE IQUIQUE

Reverse inscription: 21 | DE | MAYO | DE | 1879 within a laurel wreath

Size: 24 mm

Metal: Gilt silver

Reference: Gillingham 1932, 114–16; Barac 2009, 238

Ch18. *La Medalla por el Combate Naval de Angamos*

Because Chile had to neutralize the steam-powered armored *Huáscar*, the flagship of the Peruvian navy, before it could send its army north by sea, Chilean commander General Manuel

Baquedano sent the fleet north in two squadrons to search for it. A Chilean squadron with the *Cochrane, Blanco Encalada, Loa,* and *Covadonga* met the *Huáscar* on October 8, 1879, as it was sailing north near Angamos along with the *Unión.* The Chilean ships cornered the *Huáscar,* but the faster *Unión* escaped. In the exchange of fire, Peru's naval commander, Admiral Miguel Grau, was killed by a shell. The *Huáscar*'s guns were all damaged, and the ship was unable to fight. The crew finally surrendered, and the ship was taken over by Chilean marines. With the capture of the *Huáscar,* Chile gained control of the seas and was able to send its army north.

Instituted: 1881

Obverse: Bust of General Manuel Baquedano, ¾ left, within a laurel wreath

Obverse legend: AL EJERCITO Y ESCUADRA | EL PUEBLO CHILENO

Reverse: Naval combat scene

Reverse legend: RECUERDO DE LA CAMPANA | 1879–80–1881

Size: 36 mm

Metal: White metal

Designer: V. Prinz

Reference: Gillingham 1932, 116; Barac 2009, 238

* * *

THE LAND WAR dragged on for four years. Bolivia withdrew from the conflict in the first year of the war. Chile occupied Atacama, then Peru's Department of Tarapacá with its port at Arica, followed by the occupation of Lima itself. Peruvian officers raised an irregular army in the mountains and waged a long guerrilla war in the high Andes. Chile annexed Bolivia's litoral province and eventually Peru's Department of Tarapacá and the port of Arica. Chile authorized medals for its military in what became Chile's most important war in terms of casualties and territorial expansion.

*Ch19. *La Estrella por la Campaña de Bolivia y el Peru*

Chile authorized a Star for the Bolivian and Peruvian Campaign with 12 bars for each of the major land battles.

Instituted: September 1, 1880

Classes: Senior officers,* other officers, enlisted men*

Obverse disc: Head of Athena, right; officers: gold on a red enameled field

Obverse legend: CAMPANA A BOLIVIA I EL PERU on a blue enameled band

Reverse inscription: DE | 14 DE FEBRERO | DE 1879 | A | 7 DE JUNIO | DE | 1880 on a blue enameled field surrounded by a red enameled band

Shape: Ball-tipped star (senior officers: white enameled; enlisted men: faceted) with 7 rays in each angle; senior officers: suspended from a helmet and flags

Size: 40 mm

Metal: Senior officers: gold; other officers: gilt silver; enlisted men: silver

Ribbon: Red, white, blue

Bars: 12, bearing the names of battles, in the same metal as the medal; see below for details of the battle inscribed on each bar, arranged alphabetically

Reference: Gillingham 1932, 117–18; Barac 2009, 238

The twelve bars were awarded for the following battles:

*(a) *Anjeles (Los Angeles)*

Chile invaded Peru by landing three divisions of troops at the port of Ilo in late February 1880. The army moved inland toward the city of Tacna, while the Peruvians settled behind a blocking position at Los Anjeles hill

Ch 19   Ch 19

in open country. The Chileans flanked the Peruvians by climbing steep embankments, while making a frontal assault on the main Peruvian line. The Peruvians retreated, leaving the road to Tacna open.

*(b) *Antofagasta*

Chile landed troops in the Bolivian port of Antofagasta in an unopposed operation on February 14, 1879. This was the first military initiative of the War of the Pacific.

*(c) *Arica* (Reverse: Junio 7 1880)

The port of Arica was the last remaining stronghold in southern Peru following the fall of Tacna. The Chilean navy had been blockading the port, and Arica's supply by land was cut off when the Chileans occupied Tacna. The Peruvian defenses were built around the Moro de Arica, a steep, 140-meter-high hill dominating the port. The Peruvians concentrated their artillery there.

The Chileans launched a frontal assault and overwhelmed the defenders. Most of the Peruvians soldiers were killed, including their commander, Colonel Francisco Bolognesi.

*(d) *Calama*

On March 23, 1879, advancing Chilean troops from Antofagasta encountered Bolivian soldiers entrenched along the Topáter River near Calama. The numerically superior Chilean soldiers overran the Bolivian defenses. Although a minor encounter in terms of casualties, this was the first land battle of the war.

(e) *Chipana*

On April 12, 1879, the Peruvian corvette *Unión* and gunboat *Pilcomayo* engaged the Chilean corvette *Magallanes* near the Bolivian port of Huanillo. The Peruvians inflicted heavy damage on the *Magallanes*, which escaped south.

(f) *Chorillos*

As the Chilean army threatened Lima, Peru fortified a first line of defense anchored on the suburb of Chorillos. The Chileans, numerically superior and better equipped, launched their assault on January 13, 1881, forcing the Peruvians to retreat to Miraflores.

(g) *Miraflores*

The Battle of Miraflores was fought on January 15, 1881. This was Lima's last defense against the Chileans, who overwhelmed the defenders and occupied the city two days later. This battle ended the Peruvian government's involvement in the war. An irregular Peruvian army fought Chilean troops in the mountains until their final defeat at the Battle of Huamachuco in 1883.

*(h) *Pisagua* (Reverse: Noviembre 2 1879)

The Chilean navy landed troops at the port of Pisagua in November 1879 and overwhelmed its Bolivian garrison. The Chileans then moved inland to start their land campaign.

*(i) *San Francisco* (*de Dolores*) (Reverse: Noviembre 19 1879)

On November 19, 1879, an allied army attacked the Chilean troops threatening the port of Iquique. The two armies met near the twin hills of San Francisco and the railroad station of the Dolores Mining Company. The Chileans dominated the high ground with their cannon and Gatling guns. Both sides suffered heavy losses. The battle was indecisive, but the Bolivians under the command of their President Hilarión Daza withdrew and returned to Bolivia.

(j) *Sorpresa de Iquique*

*(k) *Tacna* (Reverse: Mayo 26 1880)

Following its victory at Los Anjeles, the Chileans advanced to Tacna, with its reinforced garrison. The numerically superior Chilean army overran the allied lines. The Bolivians abandoned their Peruvian allies and withdrew from the war. The battle allowed the Chileans to occupy Tacna and march south to Arica.

*(l) *Tarapacá* (Reverse: Noviembre 27 1879)

On November 27, 1879, a Chilean force attacked a numerically superior allied army near Tarapacá on Peruvian territory. The Chileans were defeated with heavy casualties. Despite their victory, the Peruvians retreated north to Arica.

*Ch20. *La Estrella por el Combate de Tarapacá*

Despite suffering heavy casualties and losing this battle, Chile authorized a star for its officers for bravery in one of the war's early battles. Although Peru is considered to have won the battle, it withdrew, leaving the Chileans in control of the land.

Instituted: 1881

Obverse inscription: TARAPACÁ

Reverse inscription: 27 DE | NOVIEMBRE | DE 1879

Shape: 6-armed star with 2-pointed ends and 3 rays in each angle, suspended from an enameled wreath

Size: 35 mm

Metal: Gilt

Ribbon: Red, white, red

Reference: Gillingham 1932, 117; Barac 2009, 238

* * *

HAVING consolidated its control of Atacama, Chile sent its navy north with an army to take Lima. The Chileans landed at Pisco and advanced with some twenty thousand men. The main Peruvian defensive lines were anchored around two Lima suburbs: Chorillos and

Ch 20   Ch 20

Miraflores. Many of the Peruvian defenders were civilians pressed to defend their city. The Chileans overran the two defensive lines on separate days. On January 18, 1881, both Lima and Callao surrendered.

*Ch21. *La Estrella por la Campaña de Lima*

Chile authorized a star to its officers and men who took part in the campaign starting with the landing in Pisco and ending with the occupation of Lima.

Instituted: By law on January 14, 1882

Classes: Senior officers, junior officers,* enlisted men*

Obverse disc: Star

Obverse legend: CAMPAÑA DE LIMA | 1881 on a blue enameled band

Reverse disc: Star

Reverse legend: REPUBLICA DE CHILE on a blue enameled band

Shape: Ball-tipped star with 2-pointed ends and 3 laurel leaves in each angle; enameled for senior officers; faceted for junior officers and enlisted men

Size: 43 mm

Metal: Senior officers: gold; junior officers: gilt silver; enlisted men: silver

Ribbon: Red, white, red

Bars: 5: *Angamos, Chorillos, Miraflores, San Francisco, Tarapacá*

Reference: Gillingham 1932, 115 and 118; Barac 2009, 239

Ch 21

Ch 21

* * *

DESPITE Lima's surrender, a group of Peruvian officers under the command of Colonel Andrés Cáceres started a guerrilla war against the Chileans in the Peruvian highlands. The war lasted for two years, as Cáceres kept one step ahead of the Chileans. The last battle of the war was fought near the highland town of Huamachuco at the head of the Cordillera Blanca in the Department of Libertad on July 10, 1883.

*Ch22. *La Cruz de Huamachuco*

The battle of Huamachuco pitted Cáceres's Ejército de la Sierra against a Chilean expeditionary force commanded by Colonel Alejandro Gorostiaga. Cáceres attacked the Chileans above the town of Huamachuco in a traditional military operation. The battle seesawed back and forth, but the Chileans finally won after killing much of Cáceres's officer corps. Cáceres himself escaped, but was no longer able to challenge the Chileans militarily. Peru's leaders negotiated the Treaty of Ancón on October 23, 1883, ending the war. Under this treaty, the Departments of Tacna and Arica were to be administered by Chile for ten years, with definitive sovereignty to be decided by a plebiscite. This part of the treaty was never carried out. Subsequent negotiations brokered by the United States awarded the Department of Tacna to Peru and the Department of Arica to Chile. This decision was ratified in the Treaty of Lima on June 3, 1929.

Ch 22

Ch 22

Instituted: By law on December 27, 1883

Classes: Officers, junior officers, enlisted
men*

Obverse disc: Star on a gold field

Obverse legend: HUAMACHUCO | JULIO 10
1883 on a blue enameled band

Reverse disc: 3 mountains, enameled for officers, gilt on a blue enameled disc for junior
officers and enlisted men, surrounded by a
red enameled band with branches below and
stars above

Shape: Ball-tipped Maltese cross with concave
pointed ends, enameled red for officers

Size: 43 mm

Metal: Officers: gold; junior officers, enlisted
men: silver

Ribbon: 4 red, 4 white

Reference: Gillingham 1932, 119–21; Barac
2009, 239–40

* * *

AT LEAST three Chilean cities authorized medals to their officers and men who fought in the
War of the Pacific.

*Ch23. *La Medalla de Valparaiso a sus
Valientes*

The city of Valparaiso played a key role in the
war. The Chilean navy was based there, and
control of the sea was critical to Chile's land
campaign. Valparaiso authorized three medals for members of army units recruited in the
city.

*Ch23a. *Variant 1*

Obverse: Arms of the city of Valparaiso

Obverse legend: VALPARAISO A SUS
VALIENTES on a blue enameled
band

Reverse: 3 stars in a laurel wreath

Reverse outer legend: CAMPAÑA CONTRA EL
PERU Y BOLIVIA | 1879–1881

Reverse inner legend: BATALLON CIVICO |
DE | ARTILLERIA NAVAL

Shape: Round, surrounded by a laurel wreath,
suspended from a condor

Size: 31 mm

Metal: Gold, silver*

Ribbon: Blue, red

*Ch23b. *Variant 2*

As above, except:

Reverse inner legend: BATALLON
VALPARAISO*

Metal: Gold, silver*

*Ch23c. *Variant 3*

As above, except:

Reverse inner legend: REJIMENTO
VALPARAISO

Metal: Gold, silver*

Reference: Gillingham 1932, 120; Barac 2009,
239

Ch 24

Ch 24

Ch 25

Ch 25

*Ch24. *La Medalla por la Campaña 1879–80–81*

The Medal for the Campaign of 1879–80–81 was awarded to the officers and men who participated in the Atacama and Tacna campaigns as well as the occupation of Lima. All of these operations were commanded by General Manuel Baquedano.

> Obverse: Bust of General Baquedano, ¾ left, within 2 laurel branches
> Obverse legend: EL PUEBLO CHILENO | AL EJERCITO Y ESCUADRA
> Reverse disc: 3 warships on water
> Reverse legend: RECUERDO DE LA CAMPAÑA | 1879–80–1881
> Size: 36 mm
> Metal: White metal
> Engraver: V. Prinz
> Ribbon: Red
> Reference: Brinkmann 2012, 2:12

*Ch25. *La Medalla de Miraflores*

The town of Quillota, just north of Valparaiso, awarded a simple medal to its soldiers who fought in the Battle of Miraflores, the last battle before Lima fell.

Obverse inscription: QUILLOTA | A | SUS | HIJOS

Reverse inscription: MIRAFLORES | ENERO 15 | 1881 within 2 laurel branches

Shape: Round, with a broad suspension loop

Size: 29 × 24 mm

Metal: Silver

Ribbon: White, red

Reference: Gillingham 1932, 121; Barac 2009, 240

Provenance: A. Menke

Ch26. *La Medalla por el Batallon de Aconcagua*

The citizens of Aconcagua resident in Santiago awarded a silver medal to the members of the battalion that bears the name of their valley north of Santiago.

Instituted: 1884?

Obverse: Arms of Chile surmounted by 3 plumes and superimposed on 2 crossed flags

Obverse legend: AL BATALLON ACONCAGUA | 1884

Reverse inscription: LOS ACONCAGUINOS | RESIDENTES | EN SANTIAGO within a laurel wreath

Size: 24 mm

Metal: Silver

Reference: Gillingham 1932, 121; Barac 2009, 240

*Ch27. *La Cruz por la Campaña de la Sierra del Peru*

The Medal for the Campaign of the Peruvian Mountains was awarded to the men who pursued an elusive Peruvian army in the high valleys of the Andes in Peru. The campaign lasted for two years and did not end until the Battle of Huamachuco.

Ch 27

Obverse disc: Shield with star, enameled blue above and red below

Obverse legend: CAMPAÑA DE LA SIERRA DEL PERU | 1879–1884

Shape: Maltese cross with intersecting semi-circles in each arm

Size: 37 mm

Metal: White metal

Ribbon: White with narrow red, blue, white center stripes

Provenance: A. Menke

Peacetime (1883–present)

THE WAR OF THE PACIFIC was Chile's last foreign war. However, the country itself was to fight a civil war in 1891 between liberals and conservatives over the constitutional powers of the executive and legislative branches of government. The constitutional president José Manuel Balmaceda, a political liberal, favored free trade and a secular education, which were opposed by the country's economic elite, who were well represented in the parliament and the Catholic Church. The two sides failed to reach a compromise over the 1891 budget, and the president assumed dictatorial powers. The navy and part of the army sided with parliament, while most of the army supported Balmaceda. The conservatives organized a Junta de Gobierno in Iquique and began assembling an army. The two sides fought several inconclusive battles, until the Battle of Placilla near Viña del Mar on August 28, 1891, which was won by the conservatives. Balmaceda sought asylum the following day in the Argentine Embassy and later committed suicide.

*Ch28. *La Medalla "Honor a la Marina y al Ejército"*

President Balmaceda appointed General Baquedano to replace him, and the Congress returned to Santiago. Chile authorized a medal for the officers and men of the navy as well as those army men who sided with the conservatives.

Obverse: Arms of Chile
Obverse legend: CAIDA DE LA DICTADURA | 29 AGOSTO 1891
Reverse inscription: HONOR | A LA MARINA | I AL | EJÉRCITO | CONSTITUCIONAL | CHILE
Size: 29 mm
Metal: Bronze
Reference: Medina 1901, 162

* * *

THE CHILEAN military generally stayed out of domestic politics for eighty years following the 1891 civil war. Chile has created an extensive array of peacetime decorations and medals for members of its armed forces as well as foreign officers and civilians who have provided meritorious service to the Chilean armed forces. These services include outstanding contributions to the efficiency, prestige, and loyalty to the armed forces and the nation.

*Ch29. *La Cruz a los Instructores Alemanes*

Chilean military officers were impressed with the German victory over France in the Franco-Prussian War of 1870–71. Some years after the War of the Pacific, the Chilean government requested military assistance from the Prussian kaiser to train the Chilean army and raise its level of discipline. This assistance laid the foundation for Chilean military doctrine and training. The German army provided technical assistance to Chile up to World War II. In 1897, Chile authorized a medal for its German instructors.

Instituted: 1897

Obverse disc: Star within a laurel wreath

Obverse inscription: On the upper arm: REPUBLICA | DE | CHILE; on the left arm: a gun carriage; on the right arm: a tower; and on the lower arm: 1897

Reverse disc: Arms of Chile

Reverse inscription: On the upper arm: EL MINISTERIO | DE | GUERRA; on the left arm: crossed sabers; on the right arm: crossed bugle and rifle: on the lower arm: A LOS | INSTRUCTORES | ALEMANES

Shape: Cross pattée with convex ends

Size: 32 mm

Metal: Gold, silver, brass*

Ribbon: Red, blue, white

Reference: Gillingham 1932, 122; Barac 2009, 240

Ch30. *La Medalla por el Acuerdo Argentina-Chile de 1902*

The border between Chile and Argentina remained a matter of controversy between the two countries throughout the nineteenth century. In 1856, they agreed that the border should temporarily be the one drawn by Spain until such time as they could negotiate a definitive agreement. In 1881, Chile recognized Argentina's sovereignty over Patagonia, and Argentina accepted Chile's right to the Straits of Magellan. Both sides agreed that the border follow the highest points in the Andes that divided the waters flowing to the Atlantic and Pacific. In May 1902, they signed a General Arbitration Agreement to settle any future differences by binding international arbitration. They also signed a convention limiting naval armaments. Chile authorized a medal for the diplomats and politicians who negotiated the agreement.

Instituted: 1902

Obverse: 2 warships

Obverse legend: INDE PAX UTRIUSQUE PONTI

Reverse: Mountain with rainbow above

Reverse legend: PACTIONES ARGENTINO CHILENSES | 28 MAII MCMII

Size: 26 mm

Metal: Gold, silver

Reference: Barac 2009, 240

* * *

AFTER World War II, Chile authorized an array of medals for its military in peacetime and in war for distinguished service, merit, and bravery.

Ch31

*Ch31. *La Gran Cruz por la Conducción Militar Político-Estratégica*

The Grand Cross for Military Political-Strategic Leadership is awarded to the commanders in chief of the different branches of the armed forces for strategic leadership.

Regulated: By Supreme Decree No. 19 on February 11, 2005

Obverse disc: Arms of Chile within a blue enameled band

Shape: Red and white enameled cross superimposed on an 8-pointed faceted star with 5 rays in each angle. The emblems of the 4 branches of the armed forces are displayed between the angles of the cross

Size: 63 mm

Metal: Silver

Reference: Chile 2005, 9 and 162

*Ch32. *La Condecoración "Al Valor"*

The Decoration for Valor is awarded to personnel of the Chilean armed forces in peacetime for acts of valor when faced with risk of death in

Ch 32a

carrying out orders or based on personal initiative. There is also a wartime version.

*Ch 32a. *Peacetime version*

The decoration may also be awarded to foreign military personnel.

Instituted: By Supreme Decree No. 2,007 on October 30, 1945

Regulated: By Supreme Decree No. 19 on February 11, 2005

Branches: Army,* navy*

Obverse inscription: AL | VALOR

Shape: Army: star suspended from an eagle with wings displayed; navy: ball-tipped red enameled star with anchor intertwined

Size: Army: 39 mm; navy: 44 ×45 mm

Metal: Gilt

Ribbon: Blue, red, blue [variant: red, blue, red]

Ch32b. *Wartime version*

The decoration comes in two classes. When awarded for the first time, the recipient receives the second class; if eligible for a second award, the recipient receives the first class. Additional awards are recognized by placing a gold star on the ribbon. A metal bar is attached to the ribbon bearing the year the conflict began.

> Instituted: By Supreme Decree No. 2,007 on October 30, 1945
> Regulated: By Supreme Decree No. 19 on February 11, 2005
> Branches: Army, navy
> Classes: 1st, 2nd
> Obverse inscription: AL | VALOR
> Shape: Army: star suspended from an eagle with wings displayed; navy: ball-tipped red enameled star with anchor intertwined
> Size: Army: 39 mm; navy: 44 × 45 mm
> Metal: Steel
> Ribbon: Blue, red, blue
> Reference: Chile 2005, 22–23 and 168

Ch33. *La Condecoración "Ministro de Defensa Nacional"*

The decoration "Minister of National Defense" is awarded in peacetime to Chilean and foreign nationals with the rank of cabinet minister for contributing to the national defense of Chile and promoting international understanding. It is issued in two versions.

Ch33a. *La Medalla "Del Ministro de Defensa Nacional"*

> Regulated: By Supreme Decree No. 19 on February 11, 2005
> Obverse disc: National emblem on a red enameled field surrounded by a blue enameled band
> Obverse legend: MINISTERIO DE DEFENSA NACIONAL | CHILE

> Shape: Two 8-pointed concentric suns with 4 rays in the angles suspended from an oval wreath
> Size: 45 mm
> Metal: Gilt
> Ribbon: Blue neck ribbon

Ch33b. *La Medalla "Al Honor Nacional"*

> Regulated: By Supreme Decree No. 19 on February 11, 2005
> Obverse disc: Arms of Chile
> Obverse legend: AL HONOR NACIONAL
> Shape: Cross pattée surrounded by a wreath
> Size: 40 mm
> Metal: Silvered
> Ribbon: Blue, white, red
> Reference: Chile 2005, 23–25, and 170–71

Ch34. *La Condecoración "Orden del Mérito Naval"*

The decoration "Order for Naval Merit" is awarded to general officers and civilians, both nationals and foreign, who have advanced the interests of the Chilean navy and have helped it accomplish its mission. The decoration comes in three classes: Commander, Officer, and Knight. The description of Commander has been separated from the other two grades because their designs differ.

Ch34a. *Commander*

> Obverse disc: Anchor and star on a blue enameled field
> Obverse inscription: ARMADA DE CHILE | ORDEN DEL MERITO NAVAL on a blue enameled band
> Shape: Red and white enameled cross pattée with a crown above the upper arm, superimposed on an 8-pointed faceted star with 4 rays in each angle
> Size: 85 mm

Metal: White metal

Ribbon: Red, blue, red sash

Ch34b. *Officer and Knight*

Obverse disc: Anchor beneath a star on a white enameled field

Obverse legend: ARMADA DE CHILE | ORDEN DEL MERITO NAVAL on a blue (Officer) or red (Knight) enameled band.

Shape: 2 concentric, 8-pointed gilt suns with 5 rays in the angles suspended from a copihue wreath (Officer) with a star in the center or a wreath (Knight)

Size: 45 mm

Metal: Gilt

Ribbon: Blue with red edge stripes neck ribbon

Reference: Chile 2005, 36–38, and 181–82

Ch35. *La Medalla "Al Mérito por Servicios Distinguidos en Operaciones de Paz"*

The medal "For Merit for Distinguished Services in Peacekeeping Operations" is given to officers, permanent staff, crew, and civilians who have completed their mission in a multinational peacekeeping operation. Chile has participated in four United Nations peacekeeping missions: UNTSO, monitoring a cease-fire on the Golan Heights, the very first UN peacekeeping mission; UNMOGIP, supervising a cease-fire along the Line of Control between India and Pakistan; UNFILYP, controlling the partition between the Turkish and Greek zones of Cyprus; and MINUSTAH, securing a stable government, helping recovery from natural disasters, and promoting human rights in Haiti. Chile also provided a military contingent in Bosnia and Herzegovina as part of a European Union mission in the former Yugoslavian nation. Chile has suffered casualties among its participants in these missions.

Regulated: By Supreme Decree No. 19 on February 11, 2005

Classes: Officers and senior NCO's; permanent staff and junior enlisted men; civilian employees

Obverse disc: Globe on a blue enameled field

Obverse legend: OPERACIONES DE PAZ on a white enameled band

Shape: Round, with the disc surrounded by a wreath and a blue flag with the emblem of the Ministry of National Defense flying above the disc

Size: 44 mm

Metal: Officers and senior NCO's: gilt; permanent staff and junior enlisted men: silvered; civilian employees: steel

Ribbon: Red, blue

Reference: Chile 2005, 51–52, and 196

Ch36. *La Medalla "Del Estado Mayor de la Defensa Nacional"*

The medal "From the Chief of Staff of National Defense" is awarded to foreign officers who distinguished themselves in improving military cooperation and understanding between the Chilean armed forces and another state. The medal is also awarded to Chilean officers stationed abroad or at home who have performed a comparable service.

Regulated: By Supreme Decree No. 19 on February 11, 2005

Obverse disc: Emblem of the General Staff of the Armed Forces on a red enameled field surrounded by a blue enameled band with white stars

Shape: 2 concentric 8-pointed gilt suns with 4 rays in each angle suspended from a gilt copihue wreath

Size: 45 mm

Metal: Gilt

Ribbon: Blue neck ribbon

Reference: Chile 2005, 53, and 197

Medals in Time of War

The medals listed below are restricted to times of war, including internal violence. The Decoration for Valor (Ch32, above) is also awarded in wartime for heroic acts at personal risk.

Ch37. *La Condecoración "Al Mérito de Guerra"*

The decoration "For Merit in Wartime" is awarded to personnel of the armed forces for contributing significantly to the success of a military operation above and beyond the call of duty. Stars are placed on the ribbon for additional awards of the same decoration.

> Instituted: By Decree Law No. 142 in 1973
> Regulated: By Supreme Decree No. 19 on February 11, 2005
> Obverse disc: Arms of Chile on a white enameled field
> Shape: Star superimposed on an open wreath, suspended from an open wreath
> Size: 47 mm
> Metal: Oxidized copper
> Ribbon: Red center stripe edged in white with two wide blue edge stripes bisected by a narrow white stripe
> Reference: Chile 2005, 74–75 and 212

*Ch38. *La Condecoración "Servicios Distinguidos"*

The decoration for "Distinguished Services" is awarded after hostilities have ended to those who fought honorably. This decoration was awarded to many of the officers and men who participated in the "Pronunciamiento" that overthrew the democratically elected government of President Salvador Allende on September 11, 1973. There are three classes, distinguished by the number of stars on the bar and stripes on the ribbon. The medal is awarded by all four branches of the armed forces, each one identified by the color of the ribbon.

> Instituted: By Decree Law 142 in 1973
> Regulated: By Supreme Decree No. 19 on February 11, 2005
> Classes: Senior officers, junior officers, enlisted men
> Branches: Army,* navy,* air force,* carabineros*
> Shape: Star suspended from a bar with stars (1, 2, or 3), which denote class
> Size: 47 mm
> Metal: Oxidized copper
> Maker: Hours, Santiago
> Ribbon: Army: red-orange; navy: dark blue; air force: light blue; carabineros: green. Senior officers: 3 yellow stripes; junior officers: 2 yellow stripes; enlisted men: 1 yellow stripe. A metallic bar may be added with the date of specific actions
> Reference: Chile 2005, 75–77 and 213
> Provenance Air force: A. Menke

*Ch39. *La Estrella "XI de Septiembre"*

The Star of September 11 was awarded to members of the four branches of the armed forces for participating in the 1973 coup against President Salvador Allende. The star is the same for all four branches of the armed forces, except for the ribbon.

> Branches: Army,* navy,* air force,* carabineros
> Obverse disc: Enameled to match ribbon; inscription flanked by chains, star above

Ch 38

Ch 39

Ch 39

Obverse inscription: 11–IX–1973 |
  11–IX–1983

Shape: Badge: Ball-tipped star with 5 rays in
  each angle

Star shape: Ball-tipped star superimposed on
  a 32-pointed sun

Size: Badge: army: 45 mm; air force, navy: 48
  mm. Star: 61 mm

Metal: Badge: army: oxidized bronze; navy:
  gilt; air force: bronze. Star: gilt

Maker: Air force: Milled, Santiago

Ribbon: Army: red-orange; navy: dark blue;
  air force: light blue; carabineros: green

Provenance: Navy: A. Menke

*Ch40. *La Medalla "Misión Cumplida"*

Chile instituted four medals, one for each
branch of the armed forces, recognizing military personnel for their service during and after
the 1973 coup d'état. The design is the same for
all four medals, except for the ribbon.

Branches: Army,* navy,* air force,*
  carabineros*

Obverse: Half-length winged woman with
  broken shackles

Obverse legend: POR CHILE | MISION
  CUMPLIDA

Reverse: Arms of Chile

Ch 40

Reverse legend: LA PATRIA ESTA POR SOBRE NEUSTRAS VIDAS

Size: 39 mm

Metal: Army: oxidized bronze; navy: bright patina; air force: dark patina; carabineros: silvered

Ribbon: Army: red-orange; navy: dark blue; air force: light blue; carabineros: green

MEDALS OF THE CARABINEROS

CHILE's militarized national police force, better known as the carabineros, is considered one of the four branches of the armed forces, and its organizational structure is similar to the other three branches. It operates throughout the country with carabinero stations in every town. The carabineros have authorized an array of crosses and decorations of merit for their members.

*Ch41. *La Cruz "Al Valor"*

The cross "For Valor" is awarded to carabineros in peacetime who have risked their lives while performing their duties.

Obverse inscription: AL | VALOR on a white enameled disc

Obverse legend: CARABINEROS DE CHILE

Shape: White enameled Maltese cross on a band on a 12-pointed sun with 5 rays in each angle, suspended from the claws of a flying gilt condor

Size: 42 mm

Metal: Gilt

Ribbon: Green, yellow

Ch 40

Ch 41

Ch 42

*Ch42. *La Cruz "Honor al Mérito"*

The cross "Honor in Merit" is awarded to Chilean and foreign individuals who have provided meritorious service to the carabineros; the cross "For Merit" is awarded for the same purposes but at a lower level of distinction.

Classes: Honor in Merit, For Merit*
Obverse disc: Crossed gilt rifles beneath a gilt star on a white enameled field surrounded by a wreath

Obverse legend: AL MERITO

Shape: Green enameled cross pattée with convex ends, with 11 gilt rays on the arms, surmounted by a wreath

Size: 50 mm

Metal: Honor in Merit: gilt; For Merit: silvered

Ribbon: Green neck ribbon

Medals for Disaster Relief

The two leading organizations for disaster relief in Chile are the Chilean Red Cross and the Civil Defense. In April 1879, Chile agreed to adhere to the Geneva Convention. By decree on November 15, 1879, Chile placed a red cross on its ambulances, field hospitals, and medical personnel, including nurses, during the War of the Pacific. After the war's end, Chile disbanded its Red Cross units. In 1903, a group of Chileans in Punta Arenas led by Vittorio Cuccuini agreed to build a hospital for local residents. This initiative led to the creation of the Chilean Red Cross, which was recognized by presidential decree on May 31, 1905. The Chilean Red Cross provides disaster relief, prepares for future disasters, and promotes public health.

*Ch43. *La Medalla "Cruz Roja de Chile"*

Ribbon: White with red center and edge stripes

*Ch43a. *Class A*

Obverse: Red enameled cross with arms of Chile surrounded by enameled wreath

Reverse: White enameled star within wreath

Reverse inscription: CRUZ ROJA | DE | CHILE

Size: 32 mm

Metal: Gilt

*Ch43b. *Class B*

Obverse: Cross

Obverse legend: CRUZ ROJA DE CHILE

Reverse: Star within wreath

Size: 27 mm

Metal: Gilt

Ribbon: White

Ch 43a, b

Ch 43a, b

Ch 45

Ch 45

Ch44. *La Medalla de Honor de la Cruz Roja Chilena*

Classes: 1st, 2nd

Obverse: Gilt arms of Chile superimposed on a red enameled cross on a blue enameled field

Shape: Round, surrounded by a green enameled laurel wreath suspended from a gilt wreath

Ribbon: White with red, white, and blue edge stripes neck ribbon

Reference: http://www.cruzrojaamericana .org/imagesup/phototemplate.hhm06.swf, accessed January 25, 2013

*Ch45. *La Cruz de la Cruz Roja Chilena*

Obverse disc: Enameled gilt-edged red cross on a white field surrounded by concentric gilt, blue, gilt circles

Reverse disc: Gilt star on a white field surrounded by concentric gilt, blue, gilt circles

Shape: Gilt edged enameled (red for one variant,* white for another*) cross suspended from wreath

Size: 28 mm

Ribbon: White with narrow blue, white, red edge stripes

*Ch46. *La Cruz de Caridad de la Cruz Roja*

Obverse legend: CARIDAD

Shape: Gilt edged red enameled Greek cross in an enameled wreath

Size: 31 mm

Ribbon: Red

Ch 46

MEDALS OF THE CIVIL DEFENSE

THE CIVIL DEFENSE was created on July 14, 1947. It provides relief services for the victims of armed conflict and natural disasters caused by earthquakes, fires, floods, and epidemics. Civil Defense coordinates the actions of other organizations to carry out its mission.

Ch48

Ch47. *La Medalla al Mérito de la Defensa Civil*

    Obverse: Enameled DC intertwined with star in center

    Obverse inscription: DEFENSA CIVIL | CHILE on a white enameled field

    Obverse legend: AL VALOR on a silver band

    Shape: Round, edged by a silver laurel wreath

    Size: 32 mm

    Metal Silver

    Ribbon: Blue, white, red

*Ch48. *La Estrella de la Defensa Civil*

    Obverse disc: Enameled DC intertwined with star in center on a white enameled disc

    Obverse legend: DEFENSA CIVIL | CHILE

    Shape: Silver star with 5 rays in the angles

    Size: 38 mm

    Metal: Silver

    Ribbon: Blue, white, red

    Provenance: A. Menke

ORDERS

ALTHOUGH Chile created a Legion of Honor with similar characteristics to an order, the country did not formally consolidate an order until 1929. Republican sentiment identified orders with noble privilege. Chile's first two orders are restricted to foreign nationals, and it was not until well after World War II that it instituted orders that could be awarded to its own citizens.

Ch49. *La Cruz de la Legión de Mérito*

The Cross of the Legion of Merit, instituted by Bernardo O'Higgins on June 1, 1817, is generally considered an order. The cross has three grades, much like other orders of merit, but it was given only to combatants in the Battle of Chacabuco in 1817. Recipients went through a formal investiture ceremony at which they were required to swear allegiance to the republic. The Cross of the Legion of Merit was awarded to both Chilean and Argentine military for their participation in the battle of Chacabuco that led to Chile's declaration of independence. There are two versions of this cross. The medals do not look alike, although they use the same ribbon.

The decoration was inspired by the French Legion of Honor. The first version was created by Bernardo O'Higgins, who became the first president of the Council of the Legion of Honor. Some of his officers had fought with Napoleon and had received the French decoration. The proposal to create this new honor was drawn up by a Spaniard, Antonio Arcos, who had himself served in the French Imperial Army. O'Higgins submitted his proposals for the order to the Lautarino Lodge, a secret society whose members conspired against colonial rule, as well as to José de San Martín.

The Legion of Honor had much in common with some ancient European orders of chivalry. Legionnaires were made the equivalent of army officers, and guards were required to present arms in their presence. Members of the order could be judged only in special war councils consisting of other members of the order. This provision went back to the medieval Spanish *fueros.* Notaries and judges could take evidence from a Legionnaire only in his home or in writing. The order's statutes provided for pensions: one thousand pesos per year for Grand Officers, five hundred pesos for Major Officers, and so forth. The government took measures to transfer properties of Chilean royalists, who had fled the country, to the Legion's Treasury. All of these benefits to a select group of the military eventually caught the attention of the Chilean Senate, where an acrimonious debate broke out over whether these benefits were consistent with republican principles. O'Higgins refused to support any law that weakened the rights of the Legionnaires, but the Senate persisted. Finally, on July 21, 1825, all of the remaining funds of the Legion were transferred to the General Treasury of the Republic.

The Cross of the Legion of Merit was instituted in 1817 as a silver medal for combatants, and this medal was later designated as Legionnaire. A few years later, Chile instituted two new grades: Grand Officer and Officer, with a more elaborate design intended for officers. The higher classes include a diamond-studded gold breast star, a silver and black enameled breast star, and two knights badges (described

below), as well as tailor-made designs for senior commanders.

*Ch49a. *Version 1*

Instituted: By Bernardo O'Higgins on June 1, 1817

Grades: Legionnaire

Obverse disc: Erupting volcano surrounded by 8 mountain peaks

Obverse legend: HONOR Y PRAEMIO AL PATRIOTISMO

Obverse inscription: O'HIG.S INST. on a ribbon above

Reverse disc: Column

Reverse legend: LEGION DE MERITO DE CHILE

Reverse inscription: LIBERTAD on a ribbon above

Shape: 8-armed star with 4-part arms and a laurel wreath in the angles, suspended from a knot

Size: 32 × 30 mm

Metal: Silver

Ribbon: Blue

Reference: Medina 1901, 92–111; Eyzaguirre 1934, 7–51; Gillingham 1932, 96–98; Barac 2009, 241

Ch 49b
Officer

Ch 49b
Officer

*Ch49b. *Version 2*

Instituted: 1820

Grades: Grand Officer, Officer,* and later Noncommissioned Officer

Obverse disc: Enameled mountain peaks with 1 erupting volcano

Obverse legend: LEGION DE MERITO DE CHILE on a blue enameled band

Obverse inscription: OHIG.S.YNST on a blue enameled ribbon above

Reverse disc: Enameled column

Reverse legend: HONOR Y PREMIO AL PATRIOTISMO on a blue enameled band

Reverse inscription: LIBERTAD on a blue enameled ribbon above

Shape: Ball-tipped white enameled star with three 2-pointed rays in each angle and an enameled wreath in the angles

Size: 40 mm

Metal: Grand Officer: gold; Officer: gilt silver

Reference: Gillingham 1932, 96–98; Barac 2009, 241

Provenance: A. Menke

*Ch50. *La Medalla al Mérito*

Many years passed before the country instituted another order of merit. At the beginning of the twentieth century, Chile created a medal for foreign military instructors who taught Chilean officers studying abroad. Chile wanted to create a well-trained professional officer corps, because of the lessons learned during the War of the Pacific. In particular, the Chileans wanted to learn Prussian army tactics and discipline. However, Chile had already created a medal specifically for Prussian military instructors in 1897 (see above, Ch29). The Ministry of War created a service medal to recognize military instructors from all nations.

*Ch50a. *Version 1*

Instituted: By Decree No. 1,350 of the Ministry of War on September 14, 1906, creating and 1st and 2nd classes

Modified: By Decree No. 731 of the Ministry of War on June 3, 1910

Regulated: By Decree No. 1,300 of the Ministry of War on May 18, 1911

Grades: 1st, 2nd*

Obverse disc: Female head, right

Obverse inscription: REPUBLICA DE CHILE

Reverse disc: Laurel branch

Reverse inscription: AL MERITO

Shape: Ball-tipped star with a laurel wreath in the angles, suspended from a condor with wings displayed and inverted

Size: 43 mm

Metal: 1st: gold; 2nd: silver

Maker: Casa de la Moneda, Santiago

Ribbon: Red, white, blue

Reference: Eyzaguirre 1934, 55

Ch 50a
2nd grade

Ch 50a
2nd grade

Ch 50b
Grand Officer,
1st and 2nd
grades

Ch 50b
Grand Officer,
1st and 2nd
grades

*Ch50b. *Version 2*

In 1911, the Medal for Merit was divided into three grades to recognize the different ranks of officers receiving it. Chile upgraded the medal in 1924, when the category of Grand Officer was added to be awarded to foreign heads of state.

> Reinstituted: By Decree No. 2,038 of the Ministry of War on August 31, 1911, creating 3 grades of the medal

> Regulated: By Decree No. 1,680 of the Ministry of War on September 6, 1915, making civil servants and civilians eligible to receive the medal

> Modified: By Decree 333 of the Ministry of Foreign Affairs on April 4, 1924, adding the grade of Grand Officer

> Modified: By Decree No. 208 of the Ministry of Foreign Affairs on March 11, 1925, authorizing the ministry to award the medal to foreign civilians

Grades: Grand Officer, 1st,* 2nd,* 3rd

Obverse disc: Female head, right

Obverse inscription: REPUBLICA DE CHILE

Reverse disc: Laurel branch

Reverse inscription: AL MERITO

Shape: Ball-tipped star (1st: white enameled; 2nd: blue enameled) with a laurel wreath in the angles, suspended from a condor with wings displayed and inverted

Size: 1st: 48 mm; 2nd: 42 mm; 3rd: 41 mm

Metal: 1st, gilt; 2nd, 3rd: silvered bronze

Ribbon: Blue, white, red; 1st: neck ribbon; 2nd: with rosette

Reference: Eyzaguirre 1934, 57–58

Ch 50c
Commander star

*Ch50c. *Version 3*

This version was in effect from 1925 to 1929.

Modified: By Decree Law No. 643 of the Vice President on October 26, 1925

Grades: Grand Cross, Grand Officer, Commander with Star,* Commander, Officer, Knight

Obverse disc: Enameled arms of Chile

Obverse legend: [Name of rank] | ORDEN DEL MERITO on a blue enameled band

Star shape: Red enameled ball-tipped star with an enameled wreath in the angles (with anchors in the upper 2 angles for navy, with a star on the upper point for Commander with Star), superimposed on a 20-pointed sun with 26 rays the angles

Size: 80 mm

Metal: Gilt

Reference: Eyzaguirre 1934, 58

*Ch50d. *Version 4*

Chile reinstituted the Order of Merit of Chile in 1929 by renaming O'Higgins's Legion of Merit. The government wanted to reinstate the original Legion of Merit, which had never officially been abolished. The new order was to be given to foreign civilians in recognition of meritorious service to Chile. The order is administered by the Ministry of Foreign Affairs and is often awarded on the basis of reciprocity with friendly nations. This is Chile's highest order. The first head of state to receive the collar of the order was Augusto B. Leguía, president of Peru in 1929.

Regulated: By Supreme Decree No. 927 of the Ministry of Foreign Affairs on June 20, 1929

Modified: By Supreme Decree No. 1,756 of the Ministry of Foreign Affairs on November 25, 1929

Modified: By Supreme Decree No. 470 of the Ministry of Foreign Affairs on July 13, 1978

President: President of the Republic

Grades: Collar, Grand Cross,* Grand Officer, Commander, Officer,* Knight*

Ch 50d
Grand Cross

Ch 50d
Officer

Ch 50d
Officer

Obverse disc: Female head, right, in a gilt
field

Obverse legend: REPUBLICA DE CHILE on a
gilt band

Reverse disc: Laurel branch

Reverse legend: AL MERITO

Shape: Ball-tipped star (Grand Cross, Grand
Officer, Commander: white enameled; Officer: blue enameled; Knight: red enameled) with a laurel wreath in the angles, suspended from a condor with wings displayed
and inverted

Star disc: Enameled arms of Chile

Star legend: ORDEN DEL MERITO | CHILE on
a blue enameled band

Star shape: Ball-tipped, gilt-edged white

enameled star (Commander: red enameled with star on upper point) with a laurel wreath in the angles superimposed on
a 10-pointed sun with 8 rays in each angle
(Commander: 20-pointed sun with 6 rays in
each angle)

Size: Badge: Grand Cross: 45 mm; Officer,
Knight: 40 mm. Star: 80 mm

Metal: Gilt

Ribbon In 1929: blue, white, red; after 1929:
blue; Grand Cross has narrow red edge
stripes

Reference: Eyzaguirre 1934, 58–62; Gillingham 1932, 98–99

Provenance: Grand Cross: Alexandru
Cretzianu

Ch 50d
Knight

Ch 50d
Knight

*Ch51. *La Orden de Bernardo O'Higgins*

In 1956, the Ministry of Foreign Affairs added two more grades to the Order of Merit immediately below the grade of Knight: *la Medalla Bernardo O'Higgins de Primera Clase* and *la Medalla Bernardo O'Higgins de Segunda Clase*. Later, these two medals were separated from the Order of Merit and folded into a completely new order: the Order of Bernardo O'Higgins. This order is awarded only to foreign civilians. It is Chile's second-highest order.

Modified: By Supreme Decree No. 303 of the Foreign Affairs Ministry on April 18, 1967

Modified: By Supreme Decree No. 464 on July 12, 1968

Modified: By Supreme Decree No. 435 on May 10, 1985

Grades: Grand Cross (from 1968),* Grand Officer, Commander, Officer, Knight*

Classes: Knight 1st,* 2nd*

Obverse disc: Bust of O'Higgins, right

Obverse legend: BERNARDO O'HIGGINS | CHILE on a band

Shape: Ball-tipped star edged in white enamel and gilt-rimmed (no enamel on Knight), superimposed on same, with 3 floriate rays in each angle

Size: Badge: 45 mm. Star: 62 mm

Metal: Grand Cross, Knight, 1st: gilt; 2nd: silver

Maker: Hours, Santiago

Ch 51
Grand Cross

Ch 51
Knight 1st Class

Ch 51
Knight 2nd Class

*Ch 52. *La Orden al Mérito Docente y Cultural Gabriela Mistral*

The Gabriela Mistral Order of Teaching and Cultural Merit recognizes the pen name of Lucila de María del Perpetuo Socorro Godoy Alcayaga, a Chilean poet and the first Latin American to win the Nobel Prize for Literature, in 1945. The Grand Officer has been awarded to artists and writers such as Paul McCartney, Gabriel García Márquez, and Roberto Matta.

Instituted: By Decree No. 655 in 1977

Grades: Grand Cross,* Grand Officer, Commander, Knight* or Dame

Obverse disc: Bust of Gabriela Mistral, left, on a gilt field

Shape: Grand Cross: gray enameled ball-tipped star with laurel wreath in the angles, suspended from an open book with inscription EDUCA | CION; Knight: 8-pointed sun with 4 rays in each angle, attached to an open book with inscription EDUCA | CION

Ribbon: Grand Cross: red edged in blue; other grades: blue, white, red

Reference: Burke's Peerage 2006, 995–96

* * *

MORE RECENTLY, Chile has instituted new orders designed to recognize outstanding Chilean artists, educators, and intellectuals who have contributed to promoting the nation's culture.

Ch 52
Grand Cross star

Ch 52
Knight

Ch 52
Grand Cross badge

Star shape: Gray enameled 5-pointed star with laurel wreath in the angles, attached to an open book with inscription EDUCA│CION

Size: Badge: Grand Cross: 45 mm; Knight: 55 × 45 mm. Star: 86 × 76 mm

Metal: Grand Cross: gilt; Knight: silver, with bronze disc and book

Ribbon: Gray with red, white, blue center stripes

Reference: Burke's Peerage 2006, 998

Ch 53. *La Condecoración por Servicios Meritorios a la República*

Chile also instituted a new award classified as an order called the Decoration for Meritorious Service to the Republic. The decoration is awarded only to Chilean citizens for having provided a particularly relevant service to the nation.

Instituted: By Decree No. 435 on May 10, 1985

Regulated: By Decree No. 653 on August 3, 1988

Grades: Grand Officer, Commander, Knight

Obverse disc: Enameled arms of Chile in a red enameled field

Obverse legend: REPUBLICA DE CHILE | HONOR Y MERITO

Reverse disc: Enameled arms of Chile

Reverse legend: DIOS PATRIA LIBERTAD

Shape: Grand Officer: red enameled 8-pointed star suspended from an oval laurel wreath; Commander, Knight: white enameled Maltese cross with 2 concentric laurel wreaths in the angles (Knight: 1 wreath)

Size: Grand Officer: 64 mm; Commander, Knight: 63 mm

Metal: Grand Officer: gold; Commander, Knight: silver

Ribbon: White with red, white, blue center stripes

Reference: http://www.es.wikipedia.org/wiki/Ordenes_condecoraciones_y_medallas_de_Chile, accessed February 27, 2013

Ch54. *La Orden al Mérito Artístico y Cultural Pablo Neruda*

The Pablo Neruda Order for Artistic and Cultural Merit is awarded to Chilean and foreign nationals for their contribution to cultural development. Pablo Neruda (1904–73) is the pen name of Naftalí Ricardo Reyes Basoalto. Neruda was considered Chile's most prominent poet, and he received the Nobel Prize for Literature in 1971. He also served as Chile's ambassador to France and was elected to the Chilean Senate for the Communist Party. The order was created to coincide with the one hundredth anniversary of his birth.

Instituted: By the National Council of Culture and the Arts of Chile in 2004

COLOMBIA

THE CITY OF BOGOTÁ declared its independence from Spain on July 20, 1810, which is regarded as Colombia's independence day. However, other Colombian cities claimed their own sovereign rights, and fighting broke out among them. Spain took advantage of this discord and sent troops to retake the country in 1816. Three years later Simón Bolívar returned to Venezuela from exile and rebuilt his army, which he then led over the Andes. He defeated the royalist army at Boyacá on August 27, 1819. In that same year, the Congress of Angostura established the Republic of Gran Colombia, which included all of the territory administered by the viceroy of New Granada. As Argentina had done earlier, Gran Colombia spearheaded republican efforts to expel royalist forces, first from the neighboring countries of Venezuela and Ecuador and then from both Peru and Bolivia. Gran Colombia authorized medals not only for its own troops, but also those of its allies.

Republican fervor to expel Spain did not survive regional quarrels, which degenerated into a shifting civil war lasting well into the twentieth century. First, the federalists fought the centralists during the "Patria Boba" wars. Following independence, the country was divided along regional lines during the War of the Supremes. The country then split between conservatives and liberals, as in most of Latin America. The worst conflagrations occurred during "La Violencia" in the middle of the nineteenth century and the "Thousand Days War" at the turn of the twentieth century. Colombia instituted a few medals for the War of the Supremes, but otherwise refrained from awarding medals until it created decorations for its participation in the Korean War, the only war Colombia has fought on foreign soil after the expulsion of the Spaniards. More recently the country instituted an array of military medals for its armed forces engaged in fighting leftist insurgents, drug cartels, and paramilitary forces.

Colombia did not institute its first order for merit until shortly before World War I. Over time it created an array of orders with emphasis on its military and service to the nation.

MEDALS

Co1. *La Medalla por la Batalla de Bajo Palacé*

Cities and departments in New Granada authorized military medals during the War of Independence against Spain. The first battle in Colombia's War of Independence took place along the Palacé River near the city of Popayán on March 28, 1811. An untrained revolutionary force from Cali under the command of Antonio Baraya threatened Popayán, a royalist stronghold. Its garrison under the command of the governor of Popayán, Miguel Tacón y Rosique, met the rebels at a bridge over the Palacé River. The revolutionaries defeated the royalists and occupied Popayán. The city council ordered a medal to be struck for the victors.

> Instituted: By the Cabildo of Popayán in 1811
>
> Obverse: 3 crosses and a mountain range above the arms of Popayán
>
> Reverse: Arms of the city of Cali
>
> Reference: Gillingham 1932, 127

* * *

THE LITERATURE mentions medals authorized for other battles during the War of Independence, but without any description or illustration. Many of the early military awards were *escudos*, or patches, attached or sewn onto the recipient's uniform. The patch would typically carry the name of the place where the battle took place. Such patches are known to have been issued for specific battles, including Bambula (1813), La Victoria (1813), Bocachica (1814), Carabobo (1814), Calibio (1814), Quebrada Honda (1816), Retreat from Ocumare (1816), Alalcran (1816), Juncal (1816), Mucuritas (1817), San Félix (1817), Boyacá (1820), Chancay (1821), Lima (1821), Magdalena (1820, 1821), Riobamba (1822), Armada de Colombia (1823), Maracaibo (1823), and Pasto (1839).

In 1816, Bolívar returned from exile and formed a new army in Venezuela. He succeeded in capturing parts of eastern Venezuela around Angostura, where he set up a provisional government. However, he was less successful at dislodging the royalists from the north, and the fighting settled into a military stalemate. Bolívar temporarily abandoned Venezuela and led his troops over the Andes to liberate Colombia. Despite suffering heavy losses during the long march, Bolívar replaced his losses in Gran Colombia and overcame a royalist army at Boyacá under the command of Lieutenant Colonel José María Barreiro.

Co2. *La Cruz de Boyacá*

Bolívar decisively defeated Barreiro on August 7, 1819, at the Bridge of Boyacá just as the royalist forces were crossing it. Bolívar attacked by surprise; half of the royalist army was taken prisoner, with only light casualties among the republicans. Bolívar entered Bogotá three days later and declared independence. A month later, the Popular Assembly, meeting in Bogotá, authorized Colombia's first military medals as a sovereign nation. Two decorations were instituted for the battle at Boyacá: a cross and a medal.

> Instituted: By the Popular Assembly on September 9, 1819
>
> Classes: Chiefs, officers, enlisted men
>
> Obverse inscription: VENCEDOR D[E] BOYACA above crossed laurel branch and sword with a cross pattée in the center

Shape: Cross

Metal: Chiefs: gold; officers: silver; enlisted men: bronze

Ribbon: Green

Reference: Posada 1938, 59–62; Gillingham 1932, 125; Barac 2009, 304; Rosa 1891, 246–47

Co3. *La Medalla de Boyacá*

Instituted: By the Popular Assembly on September 9, 1819

Classes: Officers, enlisted men

Obverse: Cross pattée encircled by a laurel wreath

Obverse inscription: BOYACA

Shape: Oval

Size: 25 × 20 mm

Metal: Officers: silver; enlisted men: bronze

Reference: Barac 2009, 304

Co4. *La Medalla de Cundinamarca*

Colombia instituted two medals for its officers and men who fought the royalists during the War of Independence in Cundinamarca.

Instituted: By decree on January 6, 1820

Classes: Senior officers, junior officers, enlisted men

Obverse: Double-headed eagle

Obverse legend: ALEXANDRO

Reverse inscription: LIBER | TADOR | DE | CUNDINA | MARCA within a laurel wreath

Size: 25 mm

Metal: Senior officers: gold; junior officers, enlisted men: silver

Ribbon: Bright red

Reference: Gillingham 1932, 126; Barac 2009, 304

Co5. *La Medalla de Cundinamarca*

Instituted: By Law of the Congress of Angostura on January 14, 1820

Classes: Generals, officers, enlisted men, civilian officials, private citizens

Obverse inscription: CUNDINAMARCA LIBERTADA 1819 on a red enameled field surrounded by a green enameled laurel wreath

Metal: Generals: gold with emeralds; officers, civilian officials: gold; enlisted men, private citizens: silver

Ribbon: Military: red; civilians: light blue

Reference: Posada 1938, 64–65

* * *

BOLÍVAR next turned his attention to his native Venezuela, where a strong royalist army still occupied much of the country. Bolívar first threatened Valencia. The royalist commander, General Miguel de la Torre, chose to take a stand on the plain of Carabobo to the west of Caracas. Bolívar defeated de la Torre at the Battle of Carabobo on June 24, 1821, inflicting heavy casualties on the royalists. De la Torre retreated into Puerto Cabello in good order, but the battle ended Spanish control of Venezuela.

Co6. *La Medalla de Puerto Cabello*

Spain was able to hold much of the Venezuelan coast for two more years, thanks to its control of the sea. The royalists surrendered Puerto Cabello on November 8, 1823, and sailed to Cuba, never to return. Gran Colombia authorized a medal for the mostly Venezuelan officers and men who participated in the final siege of Puerto Cabello.

Instituted: By Decree of the Vice President, General Santander, on December 7, 1823

Classes: Chiefs, officers, enlisted men

Obverse inscription: VENCEDOR EN PUERTO CABELLO | AÑO 13

Metal: Chiefs, officers: gold; enlisted men: silver

Ribbon: Bright red

Reference: Posada 1938, 87–88

* * *

Soon after the Battle of Carabobo, revolutionaries in Guayaquil pushed royalist forces from the coast. However, efforts to expel them from the highlands failed. They called on Bolívar for help. He gathered a force of Gran Colombian soldiers and sent them south under the command of General Antonio José de Sucre. This force joined up with the revolutionaries from Guayaquil, as well as an army sent north by San Martín under the command of then Colonel Santa Cruz.

Co7. *La Medalla de la Batalla de Pichincha*

Soldiers from five Latin American countries defeated the royalist army under the command of Colonel Basilio García de Bombondá near the Pichincha volcano on May 24, 1822. Quito surrendered the next day, thereby ending Spanish rule in Ecuador. Colombia authorized a medal for the Peruvian troops participating in the battle.

Instituted: By Decree of Simón Bolívar on June 18, 1822

Classes: Officers, enlisted men

Obverse disc: 3 mountain peaks

Obverse legend: LIBERTADOR DE QUITO EN PICHINCHA

Reverse inscription: GRATITUD DE COLOMBIA A LA DIVISION DEL PERU with 2 laurel branches in the center

Shape: Oval

Size: 30 × 25 mm

Metal: Officers: gold; enlisted men: silver

Ribbon: Red, blue, yellow

Reference: Posada 1938, 78; Gillingham 1932, 127–28; Barac 2009, 305

* * *

While in Guayaquil, Bolívar met with Argentine General San Martín to discuss how to defeat the remaining royalist forces in Peru. As a result of the meeting, San Martín resigned and sailed away in self-imposed exile to Europe, never to return. Meanwhile, the military situation in Peru had deteriorated. The revolutionaries could not defeat the royalists on the battlefield, and both sides suffered from discord. The Peruvians asked Bolívar to take command of the revolutionary forces in Peru. Bolívar accepted and moved to Trujillo to assemble and train a new army. In July 1824, he marched his army up into the highlands, where it defeated the royalists under the command of General José Canterac at the Battle of Junín on August 6, 1824. It appears that Sucre issued a medal to his men in December 1824 and that Bolívar issued another one a week later.

Co8. *La Medalla de Ayacucho*

Viceroy de la Serna marched north from Cuzco to engage General Sucre. After several weeks of maneuvering, the two armies met on the plains of Ayacucho on December 9, 1824. Sucre's army, consisting mainly of Gran Colombians, took up defensive positions. The royalists attacked in good order but were unable to penetrate the revolutionaries' lines. Their mainly creole troops surrendered instead, along with most of the royalist officers. The Battle of Ayacucho marked the end of effective Spanish rule in South America. Peru made Sucre a marshal. Ten days later Marshal Sucre authorized a medal for the Gran Colombian troops who fought at Ayacucho.

Instituted: By Decree of Marshal Sucre on December 19, 1824

Classes: Chiefs, officers, enlisted men

Obverse inscription: COLOMBIA A SUS BRAVOS EN EL PERU within a laurel wreath

Reverse: Sword crossed by a rifle

Reverse legend: VENCEDOR EN AYACUCHO 9 DE DICIEMBRE AÑO 14

Metal: Chiefs, officers: gold; enlisted men: silver

Ribbon: Red, blue, yellow

Reference: Posada 1938, 92–93; Gillingham 1932, 128; Barac 2009, 305; Argentina 1910, 3, 106

Co9. *La Medalla de Ayacucho*

Instituted: By Decree of Bolívar in Lima, December 27, 1824

Classes: Generals, chiefs, officers, enlisted men

Obverse Crossed laurel branches

Obverse legend: AYACUCHO

Reverse: [Name of the recipient]

Shape: Oval, suspended from an oval wreath

Metal: Generals: enameled with diamonds; chiefs, officers: gold; enlisted men: silver

Ribbon: White, red

Reference: Posada 1938, 93

Co10. *La Medalla de Cochabamba*

Despite the royalist defeat at Ayacucho, the commander of the royalist garrison in Cochabamba remained loyal to Spain. In 1825, the people of Cochabamba rose up and defeated the royalists. Marshal Sucre authorized a medal for the Cochabambino insurgents.

Instituted: By Decree of Marshal Sucre on February 9, 1825

Classes: Chiefs, officers, enlisted men

Obverse inscription: LA PATRIA A LOS FIELES DE COCHABAMBA: 14 DE ENERO DE 1825

Reverse: [Name of the recipient]

Metal: Chiefs, officers: gold; enlisted men: silver

Ribbon: Green

Reference: Posada 1938, 109–10

* * *

BOLÍVAR assigned his two chief military lieutenants, Antonio José de Sucre and Andrés de Santa Cruz with their Gran Colombian troops to maintain order in the newly created republics of Peru and Bolivia. However, with the defeat of the royalist forces, Peruvian leaders no longer shared common interests with the Gran Colombians. The Peruvians not only sought to exercise sovereignty over their own territories, but to expand their borders, particularly in Ecuador to the north. Peruvian troops under José de la Mar and Agustín Gamarra marched north. The Peruvian fleet blockaded the port of Guayaquil to prevent the Gran Colombians from reinforcing their positions. The Gran Colombian army under the Sucre took Cuenca and sought to face the advancing Peruvian army at Tarqui.

Co11. *La Medalla de la Batalla de Tarqui*

The Gran Colombians attacked the Peruvians at Portete de Tarqui near the highland town of Cuenca in the early morning of February 27, 1829. The Gran Colombians controlled a critical ravine, which limited the Peruvians ability to maneuver. The Gran Colombians won the battle ending Peru's goal of annexing Ecuador. On September 22, 1829, the two sides signed the Treaty of Guayaquil, which ceded most of Ecuador to Gran Colombia. On the same day of the battle, Sucre authorized a medal for the

Gran Colombian troops who fought at Portete de Tarqui.

Instituted: By Decree of Marshal Sucre on February 27, 1829

Classes: Officers, enlisted men

Obverse inscription: VEN | GADOR | ES DE |

COLOMBIA | EN TAR | QUI above a crossed rifle and a lance

Shape: Oval suspended from a metallic wreath

Metal: Officers: gold; enlisted men: silver

Ribbon: Green

Reference: Gillingham 1932, 128; Barac 2009, 305; Rosa 1891, 308–10

THE WAR OF THE SUPREMES

IN 1839, the constitutional government in Bogotá faced a series of insurrections that became known as the Guerra de los Supremos, or caudillos, who rose up in the name of regional autonomy. On October 28, 1840, federalist forces were advancing on Bogotá. A government army defending the capital defeated the federalists at Buenavista. On January 9, 1841, government forces defeated a federalist army under the command of General González at Altos de Aratoca. González escaped but died of malaria shortly thereafter. In 1840, Supreme leader Pedro Carmona from the north coast rose up against the central government. After initial successes, he moved inland with his troops but was defeated by General Tomás Cipriano de Mosquera in April 1841 at Tescua. The Colombian Congress authorized two medals for its military who fought in the battles ending with the defeat of the insurgents.

Co12. *La Medalla por las Batallas de Buenavista, Aratoca, Riosucio, y Tescua*

This medal was awarded to the officers and men who opposed regionalist forces at the Battles of Buenavista, Aratoca, Riosucio, and Tescua.

Instituted: By Presidential Decree on May 7, 1841

Classes: Generals, chiefs, officers, enlisted men, volunteers

Obverse: JHS, LIBERTAD Y VALOR

Reverse: [Names of battles in which the recipient fought]

Metal: Generals, chiefs: gold; officers, volunteers: gilt silver; enlisted men: silver

Ribbon: Red, blue, yellow

Reference: Posada 1938, 121–22

Co13. *La Medalla por la Batalla de Salamina*

The Department of Antioquia rose up against the central government in 1840, led by Salvador Córdoba in the name of greater regional autonomy. He was defeated at the Battle of Salamina on May 5, 1841, and executed shortly thereafter. The Congress authorized a medal for the victors and a special one in gold to Ana María Martínez, who volunteered to fight with the government army.

Instituted: By Presidential Decree on May 28, 1841

Classes: Chiefs, officers, enlisted men, volunteers

Obverse: LIBERTAD Y ORDEN

Reverse: VENCEDOR EN SALAMINA EN 5 DE
   MAYO DE 1841

Metal: Chiefs: gold; officers, volunteers: gilt
   silver; enlisted men: silver

Ribbon: Red, blue, yellow

Reference: Posada 1938, 121

* * *

SOME twenty years later, a Colombian president, Tomás Cipriano de Mosquera, supported Ecuadorian dissidents with the hope of reincorporating Ecuador into Colombia. Instead, Ecuador sent an army under General Juan José Flores into southern Colombia in reprisal. Mosquera himself commanded a Colombian army that marched south to face the Ecuadorians. The two sides met at Cuaspud on December 6, 1863. The Colombians defeated the numerically superior Ecuadoreans, capturing thousands of prisoners. Mosquera did not press his advantage, and the two countries signed an armistice, which confirmed the independence and borders of Ecuador. This was the last battle fought by Colombian soldiers in neighboring countries.

Co14. *La Cruz por la Batalla de Cuaspud*

Mosquera authorized a cross for his victorious troops.

Instituted: By Presidential Decree on December 7, 1863

Classes: Generals and secretaries of state, colonels, chiefs, officers, enlisted men

Obverse inscription: 6 | DE D^{ICE} DE | 1863

Obverse legend: COLOMBIA A SUS
   DEFENSORES

Reverse: [Name of the recipient]

Shape: Ball-tipped Maltese cross with 2-pointed ends and a wreath in the angles, surmounted by a metallic band

Metal: Generals and secretaries of state: white enamel; colonels: red enamel; chiefs up to Lt. Col.: blue enamel; officers: gold; enlisted men: silver

Ribbon: Red, blue, yellow neck ribbon

Reference: Posada 1938, 132–33

* * *

IN 1919, the government authorized the Centennial Cross for Boyacá exactly one hundred years after the Battle of Boyacá. This medal was originally awarded to Colombia's military. Various modifications were made over the years, and it eventually evolved into the country's highest award—the Order of Boyacá (Co27, below).

*Co15. *La Cruz por el Centenario de Boyacá*

The Cross for the Centenary of Boyacá was bestowed for military and diplomatic service to the nation. The original Cross of Boyacá that was reportedly given to Bolívar passed into disuse, but the decoration was never formally abolished. The new medal drew its inspiration from the Cross of Boyacá without formally being tied to it.

Instituted: By Decree No. 1,667 on August 9, 1919

Modified: By Decree No. 513 on April 17, 1922, making foreigners eligible to receive the medal

Replaced: 1930 by the Order of Boyacá

Classes: Officers, enlisted men*

Obverse disc: Bust of Bolívar, left

Obverse legend: COLOMBIA | CENTENARIO DE
   BOYACA on a blue enameled band

Reverse inscription: 1819 | 7 de Agosto | 1919
   on a blue enameled field

Shape: Blue enameled Maltese cross with concave pointed ends

Size: 50 mm

Metal: Officers: silver; enlisted men: bronze

Ribbon: Half yellow, blue, red

Reference: Gillingham 1932, 128–30; Barac 2009, 305

THE KOREAN WAR (1950–1953)

COLOMBIA remained neutral during the two world wars. However, it participated from 1951 to 1954 in the Korean War, sending a battalion of ground troops and a frigate, the *Almirante Padilla*, to fight in Korea as part of the United Nations military response to the North Korean invasion of South Korea—the only South American country to do so. Most of the Colombian troops fought with the Infantry Battalion No. 1 "Colombia" that was formed by Decree No. 3,927 in December 1950. Columbian forces suffered 608 casualties, including 130 killed and 448 wounded, almost all of them in the army. In 1952, Colombia authorized two medals for meritorious service in wartime or international conflict: the Iron Cross and the Bronze Star.

*Co16. *La Cruz de Hierro*

The Iron Cross is given for acts of valor or meritorious acts above and beyond the call of duty during war or international conflict. To date, this medal has been conferred only on Colom-

Co 16

Co 16

bian military personnel for participating in the Korean War. Additional awards are indicated by a bronze oak leaf mounted on the ribbon.

Instituted: By Decree No. 812 on March 27, 1952

Obverse: Arms of Colombia

Reverse: Korean *taeguk* symbol

Reverse inscription: ACCION CAMPAÑA | DISTINGUIDA DE | DE VALOR COREA

Shape: Cross pattée

Size: 45 mm

Metal: Black enameled silver

Ribbon: White with Korean *taeguk* symbol in the center and the Colombian national colors (red, blue, and yellow) on the borders

Reference: Colombia 2010, 7–8

*Co17. *La Estrella de Bronce*

The Bronze Star was awarded for military merit or devotion to duty in action overseas. It is given to all military personnel who serve in an international war. To date, this medal has only been awarded to Colombian military personnel during the Korean War.

Instituted: By Decree No. 812 on March 27, 1952

Obverse disc: Arms of Colombia

Reverse disc: Korean *taeguk* symbol

Reverse inscription: CAMPAÑA DE COREA

Shape: Star

Size: 42 mm

Metal: Bronze

Ribbon: White with the Korean *taeguk* symbol in the center and narrow red, blue, and yellow edge stripes

Reference: Colombia 2010, 7–8

*Co18. *La Medalla en Bronce por Servicio con el Batallon de Infantería "Colombia" en Corea*

This medal was awarded to the 4,000 Colombian officers and men who fought in Korea with the "Colombia" battalion.

Obverse: Soldier holding flag with enameled Colombian colors atop a mountain

Reverse: Lion rampant in a shield (emblem of the "Colombia" Battalion)

Reverse legend: BATALLON DE INFANTERIA "COLOMBIA"

Reverse inscription: HONOR | AL DEBER CUMPLIDO in a box

Shape: Round medal with a wreath along the lower edge

Size: 33 × 32 mm

Metal: Bronze

Ribbon: Rainbow colors with a brooch inscribed COLOMBIA

Reference: http://www.elgrancapitan.org/foro/viewtopic.php?t=14301, accessed July 13, 2012

Peacetime Awards

COLOMBIA has contributed observers to three United Nations peacekeeping operations: UNPROFOR, in the former Yugoslavia; MINUGUA, in Guatemala; and the United Nations Emergency Force (UNEF) in the Middle East. While Colombian participants in these operations may have received UN medals for their service, Colombia did not institute its own medals for these operations.

Following the Korean War, Colombia authorized new military medals for merit, distinguished service, and valor. These medals are awarded for service inside Colombia, many of them for acts of bravery related to guerrilla insurgencies and the drug wars.

*Co19. *La Cruz por Servicios Distinguidos en Orden Público*

The Cross for Distinguished Service in Preserving Public Order is awarded to military personnel for acts of courage or distinguished merit while controlling civil disturbances inside the country. Additional awards are indicated by small stars or 16-pointed suns on the ribbon.

Co 19

> Instituted: By Decree No. 803 on March 27, 1952
>
> Regulated: By Decree No. 55 on January 11, 1963, and No. 581 on March 30, 1975
>
> Regulated: By Decree No. 1,880 in December 1988
>
> Obverse disc: Arms of Colombia
>
> Reverse legend: SERVICIOS DISTINGUIDOS
>
> Reverse inscription: ORDEN | PUBLICO
>
> Shape: Maltese cross, crossed sword and rifle in angles
>
> Size: 48 mm
>
> Additional awards: 2nd: bronze star; 3rd: bronze and silver stars; 4th: bronze, silver, and gold stars; 5th: bronze, silver and 2 gold stars; 6th: bronze, silver and 3 gold stars; 7th: gold sun on a circlet of laurel; 8th: 2 gold suns on laurel circlets; 9th: 3 gold suns on laurel circlets; 10th: 4 gold suns on laurel circlets
>
> Metal: Silver
>
> Ribbon: Lead gray with yellow, blue, and red edge stripes
>
> Reference: Colombia 2010, 11–12

Co20. *La Cruz Militar al Valor*

Colombia's military has been called upon to combat leftist insurgencies, drug trafficking, and renegade military forces inside the country. The Military Cross for Valor is awarded to officers and enlisted men of the armed forces for valor or initiative in combat in peacetime for maintaining and reestablishing

Co 19

public order. Additional awards are indicated by small bronze, silver or gold stars on the ribbon.

Instituted: By Decree No. 2,281 on November 10, 1998

Obverse disc: Arms of army, navy, or air force

Reverse: DESAFIE LA MUERTE POR SALVAR LA PATRIA

Shape: Cross pattée with rounded ends and rays at the edges, superimposed on a round medal

Size: 50 mm

Metal: Silver

Ribbon: Olive green, red, olive green

Reference: Colombia 2010, 8–9

Co21. *La Medalla Militar "Herido en Acción"*

The Wounded in Action Medal is given to military and civilian personnel of the three branches of the armed forces for wounds sustained in combat or as a result of enemy action. The number of awards is indicated by the number and metal of stars on the ribbon.

Instituted: By Decree No. 1,816 of the Ministry of National Defense on May 24, 2007

Modified: By Decree No. 4,949 of the Ministry of National Defense

Obverse: Arms of the army, navy, or air force below inscription HERIDO EN ACCION

Reverse legend: MEDALLA MILITAR | HERIDO EN ACCION

Shape: 16-pointed sun with small stars between the angles

Additional awards: 1st: bronze star; 2nd: bronze and silver stars; 3rd: bronze, silver, and gold stars; 4th: bronze, silver, and 2 gold stars; 5th: bronze, silver, and 3 gold stars

Size: 45 mm

Metal: Silver

Ribbon: Royal blue with medium yellow and narrow red and blue edge stripes

Reference: Colombia 2010, 9–11

Co22. *La Cruz Militar "Campaña del Sur"*

The Military Cross for the "Southern Campaign" is awarded to the officers, NCO's, enlisted men, and marines who participate in planning, supporting, and carrying out military operations by the Joint Task Force in the Departments of Caquetá, Guaviare, and Meta in southern Colombia. This task force is charged with attacking armed groups affiliated with drug dealers and allied leftist guerrilla forces and with providing law and order in those three departments.

Instituted: By Decree No. 1,816 on March 24, 2007

Obverse disc: Enameled symbols of the armed forces

Reverse inscription: CAMPANA DEL SUR

Reverse legend: FUEREZAS MILITARES DE COLOMBIA | DIOS Y VICTORIA

Shape: Cross pattée with upper arms enameled yellow, blue, red, with an omega in the lower arm

Size: 50 mm

Metal: Gilt

Ribbon: Red, blue, light blue

Reference: Colombia 2010, 12–13

Co23. *La Medalla Militar "Fe en la Causa"*

The Military Medal "Faith in the Cause" is awarded to officers, NCO's, soldiers, and civilian members of the army who promote peace, order, and democracy in Colombia. The medal is also given to Colombian and foreign individuals

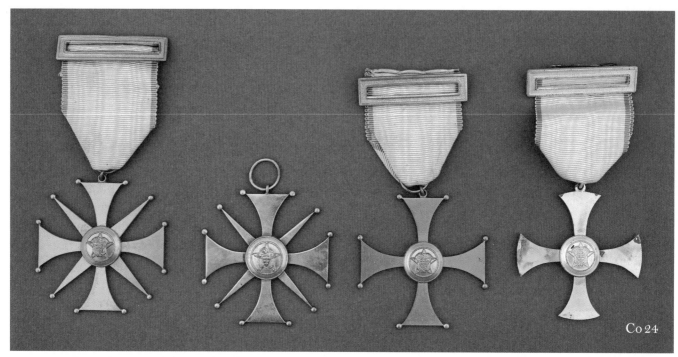

and institutions that have provided meritorious service to the army. The requirements for receiving this medal emphasize respect for human rights and suppression of armed insurgents.

Instituted: By Decree No. 2,066, on June 13, 2011

Obverse: Arms of the Army on a silver star, ribbon beneath inscribed PATRIA HONOR LEALTAD

Reverse: Seven pillars

Reverse inscription: DIGNIDAD EQUILIBRIO EQUIPO

Shape: Round within a laurel wreath, suspended from a crown

Size: 55 mm

Metal: Silvered and gilt

Ribbon: Red with 8 embroidered colored stripes representing the 8 branches of the army. The army emblem FE EN LA CAUSA is placed in the center of the ribbon.

Reference: Colombia 2011, 1–2

*Co24. *La Cruz "Policiaca al Valor"*

The Police Cross for Bravery is awarded to personnel of the national police for acts of bravery above and beyond the call of duty. The Colombian police have often taken the lead, along with the armed forces, in controlling leftist insurgencies, drug trafficking, and renegade military units.

Classes: Military,* civilian,* each with 1st* and 2nd* class

Obverse disc: Arms of Colombia on a star

Reverse inscription: AL VALOR

Shape: Ball-tipped cross pattée (with single ball-tipped ray in each angle for military; civilian 2nd class not ball-tipped, and ends rounded)

Size: 1st: 56 mm; 2nd, military: 56 mm; civilian: 50 mm

Metal: 1st: gilt; 2nd: silvered

Maker: Fibo, Bogotá

Ribbon: White with narrow green edge stripes

*Co25. *La Cruz Policiaca "Servicios Distinguidos"*

Obverse disc: Arms of Colombia

Reverse legend: SERVICIOS DISTINGUIDOS

Co25

Co25

Shape: Green enameled Maltese cross with 2-pointed ends and a laurel wreath in the angles

Size: 47 mm

Metal: Silver

Ribbon: Green with narrow white edge stripes

ORDERS

COLOMBIA instituted its first order of merit in 1913, nearly one hundred years after the Battle of Boyacá. This first order became the country's highest military award. Most of the orders subsequently created in Colombia were also awarded to the country's military. It was not until after the Korean War that Colombia began creating orders for developing the nation's economy and promoting democracy.

*Co26. *La Orden Militar de San Mateo*

In 1913, Colombia created the Military Order of San Mateo to recognize acts of exceptional valor in the defense of the nation from external enemies. It was not intended as an award for domestic violence, such as civil war, or for international conflict not involving Colombia. This order is the country's highest military order.

The order is named after San Mateo, a town in what is now Venezuela. A battle was fought there in 1814 between Simón Bolívar's men and royalist forces. The order recognizes in particular the sacrifice made by one of Bolívar's captains, Antonio Ricuarte. Royalist forces were advancing toward the main house of an estate, which contained a large store of munitions and gunpowder. Had they succeeded in capturing the house, they would have been able to resupply themselves with ammunition and complete their victory. Instead, Captain Ricuarte stayed behind in the house as his men retreated. When the house was full of royalist troops replenishing their munitions, he lit a fuse, which blew up the house, killing many enemy soldiers. Bolívar took advantage of the confusion to counterattack and carried the day.

Instituted: By Law No. 40 in October 1913

Regulated: By Decree No. 349 in March 1914

Grades: I, II, and III* Class

Obverse disc: Bust of Ricuarte, right, on a red enameled field

Obverse inscription: 1814 RICUARTE 1914

Reverse inscription: I [II or III] CLASE

Reverse legend: COLOMBIA | Orden Militar de San Mateo

Shape: Ball-tipped Maltese cross with 2-pointed ends and a laurel wreath in the angles; III: black enameled with green enameled wreath

Size: 56 × 53 mm

Metal: I: gilt; II: silver; III: iron

Maker: J. H. Werner, Berlin

Ribbon: Half yellow, blue, red

Reference: Posada 1938, 131–35; Gillingham 1932, 130; Barac 2009, 305; Colombia 2010, 6–7

*Co27. *La Orden de Boyacá*

The Order of Boyacá is awarded to Colombian nationals and foreigners, both civilian and military, for rendering exceptional service to the nation in time of war or while maintaining

Co 26
III Class

Co 26
III Class

public order. It is the country's highest civilian award. It is sometimes given in recognition of fifty years of military service.

Bolívar first reportedly received it shortly after the Battle of Boyacá. It was first awarded on August 8, 1819, to soldiers who fought at that battle. The order was ignored during the rest of the nineteenth century. The name was preserved with the Cross for the Centenary of Boyacá in 1919 (see above, Co15). By Decree No. 513 in 1922, eligibility was extended to foreign military and diplomats. In 1930, the cross was renamed the Order of Boyacá, and eligibility was extended to civilians. The statutes of the order were first published in 1954. The order was modified in 1980 to create the Grand Collar, which may be conferred only on heads of state. The silver cross is conferred only on national and foreign institutions.

Recipients of the collar have included Rafael Ángel Calderón Fournier, president of Costa Rica; HM Queen Elizabeth II; Juan Carlos Wasmosy, president of Paraguay; Alejandro Toledo, president of Peru; and Lucio Borbúa, president of Ecuador.

Instituted: By Decree No. 1,247 on August 6, 1930

Modified: By Decree No. 94 in 1935, modifying the statutes

Regulated: By Decree No. 1,396 on August 16, 1954

Modified: December 1980

Grand Master: President of the Republic

Grades: Grand Collar, Extraordinary Grand Cross,* Grand Cross, Grand Officer, Silver Cross, Commander, Officer, Knight*

Obverse disc: Bust of Bolívar, left

Obverse legend: ORDEN | DE BOYACA on a blue enameled band

Reverse inscription: REPUBLICA | DE | COLOMBIA on a blue enameled field

Co 27
Extraordinary
Grand Cross

Co 27
Extraordinary
Grand Cross star (reverse)

Co 27
Extraordinary
Grand Cross badge (reverse)

Co 27
Knight

Co 27
Knight

Shape: Gold-rimmed, blue enameled Maltese cross

Star shape: Badge on a silver 8-pointed faceted star with three 3-part rays in each angle

Size: Badge: Grand Cross: 60 mm; Knight: 47 mm. Star: 80 mm

Metal: Gilt silver

Maker: Fibo, Bogotá

Ribbon: Dark blue with narrow red, green, and yellow edge stripes

Reference: Posada 1938, 135–51; Barac 2009, 305; Burke's Peerage 2006, 1032–33

*Co28. *La Orden al Mérito Militar "Antonio Nariño"*

The Order of Military Merit "Antonio Nariño" is an award for meritorious military service in discipline, scientific research, and other non-combat-related areas.

Antonio Nariño was one of the early proponents of independence for Gran Colombia. He translated the Déclaration des Droits de l'Homme into Spanish. He was arrested several times for subversion but managed to escape. During the War of Independence, he commanded the Army of the South. Eventually, he was captured and exiled to Spain. He was returned after Gran Colombia obtained its independence and then ran unsuccessfully for president of the country against Bolívar. He is best remembered for a statement he made from his deathbed: "I loved my country; history will decide how much"—a refrain that has been enshrined in the country's national anthem.

Instituted: By Decree No. 1,415 on June 13, 1942

Regulated: By Decree No. 659 on March 21, 1944, and Decree No. 805 on March 27, 1952

Regulated: By Decree No. 1,880 on September 12, 1988

Grand Master: President of the Republic

Grades: Grand Cross, Grand Officer, Commander, Officer,* Knight,* Member*

Obverse disc: Bust of Nariño, left

Reverse inscription: AME | A MI PATRIA | CUANTO FUE | ESE AMOR | LO DIRA | LA HISTORIA

Shape: Maltese cross with 2-pointed ends and crossed swords and leaves in each angle

Star: Badge on silver 8-pointed star

Size: 45 mm

Metal: Grand Cross, Grand Officer, Commander: gilt; Officer: silvered; Knight: antique silvered; Member: bronze

Makers: Fibo, Bogotá, and Metalfischer, Bogotá

Ribbon: Half yellow, blue, red; except member: yellow

Reference: Colombia 2010, 18–19; Burke's Peerage 2006, 1035

*Co29. *La Orden al Mérito Naval "Almirante Padilla"*

The Order of Naval Merit "Admiral Padilla" is awarded to navy personnel for acts of courage or outstanding service to the navy. The order is named after Admiral Padilla, who founded the Colombian navy in 1823. He accompanied Simón Bolívar on his final expedition from Haiti, which landed at Ocumare, and began his successful campaign to liberate South America from Spanish rule.

Instituted: By Decree No. 2,409 on July 8, 1947

Regulated: By Decree No. 805 on March 27, 1952

Grand Master: President of the Republic

Grades: Grand Cross, Grand Officer, Commander,* Officer, Knight, Member

Co 28
Officer, Knight, Member

Co 28
Officer, Knight, Member

Co 29
Commander

Co 29
Commander

Obverse disc: Bust of Padilla, left

Obverse legend: ORDEN NAVAL | AL
ALMIRANTE PADILLA 1823–1947

Reverse disc: Anchor superimposed on enameled national colors

Shape: Ball-tipped Maltese cross with
2-pointed ends and 5 flat-ended rays in each
angle, suspended from a spread-winged
condor

Size: 47 mm

Metal: Grand Cross: silver; Grand Officer:
gilt silver; Commander: gilt; Officer: silvered; Knight: antique silvered; Member:
bronze

Ribbon: Aquamarine with narrow white
stripes, depending on rank; Member:
aquamarine

Reference: Colombia 2010, 20; Burke's Peerage 2006, 1035; Werlich 1974, 97

*Co30. *La Orden al Mérito Sanitario "José Fernández Madrid"*

The José Fernández Madrid Order of Health
Merit is awarded for heroism, military spirit,
discipline, work ethic, and scientific research in
the field of medicine. José Fernández Madrid
acted briefly as president of the United Provinces of New Granada in 1816. He was captured
by royalist troops and sent to Havana, where
he supported himself by practicing medicine.
He returned to Colombia in 1825.

Instituted: By Decree No. 2,423 on July 22,
1950

Regulated: By Decree No. 805 on March 27,
1952

Grand Master: President of the Republic

Grades: Grand Cross (star), Grand Officer,
Commander, Officer, Knight,* Member

Obverse disc: Bust of Fernández Madrid, ¾
left

Obverse legend: ORDEN | J. FERNANDEZ
MADRID

Co 30
Knight

Co 30
Knight

Reverse disc: Caduceus

Reverse legend: REPUBLICA DE COLOMBIA | SANIDAD MILITAR

Shape: Disc attached to surrounding wreath by a green enameled Maltese cross with rounded ends

Size: 50 mm

Metal: Grand Cross: silver; Grand Officer: gilt silver; Commander: gilt; Officer: silvered; Knight: antique silvered; Member: bronze

Maker: Meco, Bogotá

Ribbon: Officer, Commander, Knight: white with yellow, blue, and red edge stripes; Member: white

Reference: Colombia 2010, 21–22; Burke's Peerage 2006, 1036

*Co31. *La Orden al Mérito Militar "José María Córdova"*

The José María Córdova Order of Military Merit recognizes acts of valor or outstanding service by Colombian military personnel. It has also been bestowed on foreign officers. The order is named for a hero of the War of Independence who commanded Colombian troops at the decisive Battle of Ayacucho in Peru against the royalist army.

Instituted: By Decree No. 3,950 on December 23, 1950

Regulated: By Decree No. 805 on March 27, 1952

Grand Master: President of the Republic

Grades: Grand Cross (star), Grand Officer (star),* Commander, Officer, Knight, Member*

Obverse disc: Bust of Córdova, ¾ left

Obverse legend: ORDEN AL MERITO | JOSE MARIA CORDOVA on a gray enameled band

Reverse inscription: ARMAS | A | DISCRECION | PASO DE | VENCEDORES

Co 31
Grand Officer star

Shape: Round disc attached to band by a black enameled Maltese cross with rounded ends and a red enameled triangle on each arm

Star shape: Disc superimposed on an 8-pointed gilt star, each arm of which has 5 parts

Size: Badge: Member: 44 mm. Star: 80 mm

Metal: Grand Cross: silver; Grand Officer: gilt silver; Commander: gilt; Officer: silvered; Knight: antique silvered; Member: bronze

Maker: Joyería Granados, Bogotá

Ribbon: Commander, Officer, Knight: red with yellow, blue edge stripes; Member: red

Reference: Colombia 2010, 19–20; Burke's Peerage 2006, 1036

*Co32. *La Estrella Cívica*

The Civic Star is awarded to members of the national police force for outstanding service in protecting the life, honor, property, and rights of Colombian nationals.

Instituted: By Decree No. 2,358 in 1953
Modified: By Decree No. 2,612 in 1966

Co 31
Member

Co 31
Member

Co 32
Ordinary Civil Grand Officer star

Co 32
Commander

Grades: Extraordinary Civil Grand Cross, Ordinary Civil Star, Ordinary Civil Grand Officer (star)*, Commander,* Officer, Member

Obverse: Enameled arms of Columbia on star

Obverse inscription: VIS JURI DE SERVIAT on ribbon above star

Reverse inscription: ESTRELLA CIVICA | CATEGORIA | [grade]

Shape: Enameled arms of Colombia on a star superimposed on a green enameled Maltese cross with 2-pointed ends surrounded by 2 laurel branches

Size: 57 × 52 mm; star: 89 × 82 mm

Metal: Badge: gilt, silvered; star: silver
Ribbon: White, green

Provenance: Commander: A. Menke

*Co33. *La Orden Militar 13 de Junio*

The Military Order of June 13 was given to the military supporters of President Gustavo Rojas Pinilla to commemorate the first year of his dictatorship.

Co 32
Commander

Co 33

Co 33

Instituted: By Decree of President Rojas Pinilla on May 19, 1954

Rescinded: On October 1, 1959

Grades: 7

Obverse inscription: 13 | DE JUNIO on a white enameled disc

Obverse legend: FUERZAS ARMADAS | DE COLOMBIA on a green enameled band surrounded by a laurel wreath

Reverse inscription: PAZ JUSTICIA Y LIBERTAD

Shape: Gold-rimmed, white enameled Maltese cross with 2-pointed ends and the emblem of each branch of the armed forces on a wreath in the angles

Star shape: Badge on 8-pointed star with 7 rays in each angle

Size: 60 mm

Metal: Gilt bronze

Ribbon: White with 6 narrow green stripes, edged in yellow, blue, and red stripes

Reference: Werlich 1974, 98

*Co34. *La Orden de San Carlos*

The Order of Saint Charles is Colombia's second-highest award. It is bestowed on civilians and military, both national and foreigners, for extraordinary service to the nation in the field of international relations.

Instituted: By Decree No. 2,397 on August 16, 1954

Modified: By Decree No. 3,363 in 1980

Modified: By Decree No. 2,169 on July 9, 1986

Modified: By Decree No. 1,220 in 2001

Grand Master: President of the Republic

Grades: Collar, Grand Cross with gold star, Grand Cross,* Grand Officer, Commander, Officer,* Knight

Obverse: Gilt shield with arms of Colombia

Reverse inscription: Orden de San Carlos

Badge shape: Green enameled cross with lobed ends; Grand Cross: 2 silver 2-pointed

Co 34
Grand
Cross

Co 34
Officer

Co 34
Grand Cross badge (reverse)

rays in each angle; Officer: 3 gilt 2-pointed
  rays in each angle
Star shape: Badge with 3 silver 2-pointed rays
  in each angle
Size: Badge: Grand Cross: 50 mm; Officer: 40
  mm. Star: 70 mm
Metal: Grand Cross: silver; Officer: bronze
Maker: Medallas Colombianas Ltda., Bogotá
Ribbon: Green with two narrow yellow edge
  stripes
Reference: Burke's Peerage 2006, 1033–34;
  Werlich 1974, 97

*Co35. *La Orden del Mérito Industrial*

The Order of Industrial Merit is given to national and foreign individuals and to institutions that provide a meritorious service to the
nation's industry. The order may be bestowed
on foreign heads of state, heads of foreign missions, and cabinet ministers.

Co 34
Officer

Co 35
Grand Cross star (obverse)

Co 35
Officer

Co 35
Grand Cross star (reverse)

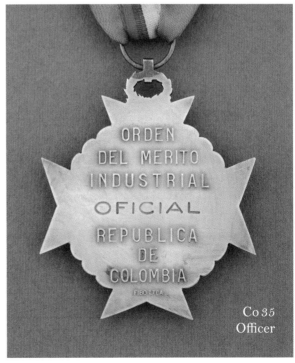

Co 35
Officer

Instituted: By Decree No. 2,898 in 1954

Modified: By Decree No, 1,190 in 1984

Modified: By Decree No. 572 in 1998

Substituted: By Decree No. 1,760 on August 23, 2012, rescinding Decree Nos. 2,898 in 1954, 1.190 in 1984, and 572 in 1998

Grades: Grand Cross,* Grand Officer, Officer,* Knight

Obverse disc: Shirtless worker holding hammer over image of city

Reverse inscription: ORDEN | DEL MERITO | INDUSTRIAL | [grade] | REPUBLICA | DE | COLOMBIA

Shape: Silver-edged light blue enameled Maltese cross with 2-pointed ends and a laurel wreath in the angles, suspended from a laurel wreath

Size: 53 mm

Metal: Silvered

Maker: Fibo, Bogotá

Ribbon: Blue with narrow yellow, blue, and red center stripes

Reference: http://www.wsp.presidencia .gov.co.Decreto_1760_del_23_de_agosto_ de_2012.pdf, accessed September 3, 2012

Provenance: A. Menke

Co36. *La Orden del Mérito Comercial*

The Order of Commercial Merit is awarded to individuals and institutions, both national and foreign, that provide meritorious service to the development of the national economy.

Instituted: By Decree No. 1,953 on August 14, 1979

Modified: By Decree No. 2,664 on October 26, 1984

Modified: By Decree No. 1,124 on May 30, 2012

Reference: http://www.mincomercio.gov.co/ decreto_2664_de_1984.pdf, accessed September 3, 2012

Co37. *La Orden Nacional al Mérito*

The National Order of Merit is a more recent order and is bestowed on national and foreign individuals and institutions rendering extraordinary services to the nation and for special acts of valor.

Instituted: By Decree No. 3,086 on November 6, 1981

Modified: By Decree No. 1,219 in 2001

Grand Master: President of the Republic

Grades: Extraordinary Grand Cross, Grand Officer, Silver Cross, Commander, Officer, Knight

Obverse disc: Female head, ¾ right

Obverse legend: REPUBLICA DE COLOMBIA | AL MERITO on a white enameled band

Shape: Gilt edged, red enameled cross pattée with a metallic wreath and 5 rays in each angle

Size: Silver Cross: 73 mm; Knight: 50 mm

Metal: Gilt and silver

Ribbon: Grand Cross: red with narrow white edge stripes; Officer, Knight: red

Reference: Burke's Peerage 2006, 1034–35

*Co38. *La Cruz de la Fuerza Aérea al Mérito Aeronáutico* (*Antonio Ricuarte*)

The Air Force Cross for Aviation Merit is awarded for courage and outstanding service to the Colombian air force. The portrait on the reverse is that of Antonio Ricuarte Lozano (1786–1814), who was a captain in Bolívar's army who acted heroically at the battle at the Hacienda of San Mateo (see Co26, above).

Instituted: By Decree No. 164 on January 31, 1983

Grades: 6

Obverse: Winged arms of the air force, within a circlet of laurel

Reverse disc: Bust of Antonio Ricuarte, left, on a blue enameled field

Co 38

Co 38

Shape: Cross terminated in stylized condor claws attached to a condor with displayed wings; lower arm of reverse inscribed F | A C

Size: 63 × 53 mm

Metal: Bronze, white metal

Maker: Metal Fischer, Bogotá; Huguenin, Le Locle, Switzerland

Ribbon: Grand Cross: blue with yellow, blue, red center stripes; other grades: sky blue with narrow yellow edge stripes

Reference: http://en.wikipedia.org/wiki/Colombian_military_decorations, accessed January 26, 2012

Co39. *La Orden del Congreso Nacional y Orden de la Democracía**

The Order of the National Congress and the Order of Democracy are awarded to national and foreign citizens for service in support of democracy and friendship among nations. The order is separated into two divisions: the Order of the National Congress and the Order of Democracy. The design of the two badges is identical, except for the inscription and the color of the ribbon.

C39a. *La Orden del Congreso Nacional**

Grades: Extraordinary Grand Cross, Grand Cross,* Grand Officer, Commander, Officer, Knight

Obverse disc: Image of the National Congress building

Obverse legend: ORDEN DEL CONGRESO DE COLOMBIA on a red enameled band

Shape: Red enameled Maltese cross with 2-pointed ends and a wreath in the angles

Star shape: Badge superimposed on an 8-pointed sun with 6 rays in the angles

Size: Badge: Grand Cross: 51 mm. Star: 80 mm

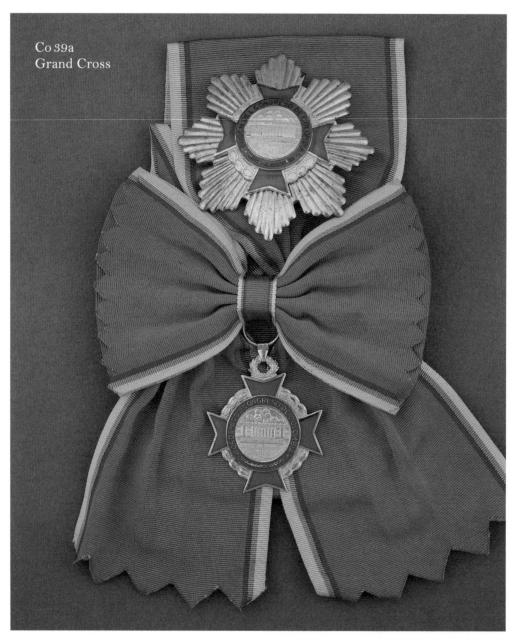

Co 39a
Grand Cross

Metal: Gilt silver

Maker: Metal Fischer, Bogotá

Ribbon: Orange with red, blue, yellow edge
stripes

Reference: http://en.wikipedia.org/wiki/
°Colombian_military_decorations,
accessed January 26, 2012

Provenance: A. Menke

*Co39b. *La Orden de la Democracía*

The same as the Order of the National Congress except:

Obverse legend: ORDEN DE LA DEMOCRACIA
on a red enameled band

Maker: B. H. Joyería

Ribbon: Wide yellow, blue, red

Provenance: A. Menke

Co 39b
Grand Cross

COSTA RICA

IN 1824, Costa Rica joined its neighbors in forming the Federal Republic of Central America after Mexico allowed the region to secede. Costa Rica tried to avoid involving itself in the emerging conflict between the region's conservatives and liberals. In 1839, the Federal Republic of Central America was dissolved, and Costa Rica became an independent republic. It held its first presidential elections in that year and chose Juan Mora Fernández as president. The country's highest order is named after him. Independence strengthened the country's resolve to stay out of Central America's continuing conflict between conservatives and liberals.

In 1846, an American filibuster, William Walker, landed in Nicaragua with his armed followers at the invitation of Nicaraguan liberals, who offered him concessions in exchange for defeating their conservative enemies in the city of Granada. Walker was later elected president of Nicaragua. Costa Ricans opposed Walker's interference in Central American affairs, organized an army, and defeated him on the battlefield. Costa Rica awarded a medal (probably two) to its troops, the first and only military medal for armed conflict in the country's history.

Costa Rica has generally enjoyed domestic peace and elected governments. In 1948, José Figueres Ferrer led a brief uprising after a disputed presidential election, which resulted in significant casualties. In 1953, a new constitution provided for universal suffrage and abolished the army. More recently, Costa Rica instituted an array of peacetime medals for loyalty, merit, and valor for its security forces, which protect the nation's borders, fight drug trafficking, and provide emergency assistance in natural disasters.

Costa Rica has an active Red Cross Society, which cooperates closely with government agencies to provide medical assistance and disaster relief, for which it awards its own medals.

MEDALS

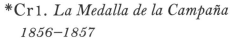

*Cr1. *La Medalla de la Campaña*
   1856–1857

The Medal for the 1856–1857 Campaign was awarded to the Costa Rican veterans of the war against the American filibuster William Walker during the 1895 inaugural ceremony of the monument to those killed in that war. In 1856, a Costa Rican army under the command of General José Joaquín Mora, brother of the country's president, attacked Walker's forces under Louis Schlessinger at Santa Rosa ranch on March 20. The Costa Ricans defeated the filibusters after suffering heavy casualties. The Costa Ricans pursued the surviving filibusters into Nicaragua, and the two sides fought a second battle at the strategic town of Rivas. The filibusters defended themselves inside the town, but were again defeated. Walker escaped from Rivas, but was pursued by forces from El Salvador and Honduras. He was deported to the United States, where he received a hero's welcome. He returned twice to Central America,

but was unable to reassert his authority. On his second trip, the British confined him to a warship and handed him over to the Hondurans, who executed him.

Costa Rica's successful military campaign against the filibusters produced its national heroes, including Juan Santamaría, a young volunteer, who was shot while torching a building defended by filibusters. A woman volunteer, Francisca Carrasco, grabbed a rifle and fought off a group of filibusters. She was reportedly given a medal for her heroism.

Obverse: Monument to those killed fighting
   William Walker

Obverse legend: MONUMENTO NACIONAL

Obverse inscription: 15 DE SET | 1895

Reverse inscription: A | LOS SOLDADOS | DE
   LA CAMPAÑAS | DE 1856 Y 1857 | LA
   PATRIA | RECONOCIDA

Size: 26 mm

Metal: Silver

Provenance: A. Menke

Cr 2

*Cr2. *La Cruz "Al Mérito Distinguido"*

Nothing is known about the events related to this medal or the intended recipients. Like Cr1, above, it may well also have been connected with the fight against William Walker in Nicaragua.

Obverse disc: COSTA | RICA

Obverse legend: AL MERITO DISTINGUIDO

Shape: Ball-tipped Maltese cross with 2-pointed ends suspended from a bar with laurel branches

Size: 36 mm

Metal: Gilt

Ribbon: Red

Provenance: A. Menke

Cr3. *La Medalla "Servicios Distinguidos"*

The Medal for Distinguished Services is awarded to Costa Rican and foreign nationals for their service of interest to Costa Rica.

Obverse: Arms of Costa Rica

Obverse inscription: AMERICA CENTRAL on ribbon above arms

Reverse: SERVICIOS DISTINGUIDOS

Ribbon: Blue, white, wide red, white, blue

Reference: Werlich 1974, 99

Cr4. *La Medalla de la Cruz Roja Costarricense*

The Red Cross Society of Costa Rica provides a range of humanitarian and disaster relief services throughout Costa Rica. It was founded in 1885 and belongs to the International Federation of the Red Cross and Red Crescent Societies. The Society operates an extensive ambulance service, which it manages by agreement with the government's social security agency and health services. The Costa Rican Red Cross Society has authorized at least one medal and an order that it awards to its members and non-members who provide meritorious service.

Instituted: By the Red Cross Society of Costa Rica

Obverse disc: A female standing, top, to the left of the altar of the Fatherland, against which she holds a laurel wreath. A tablet stands on the altar inscribed PRO PATRIA. At the top are clouds containing the faces of wounded and dead.

Obverse legend: CRUZ ROJA COSTARRICENSE | NEUTRALIDAD Y CARIDAD

Reverse: Cross inscribed 1933

Size: 38 mm

Metal: Gilt

Ribbon: White with a small red cross

Reference: Guille 1952, 5

* * *

IN 1949, Costa Rica abolished its military and replaced it with a Guardia Civil, which assumed responsibility for defending national sovereignty; mounting a defense against terrorism, narcotics trafficking, and criminal activity; and providing routine police services. In 1996, Costa Rica created the Ministry of Public Security, which assumed overall responsibility for policing and internal security. The ministry created the Fuerza Pública, which replaced the Civil Guard. In 2012, the ministry regulated three types of decorations for its uniformed officers: "For Service," "Wounded in the Line of Duty," and "For Valor." No details are currently available about these medals.

ORDERS

Costa Rica has instituted only one order for merit.

*Cr5. *La Orden Juan Mora Fernández*

The Order of Juan Mora Fernández is awarded to foreign nationals for distinguished service of interest to Costa Rica. It is most frequently given for diplomatic purposes or for reasons related to the country's foreign relations. It is named after Costa Rica's first head of state, who was also a political reformer. Recipients of the Grand Cross with golden star include Vicente Fox Quesada, president of Mexico; Fernando Henrique Cardoso, president of Brazil; and Lucio Gutiérrez Borbúa, president of Ecuador.

Instituted: By Decree No. 20,572 on July 11, 1991

President: President of the Republic

Grades: Grand Cross with gold star,* Grand Cross with silver star, Commander, Officer, Knight

Obverse disc: Bust of Fernández, ¾ left

Obverse legend: JUAN MORA FERNANDEZ on a blue enameled field

Reverse disc: Arms of Costa Rica

Reverse inscription: AL MERITO | REPUBLICA DE COSTA RICA

Shape: White enameled 5-armed star with 2-pointed ends and 7 faceted rays in each angle

Star shape: Same as badge, but 7 pointed rays in each angle

Cr 5
Grand Cross

Cr 5
Grand Cross
(reverses)

Cr 6
Grand Cross star

Size: Badge: 59 mm. Star: 95 mm

Metal: Gilt

Ribbon: Red with narrow white, blue, white
edge stripes

Reference: http://www.es.wikipedia.org/wiki/
Orden_Nacional_Juan_Mora_Fernandez,
accessed April 2, 2013

* * *

THE Red Cross Society of Costa Rica awards
its own order to members and nonmembers for
meritorious service to the Society.

*Cr6. La Orden de Honor y Mérito de la Cruz Roja Costarricense

The Costa Rican Order of Honor and Merit has
the same design as the Red Cross Orders for
Mexico and Cuba. They were all originally designed and made by Vilardebó y Riera, Havana.

Grades: Grand Cross (star),* Commander

Obverse disc: Enameled arms of Costa Rica

Obverse legend: ORDEN DE HONOR Y
MERITO | NEUTRALIDAD Y CARIDAD on a
white enameled band

Shape: Gilt-rimmed, red enameled cross with
5 rays in the angles superimposed on an
8-pointed faceted star with 5 rays in the angles, suspended from a green enameled laurel wreath

Size: Commander 62 mm. Grand Cross star:
85 mm

Metal: Gilt silver

Designer: Vilardebó y Riera, Havana

Maker: Vilardebó y Riera, Havana

Ribbon: Red, white, red with 2 white edge
stripes

CUBA

CUBA's independence dates back to May 20, 1902, some four years after the United States defeated Spanish forces on the island during the Spanish-American War. Although independent, Cuba had to accept several conditions imposed by the United States, particularly the Platt Amendment, which gave the United States the right to intervene militarily in the island.

Cubans opposed to Spanish rule first rose up in 1868. The struggle lasted for some ten years but was eventually suppressed by Spain. It resumed in 1895 when José Martí landed in Cuba with his supporters. Although Martí was killed shortly after the landing, his followers continued fighting until the Spanish-American War.

Cuba's medals following its independence were awarded to those who fought the Spanish both during the country's war of independence and those who cooperated with the Americans. Cuba instituted its first orders for its military just before the outbreak of World War I, the first awards not related to Cuba's struggle for independence. Shortly thereafter, the Cuban Red Cross instituted its own order for meritorious service. Cuba declared war on Germany during World War I, although the country's involvement did not extend beyond searching for German submarines off Cuba's shores.

In September 1933, the Cuban military orchestrated a coup d'état, which unilaterally abrogated the Platt Amendment. A year later, a Cuban sergeant, Fulgencio Batista, took control of the government and ruled Cuba until Fidel Castro overthrew him in January 1959. Batista created medals for the military who remained loyal to him throughout the 1933 military takeover. He also instituted a number of orders designed to promote the national economy.

During its first fifty years of independence, Cuba issued an array of civilian and military orders for merit, many of them attractively designed and made by a private Cuban firm, Antigua Vilardebó y Riera of Havana.

Cuba's history, international relations, internal politics, and its official awards all changed after Castro entered Havana on January 1, 1959, at the head of his rebel army. He nationalized businesses, farms, and homes in the name of his revolution. He arrested and executed political opponents, causing a mass exodus of Cubans in search of political asylum. His relations with the United States deteriorated, and President Eisenhower authorized the Central Intelligence Agency to fund an invasion of Cuba by Cuban exiles. On April 17, 1961, with President Kennedy now in office, Cuban exiles landed at the Bay of Pigs with the intent of promoting an internal rebellion against Castro. The Cuban military killed or captured all of the invaders within a few days. Castro then forged an alliance with the Soviet Union and authorized the stationing of Soviet ballistic missiles on Cuban soil. This led to the October 1962 Cuban missiles crisis. The United States forced the Soviet Union to remove its missiles from Cuba and promised never to invade the island. Castro undertook to arm, train, and support left-wing insurgencies throughout much of Latin America. The only successful insurgency were the Sandinistas in Nicaragua. Internally, Castro created a planned economy and introduced rationing of basic foodstuffs. He promoted literacy and medical care for the entire population. Politically, the Communist Party assumed sole control of the country, backed by a powerful security force that suppressed dissent.

Shortly after taking power, Castro abolished, rescinded, or simply stopped awarding the medals and orders he inherited from Batista. Instead, he gradually replaced them with his own medals and orders, which he used to promote his revolutionary goals. In 1978, Cuba issued a decree setting out the philosophy of an array of new revolutionary medals and orders. In 1979, the country instituted the new awards, complete with their individual decrees and regulations. All of them were designed to strengthen the armed forces, the security apparatus, and the sociopolitical goals of the revolution.

MEDALS

REBELLION AND INDEPENDENCE (1868–1913)

CUBA's insurrection against Spanish rule, known as the Ten Years' War, began in 1868. Carlos Manuel de Céspedes proclaimed his *Grito de Yara*, freed his slaves, and took up arms against Spain. This first insurrection ended with the surrender of the revolutionary army, but Spain suffered significant casualties. The second major uprising started in 1895 under José Martí and ended when Spain was defeated in the Spanish-American War.

*Cu 1. *La Estrella de Máximo Gómez*

The Star of Máximo Gómez is believed to have been awarded by Gómez to his officers during Cuba's War of Independence (1895–98). From its rudimentary construction, it is clear that the medal was made in a private metal workshop.

Máximo Gómez (1836–1905) became the military commander of Cuba's Ten Years' War against Spain (1868–78) for its independence. Faced with better armed Spanish forces, Gómez resorted to using guerrilla tactics. He led many "machete" charges against the Spanish lines.

Obverse: Bust of Gómez, ¾ left

Reverse: Arms of Cuba draped with
  flags

Shape: Disc suspended from star with disc
  enameled with flags and star

Size: Disc: 24 mm; star: 31 mm

Metal: White metal

Provenance: A. Menke

*Cu2. *La Cruz al Mérito Mambí*

The Cross for Merit Mambí was awarded to
Cuban nationalist combatants by the Association of Veterans, who fought the Spanish military during Cuba's War of Independence from
1895 to 1898. The cross was awarded from
1898 until 1917. When awarded to a woman,
the ribbon was changed to a bow.

*Cu2a. *Version 1*

Instituted: 1911

Obverse disc: Soldier holding a rifle on a
  white enameled field

Obverse legend: HONOR | PATRIA LIBERTAD
  on a blue enameled band

Shape: Ball-tipped, blue enamel–edged
  Maltese cross with 2-pointed ends and
  crossed swords in the angles, surmounted
  by fasces with helmet atop

Size: 44 × 35 mm

Metal: Gilt

Ribbon: Red, white, blue

Provenance: A. Menke

Cu2b. *Version 2*

Size: 26 × 23 mm

Metal: Silver

Cu3. *La Medalla de la Independencia*

It was not until 1913 that Cuba finally authorized medals for the officers and men who fought the Spanish during the four-year War of Independence. The Medal for Independence was awarded to all the men who joined the Liberation Army from the time of its foundation until February 24, 1898. The Communist government reaffirmed the validity of the medal in 1979, even though all of its recipients have died and the medal is no longer awarded.

> Instituted: By Presidential Decree No. 129 on June 12, 1913
>
> Modified: By Presidential Decree No. 502 on July 31, 1913, making civilians who served the cause of the revolution up until August 24, 1899, eligible to receive the medal
>
> Grades: Generals, chiefs, other officers, enlisted men
>
> Obverse: Head of Liberty, left
>
> Obverse legend: LA PATRIA A SUS LIBERTADORES
>
> Reverse disc: Arms of Cuba
>
> Reverse legend: GUERRA DE INDEPENDENCIA DE CUBA | 1895–1898
>
> Size: 35 mm
>
> Metal: Generals and chiefs: gilt; other officers: silver; enlisted men: bronze
>
> Ribbon: Cuban national flag; some have an enameled metallic ribbon
>
> Reference: Arista-Salado 2010–11, 1:269–70; Barac 2009, 324; Guille 1952, 7

*Cu4. *La Medalla de los Emigrantes Revolucionarios Cubanos*

The Medal of the Revolutionary Cuban Emigrés was awarded to Cubans living abroad who worked or fought for the country's independence. José Martí spent time in Florida organizing his return to Cuba. The Communist government of Cuba reaffirmed the validity of this

Cu 4

Cu 4

medal in 1979, even though its awardees have died and the medal is no longer being issued.

Instituted: By Presidential Decree No. 918 on October 10, 1913

Modified: By Presidential Decree No. 1,509 on September 20, 1929, which transferred the responsibility for accrediting the eligibility of candidates from the Association of Cuban Revolutionary Emigrés to the secretary of state (secretaría de gobernación)

Obverse: Bust of Martí, ¾ left

Obverse legend: EMIGRADOS REVOLUCIONARIOS CUBANOS

Obverse inscription: 1865–1895

Reverse disc: Arms of Cuba

Reverse legend: CUBA A SUS SERVIDORES | 10 OCTUBRE 1913

Shape: Triangle with rounded corners

Size: 40 × 37 mm

Metal: Gilt

Ribbon: Cuban national flag

Reference: Arista-Salado 2010–11, 1:270–72; Guille 1952, 7

Provenance: A. Menke

Cu5. *La Medalla de los Conspiradores por la Independencia*

The Medal of the Conspirators for Independence was awarded to persons who conspired against Spain between 1868 and 1895, prior to the Spanish-American War. Awardees could request a medal at their expense on the condition that they would receive the corresponding certificate from the Association of the Conspirators for Independence, a private organization.

Instituted: By Presidential Decree No. 670 on February 10, 1922

Obverse: Bust of Martí

Obverse legend CONSPIRADORES POR LA INDEPENDENCIA | 1865 1895

Reverse disc: Arms of Cuba

Reverse legend: MEDALLA DE HONOR

Shape: Oval

Size: 36 × 22 mm

Metal: Gold

Ribbon: Red, white, blue

Reference: Arista-Salado 2010–11, 1: 275–76

WORLD WAR I (1917–1919)

CUBA DECLARED WAR on the German Empire on April 7, 1917. Its role was limited to patrolling the waters around the island for German submarines. Cuba never sent ground forces to fight in Europe. Cuba authorized two medals for its military, including a Cuban version of the allied Victory Medal.

*Cu6. *La Medalla de Servicio por la Guerra 1917–1919*

The Medal for War Service 1917–1919 was awarded to Cuban navy personnel, who patrolled the local waters for German submarines.

Instituted: By Presidential Decree No. 1,359 on July 15, 1921

Obverse: Silhouette of a submarine with a rising sun in the background

Obverse inscription: 1917–1919

Reverse inscription: CAMPAÑA | POR | LA HUMANIDAD | LA JUSTICIA | Y EL | DERECHO above the arms of Cuba and surrounded by an oak and laurel wreath

Size: 30 mm

Cu 6

Cu 6

Metal: Bronze

Ribbon: Red, black with a narrow white center stripe

Reference: Arista-Salado 2010–11, 1:275; Barac 2009, 324

*Cu7. *La Medalla de la Victoria Aliada*

After the Allies agreed to issue a victory medal with a common shape and ribbon, Cuba redesigned its own World War I Victory Medal.

Instituted: By Presidential Decree No. 1,359 on July 21, 1921

Modified: By Presidential Decree No. 905 on June 10, 1922, which unified the ribbon and modified the design of the obverse and the reverse

Modified: By Presidential Decree No. 1,411 on September 29, 1922, which affirmed the validity of both versions of the same medal

Modified: By Presidential Decree No. 1,155 on August 27, 1924, making Cuban army personnel on active duty during World War I eligible to receive the medal

Modified: By Presidential Decree No. 75 on January 20, 1926, extending eligibility among the military

Obverse: Figure of Victory

Reverse: Arms of Cuba

Reverse legend: LA GRAN GUERRA POR LA CIVILIZACION

Reverse inscription: FRANCIA BELGICA | INGLATERRA ITALIA | ESTADOS SERVIA | UNIDOS MONTENEGRO | RUMANIA PORTUGAL | BRASIL JAPON | RUSIA CHINA | GRECIA

Size: 30 mm

Metal: Bronze

Ribbon: Rainbow colors

Reference: Arista-Salado 2010–11, 1:272–74; Guille 1952, 6; Barac 2009, 324

THE INTERWAR PERIOD

*Cu8. *La Medalla de las Campañas de la Marina de Guerra*

The Medal for Navy Campaigns was awarded to navy personnel engaged in military actions since 1902. Ribbon bars suggest that the medal was awarded for action during World War I and the coup d'état of September 4, 1933.

Instituted: By Presidential Decree No. 1,359 on July 15, 1921

Obverse: Star superimposed on an anchor

Obverse legend: MARINA DE GUERRA | SEMPER FIDELIS

Reverse: Cuban arms surrounded by an oak and laurel wreath

Size: 30 mm

Metal: Bronze

Maker: Chobillon, Paris

Ribbon: White with narrow blue edge stripes (bars: FEBRERO 1917, SEPTIEMBRE 1933, MARZO 1935)

Reference: Guille 1952, 6; Barac 2009, 326

*Cu9. *La Medalla de Marte (o Tiempo de Servicio)*

The Medal for Mars was awarded to army and navy officers for years of honorable service. It originally was given for five years of service, but in 1946 that requirement was reduced to two years. Recipients were given a gilt star to place on the ribbon for each additional five-year period of service. This medal often appears on bars also containing medals from the coup d'état of 1933 with a scroll inscribed LIBERTAD.

Instituted: By Presidential Decree No. 550 on
April 29, 1926

Modified: By Presidential Decree No. 1,106
on May 4, 1946, reducing the initial term of
service to 2 years

Modified: By Presidential Decree No. 4,219
on November 14, 1952, reversing Decree
1,106

Suspended: By Decree Law No. 13 of the
Council of Ministers on January 13, 1959

Obverse: Bust of the helmeted Roman god
Mars, left

Reverse: Arms of Cuba and inscribed PATRIA
HONOR DEBER

Size: 35 mm

Metal: Gilt (on bar of 3),* silver (on bar of
3),* bronze*

Ribbon: Red, white, blue

Reference: Arista-Salado 2010–11, 1:276–77

*Cu10. *La Medalla de los Veteranos de la
Guerra Hispano-Americana*

More than thirty years after the Spanish-
American War, it was deemed appropriate
to issue this medal for Cuban nationals who
fought with the American forces against Spain.
It became controversial, as many Cubans are
unhappy with the way the United States negotiated Cuba's independence.

Instituted: By Decree Law No. 867 on February 13, 1935

Modified: By Decree Law No. 2,486 on September 4, 1940

Obverse: Head of Liberty in Phrygian cap and
laurel wreath, left; star with rays

Obverse inscription: CUBA | A LOS |
VETERANOS | DE LA | GUERRA |
HISPANO- | AMERICANA

Cu 9, Cu 12, Cu 13
(obverses)

Cu 13, Cu 12, Cu 9
(reverses)

Cu 9, Cu 12, Cu 13
(obverses)

Cu 13, Cu 12, Cu 9
(reverses)

Reverse: Arms of Cuba, flanked by laurel branches

Reverse inscription: FIRST, | THAT THE | PEOPLE OF THE | ISLAND OF CUBA | ARE, AND OF | RIGHT OUGHT | TO BE FREE AND | INDEPENDENT | FROM THE JOINT | RESOLUTION OF | APRIL 20TH | 1898

Size: 36.5 mm

Metal: Silver

Maker: Vilardebó y Riera, Havana

Ribbon: Cuban national flag

Reference: Arista-Salado 2010–11, 2:281–83; Barac 2009, 324

THE COUP D'ETAT OF SEPTEMBER 4, 1933

ON SEPTEMBER 3, 1933, a protest by army NCO's over pay and other working conditions spun out of control. The mutineers formed the Provisional Revolutionary Government in alliance with dissident politicians and younger army officers. It unilaterally abrogated the Platt Amendment, gave women the right to vote, decreed an eight-hour workday and a minimum wage, and approved an agrarian reform. The next year, one of the insurgent NCO's, Fulgencio Batista, overthrew the government with support from the United States. Cuba went on to elect several provisional presidents, but Batista effectively ran the government as a dictator until he fled the country on January 1, 1959, when Fidel Castro's forces entered Havana.

*Cu11. *La Medalla de Servicios Distinguidos*

The Medal for Distinguished Services is believed to have been awarded to Cuban military who supported the 1933 coup d'état.

Obverse: Fasces surmounted by a Phrygian cap, flanked by oak and laurel branches

Obverse legend: HONOR DEBER VALOR

Reverse inscription: CUBA

Reverse legend: POR SERVICIOS DISTINGUIDOS A LA PATRIA

Size: 36 mm

Metal: Gilt bronze

Ribbon: Red, white, red, white, red

Reference: Barac 2009, 325

*Cu12. *La Medalla del 4 de Septiembre*

The Medal for September 4th was awarded to officers on active duty on September 4, 1933, who had supported the coup d'état. Eligibility

was extended to officers entering active service between September 4 and November 9, 1933, as well as to civilians who supported the coup and joined the Cuban armed forces after November 9, 1933. The diameter of the two medals may vary slightly according to the maker. The medal was abolished in 1944 following the election of Ramón Grau, but reinstated when Batista returned to power in 1952.

Regulated: By Presidential Decree No. 236 on January 12, 1937

Abolished: By Presidential Decree No. 4,262 on November 30, 1944, annulling Decree No. 236

Reinstated: By Presidential Decree No. 424 on March 10, 1952, annulling Decree No. 4,262

Suspended: By Decree Law No. 13 of the Council of Ministers of January 13, 1959

Obverse: Symbols of branches of the armed forces

Obverse legend: CUBA

Reverse inscription: 4 SEPT. | 1933

Size: 30, 35, 38 mm

Metal: Gilt (on bar of 3),* silver (on bar of 3),* bronze*

Ribbon: Blue, white, red, yellow, green. When awarded with other medals, the ribbons may be suspended from a wide clasp with the word "Libertad"

Reference: Arista-Salado 2010–11, 1:283–88; Barac 2009, 325

*Cu13. *La Medalla Conmemorativa del 4 de Septiembre*

The Commemorative Medal for September 4th was awarded to all members of the armed forces after completing one year of continuous service. The purpose of the medal was to remind new members of the armed forces of the significance of the 1933 coup d'état.

Instituted: By Presidential Decree No. 236 on January 12, 1937

Abolished: By Presidential Decree No. 4,262 on November 30, 1944

Reinstated: By Presidential Decree No. 424 on March 10, 1952

Suspended: By Decree Law No. 13 of the Council of Ministers on January 13, 1959

Obverse: 2 hands shaking. The left hand's sleeve is decorated with the chevrons of a first sergeant, the same rank as Batista, while the right sleeve is from a civilian suit, symbolizing the union of military and civilians who carried out the coup d'état. A semicircle above the hands displays the symbols of the branches of the armed forces. Oak and laurel branches below the hands flank a fasces

Obverse legend: 4 SEPT DE 1933 | PATRIA
ORDEN JUSTICIA

Reverse medallion: Star

Reverse legend: A LA PERPETUIDAD DEL
4 DE SEPTIEMBRE

Size: 35, 38 mm

Metal: Gilt (on bar of 3),* silver (on bar of
3),* bronze*

Ribbon: Equal blue, red, yellow, and green
stripes, and one wide central white stripe.
When awarded with other medals, the
medal may be hung from a wide suspension
bar with the inscription "POR LA LIBERTAD
DE CUBA"

Reference: Arista-Salado 2010–11, 1:285–88;
Barac 2009, 325

* * *

THE ONLY other medal issued by Batista before the second World War was for participa-

tion of Cuban individuals in the Spanish Civil
War.

***Cu14. *La Medalla del Combatiente
Internacionalista***

Cuba awarded a medal for Cuban volunteers
who fought on the Republican side in Spain's
civil war.

Obverse: Cuban flag superimposed on Spanish
flag atop an outline of a map of Spain

Obverse legend: POR VUESTRA LIBERTAD Y
LA NUESTRA

Reverse inscription: ESPAÑA | 1936 | 1939

Reverse legend: COMBATIENTE
INTERNACIONALISTA

Size: 33 mm

Metal: Bronze

Ribbon: Orange

World War II (1941–1945)

Cuba authorized one medal for Cuban nationals who served during World War II. Medals were awarded to those who joined the armed forces of one of the Allied nations, helped to organize civil defense, engaged in counterespionage, and worked on internal security.

*Cu15. *La Medalla de los Veteranos en la Segunda Guerra Mundial*

Instituted: By Presidential Decree No. 2,754 on August 19, 1948

Modified: By Presidential Decree No. 5,017 on November 21, 1949, which removed civilians from eligibility

Obverse: Soldier with a rifle and grenade surrounded by a laurel wreath

Obverse inscription: ABNEGACION | VALOR | HONOR

Reverse: Globe with western hemisphere

Reverse inscription: VETERANOS | DE LA | SEGUNDA | GUERRA MUNDIAL

Shape: Rectangle

Size: 36 × 29 mm

Metal: Bronze

Ribbon: Red, white, blue

Reference: Arista-Salado 2010–11, 1: 296–99

Provenance: A. Menke

POSTWAR MEDALS OF THE BATISTA REGIME

*Cu16. *La Medalla Oficial Conmemorativa del Primer Centenario de la Bandera de Cuba*

In an effort to consolidate his personal leadership through identification with patriotic symbols, Batista issued a medal to participants in the celebration of the centennial of the Cuban flag. The flag had been created in 1848 by General Narciso López in response to patriotic groups opposed to Spanish colonial rule; it has remained unchanged since then. The medal recognizes the taking of the town of Cárdenas on the north coast of Cuba by López during an unsuccessful attempt to mobilize the town's residents against Spanish rule.

Instituted: By Presidential Decree No. 4,248 on December 4, 1950

Obverse: Cuban flag

Obverse legend: MEDALLA CONMEMORATIVA

Obverse inscription: 1950 | AÑO | DEL CENTENARIO | DE LA BANDERA | DE CUBA

Reverse: Fort with flames to left

Reverse legend: TOMA DE CARDENAS POR NARCISO LOPEZ

Reverse inscription: 19 | DE MAYO DE | 1850

Size: 45 mm

Metal: Bronze

Ribbon: Red, white, blue

Reference: Arista-Salado 2010–11, 1:299

Cu 16

Cu 16

Cu 17

Cu 17

Cu 18

Cu 18

*Cu 17. *La Medalla del 10 de Marzo*

In 1944, Ramón Grau was elected president, and the country returned to constitutional rule. Batista carried out another coup d'état on March 10, 1952, and regained the presidency. As in 1933, he relied on the loyalty of the armed forces to consolidate his hold on power. He authorized a medal to reward those who remained loyal to him. The Medal for March 10th was awarded to all the members of the army, navy, and national police on active duty on March 10, 1952, who remained on active duty until December 3 of that same year (the date of the decree).

> Instituted: By Presidential Decree No. 4,440 on December 3, 1952
> Obverse disc: White enameled crescent on a blue enameled field
> Obverse legend: 10 DE MARZO DE 1952
> Reverse disc: Fasces on white enameled field

> Shape: Cross with ends in the shape of an anchor
> Size: 45 mm
> Metal: Bronze
> Ribbon: Yellow, white, blue, with shield enameled with arms of Cuba
> Reference: Arista-Salado 2010–11, 1:299–301
> Provenance: A. Menke

*Cu 18. *La Cruz "Maceo"*

The Maceo Cross was given to the soldiers who defended the Moncada Barracks from the attack launched by Fidel Castro on July 26, 1953. The defenders killed or captured all of the attackers. Castro was sent to prison, but later released under an amnesty. José Antonio de la Caridad Maceo y Grajales (1845–98) was second-in-command of Martí's Cuban Army of Independence. Maceo was influenced by the ideals of the French Revolution and became a

Freemason. Skilled in fighting a guerrilla war for many years against superior Spanish forces, he was finally killed in combat. Two monuments to his memory have been erected in Santiago and Havana.

> Instituted: By Presidential Decree No. 3,055 on November 23, 1953
>
> Obverse disc: Bust of Lt. General Antonio Maceo, ¾ left
>
> Obverse legend: VALOR EN ACCION

Reverse inscription: REGIMIENTO 1 | MACEO | CRUZ DE HONOR | 26-JUL-953

> Shape: Gild edged red enameled cross on a longer, narrower cross, with a gilt wreath in the angles
>
> Size: 45 mm
>
> Metal: Gilt
>
> Ribbon: Red edged in white with 2 black edge stripes
>
> Reference: Arista-Salado 2010–11, 2:274–77

MEDALS OF THE CUBAN RED CROSS

THE CUBAN RED CROSS SOCIETY was founded in 1909 and was accepted by the International Committee of the Red Cross in the same year. Cuba joined the International Federation of the Red Cross Societies in 1919. The Cuban Red Cross Society authorized at least three medals for merit.

Cu19. *La Medalla de Servicios Distinguidos de la Cruz Roja Cubana*

The Medal for Distinguished Service of the Cuban Red Cross was awarded to persons who distinguished themselves in carrying out the mission of the Cuban Red Cross. After the Cuban Revolution, the medal was officially annulled, in 1978.

> Instituted: By the Cuban Red Cross Society on April 29, 1953
>
> Sanctioned: By Presidential Decree No. 2,243 on August 10, 1953
>
> Annulled: By Decree Law No. 17 on June 28, 1978
>
> Obverse: Bust of Henri Dunant
>
> Obverse legend: CRUZ ROJA CUBANA | HENRI DUNANT 1864–1953
>
> Reverse: Cross
>
> Reverse legend: MEDALLA POR SERVICIOS DISTINGUIDOS A LA CRUZ ROJA CUBANA
>
> Size: 35 mm

> Metal: Gold, silver, bronze (according to the rank of the recipient)
>
> Ribbon: Red, white
>
> Reference: Arista-Salado 2010–11, 1:302, 2:273–74

*Cu20. *La Medalla al Mérito de la Cruz Roja Cubana*

> Obverse: Nurse attending a wounded soldier on a battlefield
>
> Obverse legend: CRUZ ROJA CUBANA | RECONOCIMIENTO AL MERITO on a white enameled band
>
> Size: 30 mm
>
> Metal: Gilt with red enamel; gilt with white enamel* (on ribbon bar with Cu21 and Cu60a); silver (on ribbon bar with Cu21 and Cu60a)
>
> Maker: Vilardebó y Riera, Havana
>
> Ribbon: White with 2 narrow red side stripes on each side; red with narrow white center stripe
>
> Provenance: A. Menke

*Cu21. *La Medalla por Tiempo de Servicio de la Cruz Roja Cubana*

The Cuban Red Cross Medal for Time of Service was awarded for years of loyal and honorable service.

Obverse: Red enameled Greek cross with a green enameled wreath in the angles

Obverse legend: CONSTANCIA HONOR ABNEGACION | 1909–1935

Reverse: Arms of Cuba

Metal: Gilt (on ribbon bar with Cu20 and Cu60a)

Ribbon: White with one enameled red cross for each 5-year period of service

Provenance: A. Menke

THE SOCIALIST REVOLUTION, 1959

ON JANUARY 1, 1959, Fidel Castro's rebel army entered Havana. Within two weeks of taking power, the new government had suspended medals associated with the Batista regime. The government did not annul them until 1978, when it laid out the basis for creating an array of new medals designed to reward individuals and organizations for supporting its revolutionary principles and for strengthening the socialist government and its armed forces.

In 1979, Cuba undertook a wholesale restructuring of its orders and medals. Today, Cuba awards a full array of meritorious medals covering every phase of the country's military, political, economic, cultural, and sports life. Most of the new medals are named after deceased cadre of the 26th of July Movement and leaders of Castro's rebel army. These medals generally emulate selected heroes of the revolution as well as recognize merit by the recipient per se. Every award conveys an ideological message to the awardee.

Cuba assisted revolutionary movements in Latin America, and some of its new medals are named after individuals like Ernesto "Che" Guevara, who supported these insurgencies. Cuba also sent thousands of troops, tanks, artillery, and aircraft to assist leftist governments in Angola and Ethiopia. Cuba issued medals to its expeditionary forces for both campaigns.

Unless otherwise indicated, all of the new medals described below were instituted by Decree Law No. 30 on December 10, 1979, and regulated on December 12, 1979; the reverse of the medal displays the arms of Cuba on the disc, while the legend is inscribed REPUBLICA DE CUBA | CONSEJO DEL ESTADO. Cuban ribbons follow the Soviet system of folding the ribbon into a pentagonal shape with a hard inner lining and a pin in the back. Most of the new medals are authorized by the Council of State.

*Cu22. *La Estrella de Oro*

The Gold Star is given only to those who have received the title of "Hero of the Cuban Republic." This is Cuba's highest award.

> Modified: By the Council of State on February 20, 2008
> Modified: By the Council of State on March 14, 2008
> Shape: Star
> Size: 30 mm
> Metal: Gilt
> Hanger: Enameled Cuban flag
> Reference: Arista-Salado 2010–11, 3: 183–85
> Provenance: A. Menke

*Cu23. *La Estrella de Oro del Trabajo*

The Gold Star for Labor is awarded to recipients of the order of "Hero of Labor of the Republic of Cuba." They all share the same rights and obligations. The medal is also the insignia that represents the order. This is Cuba's second-highest award.

> Regulated: By Decree Law No. 17 on June 28, 1978
> Obverse: Gear
> Shape: Star
> Size: 30 mm
> Metal: Gilt
> Hanger: Enameled Cuban flag
> Reference: Arista-Salado 2010–11, 3:185–87

Cu24. *La Medalla "Antonio Maceo"*

The Antonio Maceo Medal is given to members of the Fuerzas Armadas Revolucionarias (FAR) on active duty, in the reserves, or retired, and to the military of friendly nations, who fought for the defense, development, and consolidation of socialism in Cuba. The regulations specify a wide range of military achievements, such as shooting down an enemy plane or destroying two tanks. The regulations also detail how the recipient should behave politically after receiving the medal. It is named after Antonio Maceo Grajales (1845–96), who was at one time second-in-command of the Cuban Army of Liberation in the late nineteenth century.

> Regulated: By Decree Law No. 17 on June 28, 1978
> Obverse: Bust of Antonio Maceo
> Metal: Silvered
> Ribbon: Pentagonal; gold, light blue, red, white, red, light blue, gold of uneven widths
> Reference: Arista-Salado 2010–11, 3:187–90

Cu25. *La Medalla "Calixto García"*

The Calixto García Medal is awarded to members of the FAR on active duty, in the reserves, or retired, and to the military of friendly nations, who risk their lives to carry out their mission. The regulations specify a wide range of military accomplishments, such as destroying two artillery pieces, shooting down three helicopters, and so forth. Its regulations require the recipient to maintain a revolutionary attitude after receiving the award. The medal may be awarded posthumously.

The medal is named after General Calixto García e Iñiguez (1839–98), an early fighter for Cuba's independence. He rose quickly in the ranks and eventually succeeded Maceo as the second-in-command of the Cuban Army of Liberation. He assisted the U.S. Army when it landed near Santiago de Cuba during the Spanish-American War.

> Obverse: Bust of Calixto García
> Obverse legend: CALIXTO GARCIA
> Metal: Bronze
> Ribbon: Pentagonal; gold, red, gold, dark blue, gold of uneven widths
> Reference: Arista-Salado 2010–11, 3:190–94

Cu26. *La Medalla "Jesús Menéndez"*

The Jesús Menéndez Medal is awarded to Cuban and foreign nationals for their management, advice, and cooperation in building the labor movement in Cuba and in other countries. It is also awarded to worker collectives for achieving their production goals.

The medal is named after Jesús Menéndez Larrondo (1911–48), a union leader and politician belonging to the Popular Socialist Party. He strongly supported workers' rights and the Cuban sugar industry. He served in the House of Representatives and was killed by an army officer trying to arrest him.

> Obverse: Bust of Jesús Menéndez
> Metal: Gilt
> Ribbon: Pentagonal; red, light green, gold
> Reference: Arista-Salado 2010–11, 3:198–201

Cu27. *La Medalla "Combatiente de la Guerra de Liberación"*

The Combatant in the War of Liberation Medal was awarded to combatants in the Revolutionary Army during the War of National Liberation who subsequently remained faithful to its revolutionary principles. The medal was also given in special cases to other individuals, who provided exceptional assistance to the insurrection in keeping with its revolutionary principles.

Obverse: Figure of Fidel Castro with hills in the background (Sierra Maestra)

Size: 32 mm

Metal: Gilt

Ribbon: Pentagonal; wide olive green, narrow red, white, light blue

Reference: Arista-Salado 2010–11, 3:201–4

Cu28. *La Medalla "Combatiente de la Lucha Clandestina"*

The Combatant in the Clandestine War Medal was awarded to underground fighters during the War of National Liberation who have since then maintained an exemplary attitude based on revolutionary principles. The medal may be awarded posthumously.

The medal bears the image of Frank País Pesqueira (1934–57), a Cuban revolutionary opposed to Batista. País was an urban coordinator of the 26th of July Movement and key organizer of the underground movement. He was killed by police in Santiago.

Regulated: By Decree Law No. 17 on June 28, 1978

Modified: By the Council of State on November 24, 1981

Obverse: Image of Frank País with a police station in flames

Size: 32 mm

Metal: Gilt

Ribbon: Pentagonal; light blue, red, white, olive green, white of uneven widths

Reference: Arista-Salado 2010–11, 3:204–7

Cu29. *La Medalla "Abel Santamaría"*

The Abel Santamaría Medal is awarded to Cuban and foreign nationals for their creative work and contributions to artistic and literary culture and sports in the struggle to sustain the conquests of Cuban and international

youth and the international proletariat. It may also be given to individuals who have made exceptional contributions to the political education of youth.

Abel Santamaría Cuadrado (1927–53) early on shared opposition to Batista's coup d'état with Fidel Castro. They planned the July 26 attack on the Moncada Barracks together. After the battle, Santamaría was captured and tortured, but he never revealed any secrets before being killed. His sister Haydée shared his revolutionary spirit. An order was named after her (Cu53).

Obverse: Bust of Abel Santamaría, facing, within 2 laurel branches

Metal: Gilt

Ribbon: Pentagonal; red, narrow white, black

Reference: Arista-Salado 2010–11, 3:207–10

*Cu30. *La Medalla "Ciro Redondo"*

The Ciro Redondo Medal was awarded to fighters in the Revolutionary Army belonging to the Column 8 "Ciro Redondo," who participated in the invasion of the province of Las Villas from the Sierra Maestra in 1958, and who maintained their adherence to revolutionary principles. The medal may be awarded posthumously.

It was made by Cuba's best-known medal maker shortly before the firm was expropriated by the government.

The medal is named after Ciro Redondo (1931–57), a revolutionary in the wake of Batista's coup d'état in 1952. He joined Fidel Castro in attacking the Moncada Barracks on July 26. Redondo was captured and sent to prison but was released in a general amnesty. He was exiled to Mexico, where he rejoined Castro. He returned to Cuba on the yacht *Granma* and fought with the rebel army in the Sierra Maestra. He was captured again and killed while in captivity.

Cu 30

Instituted: 1959
Obverse: Bust of Ciro Redondo, facing
Obverse legend: COLUMNA 8 CIRO REDONDO | INVASOR
Shape: Round, suspended from a gilt broach
Size: 42 mm
Metal: Gilt
Maker: Vilardebó y Riera, Havana
Reference: Arista-Salado 2011, 3:213–16
Awarded to: Capt. Roger García S.
Provenance: A. Menke

Cu31. *La Medalla "Osvaldo Herrera"*

The Osvaldo Herrera Medal was awarded to members of the Revolutionary Army who participated in the invasion of Las Villas Province from the Sierra Maestra in 1958 and who have maintained their revolutionary principles since then. The medal may be awarded posthumously.

The medal is named after Osvaldo Herrera (1933–58), a young revolutionary, who joined the 26th of July Movement. He became a student activist at the University of Havana Law School, where he caught the attention of the police. He fled to the Sierra Maestra, where he joined Column 1, "José Martí," commanded by Fidel Castro. He was sent to organize students at Bayamo, but was arrested by the police. He committed suicide while in prison.

Obverse: Bust of Osvaldo Herrera, ¾ left
Obverse inscription: OSVALDO HERRERA
Metal: Washed gold
Ribbon: Pentagonal; blue, orange, olive green, and blue of uneven width
Reference: Arista-Salado 2010–11, 3:216–18

Cu32. *La Medalla "Eliseo Reyes"*

The Eliseo Reyes Medal is divided into two classes. The first class is awarded to members of the Ministry of the Interior and other individuals who demonstrate valor and initiative in carrying out their assigned missions in defense of the Cuban nation and maintaining socialist principles. The second class is awarded to the same group of recipients who carry out their assigned missions efficiently.

The medal is named after Eliseo Reyes Rodríguez (1940–67). He joined the July 26th Movement at the age of thirteen. Four years later, he became a messenger for Column 4 of the rebel army. He became a guerrilla fighter under Che Guevara. After the revolution, he ran the Ministry of the Interior's forces in Pinar del Rio against counterrevolutionaries. He was elected to the first Central Committee of the Cuban Communist Party. He accompanied Che Guevara to Bolivia, where he was killed in action.

Regulated: By Decree Law No. 108 on October 25, 1988

Classes: 1st, 2nd
Obverse: Bust of Eliseo Reyes
Metal: 1st: washed gold; 2nd: washed silver
Ribbon: Pentagonal; red, wide white, red
Reference: Arista-Salado 2010–11, 3:219–22

*Cu33. *La Medalla "Combatiente Internacionalista"*

The Medal of the International Fighter is awarded to Cuban military personnel on active service, in the reserves, or retired for assisting revolutionary movements in other countries.

Classes: 1st, 2nd*
Obverse: Map of the world with an enameled Cuban flag
Reverse: Arms of Cuba
Reverse legend: REPUBLICA DE CUBA | CONSEJO DE ESTADO

Size: 29 mm
Metal: 1st: gilt; 2nd: silvered*
Ribbon: Pentagonal: 1st: red with narrow blue, white, and red edge stripes; 2nd: red with narrow blue, white, red, white right edge stripes
Reference: Arista-Salado 2010–11, 3:222–25

*Cu34. *La Medalla "Trabajador Internacionalista"*

The Medal of the International Worker is awarded to Cuban workers who provide economic, health, or sport services to friendly nations, and to foreign workers who provide similar services in Cuba.

Obverse: Globe with red enameled flag
Obverse legend TRABAJADOR | INTERNACIONALISTA

Cu 34

Cu 34

Size: 30 mm

Metal: Silvered

Ribbon: Pentagonal; light blue, red, light
  blue, red, light blue

Reference: Arista-Salado 2010–11, 3:225–28

Provenance: A. Menke

*Cu35. *La Medalla "Fraternidad Combativa"*

The Combative Fraternity Medal is awarded
to Cuban and foreign nationals who have contributed to the development and consolidation
of the defense of socialism in Cuba.

Obverse: Bust of armed soldier with helmet,
  left, within olive branches

Size: 30 mm

Metal: Gilt

Cu 35

Ribbon: Pentagonal; red with narrow light
blue, white, green right edge stripes

Reference: Arista-Salado 2010–11, 3, 228–31

Cu36. *La Medalla por la Protección de las Frontieras*

The Medal for the Protection of the Frontiers is
awarded in two classes. The first class is given
to members of the Ministry of the Interior and
its collaborators who show extraordinary efficiency and sacrifice in defending Cuba's frontiers against infiltrators, illegal emigrants, and
border violations. The second class is given to
members of the Ministry of the Interior and
the militia who show vigilance and efficiency
in defending the nation's frontiers.

Regulated: By Decree Law No. 108 by the
Council of State on October 25, 1988

Classes: 1st, 2nd

Obverse: Border guard with AK 47, dog, and
a prickly pear plant, with the sea in the
background

Metal: 1st: washed gold; 2nd: washed silver

Ribbon: Pentagonal; light green, narrow red,
light green

Reference: Arista-Salado 2010–11, 3:231–35

Cu37. *La Medalla "Por la Seguridad del Orden Interior"*

The Medal for the Security of Internal Order
is awarded to members of the Ministry of the
Interior and its collaborators in assuring internal order and in fighting criminal activity.

Regulated: By Decree Law No. 108 by the
Council of State on October 25, 1988

Classes: 1st, 2nd

Obverse: Star within a pentagon and a laurel
branch in each point of the star

Metal: 1st: washed gold; 2nd: washed
silver

Ribbon: Pentagonal; olive green, white, beige,
white, olive green of uneven width

Reference: Arista-Salado 2010–11, 3:235–39

Cu38. *La Medalla por la Valentía durante el Servicio*

The Medal for Courage in the Line of Duty
is awarded to members of the Ministry of the
Interior and Cuban citizens who demonstrate
courage and initiative in saving lives and property during fires and natural catastrophes. The
medal comes in two classes. The first class is
awarded to recipients for courage and initiative.
The second class is given for effort in saving
lives and property.

Regulated: By Decree Law No. 108 of the
Council of State on October 25, 1988

Classes: 1st, 2nd

Obverse: Firefighter's helmet above 2 crossed
axes

Obverse legend: POR LA VALENTIA
DURANTE EL SERVICIO above 2 oak and
laurel branches

Ribbon: Pentagonal; red, white, dark blue,
white, red

Reference: Arista-Salado 2010–11, 3:239–42

Cu39. *La Medalla "Hazaña Laboral"*

The Medal for Labor Achievements is given
to Cuban citizens as well as Cuban and foreign worker cooperatives who maintain their
principles of the working class and contribute
significantly to the economic and social development of Cuba.

Obverse: Wheel with rounded projections
above an anvil and beneath the symbol of an
atom

Obverse legend: HAZAÑA LABORAL

Metal: Washed silver

Ribbon: Pentagonal; gold, narrow red, gold

Reference: Arista-Salado 2010–11, 3:243–46

*Cu40. *La Medalla por la Amistad*

The Medal for Friendship is awarded to foreign civilians who have provided service to Cuba in improving its international relations.

> Obverse: Star within rope
> Obverse inscription: AMISTAD
> Size: 30 mm
> Metal: Gilt
> Ribbon: Pentagonal; white with red edge stripe left and blue edge stripe right
> Reference: Arista-Salado 2010–11, 3:246–49

Cu41. *La Medalla "Romárico Cordero"*

The Romárico Cordero Medal is awarded to peasants in recognition of their active participation in increasing production and in the struggle to defend the conquests of the peasantry. The medal may also be given to Cuban and foreign leaders in building socialism.

The medal is named after Romárico Cordero Garcés (1899–1969), son of a poor peasant family, who spent his life defending the interests of poor peasants. He joined the opposition to the dictator Gerardo Machado. After his fall, Cordero helped organize peasant organizations. After the revolution, he helped peasants benefiting from the agrarian reform. He died a natural death at age seventy.

> Obverse: Bust of Romárico Cordero
> Obverse inscription: ROMARICO CORDERO
> Metal: Washed gold
> Ribbon: Pentagonal; red, white, wide light green, white, red
> Reference: Arista-Salado 2010–11, 3:249–52

Cu42. *La Medalla de la Cruz Roja Cubana*

The Medal of the Cuban Red Cross is awarded for heroic action at personal risk in assisting,

Cu 40

rescuing, or searching for someone in grave danger. Awardees are expected to follow revolutionary principles. The medal was created when Cuba reorganized its system of official awards and is not a continuation of the Red Cross medals existing at the time of the revolution. The new Red Cross Society operates as part of the International Federation of Red Cross Societies.

> Instituted: By Agreement with the Council of State on December 12, 1979
> Obverse: Bust of Commandant Manuel Fajardo on the left side and a Greek cross on the right side with a laurel wreath in a half circle
> Obverse inscription: CRUZ ROJA CUBANA
> Metal: Gilt
> Ribbon: Pentagonal; white, red, white, red, white of uneven width
> Reference: Arista-Salado 2010–11, 3:252–55

Cu43. *La Medalla Conmemorativa "Victoria de Playa Girón"*

The Commemorative Victory at the Bay of Pigs Medal was awarded to combatants who participated in the units that fought against the American-sponsored invasion in April 1961 and continued to follow revolutionary principles.

> Obverse: Image of tank
>
> Obverse inscription: GIRON
>
> Metal: Gilt
>
> Ribbon: Pentagonal; light blue, narrow white, red, green
>
> Reference: Arista-Salado 2010–11, 3:255–58

Cu44. *La Distinción del 28 de Septiembre*

The Distinction for September 28 is awarded to members of the Committee for the Defense of the Revolution (CDR), which was created on that date in 1960. Many Cubans belong to the CDR, which is a network of neighborhood committees patterned after a system pioneered by the Soviet Union. The main mission of the CDR is to report counterrevolutionary activities in each neighborhood to state security, although it also provides social services such as a blood bank, evacuation in times of weather emergencies, and organization of festivals.

> Obverse: Stylized image of man holding machete above a gilt Cuban flag, with the letters "CDR" placed below the tip of the machete
>
> Obverse legend: 28 DE SEPTIEMBRE
>
> Metal: Gilt
>
> Ribbon: Pentagonal; light blue with 2 narrow orange side stripes
>
> Reference: Arista-Salado 2010–11, 3: 282–85

MEDALS INSTITUTED AFTER 1979

Cu45. *La Medalla José Tey*

The José Tey Medal is awarded to educational workers in recognition of their active participation in the educational development of Cuba. It is also given to workers in political and social organizations who make an important contribution to education and building socialism.

The medal is named after José Tey Saint Blancard (1923–56) from Santiago, who became an early student activist against Batista. In 1955, he participated in an assault on a police station in El Caney led by Frank País. Tey organized the July 26th Movement in Santiago. He trained many of the fighters who supported Castro's landing from the yacht *Granma*. On November 30, 1956, he led a unit in an attack on Santiago, where he was killed in combat.

> Instituted: By Decree Law No. 53 on March 27, 1982
>
> Obverse: Bust of José Tey
>
> Obverse inscription: JOSE TEY
>
> Metal: Gilt
>
> Ribbon: Pentagonal; red, white, red, white, red
>
> Reference: Arista-Salado 2010–11, 3:261–64

*Cu46. *La Medalla Conmemorativa de la Alfabetización*

Cuba undertook a massive campaign to eliminate illiteracy on the island. Since then, most adult Cubans have learned how to read and write. The Commemorative Medal for Literacy was awarded to leaders and teachers of the Great National Literacy Campaign and

Cu 46

Cu 47

literacy efforts by the rebel army and subsequent literacy efforts after the revolution.

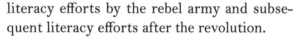

Instituted: By Decree Law No. 53 on March 27, 1982

Obverse: Lamp and open book

Obverse legend: alfabetización

Size: 30 mm

Metal: Gilt

Ribbon: Pentagonal; green, white, red, white, green

Reference: Arista-Salado 2010–11, 3:264–67

*Cu47. *La Distinción del "19 de Abril"*

The April 19th Distinction is awarded to members and former members of the intelligence and counterintelligence services, the Revolutionary National Police, and other organs of the Ministry of the Interior who plan, direct, or execute operations to detain potential

Cu 47

counterrevolutionaries. This includes personnel who provide outstanding service in interrogating, controlling, or identifying potential counterrevolutionaries. April 19 is the date that

Cuban militia and soldiers defeated the landing by Cuban exiles at Playa Girón (Bay of Pigs) in 1961. We would normally not include a distinction in our review, but decided it was important to show a medal for merit awarded to persons who arrest, interrogate, torture, and otherwise abuse persons suspected of opposing the Cuban Revolution.

Instituted: By Decree Law No. 53, on March 27, 1982

Obverse: Raised weapons surrounded by a band containing a laurel wreath

Obverse inscription: NUESTRA FUERZA | ES LA FUERZA | DEL PUEBLO

Reverse inscription: 19 | DE ABRIL

Reverse legend: MINISTERIO DEL INTERIOR

Size: 30 mm

Metal: Matte gilt

Ribbon: Pentagonal; green, red with a narrow white central stripe

Reference: Arista-Salado 2010–11, 3:388–90

Cu 49

Cu48. *La Medalla "Alejo Carpentier"*

The Alejo Carpentier Medal is awarded to Cubans for outstanding contribution to the creation, interpretation, promotion, and organization of Cuban art and culture. The medal may also be given to Cuban and foreign organizations for the same reason.

The medal is named after Alejo Carpentier y Valmont (1904–80), Cuba's most renowned novelist and intellectual. Born in Switzerland and raised in Havana and Paris, he studied architecture at the University of Havana and worked as a journalist. He became an avant-garde intellectual espousing leftist ideas, but also Afro-Cuban culture, surrealism, and Haitian history. He corresponded with the leading writers and artists of his time. He returned to Cuba after the revolution, becoming an editor at the State Publishing House. He died in Paris

Instituted: By Decree Law No. 59 on October 16, 1982

Obverse: Bust of Alejo Carpentier

Obverse inscription: ALEJO CARPENTIER

Metal: Gilt

Ribbon: Blue with one white side stripe on the left

Reference: Arista-Salado 2010–11, 3:267–70

*Cu49. *La Medalla "Lucha contra Bandidos"*

The Medal for the Struggle against Bandits is awarded to persons who aggressively hunt down the government's political opponents.

Instituted: By Decree Law No. 105 on July 13, 1988

Obverse: Militiaman carrying a Soviet-era tommy gun in the countryside

Size: 32 mm

Metal: Gilt

Ribbon: Pentagonal; red with light blue and green edge stripes on the right

Reference: Arista-Salado 2010–11, 3:282–85

Cu50. *La Medalla "Olo Pantoja"*

The Olo Pantoja Medal is awarded to members of the Ministry of the Interior on active service who have exhibited an exemplary attitude and effectively carried out their assignments, thereby assuring the security and internal order of the socialist state.

Orlando Pantoja Tamayo (1933–67), born of poor parents, became an early activist against Fulgencio Batista. He joined Fidel Castro in the Sierra Maestra. After the revolution, he became a captain in the border guards. In 1966, he joined Che Guevara in Bolivia. He was shot by Bolivian soldiers in Quebrada del Yuro along with Che Guevara in October 1967.

Instituted: By Decree Law No. 105 on July 13, 1988

Obverse: A militiaman carrying a submachine gun with mountains and palms in the background

Size: 32 mm

Metal: Gilt

Ribbon: Olive green, light blue, red stripes of uneven width

Reference: Arista-Salado 2010–11, 3:285–88

Cu51. *La Medalla "Antonio Briones Montoto"*

The Antonio Briones Montoto Medal is awarded to members of the Ministry of the Interior who carry out their assigned missions in an exemplary fashion and contribute to maintaining the security of the state and public order.

Antonio Briones Monototo (1939–67) was born in Havana. An early activist against Fulgencio Batista, he was in exile when Castro entered Havana. He became a First Lieutenant of the Ministry of the Interior's Special Forces. On May 8, 1967, he landed a group of nine Venezuelan revolutionaries on the Venezuelan coast. His boat overturned, and he sought refuge on shore. Venezuelan security forces captured him, and he died in captivity.

Reference: Arista-Salado 2010–11, 3:288–91

Cu52. *La Medalla "Combatiente de la Columna Uno José Martí"*

The "Combatant in Column One José Martí" Medal was awarded to all the members of Column One José Martí of the rebel army during the War of National Liberation. Column One was one of the units under the direct command of Fidel Castro.

Instituted: By Decree Law No. 109 on November 15, 1988

Obverse: Full-length image of José Martí in front of the Sierra Maestra

Metal: Gilt

Ribbon: Olive green, red, black, white, dark blue of uneven width

Reference: Arista-Salado 2010–11, 3:291–94

Cu53. *La Medalla "Haydée Santamaría"*

The Haydée Santamaría Medal is awarded for active participation in the cultural development of Latin America and the Caribbean and the cultural unity of the region.

Haydée Santamaría Cuadrado (1922–80) was a guerrilla fighter and political activist in Cuba. She and her brother Abel were captured after the failed assault on the Moncada Barracks on July 26, 1953. She survived captivity, but her brother was tortured and killed. A medal was created in her brother's name (Cu29). After the revolution, she helped found the Communist Party of Cuba and became a member of the Central Committee. She committed suicide in 1980 in Havana.

> Obverse: Bust of Santamaría above the inscription HAYDEE SANTAMARIA
>
> Metal: Gilt
>
> Ribbon: Pentagonal; black, light blue, red of uneven width
>
> Reference: Arista-Salado 2010–11, 3:294–97

Cu54. *La Medalla por la Defensa de la Patria y la Unidad del Barrio*

The Medal for the Defense of the Fatherland and the Unity of the Neighborhood is awarded to Cuban and foreign nationals for demonstrating valor and sacrifice in defense of the socialist revolution, to face and systematically counter antisocial and counterrevolutionary manifestations.

> Obverse: Group of houses and buildings and a representation of Revolutionary Square. Above one of the buildings is the emblem of the Committee for the Defense of the Revolution
>
> Obverse legend: POR LA DEFENSA DE LA PATRIA | Y LA UNIDAD DEL BARRIO
>
> Metal: Gilt
>
> Ribbon: Pentagonal blue, olive green white, olive green, red of uneven width
>
> Reference: Arista-Salado, 2011, 3:309–12

CUBA'S EXPEDITIONARY FORCES IN AFRICA

CUBA FOUGHT in two major conflicts in Angola and Ethiopia from 1975 to 1991. After achieving independence from colonial rule, several African countries were taken over by Marxist movements. These governments were threatened by internal and external enemies. Castro believed he had an obligation to help these regimes militarily. The Soviet Union offered some assistance, but the Cubans mainly operated independently. All of their troops were volunteers. Cuba is believed to have lost more than two thousand of its troops in combat during the sixteen years its forces were stationed in Africa. This is the only time that a Latin American nation has sent its armed forces to another continent to support an ideologically friendly nation.

In 1975, as Angola was about to declare independence, a civil war was raging among three competing groups. The capital, Luanda, was held by the MPLA, a Marxist group supported by the Soviet Union. The other two groups were supported by South Africa and Zaire, respectively. The MPLA asked Cuba for assistance, and Castro sent some thirty thousand men with armor and jet fighters. In part because of this Cuban help, the Zairean and South African troops eventually withdrew. The civil war continued, but the Cubans stayed out of the fighting. In 1988, the Angolan government undertook a major offensive against the other two groups, with Soviet assistance. The offensive failed, and the government forces retreated to Cuito Cuanavale in southern Angola. The government again asked for Cuban help. Cuban soldiers reinforced Cuito Cuanavale and eventually fended off the attacks by South Africa. Cuba withdrew its forces from Angola in 1991 in accordance with an international agreement providing for the mutual withdrawal of Cuban and South African forces from southwest Africa.

Cu55. *La Medalla por la Defensa de Cuito Cuanavale*

The Medal for the Defense of Cuito Cuanavale was awarded to Cuban military in active service, in the reserves, or retired who participated in the defense of Cuito Cuanavale against South African troops and UNITA rebels in Angola in 1988. The medal was also awarded to the military of Angola and allied nations who fought in that battle. The Cubans enabled the Angolans to hold on to Cuito Cuanavale, which led to a stalemate in the fighting and eventually to a negotiated settlement whereby both Cuba and South Africa withdrew their forces from Angola.

Cu 56

> Instituted: By Decree Law No. 103 on March 21, 1988
>
> Obverse: A map in bas-relief of Angola with a star indicating the location of Cuito Cuanavale
>
> Obverse legend: A LOS HEROICOS DEFENSORES DE CUITO CUANAVALE above a laurel branch
>
> Metal: Gilt
>
> Ribbon: Pentagonal; black, red, white, dark blue, white, red, black of uneven width
>
> Reference: Arista-Salado 2010–11, 3:273–76

*Cu56. *La Medalla "Por la Victoria Cuba-RPA"*

The Medal for the Cuba-RPA Victory was awarded to members of a Cuban expeditionary force sent to defend the People's Republic of Angola from its internal and external enemies.

> Instituted: By Decree Law No. 111 on March 20, 1998
>
> Obverse: Star beneath the flags of Cuba and Angola within olive branches
>
> Obverse inscription: POR LA VICTORIA | CUBA RPA
>
> Size: 32 mm
>
> Metal: Gilt
>
> Ribbon: Blue, white, blue, red, yellow, black
>
> Reference: Arista-Salado 2010–11, 3: 297–300

Cu 57

* * *

SOMALIA and Ethiopia were fighting a war over the Ogaden region in eastern Ethiopia. In November 1977, Somali forces were advancing into the Ogaden. The Soviet Union had recently switched sides and was supporting the Marxist government of Ethiopia. The Soviet air force began airlifting Cuban troops, some of them from Angola, to Ethiopia. By early 1978, some seventeen thousand Cuban troops in Ethiopia were fighting the Somalis in the Ogaden. By March of that year, Somalia withdrew its forces from the Ogaden. Cuban troops remained in Ethiopia for a few years but did not engage in further combat. They withdrew in 1989.

*Cu57. *La Medalla "Por la Victoria Cuba-Etiopía"*

The Cuba-Ethiopia Victory Medal was awarded to the members of a Cuban expeditionary force sent to defend the Marxist government of Ethiopia from its internal and external enemies.

Instituted: By Decree Law No. 116 on August 25, 1989

Obverse: Star above a rendering of Cuba and Ethiopia

Obverse legend POR LA VICTORIA | CUBA-ETIOPIA | 1978 1989

Size: 32 mm

Metal: Gilt

Ribbon: Pentagonal; red, white, black, red, yellow, and green

Reference: Arista-Salado 2010–11, 3:300–303

ORDERS

CUBA INSTITUTED its first orders for military merit in 1912. Shortly thereafter, it authorized a Red Cross order, followed a dozen years later by an order to promote peaceful international relations. Additional orders were instituted much later, mainly to recognize economic and cultural service to the nation.

The socialist government of Cuba significantly modified or abolished the old orders in 1979. All of the modifications as well as the creation of new orders were made in support of the political priorities of the socialist government. Loyalty to the Cuban Communist Party, and particularly continuous support of its revolutionary ideals, have been required of recipients of the new orders since 1979.

*Cu58. *La Orden del Mérito Militar* (*1912–1959*)

The Order of Military Merit was awarded for acts of heroism, capturing a wanted criminal, assistance during a natural emergency, lifesaving, and activities of importance to the armed forces. The order was also awarded for years of service. Officers qualified after twenty-five years whereas enlisted men could receive the order after sixteen years of continuous service and good conduct. Recipients of the order stood to receive a monthly cash bonus: general officers, 15 pesos; chiefs, 10 pesos; other officers, 5 pesos; and enlisted men, 2 pesos. Members of the order were encouraged to put the initials "MM" after their names when signing official documents. The order was suspended in early 1959 and abolished in 1978. The insignia for Grades I and II is a star; for III and IV, a badge. Grade III has apparently been issued with variants that changed the enameling on the arms of the cross and the wreath in the suspension. Initially the obverse and reverse arms were enameled. Some time after Batista came to power in 1933 all of the enamel was eliminated except for the obverse disc. We have not found a decree that prescribed this change.

Instituted: By Presidential Decree No. 196 on February 27, 1912, which also abolished the Certificate of Merit of the Rural Guard created in 1901 during the American occupation

Modified: By Presidential Decree No. 1,727 on November 2, 1917, which changed the requirements on the number of years of service for receiving the order

Modified: By Presidential Decree No. 99 on January 23, 1918, which added a blue distinction

Modified: By Presidential Decree No. 948 on July 21, 1924, which added 2 new distinctions: green and red|white

Modified: By Presidential Decree No. 3,842 on September 4, 1951, which created a new purple distinction

Suspended: By Decree Law No. 13 of the Council of Ministers on January 13, 1959

Rescinded: By Decree Law No. 17 on June 28, 1978

Grades: I: generals; II: senior officers;* III: other officers;* IV: enlisted men*

Obverse disc: MM intertwined: I, II on a blue enameled field; III on a black enameled field; III variant on a field enameled the color of the distinction

Obverse legend: HONOR VIRTUD VALOR: I, II III, on a metallic band; III variant on a band enameled with the color of the distinction

Reverse disc: Arms of Cuba (III: enameled)

Shape: I, II: ball-tipped Maltese cross with 2-pointed ends enameled with the color of the distinction with a laurel wreath in the angles, superimposed on a faceted 8-pointed star with 6 rays in each angle ; III: ball-tipped Maltese cross with 2-pointed ends and a laurel wreath in the angles, suspended from a laurel wreath, the disc enameled black and the arms of the cross and the laurel wreath in the suspension enameled with the color of the distinction [variant: only the disc is enameled in the color of the distinction]; IV: ball-tipped Maltese cross with a laurel wreath in the angles, suspended from a laurel wreath

Size: I: 90 mm; III: 56, 58 mm; III variant: 49, 51 mm; IV: 57 mm.

Metal: I: gilt; II: silver: III: gilt, silver: IV: bronze

Cu 58 Grade II

Cu 58
Grade III
(obverse)

Cu 58
Grade III
(obverse)

Cu 58
Grade III
(reverse)

Cu 58
Grade III
(reverse)

Cu 58
Grade IV

Cu 58
Grade IV

Cu 58 Grade III variant (obverse)

Cu 58 Grade III variant (reverse)

Ribbon: This order has an elaborate coloring system. The enamel and the ribbon are matched in the same color in each medal. Each color combination represents its own distinctive merit:

Blue: good conduct*

Blue and white: conspicuous service

Red: military merit*

Red and white: humanitarian acts

Green: special services*

White: other services*

Purple: bravery in combat

Reference: Arista-Salado 2010–11, 1:151–61; Barac 2009, 326–27

Provenance: II: A. Menke

*Cu59: *La Orden del Mérito Naval* (*1912–1959*)

The Order of Naval Merit was designed and structured in the same way as the Order of Military Merit. It was awarded for heroism, lifesaving at personal risk, assistance during a natural disaster, and extraordinary service to the navy. The order was divided into four grades; the use of color distinctions was similar to the army version, as were the monthly bonuses. Many modifications over the years were introduced into the administration of the order, including the number of years of service necessary to qualify. Members of the order were encouraged to add the initials "MN" after their names when signing official documents. The order was never awarded after the Cuban Revolution. It was suspended in 1959 and rescinded in 1978. Some known pieces are identified as Type I (Barac 2009, 328), but these follow a Spanish type rather than that prescribed in the decrees. The insignia for Grades I and II is a star; for III and IV, a badge.

Instituted: By Presidential Decree No. 1,126 on December 30, 1912

Regulated: By Presidential Decree No. 1,219 on June 30, 1921

Rescinded: By Decree Law No. 17 on June 28, 1978

Grades: I: admirals;* II: senior officers;* III: other officers;* IV: enlisted men*

Obverse disc: MN intertwined; I, II, III on an enameled field that matches the color of the distinction

Obverse legend: HONOR VIRTUD VALOR; II: on an enameled band matching the anchor

Star shape: I, II: enameled anchor (of varying color) superimposed on an enameled Maltese cross of color varying with the distinction, surrounded by a green-enameled laurel wreath on a faceted 8-pointed star with 4 rays in each angle

Badge shape: III: enameled anchor (blue for peacetime, red for wartime) superimposed on an enameled Maltese cross surrounded by a green enameled laurel wreath; IV: the same, but not enameled

Size: Badge: III: 49 mm; IV: 38 mm. Star: II: 85 mm

Metal: I: gilt; II: silver; III: gilt; IV: gilt, bronze

Maker: I: Vilardebó y Riera, Havana; III: Dator Plus Ultra; IV: gilt: Dator Plus Ultra; bronze: Vilardebó y Riera

Ribbon: According to distinction:

Dark blue: naval merit

Blue: good conduct

Blue and white: conspicuous service

Red and white: humanitarian acts

Green: special services

White: other services

Reference: Arista-Salado 2010–11, 1:162–70; Barac 2009, 328–29

Provenance: II: good conduct; III: good conduct, peacetime and wartime: A. Menke

Cu 59 Grade I star

Cu 59
Grade III badges

Cu 59 Grade II stars

Cu 59 Grade IV badges

*Cu60. *La Orden de Honor y Mérito de la Cruz Roja Cubana (1913–1978)*

The Cuban National Society of the Red Cross was approved by Presidential Decree No. 401 on May 14, 1909. The Cuban Red Cross Society was created as an entity belonging to the Cuban state, but enjoying administrative autonomy. The Society was given the right to distribute its awards. Decree No. 401 stated that the Society could issue awards of two types: Thanks (*Gracias*) and Rewards (*Recompensas*). Rewards provides for the awarding of decorations for merit.

The Order of Honor and Merit of the National Red Cross was approved in 1913. The Society awarded the order according to the importance of the merit and the rank of the recipient. This order was Cuba's most important official award until the creation of the Order of

Carlos Manuel de Céspedes in 1926. The order was abolished in 1978. The Socialist Republic of Cuba replaced this order with a new Cuban Red Cross Medal.

Instituted: By Presidential Decree No. 72 on January 31, 1913

Modified: By Presidential Decree No. 613 on March 30, 1954, which put the order under the supervision of the Ministry of National Defense, but apparently the decree was never carried out

Rescinded: By Decree Law No. 17 on June 28, 1978

Grades: I: Grand Cross;* II: Commander; III: Officer;* IV: Knight; V: Member

Obverse disc: Enameled arms of Cuba

Obverse legend: INTER INIMICOS CHARITAS [Grand Cross: INTER ARMA CHARITAS] on a white enameled band

Cu 60
Grand Cross
badge (reverse)

Reverse disc: Stylized 1909 on a blue enameled field

Reverse legend: ORDEN DE HONOR Y MERITO on a white enameled band

Shape: Grand Cross: red enameled cross with a star in each angle, suspended from a green enameled laurel wreath; Grand Officer: red enameled cross with a star in each angle superimposed on an 8-pointed star with 4 rays in each angle, suspended from a green enameled laurel wreath; Officer: red enameled cross with a star in each angle, suspended from a green enameled laurel wreath; Knight: cross suspended from a laurel wreath

Star legend: INTER INIMICOS CHARITAS ORDEN DE HONOR Y MERITO 1909

Star shape: Badge superimposed on an 8-pointed faceted star with 5 rays in each angle

Cu 60
Officer

Cu 60
Officer

Size: Badge: Grand Cross, Officer, Knight: 40 mm; Grand Officer: 48 mm. Star: Grand Cross: 90 mm; Grand Officer: 84 mm

Metal: Badge: Grand Cross: silver; Grand Officer, Officer: bronze. Star: Grand Cross: gilt silver; Grand Officer: brass

Maker: Grand Cross: Boulanger, Paris; Grand Officer: Gumersindo Suares, Havana

Ribbon: White, red, white with narrow red edge stripes. The sash for women recipients is narrower than that for men

Recipient: Grand Cross: José María Dominguez de Murta, 1910

Reference: Arista-Salado 2010–11, 1:171–76; Barac 2009, 329–30

*Cu60a. *Variant version (on ribbon bar with Cu20 and Cu21)*

Obverse: Enameled arms of Cuba with red cross at center

Obverse inscription: INTER INIMICOS CHARITAS on a blue enameled ribbon

Reverse legend: [Hand engraved]: SOCIEDAD NACIONAL CUBANA

Reverse inscription: [Hand engraved]: DE LA | CRUZ ROJA | HABANA | 1909

Size: 31 mm

Metal: Brass

Maker: Antigua Vilardebó y Riera

Ribbon: White, red, white with narrow red edge stripes, rosette

*Cu61. *La Orden Nacional de Mérito "Carlos Manuel de Céspedes"*

The Order of Carlos Manuel de Céspedes is bestowed on national and foreign citizens for merit or service to the Republic of Cuba. It was originally intended for diplomats and consular officials, special envoys, delegates to international conferences, officials of the Ministry of Foreign Affairs, and military personnel. It could also be awarded to persons for more general purposes such as defending the country's independence or promoting its national interests. Over time, the government tended to award the order for the general purpose of recognizing individual merit for promoting the country's interests and welfare. It was Cuba's highest award until the socialist revolution.

The Order is named after Carlos Manuel de Céspedes (1819–74), a revolutionary hero in the War of Independence. Cuba's struggle for independence dates back to October 10, 1868, when Céspedes, a plantation owner in the eastern part of Cuba, publicly demanded the country's independence from Spain, a call since known as the *Grito de Yara.* Céspedes was one of the first landowners to free his slaves, and he urged others to do the same. After organizing and leading a guerrilla campaign against royalist forces, he was eventually captured and executed by the Spaniards.

Instituted: By Presidential Decree No. 486 on April 18, 1926

Modified: By Presidential Decree No. 334 on February 20, 1934, changing the dates on which the order could be awarded

Regulated: By Presidential Decree No. 511 on February 15, 1943, which abolished Decrees No. 486 and 511, created the order's National Council, and specified how the order should be awarded by rank

Regulated: By Resolution of the Minister of State on March 31, 1943, detailing the organization and procedures of the National Council of the order.

Modified: By Presidential Decree No. 2,867 on October 1, 1943, allowing women, private corporations, and institutions to receive the order.

Modified: By Presidential Decree No. 3,329

Cu61a
Grand Cross star

on October 7, 1948, modifying procedures for selecting members of the order's council

Modified: By Presidential Decree No. 2,098 on October 7, 1959, rescinding all awards of the order between March 10, 1952 (when Batista returned to power) and December 31, 1958 (when Castro entered Havana)

Modified: By Decree Law No. 30 on December 12, 1979, nullified all previous regulations and changed the purpose of the order. To be eligible to receive the order, a candidate had to demonstrate support for the Cuban Revolution, the struggle for economic and social progress of the people, and for peaceful coexistence

Supreme Chief: President of the Republic; since 1979: Council of State

Cu61a
Grand Cross badge (obverse)

Cu61a
Grand Cross badge (reverse)

Cu61a
Officer

Cu61a
Officer

*Cu61a. *Version 1: pre-1979*

Grades: Grand Cross,* Grand Officer, Commander, Officer,* and Knight

Obverse disc: Bust of Céspedes, facing

Obverse legend: CARLOS MANUEL DE CESPEDES | 1868 on blue enameled band

Reverse disc: Enameled arms of Cuba

Shape: Round, surrounded by a green enameled bound laurel wreath, surrounded by 10 acanthus leaves on a blue enameled band, surrounded by a green enameled wreath (laurel only on the Grand Cross, laurel and oak on the Officer)

Star shape: 10-pointed star with faceting on alternate points, with 7 rays in each angle, superimposed on a blue enameled round disc on which are placed 10 acanthus leaves, all surrounded by a green enameled laurel wreath

Size: Badge: Grand Cross: 62 × 51 mm; Officer: 45 mm. Star: 86 mm

Metal: Badge: Grand Cross: silver; Officer: bronze. Star: brass

Maker: Grand Cross: Antigua Vilardebó y Riera, Havana; Officer: A. Chebillon, Paris

Ribbon: Blue with 5 equal blue and white stripes on the bow

*Cu61b. *Post-1979*

Obverse disc: Bust of Céspedes, facing

Obverse legend: CARLOS MANUEL DE CESPEDES | 1868 on a blue enameled band

Cu 61b

Cu 61b

Reverse disc: Arms of Cuba

Reverse legend: REPUBLICA DE CUBA | CONSEJO DEL ESTADO

Shape: White enameled star with rays in angle on a red enameled star

Metal: Gilt

Ribbon: Pentagonal: blue with narrow red, white, blue side stripes to right

Reference: Arista-Salado 2010–11, 1:177–90, 2:247–48, 3:109–11; Barac 2009, 330–31

Provenance: A Menke

*Cu62. *La Orden Nacional de Mérito "Carlos J. Finlay"*

The Order of Merit "Carlos J. Finlay" is bestowed on Cuban and foreign citizens who have made major contributions to medicine and the natural and social sciences. The order may be given to institutions and groups of people. This ministerial order is named after Carlos Juan Finlay (1833–1915), a Cuban physician and scientist. He is best known for his research on yellow fever and for showing that the mosquito was the vector transmitting the disease. The order became Cuba's second-highest order after that of Carlos Manuel de Céspedes. Its design and statutes were significantly modified in 1979.

Instituted: By Presidential Decree No. 77 on January 21, 1928

Regulated: By Presidential Decree No. 2,015 on November 30, 1928

Modified: By Presidential Decree No. 2,999 on November 25, 1939, which approved the statutes of the order and gave more importance to recognizing scientific research

Modified: By Decree No. 30 on December 10, 1979, which changed the statutes of the order, eliminated the order's National Council, and made the Council of State the head of the order

Chief: President of the Republic (until 1979), Council of State (after 1979)

Cu62a. *1928–1979*

Grades: Grand Cross (star),* Grand Officer, Commander, Officer, Knight,* and Member

Obverse disc: Head of Finlay, left; Grand Cross: on a light blue enameled field

Obverse legend: ORDEN CARLOS J. FINLAY | 1928 on a blue enameled band

Reverse disc: Enameled arms of Cuba on a white enameled field

Reverse legend: POR LA SALUD Y LA BENEFICENCIA PUBLICA on a light blue enameled band

Shape: Ball-tipped star with 3-pointed ends, enameled yellow for the outer points and a laurel wreath between the arms

Star shape: Badge on star with 5 rays in each angle

Size: Badge: Knight: 39 mm. Star: Grand Cross: 83 mm

Metal: Brass

Ribbon: Yellow

Cu62a
Grand Cross star

Cu 62a
Knight

Cu 62b

Cu 62a
Knight

Cu 62b

*Cu62b. *After 1979*

Obverse disc: Bust of Finlay, facing ¾ left, on an oval disc

Obverse legend: CARLOS J. FINLAY on a white enameled band

Reverse disc: Arms of Cuba

Reverse legend: REPUBLICA DE CUBA | CONSEJO DE ESTADO

Shape: Oval with 3 rays at top and 8 protruding balls

Size: 49 × 36 mm

Metal: Gilt

Ribbon: Pentagonal; blue with 2 yellow side and 2 yellow edge stripes

Reference: Arista-Salado 2010–11, 1:191–200, 3:156–59; Guille 1952, 7; Barac 2009, 331

*Cu63. *Orden del Mérito Policíaco* (*1936–1979*)

The Order of Police Merit was given to members of the National Police for meritorious service, bravery, and humanitarian acts. The exact nature of the merit was reflected in the color of the enamel and the ribbon, in much the same way as for the Order of Military Merit (see Cu58). Recipients of the purple grade for years of service could receive a monthly cash payment for life, depending on the grade awarded. The order was abolished in 1979. The insignia for Grades I and II is a star; for III and IV, a badge.

Instituted: By Presidential Decree No. 1,283 on May 7, 1936

Modified: By Presidential Decree No. 1,763 on June 7, 1952, adding the distinction color purple

Rescinded: By Decree Law No. 17 on June 28, 1978

Grades: I: chiefs; II: senior officers;* III: other officers;* IV: patrolmen*

Cu63
Grade III

Cu63 Grade II

Cu63
Grade III

Obverse disc: MP on a blue enameled field

Obverse legend: HONOR DEBER VALOR on a white enameled band

Reverse disc: Enameled arms of Cuba surrounded by a white enameled band

Shape: I, II: Maltese cross with 3-pointed ends with laurel sprigs between the points and three 2-pointed rays in each angle, on an 8-pointed faceted star with 5 rays in each angle; III, IV: Maltese cross with 3-pointed ends with laurel sprigs between the points and three 2-pointed rays in each angle, attached to crossed laurel branches; I, II, III: arms enameled in the color of the distinction

Size: I, II: 84 mm. III, IV: 61 × 57 mm

Metal: I: gilt silver; II and III: silver; IV: silvered nickel

Maker: Star: Vilardebó y Riera, Havana

Ribbon: According to distinction:

Red: bravery beyond the call of duty

White: intellectual merit

Blue: good conduct

Green: for years of service (IV: 20 years)

Red and White: for other services

Reference: Arista-Salado 2010–11, 1:201–6 and 2:253–55; Barac 2009, 331

Provenance: II, III: A. Menke

*Cu64. *La Orden del Mérito Intellectual "José María Heredia" (1941–1978)*

The José María Heredia Order of Intellectual Merit was awarded to eminent Cuban and foreign writers, professors, and artists who excelled in the fields of philosophy, literature, and the educational sciences. The order was originally provided with the traditional five grades of a national order, but later the number of grades was reduced to one on the grounds that an intellectual order was not suitable for a hier-

Cu 63 Grade IV badge

Cu 63 Grade IV badge

Cu 64
Commander

Rescinded: By Decree Law No. 17 on June 28, 1978

Supreme Chief: President of the Republic

Grades: Grand Cross, Grand Officer, Commander,* Officer, Knight or Dame

Obverse disc: Bust of Heredia, ¾ right, on a gilt field

Obverse legend: ORDEN DE HEREDIA on a light blue band

Reverse disc: Arms of Cuba on a white enameled field (lacking on Commander)

Shape: Ball-tipped, white enameled star surrounded by green enameled wreath

Size: Badge: Commander: 54 mm

Maker: Vilardebó y Riera, Havana

Ribbon: Blue, white, red horizontal stripes. The color was changed to white in 1956

Reference: Arista-Salado 2010–11, 1:207–10, 2:303–6

Provenance: A. Menke

archical ranking. The number of annual awards was limited to five, except in special circumstances. The order was normally conferred for the first time in the grade of Knight with promotion to higher grades being made over time. The Socialist Republic of Cuba never awarded this order, and it was abolished in 1978.

The order is named after José María Heredia (1803–37), who was a lyrical Hispanic poet committed to the ideals of Bolívar and Miranda. He was forced to flee from colonial Cuba to Boston, where he published his first book of poetry. He then traveled to Mexico, where he entered politics before he died in 1837 at the age of thirty-four.

Instituted: By Presidential Decree No. 364 on February 8, 1941

Modified: By Presidential Decree No. 470 on February 23, 1956, which modified the order's design

*Cu65. *La Orden del Mérito Agrícola e Industrial (1944–1978)*

The Order of Agricultural and Industrial Merit was awarded to individuals or institutions involved in agricultural or industrial activities for their ethical behavior and compliance with the nation's laws and government regulations. It was also bestowed on public officials whose actions merited recognition. The order awarded different titles to individual and corporate recipients. The Socialist Republic of Cuba never awarded this order, and it was abolished in 1978.

Instituted: By Presidential Decree No. 81 on January 20, 1944

Modified: By Presidential Decree No. 1,677 on June 5, 1944, changing the design

Regulated: By Resolution No. 304 on April 25, 1945

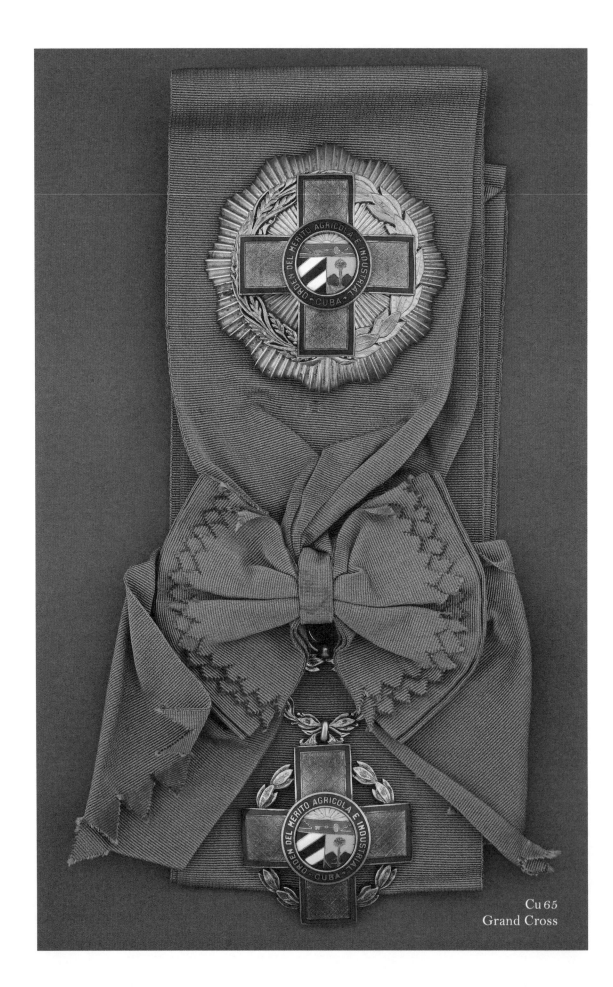

Cu 65
Grand Cross

Cu 65
Knight

Obverse legend: ORDEN DEL MERITO AGRICOLA E INDUSTRIAL | CUBA on a red enameled band

Shape: Green enameled cross with a red-enameled border: Grand Cross: wreath in each angle, suspended from a wreath

Star shape: Badge superimposed on a 12-armed rounded sun with 6 rays in each angle

Size: Badge: Grand Cross: 56 mm; Knight: 41 mm. Star: Grand Cross: 81 mm

Metal: Grand Cross badge: gilt; star: silver; Knight badge: bronze

Maker: Antigua Vilardebó y Riera, Havana

Ribbon: Green

Reference: Arista-Salado 2010–11, 1:219–221, 2:246; Barac 2009, 332

*Cu66: *La Orden del Mérito Comercial (1943–1978)*

The Order of Commercial Merit was awarded to persons or institutions for their ethical behavior and compliance with all relevant laws and government regulations. It could be awarded for negotiating favorable trade agreements with other countries. The Order had no chief but was governed instead by a council presided over by the minister of commerce. Recipients were required to have worked in their field for a minimum number of years: ten for the rank of Knight and fifty for the rank of Grand Cross. The order was never awarded by the Socialist Republic of Cuba, and it was abolished in 1978.

Instituted: By Presidential Decree No. 2,217 on June 25, 1943

Regulated: By Resolution of the Minister of Commerce on December 15, 1943

Rescinded: By Decree Law No. 7 on June 28, 1978

Grades: Grand Cross, Grand Officer,* Commander, Officer, Knight

Modified: By Resolution of the Ministry of Agriculture on January 30, 1947, changing who confers the order

Rescinded: By Decree Law No. 17 on June 28, 1978

Grades: Individuals: Grand Cross,* Grand Officer, Commander, Officer, Knight* or Dame; Institutions: Grand Diploma of Honor, Diploma of Honor, Grand Diploma of Merit, Diploma of Merit, Diploma of Distinction

Obverse disc: Enameled arms of Cuba

Cu 66
Grand Officer star

Cu 66
Grand Officer
badge

Cu 66
Grand Officer
badge

Obverse disc: Mercury, seated with caduceus, above 1943

Obverse legend: ORDEN DEL MERITO COMERCIAL | CUBA on a blue enameled band

Reverse disc: Enameled arms of Cuba surrounded by a blue band

Shape: Grand Cross and Grand Officer: white enameled cross pattée with pointed ends and 8 rays in each angle; Commander: round

Star shape: White enameled cross pattée with pointed ends and 8 rays in each angle superimposed on an 8-pointed star with five 3-part rays in each angle

Size: Badge: Grand Cross: 70 × 65 mm; Commander: 50 mm; Officer, Knight: 35 mm. Star: Grand Cross, Grand Officer: 80 mm

Metal: Grand Cross: gilt; Grand Officer: silver; Commander, Officer, Knight: gilt

Maker: Antigua Vilardebó y Riera, Havana

Ribbon: White

Reference: Arista-Salado 2010–11, 1:211–18; Barac 2009, 332

Provenance: A. Menke

Cu 67
Grand Cross star

*Cu67. *La Orden Nacional de Honor y Mérito "José Lanuza" (1944–1978)*

The José Lanuza National Order of Honor and Merit was a civilian award for individuals and institutions that promoted the integrity of the democratic system of government and the juridical relations among nations. This order was third in the ranking of Cuban orders. The Socialist Republic of Cuba never awarded this order, and it was abolished in 1978.

The order was named after José Antonio González Lanuza (1865–1917), a university professor and dean of the University of Havana Law School. He conspired with the 1895 revolution, for which he was sent to prison. He returned to Cuba under the American occupation and helped to reorganize the higher education system.

Instituted: By Presidential Decree No. 174 on February 1, 1944

Regulated: By Resolution of the Ministry of Justice on February 28, 1944

Modified: By Presidential Decree No. 2,064 on July 14, 1944, naming the members of the order's council

Modified: By Decree of the Ministry of Justice on July 26, 1950, modifying the election of the council members

Rescinded: By Decree Law No. 17 on June 28, 1978

Grades: Grand Cross with Special Distinction,

Cu 67
Grand Cross badge (obverse)

Cu 67
Grand Cross badge (reverse)

Grand Cross,* Grand Commander, Grand Officer, Commander, Officer, Knight, Member

Obverse disc: Figure of the goddess Themis, seated ¾ left

Obverse legend: INTEGRA MENS AUGUSTISSIMA POSSESSI | ORDEN LANUZA on a blue enameled band

Reverse disc: Enameled arms of Cuba

Reverse legend: REPUBLICA DE CUBA | 1944 on a blue enameled band

Shape: Gilt-edged, red enameled Latin cross suspended from a green enameled laurel wreath

Star shape: Gilt-edged, red enameled Latin cross with disc containing figure of the goddess Themis, surrounded by enameled laurel wreath on a white enameled disc with legend as for badge superimposed on a 12-pointed star with 1 ray in each angle

Size: Badge: Grand Cross: 65 × 45 mm. Star: 82 mm

Metal: Grand Cross: gold; Grand Officer: silver star

Maker: Antigua Vilardebó y Riera, Havana

Ribbon: Red

Reference: Arista-Salado 2011, 2:220–24, 249–50; Barac 2009, 332

Provenance: A. Menke

Cu68. *La Orden de Mérito de la Policia Marítima (1946–1978)*

The Order of Merit of the Maritime Police was awarded to members of the Maritime Police for valor, humanitarian acts, and personal sacrifice, entailing personal risk. Recipients could receive a monthly bonus of up to ten pesos for life. The Order used the same color-coding system used by the Orders of Military Merit and Naval Merit (Cu58, 59) to denote the nature of the merit being recognized.

Instituted: By Presidential Decree No. 2,535 on October 15, 1946

Suspended: By Decree Law No. 13 on January 3, 1959

Rescinded: By Decree Law No. 17 on June 28, 1978

Grades: I: senior officers; II: other officers; III: NCOS

Ribbon: Follows the same color-coding system used by the other military orders

Reference: Arista-Salado 2010–11, 1: 231–33

Cu69. *La Orden Nacional de Honor y Mérito "Mariana Grajales de Maceo" (1952–1978)*

The Mariana Grajales de Maceo National Order of Honor and Merit, a civilian award, was conferred on Cuban and foreign women who through their contributions to humanity and Cuba were worthy of recognition. Although

it abolished this order in 1978, Cuba created a new order bearing Grajales's name the following year (Cu80).

Mariana Grajales de Maceo (1808–93) was born in Santiago. She gave birth to thirteen children, most of whom became involved in the struggle for independence and two of whom became generals in the Revolutionary Army, including General José Antonio Maceo, second-in-command of the Revolutionary Army. She herself was active in the conflict, taking wounded from the battlefield and running hospitals.

Instituted: By Decree No. 4,066 of the Head of State on November 3, 1952

Regulated: By Presidential Decree No. 847 on March 23, 1953

Abolished: By Decree Law No. 17 on June 28, 1978

Supreme Chief: President of the Republic; co-administered by the First Lady

Obverse disc: Bust in silver of Grajales de Maceo

Obverse legend: ORDEN NACIONAL DE HONOR Y MERITO MARIANA GRAJALES MACEO surrounded by a laurel wreath

Reverse disc: Arms of Cuba

Reverse legend: LA MATERNIDAD HEROICA CREO LA NACIONALIDAD | REPUBLICA DE CUBA

Metal: Gold, silver

Ribbon: Blue, white bow

Reference: Arista-Salado 2010–11, 1:234–36, 2:267–72

Cu70. *La Orden Nacional de Mérito de la Aviación Civil (1953–1978)*

The National Order of Merit for Civil Aviation was awarded to individual Cubans and foreigners for their contribution to the development of civil aviation in Cuba. The order was abandoned after the socialist revolution and abolished in 1978.

Instituted: By Decree Law No. 801 on March 27, 1953

Regulated: By Presidential Decree No. 1,027 on May 14, 1954

Rescinded: By Decree Law No. 17 on June 28, 1978

Grades: Grand Cross, Grand Officer, Commander, and Officer

Obverse disc: Bust of Domingo Rosillo (Cuban pioneer of civil aviation) surrounded by small laurel wreaths

Obverse legend: MERITO DE AVIACION CIVIL-CUBA

Star shape: Grand Cross, Grand Officer: sun with rays

Size: Commander, Officer: 40 mm

Metal: Grand Cross, Commander: gold; Grand Officer, Officer: silver

Ribbon: Dark red

Reference: Arista-Salado 2010–11, 1:238–41, 2:281–90

*Cu71. *La Orden Deportiva Nacional* (*1954–1978*)

The National Sports Order was awarded to athletes who became world champions in their sport or who won medals in international competitions, foreign athletes who contributed to the development of sports in Cuba, and Cuban or foreign institutions that promoted sports in Cuba. The order was abolished in 1978.

Instituted: By Presidential Decree No. 60 on January 21, 1954

Regulated: By Presidential Decree No. 61 on January 21, 1954

Rescinded: By Decree Law No. 17 on June 28, 1978

Supreme Chief: President of the Republic

Obverse disc: Pointed white enameled shield with the initials CND in blue below the arms

of Cuba. Outside the shield appear sporting symbols in relief on a blue field

Obverse legend: REPUBLICA DE CUBA | ORDEN DEPORTIVA NACIONAL on a red enameled band

Shape: 8-pointed faceted star with 6 rays in each angle

Size: 65 mm

Metal: Silver

Ribbon: Red, white, blue

Reference: Arista-Salado 2010–11, 1:242–44, 2:278–81

Recipient: Rafael Emilio Fortún, sprinter 1948, 1952 Olympics

Provenance: A. Menke

Cu72. *La Orden Nacional Periodistica "Miguel de Marcos"* (*1955–1978*)

The Miguel de Marcos National Journalistic Order was instituted by President Andrès Domingo. He awarded it to Cuban and foreign journalists for eminent service to humanity, the nation, and culture in the field of journalism. It could also be conferred on institutions and journalistic societies. The order would normally be awarded in the grade of Knight with promotions to the next higher grade being awarded over time. The award could be rescinded for the defense of interests antithetical to those of Cuba.

Miguel de Marcos (1894–1954) was a lawyer by training and a writer-journalist by profession. He worked for many of Cuba's newspapers and journals over his career. De Marcos supported Fulgencio Batista and joined his Advisory Council following his 1952 revolution.

Instituted: By Decree Law No. 2,091 on January 27, 1955

Rescinded: By Decree Law No. 17 on June 28, 1978

Supreme Chief: President of the Republic

Cu 71

Grades: Grand Cross with special distinction, Grand Cross, Grand Officer, Commander, Officer, Knight

Obverse: Bust of Miguel de Marcos on a gold field above a crossed feather and sword

Obverse legend: ORDEN NACIONAL PERIODISTICA MIGUEL DE MARCOS on a white enameled band

Reverse: Arms of Cuba on a blue enameled field

Star shape: 10 swords superimposed on 10 writing pens

Metal: Badge: gilt, silver; star: silver

Ribbon: Red, blue

Reference: Arista-Salado 2010–11, 1:262–65, 2:297–302

Cu 73
Gand Cross

Cu 73
Gand Cross

*Cu73. *La Orden del Mérito Vial*

The Order of Road Merit was awarded to public officials for merit in designing and building public highways and roads. It was never awarded by the Socialist Government and was abolished in 1978.

>   Instituted: By Presidential Decree No. 1,294 on May 11, 1956
>
>   Rescinded: By Decree Law No. 17 on June 28, 1978
>
>   Grades: For individuals: Grand Cross,* Grand Officer, Commander, Knight; for collectives: Grand Diploma of Honor, Grand Diploma of Merit, Diploma of Honor, Diploma of Honor, Diploma of Distinction
>
>   Obverse disc: Image of highway interchange on a green enameled field

>   Obverse legend: ORDEN DEL MERITO VIAL | 1956 on a gray enameled band
>
>   Reverse disc: Arms of Cuba on a white enameled field
>
>   Reverse legend: REPUBLICA DE CUBA | M.O.P.
>
>   Shape: Disc surrounded by 6-pointed star with 15 rays, alternating beaded and plain, in each angle on a ball-tipped, 6-armed red and white enameled star with 3-pointed ends and an enameled laurel wreath in the angles suspended from a gilt laurel wreath
>
>   Size: 57 mm
>
>   Metal: Gilt
>
>   Ribbon: Black cordon
>
>   Reference: Arista-Salado 2011, 1:266–68
>
>   Provenance: A. Menke

Orders of the Provisional Government, 1959–1976

THE CUBAN Provisional Government after the revolution suspended most of the orders created in prior years. Only the Orders of Carlos Manuel de Céspedes and Carlos Finlay survived, and their design and purpose were radically modified. Cuba instituted a few new orders designed to recognize individual merit in favor of the revolution and its ideals. The first such order recognized those who defended the Socialist Government. A wholesale reorganization of Cuba's orders did not happen until 1979.

Cu 74a

Cu74. *La Orden Nacional Playa Girón*

The Order of Girón Beach is bestowed on Cuban and foreign citizens for the struggle against imperialism and reactionary forces, and in support of the Cuban armed forces, peace, and human progress.

The order draws its inspiration from the April 17, 1961, invasion of Cuba by a group of Cuban exiles supported and equipped by the United States Central Intelligence Agency. The invasion force was defeated by Cuban government troops, who killed or captured all of the invaders. The invasion is better known in English as the Bay of Pigs.

Instituted: By Decree Law No. 949 on July 18, 1961

Modified: December 2, 1972, limiting gold awards to people involved in worldwide revolution

Modified: By Decree No. 30 on December 10, 1979, redesigning the order

*Cu74a. *Version 1, 1961–1979*

Obverse: Map of northern Caribbean with armed Cuban soldier in the center

Obverse legend: PATRIA FUERTE

Reverse: Arms of Cuba (lacking on some examples)

Reverse legend: REPUBLICA DE CUBA |

Cu 74b

Cu 74b

CONSEJO DEL ESTADO (lacking on some examples)

Metal: Gilt,* copper*

Size: 50 mm

*Cu74b. *Version 2, post-1979*

Obverse disc: Map of northern Caribbean with armed Cuban soldier in the center

Obverse inscription: PLAYA GIRON | CUBA on a white enameled band

Reverse: Arms of Cuba

Reverse legend: REPUBLICA DE CUBA | CONSEJO DEL ESTADO

Shape: Disc above laurel branches on a circle with an enameled shooting star on a red enameled field and extending gear teeth at the bottom

Size: 45 mm

Metal: Silvered

Ribbon: Pentagonal: red, blue, white, olive, light blue

Reference: Arista-Salado 2010–11, 1:311–12, 2:359–60, 3:112–15; Burke's Peerage 2006, 1067

Provenance: A. Menke

Cu75. *La Orden Nacional "José Martí"*

The José Martí National Order is given to heads of state and of political parties for their international solidarity in fighting imperialism and neocolonialism and for their friendship with the socialist revolution in Cuba. This order was awarded to Leonid Brezhnev, secretary general of the Communist Party of the USSR.

The order is named after the Cuban revolutionary leader who organized the expedition that fought the Spanish royalist forces up until the end of the Spanish-American War. Martí fought for Cuba's independence and opposed the country's annexation by the United States.

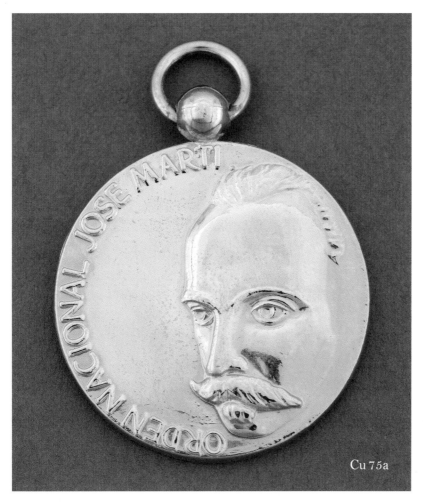

Cu 75a

He was killed in combat in 1895, soon after his expedition landed in Cuba.

> Instituted: By Decree Law No. 1,239 on December 2, 1972
>
> Modified: By Decree No. 30 on December 10, 1979

*Cu75a. *Version 1, 1972–1979*

> Obverse: Head of Martí, ¾ left
>
> Obverse legend: ORDEN NACIONAL JOSE MARTI
>
> Size: 40 mm
>
> Metal: Gilt
>
> Ribbon: Pentagonal; blue, white, red, with narrow red and blue side stripes

*Cu75b. *Version 2, post-1979*

> Obverse: Bust of Martí, ¾ left
>
> Obverse inscription: JOSE MARTI | 1853–1895 on a white enameled band
>
> Reverse disc: Arms of Cuba
>
> Reverse legend: REPUBLICA DE CUBA | CONSEJO DEL ESTADO
>
> Shape: Star with laurel wreath in the angles on a rayed sun
>
> Size: 43 mm
>
> Metal: Gilt
>
> Ribbon: Pentagonal; white with red, white, blue side stripes on the right
>
> Reference: Arista-Salado 2010–11, 1:313–15, 2:361–62, 3:105–8; Burke's Peerage 2006, 1066

Cu 75b   Cu 75b

Orders of the Socialist State,

1979 to Present

The National Assembly approved Law No. 17 on June 28, 1978, called the System of Decorations and Honorific Titles. This law established the purpose and hierarchy of awards, but did not institute or regulate any of them. This was done one year later.

As in the case of medals noted above, unless otherwise indicated, the following Cuban orders were all instituted by Decree No. 30 on December 10, 1979, and regulated on December 12, 1979. The government regulations for these orders often standardized part of the orders' design. The reverse side normally displays the arms of Cuba on a silvered disc with the legend REPUBLICA DE CUBA | CONSEJO DEL ESTADO on a silvered band (which will not be described or illustrated below). Cuban ribbons follow the Soviet system of folding the ribbon into a pentagonal shape with a hard inner lining and a pin in the back, but some of these are badges with a pin back, with the ribbon a small bar to be worn separately.

Cuban orders authorized and regulated in 1979 mainly feature the bust of a person closely identified with the 1959 socialist revolution or its ideals on the obverse, while the reverse links the recognition of these ideals with the Cuban nation and the Council of State. As is the norm when bestowing most orders of merit, the Cuban government reserves the right to rescind the recipient's membership in the order at any future date if certain conditions are not met. One condition common to all these orders is that the awardee must adhere to revolutionary principles, as defined by the Council of State, for the rest of his or her life. The acronym FAR refers to the Fuerzas Armadas Revolucionarias, which Cuba dates back to the attack on the Moncada Barracks.

*Cu76. *La Orden "Máximo Gómez"*

The Order of Máximo Gómez is awarded to members of the Cuban armed forces who distinguish themselves by leading major operations in the defense of Cuba or for merit during the War of Liberation. In exceptional cases, the order may be conferred on foreign military personnel from friendly countries.

Máximo Gómez (1836–1905) was born in Bani, Dominican Republic. He fought the Haitian army of Emperor Faustin and later joined the Spanish army. He moved with his family to Cuba, where he became one of the early fighters for Cuban independence, leading rebel forces during the 1890s.

Cu 76
2nd Grade

Grades: 1st, 2nd*
Obverse: Bust of Máximo Gómez, ¾ left
Obverse legend: MAXIMO GOMEZ
Shape: 8-pointed rayed star
Size: 45 mm
Metal: 1st: gilt; 2nd: silvered
Ribbon: Bar of 3 equal light blue, white, and red stripes followed by variable gold, red, gold, and red stripes. The center gold stripe is replaced with light blue stripes in the 2nd grade
Reference: Arista-Salado 2010–11, 3:115–19; Burke's Peerage 2006, 1067–68
Provenance: A. Menke

Cu 77

Cu 78

*Cu77. *La Orden "Antonio Maceo"*

The Order of Antonio Maceo is awarded to FAR personnel for causing significant damage to enemy forces in the field. It may be conferred on entire military units as well as foreign military personnel.

José Antonio de la Caridad Maceo y Grajales (1845–96) was born in Oriente Province. He specialized in guerrilla warfare and was promoted to lieutenant general and second-in-command of Cuba's Revolutionary Army. He was nicknamed "Bronze Titan" because of the color of his skin.

Obverse disc: Bust of Antonio Maceo, ¾ left

Obverse legend: ANTONIO MACEO, 3 stars below on a red enameled band

Shape: Disc within 2 laurel branches on star

Size: 45 mm

Metal: Gilt

Ribbon: Blue gold, white, gold, red, with 3 gold stars are placed on the ribbon

Reference: Arista-Salado 2010–11, 3:115–19; Burke's Peerage 2006, 1068

Provenance: A. Menke

*Cu78. *La Orden "Camilo Cienfuegos"*

The Order of Camilo Cienfuegos is awarded to FAR personnel on active service, in the reserves, or retired, and to friendly foreign officers for their defense of national sovereignty. The order is awarded for an array of military achievements, such as shooting down one fighter-bomber or two helicopters, destroying three or more tanks, sinking three or more boats, and so forth. It comes with a ribbon bar, but it is not suspended from a ribbon.

Camilo Cienfuegos Gorriarán (1932–59) was raised in an anarchist family. He met Fidel Castro in Mexico and sailed on the *Granma* with Castro to Cuba. Castro named him a "Comandante." Cienfuegos led one of the three columns that took the provincial capital of Santa Clara, shortly before Batista fled Cuba. He later disappeared in a plane crash in the ocean.

Obverse disc: Bust of Camilo Cienfuegos, ¾ right

Obverse legend: CAMILO CIENFUEGOS on a green enameled band

Shape: Maltese cross

Cu 79

Size: 44 mm

Metal: Gilt

Ribbon bar: Red, with narrow gold, blue right-edge stripes

Reference: Arista-Salado 3:124–28; Burke's Peerage 2006, 1068–69

*Cu79. *La Orden "Ernesto Che Guevara"*

The Order of Ernesto Che Guevara is bestowed on members of the FAR for exceptional military merit in foreign missions and in the fight against imperialism and colonialism. It is also given to foreign military personnel of friendly nations.

The Order is named for Ernesto "Che" Guevara (1928–67), an Argentine physician and guerrilla leader. Guevara met Castro in Mexico City, when the latter was exiled from Cuba. Guevara is considered to have had a major influence in converting Castro to communism. He sailed with Castro aboard the *Granma* to Cuba, eluded government soldiers, commanded a guerrilla unit in the Sierra Maestra and eventually rode with Castro into Havana following

Batista's departure. Guevara served as president of the Cuban Central Bank but soon left Cuba to launch a guerrilla campaign in Bolivia, an undertaking that led to his violent death.

Grades: 1st,* 2nd,* 3rd*

Obverse disc: Bust of Ernesto Guevara, facing

Obverse legend: ERNESTO GUEVARA | CHE on a red enameled band

Shape: 10-pointed star

Size: 45 mm

Metal: 1st: gilt; 2nd: silvered; 3rd: bronze

Reference: Arista-Salado 2010–11, 3:128–31; Burke's Peerage 2006, 1069

*Cu80. *La Orden "Mariana Grajales"*

The Order of Mariana Grajales bears the same name as an earlier order (Cu69) but is awarded for promoting the socialist revolution rather than fighting for Cuba's independence. It is awarded to Cuban women who make an extraordinary contribution to the cause of the Cuban Revolution, either internally or outside the country, or help to integrate women into society. The order may also be given to

Cu 80

Cu 81

foreign women who help to promote revolutionary ideals, the struggle against imperialism, and the liberation and independence of peoples.

The order is named after Mariana Grajales de Maceo (1808–93), who provided medical services during the War of Independence to both sides of the conflict. She was the mother of Antonio Maceo, one of the leaders of Cuba's War of Independence (see Cu77).

Obverse disc: Bust of Mariana Grajales, facing

Obverse legend: MARIANA GRAJALES | 1868–1895 on a red enameled band surrounded by 2 laurel branches with 12 sword handles protruding from the band and a star atop

Shape: Star with 9 rays in each angle

Size: 45 mm

Metal: Silvered

Ribbon: Bar with blue, white, red, edged in olive green

Reference: Arista-Salado 2010–11, 3:131–34; Burke's Peerage 2006, 1069–70

Provenance: A. Menke

*Cu81. *La Orden "Lázaro Peña"*

The Order of Lázaro Peña is awarded to Cuban and foreign workers for exceptional service in the field of labor and the national economy. It may also be conferred on national or foreign corporations and economic organizations that contribute to the economic, scientific, or cultural development of Cuba.

Lázaro Peña González (1911–74) was a labor and union leader in his youth. After the revolution, he played a major role in organizing Cuba's labor unions.

Grades: 1st, 2nd, 3rd*

Obverse disc: Bust of Lázaro Peña, ¾ left, on
a white enameled field

Obverse legend: LÁZARO PEÑA on a red
enameled band with extruding gears

Shape: Gilt-edged, white enameled star with 7
rays in each angle

Size: 45 mm

Metal: 1st: gilt; 2nd: silvered; 3rd: bronze

Ribbon: Pentagonal: black, olive green, red,
light blue, gold (1st class); the last color in
the 2nd class is white, and in the 3rd class,
brown

Reference: Arista-Salado 2010–11, 3:134–39;
Burke's Peerage 2006, 1070

Provenance: A. Menke

Cu 82

*Cu82. *La Orden "Combatiente de la Guerra de Liberación"*

The Order for Combatants in the War of Liberation is bestowed on any member of the
Cuban rebel army who demonstrated exceptional merit and defended the principles of the
revolution. In exceptional cases, the order may
also be conferred on citizens who made a significant contribution to the rebel cause.

Modified: By the Council of State, on November 24, 1981

Grades: 1st, 2nd,* 3rd (after 1981)

Obverse disc: Soldier standing in countryside
on a silvered field

Obverse legend: LIBERACIÓN | CUBA on a red
enameled band surrounded by 2 gilt laurel
branches

Shape: Star

Size: 45 mm

Metal: 1st: gilt; 2nd: silver gilt; 3rd: silvered

Ribbon: Red, black, olive green, white, blue

Reference: Arista-Salado 2010–11, 3:39–43;
Burke's Peerage 2006, 1070–71

Provenance: A. Menke

*Cu83. *La Orden "Félix Varela"*

The Order of Félix Varela is awarded to Cuban
and foreign citizens, as well as to cultural associations, for extraordinary merit in promoting
national or universal culture.

Félix Varela y Morales (1788–1853) was born
in Cuba. His criticism of slavery and colonialism
attracted the attention of the Spanish government, and he emigrated to the United States,
where he promoted religious tolerance and respect for human rights.

Grades: 1st,* 2nd

Obverse disc: Bust of Félix Varela, facing, on
a gilt field

Obverse legend: FELIX VARELA on a light
blue enameled band

Shape: 8-pointed star with a band in the
angles

Size: 47 mm

Metal: 1st: gilt; 2nd: silvered

Ribbon: Pentagonal: 1st: red, blue with a center white stripe; 2nd: same, edged in white

Reference: Arista-Salado 2010–11, 3:143–46;
Burke's Peerage 2006, 1071

Provenance: A. Menke

*Cu84. *La Orden "Julio Antonio Mella"*

The Order of Julio Antonio Mella is given to
young Cuban and foreign citizens who display
exceptional merit in a variety of areas of interest to youth.

Julio Antonio Mella (1903–29) was born into
a difficult family situation. He was expelled several times from educational institutions and the
University of Havana. He became one of the
founders of the Cuban Communist Party and
is considered a hero by the Socialist Government. He fled to Mexico, where he was murdered in 1929.

Obverse disc: Bust of Julio Antonio Mella,
facing, on a gilt field

Obverse legend: JULIO A. MELLA on a red
enameled band surrounded by silvered laurel branches

Shape: Star superimposed on a 36-pointed gilt
sun

Size: 45 mm

Metal: Gilt

Ribbon: Pentagonal: red with a light green
center stripe

Reference: Arista-Salado 2010–11, 3:146–49;
Burke's Peerage 2006, 1071

Provenance: A. Menke

*Cu85. *La Orden "Frank País"*

The Order of Frank País is awarded for exceptional merit in the field of education.

Frank País (1934–57) was the son of Spanish immigrants from Galicia, who settled in Santiago. País became active in the 26th of July Movement following Castro's attack on the Moncada Barracks. He coordinated the urban youth support for the rebels in the Sierra Maestra. Cuban police found his hiding place and executed him on the streets in 1957.

Obverse: Bust of Frank País, ¾ right, with a laurel branch to right
Obverse inscription: Frank | País

Shape: 6-pointed rayed star superimposed on 6-pointed blue enameled star

Size: 45 mm

Metal: Gilt

Ribbon: Pentagonal: white with blue left edge stripe and red right edge stripe

Reference: Arista-Salado 2010–11, 3:149–53; Burke's Peerage 2006, 1071–72

Provenance: A. Menke

*Cu86. *La Orden "Ana Betancourt"*

The Order of Ana Betancourt is given to Cuban women who actively support the Cuban Revolution and its ideals. It may also be awarded for fighting imperialism and the struggle for independence of colonies.

Ana Betancourt (1832–1901) was one of Cuba's first women revolutionaries during the rebellion that started in 1868. She joined her husband in the mountains and participated in the revolt. She spoke out against slavery and in favor of women's rights and Cuban independence. She was captured by Spanish forces in 1871 and exiled to Spain, where she died.

> Obverse: Bust of Ana Betancourt, facing, on an oval disc surrounded by oval blue and white bands
>
> Obverse inscription: ANA BETANCOURT on a red band below bust
>
> Shape: Oval, with star at top and downward facing palm branches flanking bust
>
> Size: 45 × 355 mm
>
> Metal: Gilt
>
> Ribbon: Pentagonal: red with narrow yellow side striped
>
> Reference: Arista-Salado 2010–11, 3:153–56; Burke's Peerage 2006, 1072
>
> Provenance: A. Menke

*Cu87. *La Orden "Juan Marinello"*

The Order of Juan Marinello is bestowed on Cuban and foreign citizens who fight for Cuba's ideological ideals and demonstrate exceptional merit in such areas as culture, literature, and journalism.

Juan Marinello (1898–1977) was born in Cuba and educated at the University of Havana, where he became a student leader and activist. He actively supported the Cuban Revolution from early on and died in 1977.

> Obverse: Bust of Juan Marinello, left
>
> Obverse legend: JUAN MARINELLO on a red enameled band
>
> Shape: 2 rayed trapezoids facing down and 2 rayed trapezoids facing up

Cu 87

> Size: 35 × 45 mm
>
> Metal: Gilt
>
> Ribbon: Pentagonal: red with white, blue right edge stripes
>
> Reference: Arista-Salado 2010–11, 3:159–61; Burke's Peerage 2006, 1073
>
> Provenance: A. Menke

*Cu88. *La Orden de la Solidaridad*

The Order of Solidarity is awarded to Cuban and foreign citizens, as well as organizations, for exceptional humanitarian work on behalf of Cuba and friendly nations. Cuba has provided valuable services to other developing countries,

Cu 88

Cu 89

particularly in the fields of medicine and literacy campaigns. Cuba has sent large numbers of medical personnel to countries like Angola, Haiti, Nicaragua, and Venezuela.

Obverse: Monument to José Martí

Obverse legend: SOLIDARIDAD

Shape: 12-pointed sun with 3 rays in each angle

Size: 45 mm

Metal: Gilt

Ribbon: Pentagonal: red with narrow white, blue, white center stripes

Reference: Arista-Salado 2010–11, 3:162–65; Burke's Peerage 2006, 1073–74

*Cu89. *La Orden al Mérito Deportivo*

The Order of Sporting Merit is given to Cuban and foreign citizens who display exceptional sporting ability or for developing sports in Cuba. It may also be conferred on organizations and sports institutions. Cuba has given great importance to its sporting programs. As a result, the country has produced world-class athletes, who have earned many Olympic medals.

Obverse: Olympic torch with red enameled flames with enameled Cuban flag wrapped in front, to left and right

Obverse legend: AL MERITO DEPORTIVO

Shape: Oval

Cu 90

Cu 91

Size: 45 × 30 mm

Metal: Gilt

Ribbon: Pentagonal; light blue, gold, black,
   light green, red

Reference: Arista-Salado 2010–11, 3:165–68;
   Burke's Peerage 2006, 1074

Provenance: A. Menke

*Cu90: *La Orden "Por el Servicio de la Patria en las Fuerzas Armadas Revolucionarias"*

The Order for Service to the Fatherland in
the Revolutionary Armed Forces is awarded
to members of the FAR for extraordinary merit
in carrying out their mission to defend the Socialist Fatherland and the country's territorial integrity. It is awarded successively to
the higher grade. The same grade may not be
awarded twice.

   Grades: 1st, 2nd,* 3rd

   Obverse disc: Fasces with liberty cap atop
      flanked by laurel branches

Obverse legend: POR EL SERVICIO A LA
   PATRIA on a green enameled band

Shape: Star with 7 rays in each angle

Size: 45 mm

Metal: 1st: gilt; 2nd: silvered; 3rd: copper

Ribbon: Pentagonal: red, white, dark blue,
   white, red of uneven width

Reference: Arista-Salado 2010–11, 3:
   168–71

Provenance: A. Menke

*Cu91. *La Orden "Blas Roca"*

The Blas Roca Order is given to Cuban citizens
for extraordinary merit in building socialism
in Cuba through creative works in the fields of

culture, education, science, and sports, as well as for strengthening Cuba's military power. It may also be given to foreign citizens for outstanding work in fighting imperialism and all forms of exploitation, and for demonstrating solidarity with the Cuban Revolution.

Blas Roca Caldario (1908–87) was born into a poor family and became an early militant in the Cuban Communist Party. In 1931, he was elected to the Central Committee of the Party. After the revolution, he became the first president of the National Assembly, and he served as secretary general of the Cuban Communist Party.

Cu 92

Obverse disc: Bust of Blas Roca, ¾ left

Obverse legend: BLAS ROCA | 1908–1987 on a red enameled geared band

Shape: Star

Size: 45 mm

Metal: Gilt

Ribbon: Pentagonal; red, white, dark blue, red of uneven width

Reference: Arista-Salado 2010–11, 3: 171–74

Provenance: A. Menke

*Cu92. *La Orden "6 de Junio"*

The Order of June 6 is awarded to members of the Ministry of the Interior on active duty or in retirement as well as units of the ministry for extraordinary merit in carrying out their missions and contributing to the security of the state and the maintenance of internal order. The order may also be given to foreign military and foreign military units. It may be awarded posthumously.

The order is named for the date when the Provisional Government created the Ministry of the Interior on June 6, 1961. The ministry administers Cuba's security forces to defend the socialist revolution and maintain public order.

Grades: 1st, 2nd*

Obverse disc: White-edged, red enameled shield

Obverse inscription: 6 | DE | JUNIO

Shape: Star with oak and laurel branches on silver-edged, blue enameled pentagon

Size: 43 mm

Metal: 1st: gilt; 2nd: silvered

Ribbon: Pentagonal; light blue, dark blue, white, green

Reference: Arista-Salado 2010–11, 3: 174–78

*Cu93. *La Orden "17 de Mayo"*

The Order of May 17 is given to Cuban and foreign nationals for extraordinary merit in the field of agriculture. It is also conferred on farming collectives belonging to the National Association of Small Producers. On May 17, 1946, Niceto Pérez García, a peasant activist, was assassinated. Fidel Castro signed the first Agrarian Reform Law on that date in 1959 in commemoration of that event.

Cu93

Obverse: Bust of Niceto Pérez, ¾ right

Obverse legend: 17 DE MAYO | NICETO PÉREZ on blue enameled band

Shape: 8-pointed blue enameled star on 8-pointed star on 8-pointed star with 2 red enameled semicircles in each angle

Size: 45 mm

Metal: Gilt

Ribbon: Pentagonal; alternating green, carmelite narrow stripes

Reference: Arista-Salado 2010–11, 3: 176–81

Provenance: A. Menke

DOMINICAN REPUBLIC

THE DOMINICAN REPUBLIC's struggle for independence began in 1838, when Juan Pablo Duarte, Ramón Matías Mella, and Francisco del Rosario founded "La Trinitaria," a secret society committed to expelling a Haitian army of occupation. The Trinitarios proclaimed the country's independence on February 27, 1844, with the backing of a private army assembled by a wealthy landowner, Pedro Santana. Caudillos competed for power even as Haiti invaded the country four times in an unsuccessful effort to reassert its control. In 1863, Santana signed an agreement whereby the country reverted to being a Spanish colony. Many Dominicans opposed colonial rule, and Spain withdrew two years later.

The Dominican Republic went through decades of political instability lasting until World War I, when President Woodrow Wilson ordered the U.S. Marines to take over the country. The United States administered the country until the marines withdrew in 1924. National elections were then held, and in 1924 a president was elected for a six-year term.

During this entire period beginning with the creation of La Trinitaria until the 1930 presidential elections, the Dominican Republic is not known to have instituted a single medal or order. This changed when General Rafael Trujillo Molina was elected president after an uncontested campaign. Shortly after his election, Trujillo created the country's first order of merit named after Juan Pablo Duarte, the original founder of La Trinitaria. He later created an array of orders and medals, which he used to reward loyalty to himself. He instituted one order in his name, the only Latin American ruler to do so while still in office. Some of his medals bear his effigy on the obverse.

Trujillo was assassinated in 1961. Shortly thereafter, the government abolished the orders and medals that either displayed his effigy or were named after him. Over the past half century, the Dominican Republic is known to have created only two medals and no new order of merit. Aside from that, the country continues to award the same orders and medals created by Rafael Trujillo, minus any symbol related to his regime.

MEDALS

ALL OF the Dominican Republic's early medals were instituted during Trujillo's rule. He used them to solidify loyalty among his supporters, particularly the military, which was the foundation of his power.

Trujillo created a good conduct medal for the three branches of the armed forces and the national police, each with its own design. He devised them with five stars symbolizing his rank of generalissimo. The medals are still being awarded, but the five stars were removed from all of them on December 6, 1961, following his assassination.

Do 1a

*Do1. *La Medalla "Buena Conducta"*
(*Fuerza Aérea*)

The Good Conduct Medal for the Air Force is awarded to Dominican Air Force personnel for good behavior or for years of service. In 1961, the five stars were replaced with the inscription FAD.

*Do1a. *Variant 1, before 1961*

Instituted: February 15, 1948

Obverse: Blue enameled wings elevated and displayed above the Dominican air force emblem with 5 red stars between the wing tips, all surrounded by a raised red enameled band

Shape: Round, suspended from a gilt bar inscribed either ANTIGUEDAD EN SERV. or BUENA CONDUCTA

Size: 37 mm

Metal: Bronze

Maker: N. S. Meyer, Inc., New York

Ribbon: White with narrow center green and 2 red edge stripes and a bar inscribed BUENA CONDUCTA

*Do1b. *Variant 2, after 1961*

Obverse: Blue enameled wings elevated and displayed above the Dominican air force emblem with FAD between the wing tips, all surrounded by a raised red enameled band

Ribbon: Enameled broach with the flag of the Dominican Republic and a bar inscribed BUENA CONDUCTA and further suspended from a broach with the national flag of the Dominican Republic

*Do2. *La Medalla "Buena Conducta"* (*Ejército*)

The Good Conduct Medal for the Army is awarded to Dominican Army personnel for good behavior.

Obverse disc: Arms of the Dominican Republic

Obverse legend: EJERCITO NACIONAL

Shape: Cross

Size: 36 mm

Metal: Bronze

Maker: N. S. Meyer, Inc., New York

Ribbon: Enameled broach with the flag of the Dominican Republic and a bar inscribed BUENA CONDUCTA

Do 2

Do 1b

*Do3. *La Medalla de Buena Conducta* (*Marina*)

The Navy Medal for Good Conduct is awarded to Dominican navy personnel for good conduct.

Obverse disc: Star within a green enameled wreath

Obverse legend: BUENA CONDUCTA

Reverse legend: MARINA DE GUERRA

Shape: Life preserver superimposed on an anchor

Size: 44 × 38 mm

Metal: Gilt, white metal*

Ribbon: Red, white, blue

Do 3

Do 3

Do4. *La Medalla de Buena Conducta* (*Policia Nacional*)

The Police Good Conduct Medal is awarded to members of the national police for good conduct.

Obverse: Arms of the Dominican Republic

Obverse legend: POLICIA NACIONAL | BUENA CONDUCTA

Shape: Round, suspended by a chain from a rectangular brooch with the national flag of the Dominican Republic

Size: 35 mm

Metal: Silvered, darkened silvered

Maker: N. S. Meyer, Inc., New York

*Do5. *La Medalla Conmemorativa "23 de Febrero 1930"*

Trujillo awarded this medal to his supporters in the coup d'état that brought him to power.

Instituted: On July 22, 1937

Abolished: On December 6, 1961

Obverse: Bust of Trujillo, facing

Obverse legend: DISCIPLINA Y LEALTAD | TRUJILLO

Reverse inscription: MEDALLA | CONMEMORATIVA | DEL | AVENIMIENTO | DE LA | PATRIA NUEVA | 23 DE FEBRERO | 1930

Size: 30 mm

Metal: Bronze

Maker: N. S. Meyer, Inc., New York

Ribbon: Green, white, red, yellow

Provenance: A. Menke

*Do6. *La Medalla del Mérito Municipal*

The Medal for Municipal Merit was awarded to Trujillo's supporters, probably in connection with the defeat of a group of insurgents who landed on the north coast of the island in 1959.

Do 5

Do 6

Do 5

Do 6

Instituted: 1959

Abolished: December 6, 1961

Obverse disc: Bust of Trujillo, facing

Obverse legend: MEDALLA DEL MERITO MUNICIPAL

Reverse: Arms of the Dominican Republic

Reverse inscription: REPUBLICA DOMINICANA | 1959 | ERA DE TRUJILLO

Shape: Red enameled cross pattée with pointed ends with crossed swords and a wreath in the angles

Size: 52 mm

Metal: Gilt

Ribbon: Red, white, blue

Reference: http://www.medals.org.uk/dominican-republic/dominican-republic-text.htm, accessed July 31, 2012

D07. *La Medalla del Mérito de la Mujer Dominicana*

The Medal of Merit for the Dominican Woman is bestowed on women for their contribution to humanity in the social, political, humanitarian, scientific, and artistic fields. It is conferred each year to coincide with International Woman's Day on March 8. More than one hundred medals have been conferred. It is believed to be the first medal for merit authorized after Trujillo's assassination.

Instituted: By Decree No. 3,013 on May 29, 1985

Obverse: Stylized outline of dove

Shape: Round

Ribbon: Red, white, blue

Reference: http://www.es.wikipedia.org/wiki/Sistema_dominicano_de_honores, accessed March 1, 2013; http://www.mujer.gob.do/MedallaalMérito/tabid/122/Default.aspx, accessed March 1, 2013

D08. *La Medalla Presidencial al Mérito Civil*

The Presidential Medal for Civil Merit is awarded to Dominican nationals for outstanding accomplishments at work, in the arts, and in science.

Instituted: By Decree No. 1,048-01 on October 19, 2001

Obverse: Presidential Palace beneath a Dominican flag

Obverse legend: MEDALLA PRESIDENCIAL | AL MERITO CIVIL

Reverse: Arms of the Dominican Republic

Reverse legend: GOBIERNO CONSTITUCIONAL | REPUBLICA DOMINICANA

Size: 48 mm

Metal: Silver

Ribbon: Blue, white, red

Reference: Dominican Republic 2001, 47–48

ORDERS

RAFAEL TRUJILLO founded all of the country's orders. He came to power in 1930 and ruled the country for thirty-one years until his assassination in 1961. Those orders bearing his name or politically associated with him were rescinded on December 6, 1961.

Trujillo's supporters hailed his taking power as the "Era of Trujillo," a title that Trujillo used frequently to describe his dictatorial rule. Perhaps more than any other caudillo in Latin American history, Trujillo created orders to promote his power, loyalty to himself, and standing in the community.

Do 9

*Do9. *La Orden del Mérito Militar*

The Order of Military Merit was the first order instituted by Trujillo. Himself an army officer, Trujillo created the order to recognize military officers who supported his rise to power. It is still awarded to Dominican army personnel for exemplary service. A recipient of this order may add the initials "M.M." (Mérito Militar) to his full name in all official papers and documents. The order is the second-highest in rank after the Order of Duarte, Sánchez, and Mella (see Do11). Recipients of the first three grades must pay for their order; the government provides the fourth grade free of charge.

Instituted: By Law No. 21 on October 14, 1930

Divisions: Bravery, long service,* and other service*

Grades: I, II, III, and IV (for each division)

Obverse disc: Arms of the Dominican Republic

Obverse legend: REPUBLICA DOMINICANA | MERITO MILITAR

Reverse disc: [Name of the awardee and the date of concession]

Reverse legend: EL PRESIDENTE DE LA REPUBLICA DOMINICANA

Shape: Ball-tipped star

Size: Gilt: 48 mm; bronze: 47 mm

Metal: Senior officers: gold; other officers: silver; enlisted men: bronze

Ribbon: Bravery: red; long service: blue; other services: white

Reference: Barac 2009, 392; Prober 1951, 103–4

*Do10. *La Orden del Mérito Juan Pablo Duarte*

Rafael Trujillo created the Juan Pablo Duarte Order of Merit less than a year after he took power. It became the nation's highest award and was conferred in both a civilian and a military division. In 1954, the order was renamed the Order of Duarte, Sánchez, y Mella.

Juan Pablo Duarte (1813–76) was one of the founders of the Dominican Republic. In 1838, he and others created a secret society, La Trinitaria, which sought to expel the Haitian army of occupation. He later started another society, La Filantrópica, which promoted independence through the theater. Duarte spent much of his life in exile and died in Venezuela. He is buried in Santo Domingo, along with Sánchez and Mella.

Instituted: By Decree No. 3,916 on February 24, 1931

Regulated: By Decree No. 1,112 on November 22, 1934

Modified: By Decree No. 113 on May 26, 1936

Regulated: By Reglamento No. 187 on February 16, 1939

Renamed: By Law No. 3,916 on September 9, 1954

Chief: President of the Republic

Grades: Collar issued only to the president as his seal of office; Grand Cross with gold star, Grand Cross with silver star (3 badges),* Grand Officer, Commander, Officer, Knight*

Do 10
Grand Cross badge (military)

Do 10
Grand Cross badge (military)

Do 10
Grand Cross with
silver star

Do 10
Grand Cross
badge

Do 10
Grand Cross
badge

Do 10
Knight

Do 10
Knight

Do 10 Grand Cross badge (detail)

Do 10
Grand Cross
badge
(reverse)

Obverse disc: Bust of Juan Pablo Duarte, facing, on a white enameled field

Obverse legend: JUAN PABLO DUARTE | HONOR Y MERITO

Reverse disc: Arms of the Dominican Republic on a white enameled field

Shape: Ball-tipped, white enameled Maltese cross with a center blue enameled stripe, with 5 rays in each angle, suspended from a

green enameled wreath; for military awards, the wreath has crossed swords

Trujillo example of Grand Cross badge:* suspended from a bar with a miniature of the badge with a pearl as the disc; engraved on the reverse of the bar: RAFAEL LEONIDAS | TRUJILLO | 1950

Star shape: Ball-tipped cross pattée with 5 rays in each angle with wreath surrounding the disc

Badge size: Grand Cross, Commander: 61 mm; Knight: 45 mm. Star: 86 mm

Metal: Gold and silver

Ribbon: White with a wide center blue stripe and 2 narrower side blue stripes

Reference: Barac 2009, 392; Rodríguez Cabrer 2001, 171–84

Recipient: Grand Cross: Rafael Leonides Trujillo

*Do11. *La Orden del Mérito Duarte, Sánchez, y Mella*

The Order of Merit of Duarte, Sánchez, and Mella is a continuation of the Order of Merit of Juan Pablo Duarte. When awarded to a military recipient, crossed swords are placed on the suspension wreath. Past recipients of the Grand Cross with gold star include Queen Elizabeth II; Fidel Castro, president of Cuba; and Ernesto Samper, president of Colombia.

Ramón Matías Mella and Francisco del Rosario Sánchez formed La Trinitaria in 1838 along with Juan Pablo Duarte. The three of them are considered the fathers of Dominican independence. They are buried together in Santo Domingo.

Renamed: By Law No. 3,916 on September 9, 1954

Grades: Grand Cross with gold star, Grand Cross with silver star,* Grand Officer, Commander, Officer, Knight*

Obverse disc: Busts of Duarte, Sánchez, and
  Mella, facing, in discs with laurel branches
  between, on a white enameled field

Obverse legend: DUARTE SANCHEZ Y MELLA
  | HONOR Y MERITO

Reverse disc: Arms of the Dominican Republic on a white enameled field

Shape: Ball-tipped, white enameled Maltese
  cross with a center blue enameled stripe,
  with 5 rays in each angle, suspended from a
  laurel wreath

Size: Badge: Grand Cross, Knight: 62 mm.
  Star: 80 mm

Metal: Silver

Maker: Antigua Vilardebó y Riera, Havana

Ribbon: White with a wide dark blue central
  stripe and narrow dark blue side stripes

Reference: Burke's Peerage 2006, 1083;
  Rodríguez Cabrer 2001, 199–201

Do 11
Grand Cross badge (reverse)

Do 11
Knight

Do 11
Knight

Do 11
Grand Cross with
silver star

Do 12
Grand Cross silver star

Do 12
Grand Cross badge (obverse)

*Do 12. *La Orden Heráldica de Cristóbal Colón*

The Order of Christopher Columbus recognizes distinguished service to the nation, to humanity, and in the arts and sciences. It is the third-highest order in rank of the Dominican orders. It may be conferred on Dominican and foreign citizens, both civilian and military. The collar of the order has been awarded to Rafael Angel Calderón Fournier, president of Costa Rica, and Gustavo Noboa, president of Ecuador.

Instituted: By Law No. 1,352 on July 22, 1937

Regulated: Reglamento No. 172 on February 3, 1939

Grades: Collar, Grand Cross with gold star, Grand Cross with silver star,* Grand Officer, Commander, Officer, Knight*

Obverse disc: Bust of Christopher Columbus, ¾ left

Obverse legend: Ilustre y Esclarecido

Do 12
Grand Cross badge (reverse)

Do 12
Knight (military)

Do 12
Knight (military)

Varón | Don Cristobal Colón on a white enameled band

Reverse: Enameled arms of the Dominican Republic

Shape: Red enameled, ball-tipped cross pattée with concave ends and three 2-pointed rays in each angle suspended from a laurel wreath. When awarded to military personnel, the wreath has crossed swords

Size: Badge: Grand Cross, Knight: 56 mm. Star: 70 mm

Metal: Grand Cross: gilt; all other grades: silver

Maker: Carlup Fibo, Santo Domingo

Ribbon: Red

Reference: Barac 2009, 394; Burke's Peerage 2006, 1084; Dominican Republic 1939, 3–11

Provenance: Grand Cross: A. Menke

*Do13. *La Orden Heráldica de Trujillo*

The Heraldic Order of Trujillo was awarded for loyal service to Rafael Trujillo and meritorious accomplishments related to the glory of General Trujillo, the patriot and leader. It is the only known Latin American order named after a sitting president. It was rescinded in 1961.

Instituted: By Law No. 1,517 on June 13, 1938

Rescinded: December 6, 1961

Grades: Collar, Grand Cross with gold star, Grand Cross with silver star,* Grand Officer, Commander, Officer, and Knight*

Obverse disc: Bust of Trujillo, right

Obverse legend: ORDEN DE TRUJILLO on a white enameled band, 8 stars above

Do 13
Knight
(military)

Do 13
Knight
(civil)

Do 13
Knight
(military)

Do 13
Knight
(civil)

Do 13
Grand Cross
with silver star

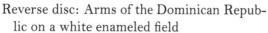
Do 13
Grand Cross badge (reverse)

Reverse disc: Arms of the Dominican Republic on a white enameled field

Reverse legend: EL CONGRESO NACIONAL | 1938 in a white enameled band

Shape: Disc flanked by 3 enameled Dominican flags on a ball-tipped white and green enameled Maltese cross with 2-pointed ends and 3 rays in each angle, suspended from a wreath. Awards for military merit have crossed swords in the wreath

Size: Badge: Grand Cross: 56 mm; Knight (civil): 50 mm, (military): 48 mm. Star: 90 mm

Metal: Silver

Maker: Grand Cross: Henri Walravens, Brussels

Ribbon: White with 2 narrow green edge stripes

Reference: Barac 2009, 393

Do 14

*Do14. *La Orden del Generalissimo*

Trujillo gave himself the title of generalissimo in addition to president and named this order for himself. It was rescinded in 1961 after his assassination.

Instituted: By Law No. 1,516 on June 13, 1938

Rescinded: December 6, 1961

Obverse: Entwined script letters RLT in green enameled wreath above 2 unfurled Dominican flags; in red enameled band beneath: ORDEN DEL GENERALISIMO

Reverse inscription: EL PRESIDENTE | DE LA | REPUBLICA DOMINICANA | AL | [raised band for recipient's name]

Size: 49 × 40 mm

Metal: Gilt, silvered,* bronze

Ribbon: Blue, white, red

Reference: Barac 2009, 394

*Do15. *La Orden del Mérito Aéreo*

The Order of Air Merit is awarded for meritorious service to the Dominican air force. Recipients may add the initials "M.A." (Mérito Aéreo) to their full names in all official papers and documents.

Instituted: By Law No. 3351-52 on August 3, 1952

Modified: By Law No. 5947 in 1962, deleting image of Trujillo and reverse legend

Grades: 1st: generals; 2nd: senior officers; 3rd: junior officers; 4th: noncommissioned officers*

Divisions: Combat, long service, other service

Obverse disc: Bust of Trujillo, right

Reverse inscription: AL | VALOR Y LEALTAD | 3 DE AGOSTO, 1952

Reverse legend: EL GENERALISIMO DR. RAFAEL L. TRUJILLO M.

Shape: Maltese cross with 2-pointed ends superimposed on sun surrounded by laurel wreath and attached to a device with the arms of the Dominican Republic flanked by laurel branches and displayed wings

Size: 72 × 58 mm

Metal: 1st: gold; 2nd: gilt; 3rd: silver; 4th: bronze

Do 15
4th grade

Do 15
4th grade

Ribbon: Combat: red; long service: blue; other service: white

Reference: http://en.wikipedia.org/wiki/Order_of_Air_Merit, accessed July 31, 2012

Do16. *La Orden del Mérito Naval*

The Order of Naval Merit is awarded for outstanding service in the Dominican navy and is divided into four classes with distinct medals with different designs and ribbons. They were all instituted by Law No. 2,043 on July 5, 1954, during the government of Rafael Trujillo. The original design of the four classes provided for five stars on the obverse symbolizing Trujillo as generalissimo. The stars were removed following his assassination in 1961.

*Do16a. *1st class: La Medalla del Mérito Naval*

The Medal for Naval Merit is awarded to sailors.

> Obverse disc: Sailing ship and torch
> Obverse legend: REPUBLICA DOMINICANA | MERITO NAVAL
> Shape: Dark blue enameled star on an anchor, surrounded by a wreath, suspended from a suspension bar with an enameled cross of the Dominican Republic
> Size: 31 mm
> Metal: Gilt,* silver, bronze
> Maker: N. S. Meyer, Inc., New York
> Ribbon: Blue, white, red

*Do16b. *2nd class: La Medalla de Honor*

The Medal of Honor is awarded to Dominican navy personnel for honorable service.

> Obverse disc: Enameled arms of the Dominican Republic
> Obverse legend: REPUBLICA DOMINICANA | MEDALLA DE HONOR
> Shape: Green enameled, ball-tipped star with a wreath in the angles and a silver anchor at the top, suspended from a blue enameled bar
> Size: 30 mm

Do 16a

> Metal: Gilt, silver,* bronze
> Ribbon: White with 2 light blue and 2 dark blue edge stripes

*Do16c. *3rd class: La Medalla de Servicio Distinguido*

The Medal for Distinguished Service is awarded to Dominican navy officers and warrant officers for distinguished service.

> Obverse: Enameled arms of the Dominican Republic attached to band by crossed anchors
> Obverse legend: SERVICIOS DISTINGUIDOS on a blue enameled band
> Shape: Round, attached to a gilt suspension bar
> Size: 30 mm

Do 16b

Do 16c

Do 16d

Metal: Gilt

Maker: N. S. Meyer, Inc., New York

Ribbon: Narrow center yellow stripe edged in
red with 2 white and green edge stripes

*Do16d. *4th class: La Medalla de Valor*

The Medal for Valor is awarded to Dominican
navy personnel for valor.

Obverse legend: REPUBLICA DOMINCANA

Obverse inscription: MEDALLA | DE | VALOR
on a white enameled field surrounded by a
raised copper wreath

Shape: White-edged, red enameled cross
pattée with convex ends

Size: 32 mm

Metal: Gold, silver, copper*

Maker: N. S. Meyer, Inc., New York

Ribbon: Purple with 2 narrow yellow side
stripes

Reference: Burke's Peerage 2006, 1085; Barac
2009, 392

*Do17. *La Orden de Mérito Policial*

The Order of Police Merit is awarded to members of the national police for merit.

Instituted: By decree on June 18, 1943

Regulated: By decree on April 19, 1964

Grades: 1st: officers;* 2nd: patrolmen*

Obverse disc: Arms of the Dominican Republic on a white enameled field

Obverse legend: MERITO | POLICIAL; 2nd: on a blue enameled band

Shape: 1st: ball-tipped, red enameled Maltese cross with 2-pointed ends and a green enameled wreath in the angles; 2nd: blue edged, white enameled modified Maltese cross with flat ends with concave edges and a green enameled wreath in the angles

Size: 50 mm

Metal: Gilt

Maker: N. S. Meyer, Inc., New York

Ribbon: 1st: red with 3 narrow white center stripes; 2nd: blue, white, green, suspended from a clasp denoting the class of the medal

Provenance: A. Menke

*Do18. *La Orden del Benefactor de la Nación*

The Order of the Benefactor of the Nation was awarded by Rafael Trujillo to his political supporters. Trujillo had named himself the "Benefactor of the Nation" to create a cult around his leadership. The order was rescinded in 1961.

Instituted: May 14, 1955

Rescinded: December 6, 1961

Grades: Silvered,* enameled bronze,* bronze*

Obverse: Bust of Trujillo, right, flanked by 2 Dominican flags with 5 stars between them

Do 17
1st grade

Do 17
2nd grade

Do 18

Reverse disc: Arms of the Dominican Republic (1st and 2nd: on a white enameled field)

Reverse legend: Outer: 25 AÑOS DE LA GLORIOSA ERA DE TRUJILLO; inner: AÑO DEL BENEFACTOR DE LA PATRIA (1st and 2nd: both on blue enameled bands)

Shape: 25-pointed sun

Size: 47 mm

Metal: Silvered, enameled bronze, bronze

Maker: Antigua Vilardebó y Riera, Havana

Ribbon: Blue, white, red

Reference: http://www.medals.org.uk/ dominican-republic/dominican-republic-text.htm, accessed July 31, 2012

Do19. *La Orden del Mérito Municipal*

This order is known only from a photo on an eBay auction in January 2013.

Instituted: 1956

Obverse disc: Bust of Trujillo, left, on a gilt field

Obverse legend: ORDEN DEL MERITO MUNICIPAL with 5 stars on a green enameled field

Reverse: Arms of the Dominican Republic

Shape: Gilt star with 7 rays in the angles

Size: 45 × 38 mm

Metal: Gilt

Ribbon: Green with red side stripes

Reference: http:/cgi.ebay.com/ws/eBay-ISAPI.d11?ViewItem, accessed January 8, 2013 (no longer accessible)

*Do20. *La Orden del Mérito 14 de Junio*

The June 14 Order of Merit was bestowed by Trujillo on his military and civilian allies for defeating a landing by Cuban-trained revolutionaries on June 14, 1959. The revolutionaries were led by Enrique Jiménez Moya and supported by President Betancourt of Venezuela and Fidel Castro of Cuba. They landed in small boats on the north coast at the fishing villages of Maimón and Estero Hondo, and by plane in an airport near Constanza. Although the attack failed, it is often credited with setting in motion an armed opposition to Trujillo.

Trujillo created the order specifically for those who fought or helped defeat the landing parties. It is divided into three variants, one for each of the landing points. A fourth variant exists, with no reference to landing spots.

Instituted: July 21, 1961

Rescinded: December 6, 1961

Grades: Senior officers, other officers, enlisted men

Divisions: Armed forces, militia

*Do20a. *Variant 1: Constanza*

Obverse disc: Bust of Trujillo, ¾ right

Obverse legend: CONSTANZA | HEROISMO Y LEALTAD

Reverse: Arms of the Dominican Republic

Reverse inscription: REPUBLICA DOMINICANA | 1959 | ERA DE TRUJILLO

Shape: Arc of 5 stars above the disc. Maltese cross with 2-pointed ends (red enameled for other officers) and a laurel wreath in the angles; armed forces: crossed rifles in the angles; militia: attached to crossed machetes at the top

Size: Military: 51 mm;* militia: 59 × 51 mm*

Metal: Senior officer: gilt; other officers: silvered;* enlisted men: bronze*

Ribbon: Red, white, blue

Engraver: Alberti

*Do20b. *Variant 2: Maimón*

Obverse disc: Bust of Trujillo, ¾ right

Obverse legend: MAIMON | HEROISMO Y LEALTAD

Reverse: Arms of the Dominican Republic

Reverse inscription: REPUBLICA DOMINICANA | 1959 | ERA DE TRUJILLO

Do 20a

Do 20a

Do 20b

Do 20b

Do 20c

Do 20c

Shape: Arc of 5 stars above the disc. Maltese cross with convex ends (green enameled for other officers) and a laurel wreath in the angles; armed forces: crossed rifles in the angles; militia: attached to crossed machetes at the top

Size: Military: 50 mm;* militia: 60 × 50 mm*

Metal: Senior officers: gilt; other officers: silvered;* enlisted men: bronze*

Ribbon: Red, white, blue

*Do20c. *Variant 3: Estero Hondo*

Obverse disc: Bust of Trujillo, ¾ right

Obverse legend: ESTERO HONDO | HEROISMO Y LEALTAD

Reverse: Arms of the Dominican Republic

Reverse inscription: REPUBLICA DOMINICANA | 1959 | ERA DE TRUJILLO

Shape: Arc of 5 stars above the disc. Maltese cross with pointed ends (enameled blue upper and lower arms and red left and right arms for senior officers; yellow for other officers) and a laurel wreath in the angles; armed forces: crossed rifles in the angles

Size: Military: 50 mm

Metal: Senior officers: gilt;* other officers: silvered;* enlisted men: bronze*

Ribbon: Red, white, blue

*Do20d. *Variant 4*

Obverse disc: Bust of Trujillo, ¾ right

Obverse legend: ORDEN AL MERITO 14 DE JUNIO

Reverse: Arms of the Dominican Republic

Reverse inscription: LEALTAD Y ABNEGACION on a white enameled band

Shape: Red enameled Maltese cross with pointed ends and a laurel wreath in the angles; crossed arms in the angles

Size: 51 mm

Metal: Silvered

Ribbon: Red, white, blue

Do 20d

Do 20d

ECUADOR

THE CITY OF GUAYAQUIL declared its independence from Spain in October 1820, but the Spanish authorities remained firmly based in Quito. In May 1821, Simón Bolívar sent republican forces under Antonio José de Sucre to help Guayaquil, but the royalists defeated him at the Battle of Huachi. Argentine General San Martín, who by then was in Lima, sent another force under Andrés de Santa Cruz north to assist Sucre. Their combined forces succeeded in defeating the royalists at the decisive Battle of Pichincha on May 24, 1822. The Cabildo of Quito proclaimed its independence and authorized Ecuador's first medal for the victors of that battle.

Once Ecuador obtained its independence from Spain, both Gran Colombia and Peru hoped to annex it and sent armies to assert their claim. The two sides met at Portete de Tarqui in 1829; Gran Colombia won the battle and created a political union with Ecuador. Over time, public opinion in Ecuador shifted in favor of independence from Gran Colombia, and Quito dissolved the union in 1830.

Ecuador's political independence quickly split the country between free trade liberals in the port city of Guayaquil and conservative landowners in the mountains centered in Quito. The split led to decades of internal armed conflict. Ecuador fought brief border wars with Colombia in 1863 and border skirmishes with Peru in 1941, 1981, and 1995. Ecuador is not known to have authorized any medals for either the internal conflicts or the fighting with its neighbors.

Ecuador instituted its first three national orders of merit at the turn of the twentieth century, followed by additional ones beginning after World War II. The country authorized an array of military medals for valor, merit, distinguished service, and loyalty in peacetime after World War II.

MEDALS

ECUADOR's War of Independence centered on defeating the royalist garrison in Quito after Guayaquil proclaimed its independence. Ecuadorean troops from Guayaquil tried to take Quito but were defeated at Huachi by royalist forces commanded by Colonel Francisco González. Bolívar then sent Sucre to reinforce Guayaquil. The combined armies advanced on Quito but were again defeated by the royalists at Huachi. Bolívar marched south from Gran Colombia but was himself defeated at Bombona by royalists under the command of Colonel Basilio García. Argentine General San Martín sent Andrés de Santa Cruz north with reinforcements from Peru. The combined forces from five Latin American countries fought the royalists commanded by Melchor de Aymeric in the foothills of the Pichincha volcano, defeating them on May 24, 1822. The royalists suffered heavy casualties, and Quito surrendered the next day. The Cabildo of Quito authorized a medal for its liberators.

Ec1. *La Medalla de la Victoria de Pichincha*

The Cabildo of Quito authorized Ecuador's first military medal for the battle of Pichincha, which ended Spanish power in Ecuador. Many of Quito's medals were awarded to men from Argentina, Chile, Colombia, Peru, and Venezuela, who made up the bulk of the revolutionary forces at the battle of Pichincha. The medal is known in at least two variants. The first variant served as a model years later when Ecuador created its highest order, the National Order of Merit.

Ec1a. *Variant 1*

Instituted: May 29, 1822
Grades: Officers, enlisted men
Obverse disc: Sun rising above 3 mountains
Obverse legend: LIBERTADOR D^E QUITO
Obverse inscription: AÑO DE | 1822
Reverse: EL CABILDO DE QUITO
Shape: 12-armed star, each arm composed of 5 rays with an interlaced wreath, suspended from an oval wreath
Size: 35 mm
Metal: Officers: gold; enlisted men: silver
Ribbon: Red, blue, yellow

Ec1b. *Variant 2*

Obverse: Shield crowned with a liberty cap bearing a sunburst, flags, and a horn of plenty
Obverse inscription: A LOS LIBERTADORES DE QUITO
Reverse inscription: YO FUI DEL EJERCITO LIBERTADOR within a laurel wreath
Shape: Oval, circular outer border of 12 arms each composed of 7 rays, with intertwined laurel wreath
Size: 42 × 38 mm
Metal: Officers: gold; enlisted men: silver
Ribbon: Red, blue, yellow
Reference: Gillingham 1932, 131–34; Barac 2009, 395

Ec2. *La Cruz de la Independencia*

The attribution of this undocumented medal to Ecuador is based on the inscription 1831, one year after Ecuador gained its independence from Gran Colombia.

Obverse inscription: 1831 on a white enameled field

Obverse legend: GUERRA DE INDEPENDENCIA on a blue enameled band

Shape: Ball-tipped, white enameled Maltese cross with 2-pointed ends surmounted by 2 green enameled scrolls

Size: 41 mm

Metal: Gold

Reference: Gillingham 1932, 134; Barac 2009, 395

* * *

FOLLOWING its independence, Ecuador suffered from many decades of internal instability between liberals and conservatives. No military medals are known to have been authorized for these conflicts. Ecuador never fought major wars with its neighbors other than minor border clashes with Colombia and Peru. Ecuador's first medals for national merit were created after World War II.

Ec3. *La Cruz al Mérito de Guerra*

The Cross for War Merit is Ecuador's highest award to the members of its armed forces. The cross is given to military personnel killed or seriously wounded in combat as a result of heroic action as well as extraordinary heroism in defense of the nation and national sovereignty. The medal may be bestowed individually or collectively. The grade of the cross is awarded in accordance with the degree of heroism or bravery. The cross is awarded by executive decree on the recommendation of a military council. It is awarded to military personnel of all branches of the armed forces.

The cross was awarded to members of the armed forces who fought a short border war with Peru known as the Cenepa War. Ecuador and Peru disagreed on the exact definition of the border around the Cenepa River. War broke out between the two countries on January 26 and ended on February 28, 1995. Fighting centered on military outposts of both countries with names like Tiwinza, Cueva de los Tayos, Coangas, Base Sur, and Base Norte. The conflict was eventually arbitrated and settled by the Brasilia Agreement of October 28, 1998.

Regulated: By Ministerial Agreement No. 459 on June 21, 1994

Modified: By Ministerial Agreement No. 925 on October 4, 2005

Classes: Grand Cross, Commander, Knight

Obverse disc: Enameled arms of Ecuador within 2 laurel branches

Obverse legend: AL MERITO DE GUERRA | [year of the action]

Shape: Maltese cross with 9 rays extending from the end of each arm and with 11 rays in each angle

Size: 85 mm

Metal: Grand Cross: gilt; Commander: silvered; Knight: bronze

Ribbon: Yellow, blue, red

Reference: Ecuador 2005, 5–7

MEDALS FOR PEACETIME SERVICE

AFTER World War II, Ecuador created a large number of military medals in peacetime, for valor, merit, distinguished service, and length of service. We have included medals for bravery and merit to the armed forces and the nation. We have excluded medals for academic merit, length of service, promotion to a higher rank or awards for technical accomplishment of interest to unit commanders.

A Cross for Military Merit is awarded to officers of the three branches of the armed forces for meritorious actions and performance of importance to the armed forces in peacetime. The army's version is called Vencedores de Tarqui; the navy is Al Mérito Comandante Morán Valverde; the air force is Al Mérito Aeronáutico Cóndor de los Andes. Although hierarchy influences who receives the Grand Cross, most of the crosses are awarded on the basis of merit and length of service. The reasons for awarding this medal are spelled out in great detail in the regulations. The design of the medal differs according to the branch of service.

*Ec4. *La Cruz al Mérito Militar de la Fuerza Terrestre "Vencedores de Tarqui" (Ejército)*

The Cross for Military Merit of the Land Forces "Conquerors of Tarqui" is awarded by the army for service in peacetime to senior government officials, army officers, and other military officers for service of importance and benefit to the army. The medal honors the officers from Colombia and Ecuador commanded by Antonio José de Sucre and Juan José Flores, who defeated a Peruvian army under the command of José de la Mar at Portete de Tarqui on February 27, 1829. The battle ended Peru's effort to expand its borders north into Ecuador.

Regulated: By Ministerial Agreement No. 459 on June 21, 1994

Modified: By General Order No. 116 on October 5, 2005

Classes: Grand Cross, Commander, Knight*

Obverse disc: Enameled emblem of the army

Reverse disc: Arms of Ecuador

Reverse legend: AL MERITO | EJERCITO DEL ECUADOR

Shape: Blue enameled, ball-tipped Maltese cross with 3-pointed ends and a laurel wreath in the angles

Size: Grand Cross: 70 mm; Commander, Knight: 60 mm

Metal: Grand Cross: gilt; Commander: silver; Knight: bronze

Ec 4

Ec 4

Ribbon: Grand Cross: cord; Commander,
  Knight: red with 2 yellow edge stripes
  hanging behind medal
Reference: Ecuador 2005, 7–13
Provenance: A. Menke

*Ec5. *La Cruz al Mérito Naval "Comandante Morán Valverde"* (*Marina*)

The Commander Morán Valverde Medal for
Naval Merit is awarded for meritorious service
to the navy in peacetime. It recognizes senior
government officials, navy officers, and other
military personnel who provide service of importance and benefit to the navy. The medal is
named for Commander Rafael Morán Valverde
(1904–58), a career navy officer. Morán commanded an obsolete Ecuadorean gunboat, the
Calderón, during the 1941 war with Peru. While
on a mission off the Ecuadorean coast, his ship
was attacked by the Peruvian destroyer *Almirante Villar*. Moran damaged the Peruvian warship, which retreated from Ecuadorean waters.
After Morán's death, Ecuador named its naval
university after him.

Regulated: By Ministerial Agreement No. 459
  on June 21, 1994
Modified: By General Order No. 116 on Oc-
  tober 5, 2005
Classes: Grand Cross, Commander,* Knight
Obverse disc: Emblem of the navy on a blue
  enameled field
Reverse disc: Arms of Ecuador
Reverse inscription: ARMADA DEL ECUADOR
  | AL MERITO
Shape: Ball-tipped, blue enameled Maltese
  cross with 3-pointed ends with a wreath in
  the angles suspended from a bar inscribed
  REPUBLICA DEL ECUADOR
Size: Grand Cross: 70 mm; Commander and
  Knight: 60 mm

Ec 5

Ec 5

Metal: Grand Cross: gilt; Commander: silver; Knight: bronze

Ribbon: Blue with 2 yellow edge stripes hanging behind medal

Reference: Ecuador 2005, 7–13

Ec6. *La Cruz al Mérito Aeronáutico "Cóndor de los Andes"*

The Medal for Aeronautical Merit "Condor of the Andes" is given by the air force for peacetime service. The medal recognizes senior government officials, air force officers, and other military personnel who have provided services of importance and the benefit to the air force. The medal also recognizes the number of years of uninterrupted service.

Regulated: By Ministerial Agreement No. 459 on June 21, 1994

Modified: By General Order No. 116 on October 5, 2005

Classes: Grand Cross, Commander, Knight

Obverse: Emblem of the air force within a laurel wreath

Reverse: AL MERITO AERONAUTICO

Shape: Ball-tipped, blue and white enameled cross with 2-pointed ends and 3 rays in each angle, suspended from a condor, right, with its wings displayed

Size: 55 mm

Metal: Grand Cross: gilt; Commander: silvered; Knight: bronze

Ribbon: Blue

Reference: Ecuador 2005, 7–13

* * *

A MEDAL of Honor and Discipline is awarded by each branch of the armed forces to its enlisted men for discipline, loyalty, esprit de corps, exemplary conduct, exceptional acts, and

Ec 7

years of service in peacetime. The purpose of this medal is the same for all three branches of the armed forces, but the medals' designs differ.

*Ec7. La Condecoración Honor y Disciplina de la Fuerza Terrestre "Caporal Luis Minacho"

The Corporal Luis Minacho Decoration for Honor and Discipline in the Army is awarded to enlisted men for discipline, loyalty, esprit de corps, exemplary conduct, and outstanding performance in the army. The class of the decoration awarded depends on the number of years uninterrupted service (1st: 12 years; 2nd: 9 years; 3rd: 6 years). The decoration may also be given to enlisted men from friendly countries for strengthening fraternal ties.

The decoration honors Corporal Luis Minacho of the Ecuadorean army, who was killed in combat during the 1941 border war with Peru.

Instituted: July 28, 1947

Regulated: By Ministerial Agreement No. 459 on June 21, 1994

Modified: By General Order No. 116 on October 5, 2005

Classes: 1st,* 2nd, 3rd

Obverse disc: Red, blue, yellow enameled concentric circles

Shape: Disc surrounded by a laurel wreath on crossed swords, surmounting a ball-tipped Maltese cross with 2-pointed ends and 11 rays in each angle. The upper arm is inscribed: MEDALLA; the left arm: HONOR Y; the right arm: DISCIPLINA; the lower arm: EJERCITO. All suspended from a brooch inscribed REPUBLICA DEL ECUADOR

Size: 54 mm

Metal: 1st: gilt; 2nd: silvered; 3rd: bronze

Ribbon: Olive green with yellow, red, blue center stripes hanging behind medal

Reference: Ecuador 2005, 13–15

Provenance: A. Menke

Ec8. *La Condecoración Honor y Disciplina de la Fuerza Naval*

The Navy Decoration for Honor and Discipline is awarded to sailors for their discipline, loyalty, esprit de corps, exemplary conduct, and outstanding effort that benefits the navy. The decoration may also be awarded to foreign sailors who have worked with the navy and strengthened friendship with Ecuador. The class of the decoration awarded depends on the number of years uninterrupted service (1st: 12 years; 2nd: 9 years; 3rd: 6 years).

Instituted: July 28, 1947

Regulated: By Ministerial Agreement No. 459 on June 21, 1994

Modified: By General Order No. 116 on October 5, 2005

Classes: 1st, 2nd, 3rd

Obverse disc: Emblem of the navy on a yellow, red, blue enameled field

Obverse inscription: HONOR Y DISCIPLINA

Shape: Cross

Size: 50 mm

Metal: 1st: gilt; 2nd: silvered; 3rd: bronze

Ribbon: Light blue with blue, red, yellow edge stripes hanging behind medal

Reference: Ecuador 2005, 13–16

*Ec9. *La Condecoración Honor y Disciplina de las Fuerzas Aéreas*

The Decoration for Honor and Discipline of the Air Force recognizes discipline, loyalty, esprit de corps, exemplary conduct, and outstanding performance in the air force in peacetime. The class of the decoration awarded depends on the number of years of uninterrupted service (1st: 12 years; 2nd: 9 years; 3rd: 6 years), for which a special bonus is awarded. The decoration may also be given to enlisted men from friendly countries who have cooperated with the air force.

Instituted: July 28, 1947

Regulated: By Ministerial Agreement No. 459 on June 21, 1994

Modified: By Ministerial Agreement No. 925 on October 4, 2005

Regulated: By General Order No. 116 on October 5, 2005

Classes: 1st, 2nd,* 3rd

Obverse disc: Emblem of the air force on concentric red, blue, yellow circles

Obverse legend: HONOR | Y DISCIPLINA

Shape: Round medal surrounded by 2 laurel branches, suspended from a bar inscribed REPUBLICA DEL ECUADOR

Ec 9

Size: 42 mm

Metal: 1st: gilt; 2nd: silvered; 3rd: bronze

Ribbon: Light blue with 1 medium yellow and 2 narrower blue and red center stripes hanging behind medal

Reference: Ecuador 2005, 13–16

Ec 10. *La Estrella Militar de las Fuerzas Armadas del Ecuador*

The Military Star of the Ecuadorean Armed Forces is awarded to officers and institutions of foreign countries for distinguished service of importance to Ecuador and its armed forces. The star is an honorific award used by Ecuador to recognize service by foreigners to the nation or its armed forces.

Regulated: By Ministerial Agreement No. 459 on June 21, 1994

Modified: By Ministerial Agreement No. 925 on October 4, 2005

Classes: Grand Star for Military Merit, Star for Military Merit, Military Star

Obverse disc: Emblems of the army, navy, and air force of Ecuador on a white enameled field

Obverse legend: GRAN ESTRELLA AL MERITO MILITAR, ESTRELLA AL MERITO MILITAR, or ESTRELLA MILITAR, depending on class

Shape: Ball-tipped star

Size: 75 mm

Metal: Grand Star for Military Merit: gilt; Star for Military Merit: silvered; Military Star: copper

Ribbon: Yellow with blue, red, and yellow edge stripes. The ribbon of the Military Star is suspended from a brooch inscribed REPUBLICA DEL ECUADOR

Reference: Ecuador 2005, 33–35

*Ec 11. *La Decoración de Mérito "Atahualpa"*

The Atahualpa Decoration for Merit is an honorific award for individuals and organizations and members of the armed forces from Ecuador and foreign countries for their loyalty and actions of benefit to the Ecuadorean armed forces. The Grand Cross has no star.

The decoration is named after Atahualpa, the Inca emperor at the time of the Spanish conquest. Atahualpa was born in Quito when it was part of the Inca Empire. Francisco Pizarro had Atahualpa executed on August 29, 1533.

Classes: Grand Cross,* Commander, Knight

Obverse disc: Bust of Atahualpa, ¾ left, surrounded by a blue enameled band

Ec 11
Grand
Cross

Obverse legend: AL MERITO | ATAHUALPA
on a yellow enameled band

Shape: Ball-tipped star with a wreath intertwined in the angles

Size: Grand Cross badge: 60 mm

Metal: Grand Cross: gilt; Commander:
silvered; Knight: bronze

Ribbon: Blue-green, red, blue-green

Reference: Ecuador 2005, 35–36

Provenance: A. Menke

*Ec12. *La Estrella de Plata*

The purpose of this medal is not known.

Obverse disc: Enameled view of mountain
and ship with sun above in band with zodiac
symbols, within an enameled wreath

Shape: Rayed star with a ray enameled yellow,
blue, red in each angle

Size: 57 mm

Metal: Silvered white metal

Ec 12

Ec 13

Maker: MECO

Ribbon: Blue, white, blue, hanging behind medal, suspended from a brooch inscribed REPUBLICA DEL ECUADOR

Provenance: A. Menke

*Ec13. *La Estrella de la Armada*

The purpose of this naval medal is not known.

Obverse disc: Eagle with spread wings on enameled flags

Obverse legend: ARMADA DEL ECUADOR | FUERZAS ARMADAS

Shape: Ball-tipped, blue enameled 6-pointed star edged in white with a laurel wreath in the angles

Size: 55 mm

Metal: Bronze

Ribbon: Blue, red, blue, hanging behind medal, suspended from a brooch inscribed REPUBLICA DEL ECUADOR

Provenance: A. Menke

*Ec14. *La Cruz de Honor de la Armada*

The purpose of this naval medal is not known.

Obverse disc: Anchor with eagle above on oval enameled field, divided horizontally, yellow, blue, red, surrounded by a rope

Obverse inscription: HONOR

Obverse legend: ARMADA | DEL ECUADOR

Ec 14

Shape: Maltese cross with flat ends with center semicircle

Size: 52 × 49 mm

Ribbon: Light blue with narrow red and blue side stripes and yellow edge stripes, hanging behind medal, suspended from a brooch inscribed REPUBLICA DEL ECUADOR

Provenance: A. Menke

*Ec15. *La Estrella de las Fuerzas Armadas*

The purpose of this medal is not known.

Classes: 1st,* 2nd*

Obverse disc: Metallic disc surrounded by narrow red, blue enameled rings

Obverse legend: FUERZAS | ARMADAS on a yellow enameled band

Shape: Crossed rifles with banner suspended on a ball-tipped star with laurel wreath entwined between the angles

Ec 15

Size: 63 mm

Metal: 1st: gilt; 2nd: bronze

Ribbon: 1st: Light blue, green, dark blue; 2nd: blue, green, light blue hanging behind medal, suspended from a brooch inscribed REPUBLICA DEL ECUADOR

Provenance: A. Menke

Ec16. *La Medalla de la Cruz Roja Ecuatoriana*

The Ecuadorean Red Cross traces its roots back to April 22, 1910, when an organizing committee of the Red Cross was created in Guayaquil, which formed three medical brigades to care for wounded soldiers in case of an armed conflict with Peru. The government recognized the Ecuadorean Red Cross as an institution of well-being and public utility on November 14, 1910. The organization was legally established with its own statutes on December 27, 1922, and recognized by the League of Red Cross Societies in 1923. The Ecuadorean Red Cross volunteers have been providing a range of medical, public health, and disaster relief services to the country for over one hundred years.

Obverse: Red cross on a white enameled field

Shape: Round, within 2 green enameled branches

Size: 50 mm

Metal: Bronze

Ribbon: White with yellow, blue, and red edge stripes suspended from a bronze brooch inscribed CRUZ ROJA ECUATORIANA

Reference: http://www.cruzrojaamericana. org/imageup/phototemplate_hhm06. swf, accessed January 25, 2013; no longer accessible

ORDERS

ECUADOR created its first order of merit in 1809, one week after insurgents formed a provisional government in Quito. The order was abandoned after the royalists recaptured the city. The first order of merit after Ecuador's independence was established in 1904.

*Ec17. *La Orden de Abdón Calderón*

The Order of Abdón Calderón is awarded to Ecuadorean and foreign military personnel for extraordinary merit. It may also be conferred on civilians who have served in the armed forces. The order was bestowed on General Dwight Eisenhower during World War II and Felipe Herrera, president of the Interamerican Development Bank.

The order is named after Captain Abdón Calderón (1804–22) in the Yaguachi Battalion that fought the royalist army at the Battle of Pichincha. Although wounded four times, he continued to lead his men until the battle ended. He died of his wounds several days later in Quito. Calderón's father had been a colonel who was captured and executed by the royalists in the first rebellion ending in 1812.

Instituted: October 22, 1904

Grades: 1st,* 2nd,* 3rd*

Obverse disc: Bust of Calderón, left, surrounded by a blue enameled band

Obverse legend: ABDON CALDERON | 1822

Reverse disc: REPUBLICA DEL ECUADOR over the first 4 signs of the zodiac

Shape: 5-armed, 12-part star with 2-pointed ends and a wreath in the angles

Ec 17
1st, 2nd, 3rd grades

Metal: 1st: gilt, 2nd: silver; 3rd: bronze

Size: 53 mm

Ribbon: Half yellow and half equal blue and red stripes, hanging behind medal, suspended from a brooch inscribed REPUBLICA DEL ECUADOR over 4 signs of the zodiac

Reference: Gillingham 1932, 135; Barac 2009, 396; Burke's Peerage 2006, 1089; Ecuador 1934, 3–5

*Ec18. *La Orden Nacional al Mérito*

The National Order of Merit is Ecuador's highest civil award. It is bestowed on Ecuadorean and foreign citizens for extraordinary service to the nation in the fields of diplomacy, science, literature, and the arts. The order was originally instituted in 1921 as the Medal of Merit, but its name was changed in 1929 to the National Order of Merit.

The collar is awarded only to heads of state; it has been bestowed on Rafael Ángel Calderón Fournier, president of Costa Rica; Juan Carlos Wasmosy, president of Paraguay; Ricardo Lagos, president of Chile; Fernando Henrique Cardoso, president of Brazil; and Rafael Hipólito Mejía, president of the Dominican Republic.

Instituted: By law on October 8, 1921, as the Medal of Merit

Renamed: December 2, 1929. as the National Order of Merit

Regulated: By Decree No. 37 on June 28, 1937

Regulated: By Executive Decree No. 3,109 on September 17, 2002, creating the grade of Grand Collar and abolishing Executive Decree No. 1,306 of November 19, 1985; Executive Decree No. 1,529 of January 30, 1986; and Executive Decree No. 1,495 of May 10, 1990

Ec 18
Grand Collar

Ec 18
Grand
Cross

Ec 18
Grand Cross star variant

Ec 18
Grand Cross star variant

Chief: President of the Republic

Grades: Grand Collar,* Grand Cross (3),* Grand Officer, Commander, Officer, and Knight*

Obverse disc: 3 mountains beneath a sun (design has changed 3 times since the order was created)

Obverse legend: REPUBLICA DEL ECUADOR | AL MÉRITO

Shape: Red enameled, 12-armed sun with 5-pointed ends and a green enameled wreath interlaced among the arms

Star disc: Enameled 3 mountains beneath a sun on oval disc; variant: 3 mountains to left, ship with flags and caduceus to right, sun above an arc with zodiac signs

Star legend: REPUBLICA DEL ECUADOR | AL MÉRITO

Star shape: Ball-tipped, silvered-sequined Maltese cross with 2-pointed ends and a laurel wreath behind; variant: cross is faceted

Collar shape: Scrollwork around the tips of the star, suspended from collar of alternating links of different patterns of scrollwork

Size: Badge: Grand Cross: 59 mm; Knight: 41 mm. Star: Grand Collar: 77 × 71 mm; Grand Cross: 81 × 72 mm, 75 × 69 mm

Metal: Grand Collar (made in 2012): gilt and white metal; badge: Grand Cross: gilt; Knight: silvered. Star: Grand Cross: silver

Maker: Collar and Grand Cross: Cejalvo, Madrid

Ribbon: Yellow with 1 narrow blue and 1 narrow red edge stripe

Reference: Burke's Peerage 2006, 1087–88; Gillingham 1932, 134; Barac 2009, 396–97; Werlich 1974, 117

*Ec 18a. *Variant*

The flags beneath the disc identify this star as Ecuadorian. Though apparently undocumented as such, it appears to be an early version of the National Order of Merit.

Obverse disc: Enameled scene of 3 mountains beneath a sun on a banner inscribed EL BIEN PUBLICO, with a ship at sail in foreground

Star shape: Eagle in flight above disc, enameled Ecuadorian flags beneath, with enam-

Ec 18
Knight

eled laurel branches to left and right, on
a 3-part Maltese cross with 8 rays with
2-pointed ends in each angle

Size: 87 mm

Metal: Gilt

Maker: Medina, Barcelona and Madrid

*Ec19. *La Orden al Mérito Aeronáutico*

The Order of Aeronautical Merit is awarded to
national and foreign citizens for outstanding
service to the Ecuadorean air force.

Instituted: October 31, 1958

Modified: 1963

Grades: Grand Cross,* Commander, Knight

Obverse shield: Gold shield with 2 enameled,
snow-capped volcanoes above 3 horizontal
stripes, enameled with the national colors

Obverse inscription: FAE in blue enamel

Reverse legend: AL MERITO AERONAUTICO

Shape: Ball-tipped, blue and white enameled
Maltese cross with 2-pointed ends and 3
rays in each angle with a laurel wreath behind, suspended from a gold globe attached
to golden condor with displayed wings

Ec 18a
Grand Cross star variant

Ec 19
Grand Cross star

Ec 19
Grand Cross badge (obverse)

Ec 19
Grand Cross badge (reverse)

Star shape: Badge on an 8-pointed sun with 5
    rays in each angle

Size: Badge: 48 mm. Star: 74 mm

Metal: Gilt silver, bronze

Ribbon: Light blue

Reference: Burke's Peerage 2006, 1090;
    Werlich 1974, 118

*Ec20. *La Orden Nacional de San Lorenzo*

The National Order of Saint Lawrence is
awarded to Ecuadorean and foreign nationals
for extraordinary civil merit. The order was
originally created as a military award in 1809
and was called the Grand Cross of Saint Lawrence. It was awarded to a number of influential
insurgents while they controlled Quito. However, when royalist forces recaptured the city,
the provisional government disbanded and the
order fell into disuse.

The order was restored in 1959 and restructured in 2001. It is now known as the National
Order of Saint Lawrence. The Grand Cross is
only awarded to heads of state. Its recipients
include Carlos Saúl Menem, president of Argentina, and Rafael Hipólito Mejía, president
of the Dominican Republic. The order is Ecuador's second-highest civil and military award.

The order is named after Saint Lawrence,
the Roman deacon who by tradition gave away
Church valuables to the poor rather than to
the emperor, for which he suffered martyr-
dom. Saint Lawrence's saint's day is August
10, which coincides with the date in 1809 when
Ecuador first proclaimed its independence.

Instituted: August 10, 1809

Restored: By Executive Decree No. 1,329 on
    August 10, 1959

Modified: June 4, 2001

Regulated: By Executive Decree No. 655 on
    September 2, 2002

Ec 20
Grand
Cross

Grades: Grand Collar, Grand Cross,* Commander

Obverse disc: Stylized letters "SLr"

Obverse legend: ORDEN DE SAN LORENZO | 10 DE AGOSTO DE 1809 on a black enameled band

Shape: Red enameled, black-edged Maltese cross with 2-pointed ends and 4 flames in each angle suspended from a wreath

Star disc: Stylized letters "SLr" in front of a grill flanked by flames on a red enameled disc

Star legend: REPUBLICA DEL ECUADOR | 10 DE AGOSTO DE 1809

Star shape: 5-armed star with 3-part arms and 2-pointed ends (sometimes partially red enameled), with 5 rays in each angle

Size: Badge: Grand Cross: 57 mm. Star: 80 mm

Metal: Gilt silver

Ribbon: Red with black edge stripes

Reference: Barac 2009, 396; Burke's Peerage 2006, 1088–89

Provenance: A. Menke

Ec21. *La Orden Nacional Honorato Vásquez*

The National Order Honorato Vásquez is given to Ecuadorean and foreign nationals for extraordinary achievement in the political and diplomatic fields. It is often bestowed on foreign ambassadors who have served at least two years in Ecuador, on the basis of reciprocity.

Honorato Vásquez (1855–1933) was a lawyer, politician, diplomat, writer, and poet from Cuenca. The government called on him to arbitrate territorial disputes with Peru and Colombia. A political conservative, he also served under liberal presidents.

Instituted: By Executive Decree No. 700 on April 25, 1985

Regulated: By Executive Decree No. 3,798-A on May 17, 1996

Regulated: By Decree No. 3,110 on September 17, 2002, abolishing Executive Decree No. 700 of April 25, 1985, and Executive Decree No. 3,798-A of May 17, 1996

Chief: President of the Republic

Grades: Grand Cross, Grand Officer, Commander

Obverse disc: Bust of Vásquez on a field, gilt for Grand Cross and Grand Officer, silver for Commander

Obverse legend: Grand Cross, Grand Officer: HONORATO VASQUEZ | ECUADOR; Commander: ECUADOR, on a blue enameled field

Shape: Maltese cross with rays in the angles

Star shape: Star within 2 laurel branches

Size: Grand Cross, Grand Officer: 80 mm; Commander: 30 mm

Metal: Grand Cross: gilt silver; Grand Officer: silver

Ribbon: Blue with red, blue, yellow edge stripes

Reference: Burke's Peerage 2006, 1089; Ecuador 2002

Ec22. *La Orden al Mérito Agrícola*

The Order of Agricultural Merit is awarded to Ecuadorean and foreign nationals for outstanding service to the country's agribusiness sector.

Obverse disc: Enameled image of snow-covered volcano

Obverse legend: REPUBLICA DEL ECUADOR on a white enameled band

Reverse inscription: MERITO AGRICOLA on a yellow enameled field, surrounded by a white enameled band

Shape: Green enameled, ball-tipped Maltese cross with a wreath in the angles, suspended from the claws of a silver condor with displayed wings

Ribbon: Red with narrow green side stripes

Reference: Burke's Peerage 2006, 1090; Werlich 1974, 11

EL SALVADOR

THE STRUGGLE for independence in El Salvador began in 1811, led by a Catholic priest, José Matías Delgado. The revolt was suppressed by royalist forces based in Guatemala. El Salvador became independent on September 15, 1821, when Central America proclaimed its independence from Spain. However, within a few months the region was incorporated into the newly formed Mexican Empire. In 1823, Mexico reverted to a republic and recognized Central America's independence. On July 23, 1823, five Central American republics, including El Salvador, formed the United Provinces of Central America, with its capital in Guatemala City. The new republic suffered from internal disputes primarily caused by a political split between liberals and conservatives. The union was dissolved in 1840, and El Salvador officially proclaimed its independence in February 1841.

El Salvador authorized one medal during the entire period leading up to its total independence. There is no literature on any other medal until well after the end of World War II. El Salvador has created an array of military medals for merit and loyalty in peacetime and one medal related to the violent insurgency affecting the country between 1980 and 1992. El Salvador created its first order of merit, named for José Matías Delgado, after World War II. El Salvador has authorized few orders and medals, with Costa Rica being the only Latin American country with fewer official awards.

Sv 1

Sv 1

MEDALS

E L SALVADOR's first known military medal was awarded as the Federal Republic of Central America was disbanding. The country took sides in the decades-long struggles between liberals and conservatives, mostly on the side of the liberals. In 1839, a Honduran liberal, Francisco Morazán, was elected chief of state of El Salvador, a position he held for less than a year. Morazán had just finished his second term as president of the Federal Republic of Central America. He was frequently challenged during this period by a conservative Guatemalan insurgent, Rafael Carrera, who became president of Guatemala.

*Sv 1. *La Medalla a Sus Leales Defensores*

The Medal for Its Loyal Defenders was probably instituted by Francisco Morazán to reward Salvadoran troops for defeating an invading army from Guatemala and Nicaragua in 1839. There is no known literature on this medal. In 1839, Rafael Carrera invaded El Salvador shortly after Morazán became head of state. Morazán, commanding a Salvadoran army, defeated the invading force at the Battle of San Pedro Perulapán on September 25, 1839. The medal was probably instituted at the end of 1839 as a reward for the Salvadoran officers and men who fought with Morazán. It has three divisions with the same design, except for the reverse inscription.

Instituted: Probably 1839

Divisions: Al Valor Distinguido,* Al Mérito,* Al Heroismo,*

Classes: Senior officers, other officers,* enlisted men*

Obverse: Bust of Morazán, left, in a general's uniform

Obverse legend: REPUBLICA DEL SALVADOR | LA PATRIA A SUS LEALES DEFENSORES

Reverse inscription: PREMIO | AL | VALOR | DISTINGUIDO [PREMIO | AL | MERITO,

PREMIO | AL | HEROISMO] within laurel branches

Shape: Round, suspended from a shield with volcano and stars above on obverse and 15 SET^{BRE} 1821 on reverse

Size: 41 × 36 mm

Metal: Senior officers: gold; other officers: silver; enlisted men: bronze

Ribbon: Red with narrow blue, white, blue center stripes

Engraver: N. Perfita

Reference: Barac 2010, 403

Provenance: Al Mérito, Al Heroismo: A. Menke

* * *

IN 1969, El Salvador instituted an array of military medals for its armed forces in both wartime and peacetime. The country had just fought a brief war with neighboring Honduras, generally known as the Football War.

Sv 2. *La Cruz al Heroismo*

The Cross for Heroism is awarded to units of the armed forces and the security forces, to military personnel, and to civilians. In wartime, the gold cross is awarded for bravery in combat. In peacetime, the silver cross is given for responding to natural disasters above and beyond the call of duty.

Instituted: By Decree Law No. 520 on October 21, 1969

Regulated: By Presidential Decree No. 82 on June 16, 1973

Classes: Gold: wartime; silver: peacetime

Obverse disc: Enameled arms of El Salvador

Obverse legend: REPUBLICA DE EL SALVADOR EN AMERICA CENTRAL

Shape: Cross with a ray in each angle

Size: 30 mm

Metal: Gold: gilt; silver: silvered

Ribbon: Blue, white, blue. The white stripe has 2 narrow blue side stripes near the center

Reference: El Salvador 1973; El Salvador 1969

Sv3. *La Medalla al Valor*

The gold Medal for Valor is awarded to units of the armed forces and of the security forces, military personnel, and civilians for valor in combat. The silver medal is awarded in peacetime for responding efficiently to natural disasters The design of the two classes is identical in all other respects.

Instituted: By Decree Law No. 520 on October 21, 1969

Regulated: By Executive Decree No. 82 on June 16, 1973

Divisions: Gold: wartime; silver: peacetime

Obverse: Red enameled V with a helmet in front within an enameled coffee wreath

Metal: Gold: gilt; silver: silvered

Ribbon: Blue, white, blue; blue stripes are divided by narrow blue-green stripes; white stripe is divided by narrow orange, red, and orange stripes

Reference: El Salvador 1973; El Salvador 1969

Sv4. *La Medalla al Servicio en Campaña*

The gold Medal for Service in the Field of Battle is awarded to units of the military and security forces for distinguishing themselves in combat. The silver medal is awarded to individuals who participated with them in action.

Instituted: By Decree Law No. 520 on October 21, 1969

Regulated: By Executive Decree No. 82 on June 16, 1973

Classes: Gold, silver

Obverse: White enameled bust of soldier in a star

Shape: Gold: round, surrounded by a laurel wreath; silver: same, superimposed on a rectangle

Size: Gold: 33 mm; silver: 23 mm

Metal: Gold: gilt; silver: silvered

Ribbon: Blue, white, blue

Reference: El Salvador 1973; El Salvador 1969

Sv5. *La Medalla de Oro por Servicios Distinguidos*

The Gold Medal for Distinguished Service is awarded to members of the armed forces and the security forces who perform meritorious professional service in the technical, teaching, and diplomatic fields, as well as to the military of friendly nations for forging closer relationships with the military of El Salvador.

Instituted: By Decree Law No. 520 on October 21, 1969

Regulated: By Executive Decree No. 82 on June 16, 1973

Obverse: Enameled torch over blue equilateral triangle within a green enameled laurel wreath

Size: 35 mm

Metal: Gilt

Ribbon: Green with white center stripe edged in blue

Reference: El Salvador 1973; El Salvador 1969

Sv6. *La Medalla "Al Mérito"*

The gold Medal for Merit is awarded to officers of the armed forces for outstanding performance in technical, teaching, and academic fields. The silver class is awarded to enlisted men and civilians for bringing prestige to the armed forces.

Instituted: By Decree Law No. 520 on October 21, 1969

Regulated: By Executive Decree No. 82 on June 16, 1973

Classes: Gold, silver

Obverse: Enameled arms of El Salvador within a star with the letter M above surrounded by a laurel wreath

Obverse legend: REPUBLICA DE EL SALVADOR EN LA AMERICA

Size: 35 mm

Metal: Gold: gilt; silver: silvered

Ribbon: Blue, white, blue

Reference: El Salvador 1973; El Salvador 1969

Sv7. *La Medalla de la Campaña Militar 1980–1992*

The Medal for the Military Campaign of 1980–1992 was awarded to military personnel for fighting insurgents grouped under the banner of the Farabundo Martí National Liberation Front (FMLN). In 1979, the Salvadoran military staged a coup d'état and ruled the country for more than ten years. Five insurgent groups operating in the country joined together operationally in the FMLN, which launched its first major offensive in 1981. Neither side was able to defeat the other militarily, and they finally negotiated and signed the Chapultepec Peace Accords in Mexico City on January 16, 1992. The agreement was subsequently respected by both sides, and the FMLN reorganized itself as one of the two leading political parties in the country. The Salvadoran military considers that it saved the country from an FMLN dictatorship and awarded this medal for that struggle.

Obverse: Star within wreath

Obverse legend: CAMPANA MILITAR | 1980 1992 within a gilt scroll

Shape: Square with indented corners within a cross made of 5 graduated straight-sided rays with the center one pointed

Ribbon: Gold, blue, white

Reference: http://www.omsa.org/photopost/showphoto.php?photo=6413, accessed on January 31, 2013

*Sv8. *La Medalla al Mérito de la Cruz Roja Salvadoreña*

The Salvadoran Red Cross was created on February 17, 1863, and was recognized by the government as an autonomous organization on March 13, 1885. It sought to relieve human suffering and promote public health. In 1914, it opened three sanatoria to combat an epidemic of tuberculosis. It was incorporated into the League of Red Cross Societies on March 24, 1925. It currently operates under the terms of Legislative Decree No. 2,233 of October 1956. The Salvadoran Red Cross awards a medal for merit to its volunteers and other individuals for meritorious service.

Obverse disc: Red enameled cross on a white enameled field

Reverse inscription: CRES (Cruz Roja de El Salvador) and the name of the recipient

Shape: 8-pointed sun with 5 rays in each
   angle

Size: 46 mm

Metal: Gilt

Ribbon: Light blue with red edge stripes and
   a red center stripe edged in white

Recipient: Jack Boddington

Provenance: A. Menke

ORDERS

EL SALVADOR did not institute any orders for merit until after the end of World
War II.

*Sv9. *La Orden José Matías Delgado*

The Order of José Matías Delgado is awarded
to Salvadoran and foreign nationals for extraordinary civil merit in the humanitarian, literary,
scientific, and artistic fields. It is El Salvador's
highest official award. The original decree reg-
ulating the order set numerical limits for each
grade; Salvadoran awardees cannot total more
than twenty-five at any one time and may not
receive the order while serving in public office.

Sv 9
Grand Cross
with silver star star (obverse)

Sv 9
Grand Cross
with silver star star (reverse)

Sv 9
Grand Cross
with silver star badge (obverse)

Sv 9
Grand Cross
with silver star badge (reverse)

The Grand Cross with gold star is awarded only to heads of state. Recipients of this grade include Juan Carlos Wasmosy, president of Paraguay; Vicente Fox, president of Mexico; and Abel Pacheco, president of Costa Rica.

The order is named for José Matías Delgado (1767–1832) regarded as the father of El Salvador's independence. Delgado was a Catholic priest and a physician. He signed the Act of Independence of the United Provinces of Central America on September 15, 1821. As chief of San Salvador, he opposed its being annexed to the Mexican Empire. Delgado later presided over the constituent congress of the Federal Republic of Central America.

Instituted: By Decree Law No. 85 on August 14, 1946

Regulated: By Executive Decree on September 27, 1946

Grand Master: President of the Republic

Grades: Grand Cross with gold star (20), Grand Cross with silver star (40),* Grand Officer (60), Commander (60), Officer (80), Knight

Obverse disc: Bust of Delgado, left

Reverse disc: Phrygian cap

Reverse legend: HONOR A LOS PROCERES | DE LA INDEPENDENCIA

Shape: Blue enameled cross with white enameled cross stripes and 5 waves in each angle, suspended from a wreath

Star reverse disc: Phrygian cap

Star reverse legend: HONOR A LOS PROCERES | DE LA INDEPENDENCIA

Star shape: Badge on 8-pointed star with 3 rays in each angle

Size: Badge: 52 mm. Star: 69 mm

Metal: Silver

Ribbon: Blue with white side stripes

Reference: Burke's Peerage 2006, 1098; El Salvador 1946

Sv 10. *La Orden del Libertador de los Esclavos José Simeón Cañas*

The Order of the Liberator of the Slaves José Simeón Cañas is awarded to heads of state and to Salvadoran and foreign citizens in recognition of their achievements of a humanitarian, scientific, educational, or philanthropic nature. It is El Salvador's second-highest award.

José Simeón Cañas (1767–1838) was a Catholic priest, theologian, philosopher, and humanist. He became the president of San Carlos University in Guatemala. In 1838, he petitioned the United Provinces of Central America to abolish slavery, reportedly the first such action in the Americas.

Instituted: By Decree Law No. 163 on October 19, 1966

Regulated: By Executive Decree on December 5, 1966

Grand Master: President of the Republic

Grades: Collar, Grand Cross, Grand Officer, Commander, Knight

Obverse disc: Bust of Cañas within an enameled circle of the national colors within a laurel wreath

Shape: Badge: 4-pointed, blue enameled, white rimmed Maltese cross

Star shape: Badge superimposed on star with 2 rays in each angle of the cross

Size: Grand Cross: badge: 70 mm. Star: 85 mm

Ribbon: Light blue with 2 narrow white side stripes

Reference: El Salvador 1988, 61–66

Sv. 11 *La Orden del Mérito Policial*

The Order of Civil Police Merit is awarded to members of the national police killed or seriously wounded in the line of duty. In exceptional cases, it may be awarded to Salvadoran and foreign nationals and institutions for rendering an important service to the community, to the nation, or to the Civil National Police.

Instituted: By Presidential Decree No. 165 on November 27, 1997

Regulated: By Presidential Decree No. 14 on January 23, 1998

Grades: 1st, 2nd, 3rd

Obverse disc: Emblem of the Civil National Police

Obverse legend: MERITO|POLICIA

Reverse disc: Arms of El Salvador

Shape: Blue enameled, metal rimmed Maltese cross with 2 gilt rays in each angle

Metal: 1st: gilt; 2nd: silvered; 3rd: bronze

Ribbon: 1st: gold with blue and white edge stripes; 2nd: silver with blue and white edge stripes; 3rd: bronze with blue and white edge stripes

Reference: El Salvador 1998

Sv 12. *La Orden al Mérito 5 de Noviembre 1811, Próceres de la Independencia Patria*

The Order of Merit 5th of November 1811, Heroes of the Independent Fatherland is awarded to Salvadorans and foreign nationals for their humanitarian, scientific, intellectual, spiritual, civic, and moral actions that lend prestige to the nation and promote human conviviality. The order was created and is administered by the legislature.

Instituted: By Decree Law No. 902 on December 3, 2011

Obverse: Angel of liberty

Obverse legend: HONOR A LOS PROCERES DE LA INDEPENDENCIA PATRIA

Reverse: Arms of El Salvador

Ribbon: Blue, white

GUATEMALA

GUATEMALA proclaimed its independence from Spain along with the rest of Central America on September 15, 1821. However, within a few months, Guatemala led the region to join the newly formed Mexican Empire. In 1823, Mexico reverted to being a republic, and it recognized Central America's independence. On July 1, 1823, Guatemala joined the four other Central American republics (present-day Costa Rica, El Salvador, Honduras, and Nicaragua) to form the United Provinces of Central America, based in Guatemala. The federation approved a constitution similar to that of the United States. The union was threatened by new political divisions between free market liberals and landowning conservatives allied with the Catholic Church. In November 1838, Honduras withdrew from the federation, and two years later it was dissolved. During this period, Guatemala is not known to have authorized any medals or orders.

In March 1840, conservative Rafael Carrera defeated the forces of Francisco Morazán, the liberal president of the Federal Republic of Central America. His victory effectively ended the federation, and he went on to rule Guatemala off and on until his death in 1865. Carrera became the leader of Central American conservatives and frequently fought his liberal opponents both in Guatemala and in other Central American republics. He is known to have authorized at least four medals for these conflicts, including one for defeating the forces of the American filibuster William Walker in Nicaragua. With the exception of the medal for fighting Walker, all of Guatemala's military medals until well into the twentieth century were awarded in connection with the unending struggle for political domination between liberals and conservatives.

In 1871, Justo Rufino Barrios led the "Liberal Revolution," which ousted the conservatives from power. He fought his neighbors in an unsuccessful attempt to reunite Central America. Barrios was killed in 1885 while fighting conservative forces in El Salvador. He is believed to have authorized only one medal for his military during his invasion of Honduras in 1872. In 1898, a conservative general, Manuel Estrada Cabrera, assumed the presidency after his predecessor was assassinated. Estrada ruled until being ousted in 1920. He faced continuous opposition from liberals both inside Guatemala and in neighboring countries. In 1906, liberal forces invaded Guatemala from El Salvador and Mexico, but Estrada mobilized a large army and defeated them, for which he authorized a cross and a medal.

Guatemala instituted its first order of merit in 1936, the Order of the Quetzal, which remains today the country's highest official award. Other orders were created after World War II. Beginning in 1947, the country began to create military medals for valor, merit, distinguished service, and loyalty in peacetime. Although Guatemala remained at peace with its neighbors after World War II, it continued to suffer from instability between left-wing insurgents and the armed forces.

MEDALS

MOST OF Guatemala's military medals during the nineteenth century were awarded to military personnel for fighting on one side or the other in the decades-long struggle between liberals and conservatives throughout Central America. Guatemala's best-known conservative, Rafael Carrera, issued four campaign medals for fighting neighboring liberals. He was followed by liberal Presidents J. Ruffino Barrios and Manuel Estrada Cabrera, who instituted four medals for fighting conservatives in neighboring countries.

*Gt1. *La Medalla de la Campaña de 1851*

The Campaign Medal for 1851 was awarded by conservative President Rafael Carrera to the Guatemalan officers and men who defeated an invasion force from El Salvador and Honduras along with exiled Guatemalan liberals at the Battle of San José La Arada in Guatemala on February 2, 1851. Liberal Salvadoran President Doroteo Vasconcelos wanted to unite Guatemala with El Salvador and Honduras in a single Central American republic. Carrera opposed Vasoncelos's idea and personally led the Guatemalan army. Carrera forced Vasconcelos from office, and the effort to unite the three countries failed. Carrera authorized a medal for his victory at San José La Arada.

Classes: Officers, enlisted men*

Obverse inscription: LA PATRIA|RECONOCI-|DA. within a laurel wreath, coffee to the left, palm to the right, tied at the top

Reverse inscription: A LOS|VENCED^S|EL 2 DE|FEBRERO|DE 1851 within a laurel wreath

Shape: Officers: oval; enlisted men: round

Size: Officers: 20 × 18 mm; enlisted men: 21 mm

Metal: Officers: gold; enlisted men: silver

Ribbon: Yellow, edged successively by narrow red, white, and light blue stripes

Reference: Guille 1952, 10

Provenance: J. Coolidge Hills, Wadsworth Athenaeum, American Numismatic Society, A. Menke

*Gt2. *La Cruz al Servicio Distinguido en la Campaña de Nicaragua, 1857*

The Distinguished Service Cross for the Nicaraguan Campaign of 1857 was awarded to the men who fought the American filibuster William Walker. In the mid-1850s, Nicaraguan liberals from León were fighting a civil war with their conservative enemies from Granada.

Gt 1

Gt 1

Gt 2

Gt 2

The president of Nicaragua, a liberal, invited an American adventurer named William Walker to bring his armed supporters to fight the conservatives. Walker's men defeated the conservatives at the first Battle of Rivas. Walker's military intervention in Nicaragua alienated most Central Americans, regardless of their political affiliation. In 1857, Guatemala joined El Salvador in sending an army that attacked Walker's stronghold at Granada, forcing him to flee. President Carrera authorized a cross for defeating Walker.

Instituted: 1857

Obverse legend: GUATEMALA AL MERITO DISTINGUIDO | 1856–1857

Obverse inscription: [Name of recipient]

Shape: Ball-tipped Maltese cross with
2-pointed ends and a laurel wreath in the
angles, with a scrolled loop at top

Size: 50 mm

Metal: Silver

Ribbon: Yellow, edged successively by narrow
red, white, and light blue stripes

Reference: Guille 1952, 10

Recipient: Eligio Custodio

Provenance: A. Menke

*Gt3. *La Cruz de Oficial de la Campaña contra El Salvador y Honduras*

Gt 3

The Officer's Cross for the Campaign against
El Salvador and Honduras was awarded to Guatemalan officers who fought in the 1863 campaign against both countries. War broke out
in 1863, again pitting Rafael Carrera against
El Salvador and Honduras. Despite an initial
setback at the Battle of Coatepeque, Carrera
prevailed, occupying San Salvador and temporarily ruling both El Salvador and Honduras.
President Carrera authorized this cross for his
military.

Obverse disc: Shield with 3 mountains surmounted by vertical stripes and radiant sun
on a red enameled field

Obverse legend: CAMPANA DEL SALVADOR Y
HONDURAS | 1863 on a blue enameled band

Reverse inscription: AL | MERITO | MILITAR
on a red enameled field

Reverse legend: REPUBLICA DE GUATEMALA
on a blue enameled band

Shape: Ball-tipped, white enameled Maltese
cross edged in green enamel with 2-pointed
ends and five 2-pointed rays in each angle
and a green enameled laurel wreath between
the angles, suspended from a green enameled wreath

Metal: Silver

Size: 40 mm

Ribbon White with 2 red center stripes

Gt 3

*Gt4. *La Medalla de la Campaña contra El Salvador y Honduras, 1863*

President Carrera awarded this Medal for the Campaign against El Salvador and Honduras to enlisted men who fought against El Salvador and Honduras in 1863.

Instituted: 1863

Obverse medallion: Laureate bust of Carrera, left

Obverse legend: RAFAEL CARRERA P^TE. DE LA R^A. DE GUATEMALA

Reverse inscription: CAMPAÑA | DEL SALVADOR | Y HONDURAS | 1863 with a triangle within rays above and oak and olive branches beneath

Size: 24 mm

Metal: Silver

Ribbon: White, yellow, light blue

Reference: Guille 1952, 10

Gt5. *La Medalla de la Campaña de 1872*

In 1872, liberal President Miguel García Granados invaded Honduras, which was ruled by a conservative general. Several battles were fought, including one at Santa Barbara. The literature gives little importance to the battle, but it coincides with the date when conservative Honduran President José María Medina was forced out of office and replaced by a provisional liberal president, Céleo Arias. Anecdotal reports claim that a young, liberal Salvadoran officer in the Guatemalan army, Carlos Ezeta, was wounded at the Battle of Santa Barbara. He later became a liberal president of El Salvador.

Instituted: By decree on September 6, 1872

Classes: Chiefs, officers, enlisted men

Obverse inscription: DEFENSA DE LA LIBERTAD | HONDURAS | SANTA BARBARA

Reverse inscription: AL MERITO Y AL VALOR

Shape: Oval surrounded by a laurel wreath

Size: 15 × 10 mm

Metal: Chiefs, officers: gold; enlisted men: silver

Ribbon: Blue

Reference: Guille 1952, 10

Gt6. *La Medalla de 1894*

The Medal of 1894 appears to be an honorific or political award and not a medal for merit. It was instituted by liberal President José María Reina Barrios. June 30, 1871, was the date when Miguel García Granados and J. Ruffino Barrios, two liberal generals, overthrew the conservative government of Vicente Cerna. García Granados became provisional president and introduced the liberal reform laws of 1871. He was killed during his invasion of El Salvador two years later and replaced by Ruffino Barrios, who carried out and expanded those liberal reforms during his twelve years in office. In 1894, Reina Barrios, uncle of Ruffino Barrios, moved García Granados's body to the general cemetery in Guatemala City and erected a large monument to his memory. The Medal of 1894 was probably awarded to commemorate this event and to honor the two founders of liberal power in Guatemala.

Instituted: 1894

Obverse: Arms of Guatemala

Obverse legend: LA PATRIA AGRADECIDA A SUS BUENOS HIJOS 1894

Reverse inscription: 30 DE JUNIO DE 1871

Reverse legend: J. RUFFINO BARRIOS | MIGUEL GARCIA GRANADOS

Size: 22 mm

Metal: Silver

Ribbon: Blue with a narrow center white stripe

Reference: Guille 1952, 11

* * *

IN 1898, liberal President Reina Barrios was assassinated and replaced by another liberal, Manuel Estrada Cabrera, who ruled for twenty-two years.

*Gt7. *La Cruz de Honor*

In 1906, rebellions broke out in Guatemala, supported by other Central American countries and fellow Guatemalan liberals. Estrada Cabrera suppressed the rebellion and instituted

Gt 7

Gt 7

a cross that he awarded to his loyal senior officers. The conflict was resolved after President
Theodore Roosevelt intervened and negotiated
an armistice.

Instituted: By Decree No. 666 on July 21,
1906

Obverse disc: Enameled arms of Guatemala
within a laurel wreath

Obverse legend: CAMPAÑA NACIONAL | 1906

Reverse inscription: HONOR AL MERITO

Shape: Ball-tipped Maltese cross with
2-pointed ends and five 2-pointed rays in
the angles

Size: 45 mm

Metal: Gilt

Ribbon: Blue, white, blue

Reference: Guille 1952, 11

Provenance: American Numismatic Society,
A. Menke

*Gt 8. *La Medalla de la Campaña
Nacional de 1906*

The Medal for the 1906 National Campaign
was awarded to military officers loyal to President Cabrera during that year's uprising

Instituted: 1906

Classes: Senior officers, other officers*

Obverse: Arms of Guatemala

Obverse legend: CAMPAÑA NACIONAL DE
1906

Reverse inscription: HONOR | AL | MÉRITO
flanked by branches

Size: 22 mm

Metal: Senior officers: gold; other officers:
silver

Ribbon: Blue, white, blue

Reference: Guille 1952, 11

Peacetime Medals

In 1923, Guatemala began to create military medals to be awarded in peacetime for valor, merit, distinguished service, and loyalty.

*Gt9. *La Cruz de Mérito Militar*

The Cross for Military Merit is awarded to Guatemalan and foreign military personnel for bravery and heroism in combat or some similar acts in comparable circumstances above and beyond the call of duty. The medal may be awarded individually or collectively. In exceptional cases, it may be awarded individually to officers of other friendly nations. It is Guatemala's highest military award.

> Instituted: By Decree No. 1,823 in August 1923
>
> Modified: By Decree No. 433 on October 15, 1947
>
> Regulated: By Executive Agreement No. 43 in 1982

Modified: December 17, 2011

Classes: 1st,* 2nd,* 3rd*

Obverse disc: Arms of Guatemala on a white enameled field

Obverse legend: merito militar | i [ii, iii] clase on a blue enameled band

Shape: 5-armed ball-tipped star with 2-pointed ends and a schematic wreath between the angles, with crossed swords above

Size: 1st, 3rd: 58 × 43 mm; 2nd: 63 × 49 mm

Metal: 1st: gilt; 2nd: silver; 3rd: steel

Ribbon: Red, white, red suspended from a gilt ribbon bar

Reference: Guille 1952, 13; Prober 1957, 260; Werlich 1974, 225; Guatemala 1982, 3–5

Gt 10

Gt 10

*Gt10. *La Cruz de Constancia en el Servicio*

The Cross for Military Loyalty is awarded to members of the armed forces for years of loyal service.

> Instituted: By Decree No. 1,823 in August 1923
>
> Regulated: By Executive Agreement No. 43 in 1982
>
> Modified: December 17, 2011
>
> Classes: 1st, 2nd, 3rd*
>
> Obverse disc: Enameled arms of Guatemala
>
> Obverse legend: CONSTANCIA EN EL SERVICIO | I [II, III] CLASE on a blue enameled band
>
> Reverse disc: Enameled arms of Guatemala
>
> Reverse legend: CONSTANCIA EN EL SERVICIO | I [II, III] CLASE on a blue enameled band
>
> Shape: Ball-tipped Maltese cross with 2-pointed ends with crossed swords above
>
> Metal: Silver
>
> Ribbon: Black with narrow red center stripe
>
> Reference: Guille, 1952, 12; Guatemala 1982, 3–5

*Gt11. *La Cruz de Servicios Distinguidos*

The Cross for Distinguished Services is awarded to Guatemalan army personnel for valor or self-sacrifice above and beyond the call of duty or, exceptionally, to foreign civilian and military personnel for distinguished service to the army.

> Instituted: By Decree No. 433 on October 15, 1947
>
> Regulated: By Executive Agreement No. 43 in 1982
>
> Shape: Ball-tipped cross pattée with concave pointed ends beneath a scroll inscribed SERVICIOS | DISTINGUIDOS

Size: 54 × 40 mm

Metal: Gilt

Ribbon: Green with narrow white side stripes suspended from a gilt ribbon bar

Reference: Werlich 1974, 225–26; Prober 1957, 260; Guatemala 1982, 6–7

*Gt12. *La Cruz de la Marina de Guerra*

The Cross for the Wartime Navy is awarded to members of the armed forces, units, and ships, and to others for heroism, merit, and distinguished service to the navy. The Cross may also be awarded to foreign military personnel and civilians.

Regulated: By Executive Agreement No. 43 in 1982

Obverse: Gilt anchor superimposed on a silvered Latin cross

Shape: 8-pointed star with 4 rays in each angle

Size: 41 mm

Metal: Gilt

Ribbon: Blue with narrow white side stripes suspended from a gilt ribbon bar

Reference: Guatemala 1982, 11–12

*Gt13. *La Cruz de la Fuerza Aérea*

The Air Force Cross is awarded to members of the armed forces, units, and squadrons for heroism, merit, and distinguished service to the air force.

Instituted: October 1947

Regulated: By Executive Agreement No. 43 in 1982

Shape: 4-bladed propeller with a green enameled laurel wreath in the angles suspended from a gilt device

Size: 45 mm

Metal: Gilt

Ribbon: Light blue with 2 narrow white side stripes, suspended from a gilt ribbon bar

Reference: Guatemala 1982, 10–11

Gt 13

Gt 15

Gt14. *La Cruz de la Fuerza de Tierra*

The Cross for Land Forces is awarded to members and individual units of the army and to others for acts of heroism, merit, or distinguished service to the army.

> Regulated: By Executive Agreement No. 43 in 1982
>
> Obverse: Insignia of infantry on upper arm; artillery on lower arm; engineers on right arm; and cavalry on left arm
>
> Reverse legend: GUATEMALA and the date of issue
>
> Shape: Cross
>
> Size: 34 mm
>
> Metal: Gilt
>
> Ribbon: Blue with narrow white edge stripes
>
> Reference: Guatemala 1982, 9–10

*Gt15. *La Medalla de Buena Conducta*

The Good Conduct Medal rewards exemplary service over a period of time.

> Classes: Gold, silver,* bronze*
>
> Shape: Stylized bird with wings raised atop a shield between 2 branches
>
> Size: 44 × 26 mm
>
> Metal: Gold: gilt; silver: silvered; bronze: bronze
>
> Ribbon: Light blue with 2 black side stripes edged in white, red, and yellow edge stripes, suspended from a gilt ribbon bar

*Gt16. *La Estrella Posthuma*

The Posthumous Star is awarded to the families of members of the armed forces who die in the line of duty.

> Obverse disc: Arms of Guatemala on a white enameled field, surrounded by a blue enameled band
>
> Shape: Ball-tipped gilt star superimposed on a black enameled circle
>
> Metal: Gilt
>
> Ribbon: Light blue, white, light blue suspended from a gilt ribbon bar

Gt 16

*Gt17. *La Cruz de la Paz*

The Cross for Peace was awarded in connection with the peace accords between the government of Guatemala and the insurgent Unidad Revolucionaria Nacional Guatemalteca, which were finalized on December 29, 1996. The agreements ended more than three decades of armed conflict in Guatemala.

Classes: Gold,* silver,* bronze*

Obverse disc: Stylized dove on glazed disc matching the color of the medal, surrounded by green enameled wreath

Obverse inscription: Paz

Shape: Ball-tipped, 4-pointed blue and white enameled cross with concave sides, with crossed sword and automatic rifle in cutout cross with concave sides

Size: 52 mm

Metal: Gold: gilt; Silver: silvered; Bronze: bronze

Ribbon: Light blue, white, light blue

Gt 17

ORDERS

GUATEMALA founded its first order 115 years after the country gained its independence from Spain. All of Guatemala's orders were created to promote economic, intellectual, medical, educational, and humanitarian goals. None were instituted primarily for military merit.

*Gt18. *La Orden del Quetzal*

The Order of the Quetzal is Guatemala's highest and also its oldest order. It is bestowed on nationals and foreigners for international, civic, scientific, literary, or artistic services of benefit to the nation. The order is named for the colorful quetzal, Guatemala's national bird, which inhabits the country's many volcanoes. It is often given to foreign nationals in reciprocity for orders received.

Gt18
Knight

Instituted: By Decree No. 2,157 on April 23, 1936

Modified: By Decree No. 2,549 on June 26, 1941, adding the grade of Commander

Regulated: On March 29, 1942

Modified: On November 26, 1951, adding the Grand Cross and Knight

Grades: Collar,* Grand Cross,* Grand Officer, Commander, Officer, Knight*

Obverse disc: Arms of Guatemala

Obverse legend: GUATEMALA AL MERITO

Reverse inscription: MCMXXXVI

Reverse legend: ORDEN DEL QUETZAL

Badge shape: Ball-tipped, 5-armed gold-rimmed star with 3-pointed ends and a silver ray in each angle; uncertain grade: ball-tipped, 5-armed star with 2-pointed ends with a green enameled quetzal curved around the right of the medallion

Star shape: Badge superimposed on 10-pointed, ball-tipped sun with 3 silvered rays in each angle

Size: Badge: Collar and Grand Cross: 58 mm;

Gt18
Knight

Gt 18
Collar

Gt 18
Collar (detail)

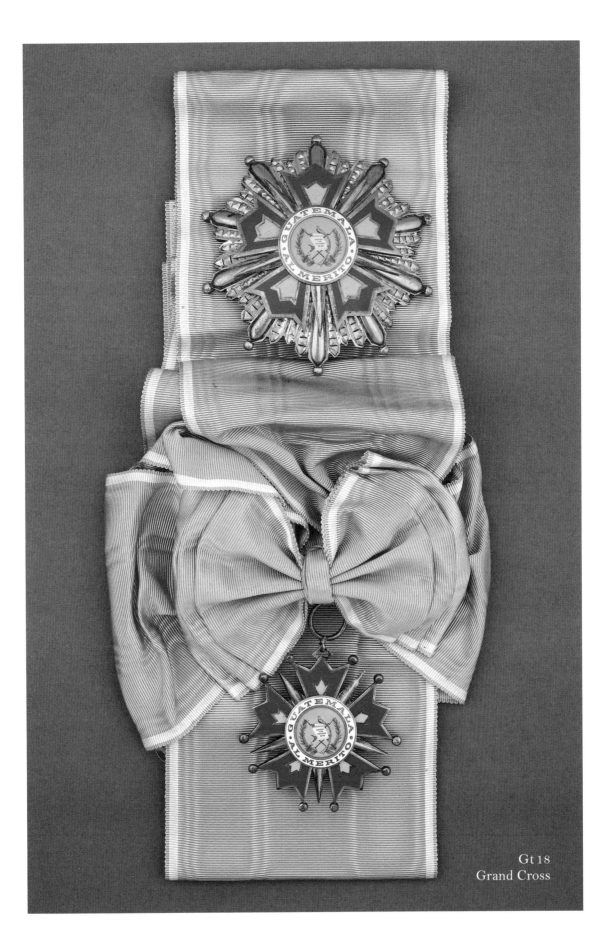

Gt 18
Grand Cross

Gt 18
Collar (reverse)

Gt 18
uncertain grade

Gt 18
Grand Cross badge (reverse)

uncertain grade: 48 mm; Knight: 42 mm.
Star: 80 mm

Collar shape: Badge suspended by a vertical
Mayan image from a link with the arms of
Guatemala in an enameled wreath, alternating with 2 plaques with human images derived from Mayan art

Metal: Collar: gilt silver; Grand Cross: silvered bronze; uncertain grade and Knight:
silver

Maker: Collar: Gardino, Rome; Grand Cross:
Cravanzola, Rome

Ribbon: Light blue with narrow white edge
stripes

Reference: Prober 1957, 259; Burke's Peerage
2006, 1174; Werlich 1974, 223

Gt19. *La Orden de la Libertad*

The Order of Liberty is awarded for service
against communism or other forms of totali-
tarianism as well as meritorious service in favor
of individual freedom and world peace, or for
distinguished service in the fields of literature,
the arts, or science.

Instituted: July 1956
Reference: Burke's Peerage 2006, 1175

Gt20. *La Orden de Rodolfo Robles*

The Order or Rodolfo Robles is awarded to Guatemalan and foreign physicians for outstanding service in the field of public health. The order is named after Dr. Rodolfo Robles (1878–1939), a distinguished Guatemalan physician, who identified and found a cure for the parasite that causes filariasis. The order has no ribbon or star.

Instituted: December 2, 1955

Obverse disc: Bust of Robles, right, on a silver field

Shape: Gold-rimmed white and blue enameled cross pattée with convex ends with gold banana stalks in the angles suspended from plaque portraying Mayan gods

Reference: Burke's Peerage 2006, 1175; Werlich 1974, 224

Gt21. *La Orden del Hermano Pedro de San José Bethancourt*

The Order of Brother Pedro de San José Bethancourt is awarded to Guatemalan and foreign citizens for contributions in the field of philanthropy and humanitarian services. The order is named for a missionary who devoted his life to the service of the poor and the relief of suffering. It is awarded once a year on April 25 at the presidential palace. The order has no star.

Instituted: June 27, 1958

Obverse disc: Father Bethancourt standing with right arm extended

Obverse legend: ACORDAMOS HERMANOS QUE UNA ALMA TENEMOS Y SI LA PERDEMOS NO LA RECOBRAMOS

Reverse legend: ORDEN DE HERMANO PEDRO DE SAN JOSE BETHANCOURT | GUATEMALA C.A.

Shape: 2 blue enameled, pointed, oval ellipses forming a St. Andrews cross

Ribbon: Gold cord ending in 2 balls

Gt22
Knight

Reference: Burke's Peerage 2006, 2:1176; Werlich 1974, 224–25

*Gt22. *La Orden de los Cinco Volcanes*

The Order of the Five Volcanoes is Guatemala's second-highest award. It recognizes extraordinary service in promoting the integration of the five Central American republics (with Panama and Belize excluded). The literature prescribes three grades, but the second piece in the collection appears to be a Knight's badge.

Gt 22
Gold Grand Cross

Gt 23

Instituted: March 25, 1961

Grades: Gold Grand Cross,* Silver Grand Cross, Grand Officer, Knight*

Obverse disc: Enameled scene of 5 volcanoes surmounted by a red cap of liberty

Obverse legend: O LOS CINCO O NINGUNO on a white enameled band with laurel wreath inside and outside

Shape: Ball-tipped, red enameled Maltese cross with 3-pointed ends and 5 rays in the angles, suspended from a green enameled laurel wreath

Size: Badge: 52 mm. Star: 84 mm

Metal: Gold Grand Cross: gilt; Knight: silvered

Maker: Cejalvo, Madrid

Ribbon: Dark blue

Reference: Burke's Peerage 2006, 1175; Werlich 1974, 223–24

*Gt23. *La Orden de Francisco Marroquín*

The Order of Francisco Marroquín is bestowed on distinguished educators and professors who make important contributions to education in Guatemala. Only five orders are awarded each year. The order is named after Francisco Marroquín (1499–1563), a Spanish-born priest, who worked to free Indian slaves from oppression. He was appointed bishop of Santiago de Guatemala and later governor of the Captaincy General. Guatemala's most famous university is named for him.

Instituted: June 25, 1964

Obverse disc: Bust of Marroquín, ¾ right, on a textured field

Obverse legend: ORDEN FRANCISCO MARROQUIN | GUATEMALA A.C. in blue enamel

Shape: 8-pointed, 6-part star

Size: 72 mm

Metal: Brass

Maker: Joyería San Antonio, Guatemala City

Ribbon: Blue, white, blue

Reference: Burke's Peerage 2006, 1176; Werlich 1974, 225

Gt24. *La Orden "Antonio José de Irisarri"*

The Antonio José de Irisarri order is an award for meritorious diplomatic service. It is named after Antonio José de Irisarri Alonso (1786–1868), a Guatemalan statesman and journalist. He held high office in Chile under Bernardo O'Higgins, including the position of minister of foreign affairs. He acted as minister plenipotentiary of Guatemala and El Salvador in the United States and helped remove the American filibuster William Walker from Central America.

Instituted: 1973

Grades: Collar, Grand Cross, Grand Officer, Commander, Officer

Obverse disc: Bronze bust of Irisarri, ½ left

Shape: Bronze circle superimposed on a red enameled cross with a blue and white enameled ray in each angle

Metal: Gilt

Ribbon: White with a blue center stripe

Reference: http://www.es.wikipedia.org/wiki/ Orden_de_Antonio_Jose_de_Irisarri, accessed April 27, 2013

*Gt25. *La Orden del Ejército*

The Order of the Army is Guatemala's highest military award and appears to be conferred only in the grade of Grand Cross. It is given to high military officials, Guatemalan and foreign, for service of major interest to the army. The design of the order is identical to the Medal for Military Merit.

Obverse disc: Gilt arms of Guatemala on a white enameled disc

Obverse legend: EJERCITO | DE GUATEMALA on a blue enameled band

Shape: Ball-tipped star with 2-pointed ends and a green enameled laurel wreath in the angles, with crossed swords above

Star shape: Badge on 10-pointed sun with 4 rays in each angle

Size: Badge: 58 × 43 mm. Star: 78 mm

Metal: Gilt

Ribbon: Red, white, red

Gt 25
Grand Cross

HAITI

JEAN-JACQUES DESSALINES declared Haiti's independence on January 1, 1804, following more than a decade of cruel and merciless warfare with France, which by this time was under the rule of Napoleon. Dessalines declared himself emperor and tried to establish his own nobility, though he is not known to have created any imperial orders. Henri Christophe replaced Dessalines and declared himself King Henry I. He also attempted to establish a royalist society and created his own order—the Ordre Royal et Militaire de Saint Henry—but no such decorations are known to have been made. King Henry committed suicide, and his nobility lost their titles.

In 1847, a Haitian general, Faustin Soulouque, seized power and proclaimed himself emperor. Faustin ruled for ten years and created a new Haitian nobility. He founded four imperial orders, which he awarded to members of his court and senior military officers. Faustin was deposed in 1859, and his nobility and imperial orders were all abolished.

In 1915, President Woodrow Wilson ordered the U.S. Marines to invade and occupy Haiti. They stayed for nearly two decades and tried to create governmental institutions. In 1918, President Philippe Sudré Dartiguenave created the country's first republican medals for civil and military merit, which are still awarded.

MEDALS

THE AWARDING of military medals in Haiti began under French colonial rule during the reign of Louis XV. In 1765, the local governor general, Count d'Estaing, authorized two nearly identical medals for mulattoes and free blacks: the Medal of Valor (military) and the Medal of Virtue (civilian). Upon the death of the recipient, his heirs were required to return the medal to the crown. It is known that both medals were awarded in accordance with the statutes, but no pieces are known to have survived to this day (Étienne 1954, 20–24).

Haiti's first military medal was authorized in 1918 by President Dartiguenave during the American occupation. Haitian military medals have also been awarded to foreign military personnel, including Americans, who served in Haiti during the occupation from 1915 to 1934. The Haitian military was abolished in 1994.

*Ha1. *La Médaille Militaire*

The Military Medal was Haiti's highest military award. It was originally bestowed on the officers and enlisted men of the Gendarmerie d'Haïti for bravery in combat against the *cacos* during the American occupation. The *cacos* were Haitian revolutionaries opposed to the Haitian government as well as to the American occupation. This medal was Haiti's first since the country became independent in 1804. Additional awards for bravery were recognized by placing a 5-mm star on the ribbon. The medal could be awarded posthumously to the closest family member if the recipient was killed in action or died a natural death. The Haitian army was disbanded in 1994 by the United States, and the medal may no longer be awarded. The Military Medals were inscribed variously to the Gendarmerie d'Haïti, the Garde d'Haïti or the Armée d'Haïti, depending on the year of issue, as the army's name was changed three times.

Ha1a. *Version 1*

Instituted: 1918
Obverse legend: LIBERTE EGALITE FRATERNITE | GENDARMERIE
Size: 35 mm
Metal: Silver
Ribbon: Red, blue
Bar: MEDAILLE MILITAIRE

*Ha1b. *Version 2*

Replaced: December 18, 1922 (shape changed)
Modified: September 27, 1938 (ribbon changed)
Modified: November 17, 1942
Modified: May 31, 1951 (name changed to Armée d'Haïti)
Obverse disc: Arms of Haiti
Obverse legend: MEDAILLE MILITAIRE
Reverse legend: ARMÉE D'HAITI
Shape: 5-armed star with 2-pointed ends and 5 rays in each angle
Size: 40 mm

Ha 1b

Ha 1b

Metal: Bronze

Maker: N. S. Meyer, New York

Ribbon: Red with narrow black edge stripes (after 1938)

Reference: Étienne 1954, 60–67

*Ha2. *La Médaille du Service Distingué*

The Medal for Distinguished Service was Haiti's second-highest military award. It was awarded to officers and men of the Gendarmerie d'Haïti for acts of heroism during a military or police action in peacetime or for exceptional service to the nation. This medal may not be awarded to a person who had previously received the Military Medal. Additional awards for meritorious service were recognized by placing a 5-mm star on the ribbon. The medal could be awarded posthumously to the closest family member, if the recipient was killed in action or died a natural death. This medal may no longer be awarded after the army was disbanded.

Instituted: By law on December 18, 1922

Modified: September 27, 1938 (size and ribbon changed)

Modified: April 17, 1940

Modified: November 17, 1942

Modified: May 31, 1951

Obverse disc: Arms of Haiti

Suspension bar: SERVICE DISTINGUE

Shape: 6-pointed star with trilobe ends to the points and oak leaves on the arms

Size: 45 mm (60 mm until 1938)

Metal: Bronze

Maker: N. S. Meyer, New York

Ribbon: Royal blue with narrow yellow edges (blue and red with yellow edges before 1938)

Reference: Étienne 1954, 67–81; Guille 1952, 15

Ha 2

Ha 3

*Ha3. *Le Brevet de Mérite*

The Certificate of Merit was awarded to anyone working with the Haitian gendarmerie in
peacetime for service to the government above
and beyond the call of duty. The certificate may
be awarded posthumously to the closest family member if the recipient was killed in action
or died of natural causes. Additional awards of
this medal to the same recipient are made with
a 5-mm silver star attached to the ribbon.

Instituted: By law on December 18, 1922

Modified: May 31, 1951, changing the inscription GENDARMERIE TO ARMÉE
D'HAITI

Obverse disc: Arms of Haiti

Ha 3

Obverse legend: REPUBLIQUE D'HAITI |
BREVET DE MERITE

Reverse legend: ARMÉE D'HAITI

Shape: 8-pointed sun of 16 rays

Size: 47 mm

Metal: Bronze

Ribbon: Green with narrow white center
stripe

Reference: Étienne 1954, 60–81

*Ha4. *La Médaille du Soldat* (*de Bonne Conduite*)

When first authorized in 1922, the Medal of the
Soldier was called the Good Conduct Medal.
It was awarded for three years of meritori-
ous service. The original law provided that a

recipient of the medal would receive an increase of US $0.50 per month for each award. The medal was awarded to enlisted men for having served three three-year tours of duty. Officers who had already received the Military Medal or the Medal for Distinguished Service were eligible for the Medal of the Soldier after twenty years of service.

Instituted: By law on December 18, 1922
Modified: May 31, 1951 (change of name)
Obverse: Arms of Haiti
Legend: In ribbons: ARMEE D'HAITI | MEDAILLE DU SOLDAT
Size: 35 mm
Metal: Bronze
Ribbon: Orange
Reference: Étienne 1954, 74–81

*Ha5. *La Médaille "Rebati Ayiti"*

The medal "To Rebuild Haiti" takes its name from a major philanthropic undertaking from the United States in 1994 to donate school and hospital supplies to Haiti. We believe it to be an official medal because the arms of Haiti are engraved on the reverse.

Obverse: 2 fists removed from shackles, dove above
Obverse legend: REBATI AYITI
Reverse: Arms of Haiti
Size: 32 mm
Metal: White metal
Ribbon: Red, edged in blue with 2 narrow yellow side stripes edged in white; bar with REBATI AYITI in scroll
Provenance: A. Menke

ORDERS

HAITI's first orders were all royal or imperial, instituted originally under Henri Christophe's kingdom of the north and later under Faustin I's Haitian Empire. These imperial orders were designed to promote loyalty and respect from the sovereign's court and his military leaders. King Henry I instituted Haiti's first order by royal edict on April 20, 1811, seven years after Haiti's declaration of independence.

Ha6. *L'Ordre Royal et Militaire de Saint Henry*

The Royal and Military Order of Saint Henry was a purely military order to be awarded to men who fought the French during Haiti's War of Independence. The only other requirement was that the recipient be a Roman Catholic. The royal decree provided for sixteen Grand Crosses, thirty-two Commanders, and an unlimited number of Knights. The decree also set aside a sum of money to reward the awardees financially each year.

The legend on the reverse of the badge reads PRIX DE LA VALEUR (reward for valor), which must have been copied from the French colonial medal of the same name that was awarded to free blacks and mulattoes for, among other things, hunting down black maroons.

No Order of Saint Henry is believed actually to have been made, although some certificates were probably bestowed. The description below is based on the royal decree creating the medal.

Instituted: By royal decree on April 20, 1811
Grand Master: Crown prince
Classes: Grand Collar, Grand Cross, Commander, Knight

Obverse disc: Bust of Saint Henry, left, in red enameled field

Obverse legend: HENRY FONDATEUR | 1811 on blue enameled band

Reverse disc: Star in red enameled field

Reverse legend: PRIX DE LA VALEUR on blue enameled band

Shape: Ball-tipped, 12-pointed sun with a ball-tipped ray in each angle

Metal: Gold

Ribbon: Grand Cross: black; Commander: red; Knight: red, blue

Reference: Étienne 1954, 26–40

THE SECOND HAITIAN EMPIRE

IN 1847, Haitian General Faustin Soulouque became president of Haiti. Two years later, he proclaimed himself emperor, with the title Faustin I. During his ten-year reign, he set out to create a court with its own nobility and hierarchy of titles and privileges. The four monarchical orders he instituted played an important role in raising the prestige of this court among the country's elite. All four of his monarchical orders were disbanded after he was deposed in 1859.

*Ha7. *L'Ordre Impérial et Militaire de Saint Faustin*

The Imperial and Military Order of Saint Faustin was awarded to military officers for bravery and loyalty to the emperor. Many of these officers were incorporated into Faustin's nobility and given titles. Like his predecessor Henri Christophe, Faustin named the order after a saint with his own name and put his bust on the reverse.

Ha7
Grand Cross
badge (reverse)

Instituted: By Emperor Faustin on September 21, 1849

Grades: Grand Cross,* Commander, Knight*

Obverse disc: Eagle atop 2 cannons in a blue enameled field

Obverse legend: DIEU MA PATRIE ET MON EPEE on red enameled band

Reverse disc: Bust of Faustin, left, in a gold field

Reverse legend: FAUSTIN IER EMPEREUR D'HAITI on red enameled band

Shape: Ball-tipped, 8-armed star with

Ha 7
Grand
Cross

Ha 7
Knight

Ha 7
Knight

2-pointed ends and a green enameled wreath in the angles. Each arm alternates red and blue enamel. The badge is suspended from a gold crown

Star shape: 8-pointed star with 6 rays in each angle

Size: Badge: Grand Cross: 70 mm; Knight: 43 mm. Star: 89 mm

Metal: Badge: Grand Cross: gilt silver; Knight: silver. Star: silver

Maker: Arthus Bertrand, Paris

Ribbon: Light blue

Reference: Étienne 1954, 44–47; Werlich 1974, 230

Provenance: Knight: A. Menke

*Ha8. *L'Ordre Civil de la Légion d'Honneur*

The Civil Order of the Legion of Honor, awarded for exceptional civil merit, was equal in rank to the military order bearing Faustin's name. It was abolished in 1859 after Faustin was deposed.

Instituted: By Emperor Faustin on September 21, 1849

Grades: Grand Cross,* Officer, Knight

Obverse disc: Imperial crown on a red enameled field

Obverse legend: HONNEUR ET PATRIE on a blue enameled field

Ha 8
Grand
Cross

Ha 8
Grand
Cross
badge
(reverse)

Reverse disc: Bust of Faustin, left, on a gold field

Reverse legend: FAUSTIN Iᴱᴿ FONDATEUR | 1849 on blue enameled band

Shape: Ball-tipped, gold-rimmed, white enameled, 7-pointed star with a green enameled wreath in the angles, suspended from an imperial crown

Star shape: Ball-tipped, gold-rimmed, 7-pointed star with (paste) diamonds with a green enameled wreath in the angles

Size: Badge: 63 mm. Star: 92 mm

Metal: Badge: gilt bronze. Star: silver

Maker: Arthus Bertrand, Paris

Ribbon: Red with a narrow light blue center stripe

Reference: Étienne 1954, 44, 48–50; Werlich 1974, 22

* * *

IN 1856, Faustin created two religious/monarchical orders. Although the Orders of Saint Mary Magdalene and of Saint Anne honored two prominent saints, they were intended to establish Faustin's legitimacy in the eyes of the Catholic Church and those of the recipients. At the investiture, a candidate was required to kneel before the emperor, declare his fidelity to the emperor and swear to obey the constitution and the laws of Haiti. Members of each order were required to attend mass with the emperor on their respective saint's day and to pray for God's blessing on the emperor and on Faustin himself.

Faustin considered that the two orders would serve the same purpose. The combined number of members for both orders was limited in the case of the Grand Cross to 40, and the Commander to 125. Candidates for receiving a higher grade must have first been awarded the Knight.

Ha9. *L'Ordre de Sainte Marie Madeleine*

Instituted: By Emperor Faustin on March 31, 1856

Grades: Collar, Grand Cross, Commander, Knight

Obverse disc: Half-length frontal image of Saint Mary Magdalene, on green enameled field

Obverse legend: DIEU SEUL on red enameled gold-rimmed band

Reverse disc: Bust of Faustin on gold field

Reverse legend: FAUSTIN Iᴱᴿ FONDATEUR on red enameled, gold-rimmed band

Shape: Ball-tipped, 6-armed star with 2-pointed ends and alternating red and black enamel and 3 rays in each angle suspended from a gold imperial crown

Star shape: Disc with gold script letter M, crowned, on a white enameled field on a ball-tipped, 6-armed black star with 2-pointed ends with (paste) diamonds and 3 rays in each angle

Metal: Collar, Grand Cross, Commander: gold; Knight: silver

Ribbon: Green with white edge stripes

Reference: Étienne 1954, 52–56; Werlich 1974, 230–31

*Ha10. *L'Ordre de Sainte Anne*

The Order of Saint Anne was conferred for exceptional service to the emperor and to the Haitian Empire. To be eligible for a higher grade, a candidate must have already received the Knight. Numerical limits were placed on the number of orders awarded.

Instituted: March 31, 1856

Grades: Collar, Grand Cross (40), Commander (120),* Knight

Obverse disc: Saint Anne standing on oval blue enameled field

Obverse legend: J'ESPERE EN ELLE on gold-rimmed, white enameled band

Reverse disc: Ornate letter A beneath a stylized heart on oval blue enameled field

Reverse legend: POUR L'EMPEREUR ET LA PATRIE on a gold-rimmed, white enameled band

Shape: Ball-tipped, gold-rimmed, red enameled 8-pointed star, suspended from an imperial crown

Size: 65 × 57 mm

Metal: Collar, Grand Cross, Commander: gold; Knight: silver

Maker: Arthus Bertrand, Paris

Ribbon: White with narrow light blue edge stripes

Reference: Étienne 1954, 52–57; Werlich 1974, 231

* * *

HAITI created its first republican order in 1926, under the presidency of Louis Borno, who served from 1922 to 1930, during the American occupation.

Ha 10
Commander

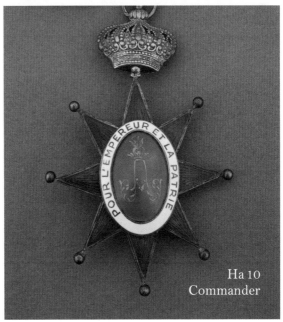

Ha 10
Commander

Ha 11
Officer

*Ha11. *L'Ordre National Honneur et Mérite*

The National Order for Honor and Merit is awarded to Haitian and foreign nationals for meritorious service in carrying out their duties in the fields of diplomatic, consular, civil, judicial, or military fields. A Haitian member may receive a higher grade only after having completed three years in the prior grade. There are no limitations on foreign membership.

Instituted: By law on May 26, 1926

Grand Master: President of the Republic

Grades: Grand Cross (30),* Grand Officer (50), Commander (75), Officer (150),* Knight

Obverse disc: Arms of Haiti

Obverse legend: MEDAILLE HONNEUR ET MERITE on a blue enameled band

Reverse disc: RÉPUBLIQUE D'HAÏTI

Reverse legend: LIBERTE EGALITE | FRATERNITE on a blue enameled band

Badge shape: White enameled Maltese cross with 2-pointed ends

Star legend: L'UNION FAIT LA FORCE

Star shape: Disc as for badge on Maltese cross with 2-pointed ends with faceted lozenges on the arms

Ha 11
Officer

Ha 11
Grand Cross badge
(reverse)

Ha 11
Grand Cross

Size: Badge: Grand Cross: 71 mm; Knight,
Officer: 41 mm. Star: 88 mm

Metal: Silver, except for Grand Cross star
awarded to heads of state: gold

Ribbon: Blue with narrow red edge stripes

Reference: Étienne 1954, 86–95; Werlich
1974, 226–27

*Ha12. *L'Ordre Jean-Jacques Dessalines le Grand Mérite Militaire*

The Order of Jean-Jacques Dessalines the
Grand for Military Merit is named after Haiti's revolutionary hero who first proclaimed
the country's independence. It recognizes outstanding military merit by members of Haiti's armed forces or members of foreign armed
forces who have performed valuable services to
Haiti. The order has no star. The current status of the order is not known, as the army has
been disbanded.

Grades: 1st, 2nd, 3rd*

Obverse: Bust of Dessalines, left

Obverse legend: ORDRE JEAN JACQUES
DESSALINES LE GRAND | MERITE
MILITAIRE on blue enameled band

Reverse: Arms of Haiti

Reverse legend: LIBERTE EGALITE
FRATERNITE | REPUBLIQUE D'HAITI

Shape: Round, surrounded by green enameled
laurel wreath

Size: 3rd: 45 mm

Metal: Bronze

Maker: Antigua Vilardebó y Riera, Havana

Ribbon: Red, black

Reference: Burke's Peerage 2006, 1182–83;
Werlich 1974, 227–28

* * *

PRESIDENT Sténio Vincent, who served from
1930 to 1941, instituted a republican order of
merit to promote inter-American solidarity

Ha 12
3rd grade

Ha 12
3rd grade

Ha 13
Grand Cross star

Ha 13
Grand Cross badge

and good neighbor policies. Haiti was seeking to expand its commercial relations with Latin America.

*Ha13. *L'Ordre Pétion et Bolívar*

The Order of Pétion and Bolívar is awarded to foreign heads of state and to Haitian and foreign career diplomats who have supported the cause of pan-Americanism. The collar is reserved for the President of the Republic, and Grand Crosses are reserved for heads of state. Haitian members must have served for five years in one grade before they may be promoted to the next grade.

During Latin America's wars of independence Simón Bolívar was given political asylum by Alexandre Pétion, then president of the southern (republican) half of Haiti. Bolívar left Haiti in 1816 with his supporters to begin

his eventually successful campaign to liberate Latin America from Spanish rule.

Instituted: October 21, 1939

Grand Master: President of the Republic

Grades: Collar, Grand Cross (20),* Grand Officer (40), Commander (60), Officer (80), Knight (100)

Obverse disc: Jugate busts of Alexandre Pétion and Simón Bolívar, left

Obverse legend: ORDRE PANAMERICAIN | PETION ET BOLIVAR 1939

Reverse disc: Arms of Haiti

Shape: 4-pointed cross superimposed on band with 3 radiating bars in interior angles, superimposed on angled 4-pointed cross with 3 small balls between each point

Star disc: Map of the western hemisphere

Star legend: ORDRE PANAMERICAIN | PETION ET BOLIVAR 1939

Ha 13
Grand Cross star (reverse)

Ha 13
Grand Cross badge (reverse)

Star shape: Cross made of 3 rays in each arm, 3 circles in each angle, 3 radiating bars connecting outer legend band

Size: Badge: Grand Cross, Grand Officer, Commander: 60 mm; Officer, Knight: 40 mm. Star: 74 mm

Metal: Badge: Grand Cross: gold; Grand Officer, Commander, Officer, Knight: gilt. Star: Grand Cross: gilt silver; Grand Officer: silver

Ribbon: Orange, green, orange

Reference: Étienne 1954, 98–104; Burke's Peerage 2006, 1183–84; Werlich 1974, 228

Provenance: A. Menke

* * *

PRESIDENT Elie Lescot, who served from 1941 to 1946, authorized Haiti's first order of merit for persons contributing to the country's economic well-being. Agriculture was and is the mainstay of Haiti's economy.

Ha14. *L'Ordre National du Mérite Agricole*

The National Order of Agricultural Merit is awarded to Haitian and foreign citizens and organizations. In the case of Haitians, the order may be bestowed on farmers who apply responsible growing techniques, as well as to individuals and institutions that contribute to Haiti's agricultural progress. The order may be given to an individual or organization that has made significant scientific advances of benefit to Haiti's agriculture. The order has no star.

Instituted: By law on January 12, 1945
Grades: Officer, Knight
Obverse: A hoe, a pitchfork, and a machete
Obverse legend: MERITE AGRICOLE
Reverse: Arms of Haiti
Reverse legend: REPUBLIQUE D'HAITI
Size: 40 mm
Metal: Officer: gilt; Knight: silver

Ribbon: Green with narrow yellow edge
 stripes
Reference: Étienne 1954, 106–8; Werlich
 1974, 229

* * *

PRESIDENT Paul Magloire, who served from
1950 to 1957, instituted three new orders for
merit in the fields of medicine, the economy, and
education. Magloire made himself the Grand
Master of two of the orders, and in each case a
gold medal was struck for the Grand Master.

*Ha15. *L'Ordre National du Travail*

President Magloire authorized the National
Order of Labor to recognize outstanding service by businessmen and laborers working in
the public sector or private enterprise. Criteria for membership include professional com-
petence, discipline, and a contribution to a profession. The order has no star.

Ha 15
Officer

Instituted: April 26, 1951
Grand Master: President of the Republic
Grades: Officer,* Knight
Obverse: Arms of Haiti
Obverse legend: REPUBLIQUE D'HAÏTI in
 raised band | DEPARTEMENT DU TRAVAIL
Reverse: Triangle with image of laborer
 within and inscription SECURITE | PROGRES
 | TRAVAIL
Reverse legend: ORDRE NATIONAL DU
 TRAVAIL in raised band
Size: 40 mm
Metal: Officer: silver; Knight: gilt silver
Ribbon: Red with narrow blue edge stripes
Reference: Étienne 1954, 109–10

Ha 15
Officer

Ha16. *L'Ordre National de l'Education*

President Magloire instituted the National
Order for Education, which recognizes teachers at the primary, secondary, and university

levels who distinguish themselves by their com-
petence, devotion, and example. Candidates
must have worked for at least fifteen years as a
teacher in a public or private school, or in the
Department of Education. The grand council
of the order may also accept anyone, regard-

less of nationality, who in its opinion has made an outstanding contribution to the country's education. Knights of the order are eligible for the grade of Officer only after teaching for five years after entering the order. The order has no star.

Instituted: By law on September 19, 1952

Modified: By law on July 7, 1953 (shape changed)

Grand Master: President of the Republic

Grades: Grand Master, Legal Council, Officer, Knight

Obverse: Open book resting on laurels

Obverse legend: EDUCATION NATIONALE | MENS AGITAT MOLEM

Reverse: Arms of Haiti

Reverse legend: REPUBLIQUE D'HAÏTI

Shape: Oval

Metal: Grand Master, Legal Council: gold; Officer: silver; Knight: bronze

Ribbon: Grand Master: purple with center white stripe and gold horizontal stripe to left of rosette; Legal Council: same but with white stripe to left of rosette; Officer: same but no horizontal stripe; Knight: same, but no rosette or horizontal stripe

Reference: Étienne 1954, 112–16; Werlich 1974, 228–29

Ha17. *L'Ordre National de la Santé*

President Magloire authorized the National Order of Health to recognize doctors, nurses, practitioners, and laboratory technicians who have carried out research to eliminate diseases. The order has no star.

Instituted: By law on July 17, 1954

Grand Master: President of the Republic

Grades: Grand Officer, Officer, Knight

Obverse: 2 crossed palms

Obverse legend: SANTÉ PUBLIQUE

Reverse: Arms of Haiti

Reverse legend: RÉPUBLIQUE D'HAÏTI

Shape: Oval

Metal: Grand Officer: gilt; Officer: silver; Knight: bronze

Ribbon: Dark blue with a narrow white center stripe

Reference: Étienne 1954, 118–20

HONDURAS

HONDURAS joined the other four Central American republics in declaring its independence from Spain on September 15, 1821. Within a few months, however, Central America joined the Mexican Empire, a relationship that lasted for two years. In 1823, Mexico overthrew its emperor, declared itself a republic, and recognized the independence of Central America.

Two Honduran leaders emerged in this period: Francisco Morazán and José Cecilio del Valle. Morazán made his military reputation by defeating conservative forces at the Battle of Trinidad in 1827, after which he served briefly as Honduras's president. In 1830, he was elected president of the Federal Republic of Central America, a post he held until the federation was dissolved a decade later. As the leading liberal of his time, Morazán frequently fought Rafael Carrera, Guatemala's conservative president. Del Valle was a lawyer who was appointed Mexican foreign minister when Central America merged with that country. He helped negotiate Central America's separation from Mexico in 1823. He returned to Central America, where he drafted the constitution of the Central American federation. Although no medals were created by Honduras for these two statesmen, the country instituted orders named after them in the middle of the twentieth century. The two orders are the country's highest official awards.

Honduras was involved in many of the wars between conservatives and liberals in Central America during the nineteenth century. However, no medals are known to have been created by Honduras during this period. The country's first medal was authorized for its military that were sent to Nicaragua in 1857 to fight the forces of American filibuster William Walker.

After World War II, Honduras began creating medals mainly for its military in peacetime. Honduras fought a brief border war with El Salvador in 1969, popularly known as the "Football War." In 2003, Honduras sent seven hundred soldiers to participate in the U.S.-led invasion of Iraq. Honduran troops worked mainly on reconstruction and did not suffer any casualties. No specific medals are known to have been created in connection with these two wars.

MEDALS

MANY OF the intra–Central American wars prior to national independence were fought between liberals and conservatives, with little regard for national origin. These were ideological wars, not territorial ones. Honduras did not authorize any military medals until well after attaining its national independence. Its first military campaign medal resulted from the adventures of the American filibuster William Walker.

Hn1. *La Medalla de la Campaña de Nicaragua 1857*

The Nicaragua Campaign Medal of 1857 was bestowed on Honduran officers and men who fought the American adventurer and filibuster William Walker in Nicaragua. Walker sought to create English-speaking colonies in the region under his personal rule. He became president of Nicaragua in 1856. His threats to occupy other parts of Central America led Costa Rica, El Salvador, Guatemala, and El Salvador to send troops to Nicaragua to defeat him. Honduran General Florencio Xatruch was put in charge of the allied armies, which defeated Walker on the field of battle. Walker surrendered to the United States Navy, which forcibly repatriated him home. In 1860, Walker was invited back to the region by English-speaking inhabitants based in Roatán. On arrival, he was arrested by the Royal Navy and turned over to Honduras, which executed him shortly thereafter.

> Instituted: 1857?
> Obverse: Rising sun with two laurel branches below
> Obverse inscription: HONDURAS
> Reverse: Smiling face of a sun
> Reverse legend: CAMPAÑA DE NICARAGUA, 1857.
> Size: 37 mm
> Metal: Gold

> Ribbon: Blue, white, blue
> Reference: Emering 2013, 33–34

Hn2. *La Condecoración del 21 de Octubre de 1956*

The Decoration of October 21, 1956, was awarded to members of the armed forces who overthrew de facto President Julio Lozano Díaz on that date and formed a military junta. Díaz had assumed presidential authority in November 1954, when the incumbent President Gálvez sought medical attention outside the country. Díaz later ran for office and was elected president in 1956, but the military junta annulled the election. He died in Miami the following year.

> Instituted: December 3, 1956
> Classes: 1st, 2nd
> Shape: Star
> Metal: Gilt
> Reference: http://www.medals.org.uk/honduras/honduras-text.htm, accessed March 6, 2012

*Hn3. *La Medalla de Juan Lindo– Civilización y Cultura*

The Medal of Juan Lindo–Civilization and Culture was instituted one hundred years following the death of Juan Nepomucemo Fernández Lindo y Zelaya (1790–1857), a conservative president of Honduras from 1847 to 1852. He rewrote the constitution and founded the Na-

Hn 3

Hn 4

Hn 3

Obverse disc: Bust of Lindo, ¾ right

Obverse legend: REPUBLICA DE HONDURAS |
1857–1957

Reverse inscription: DON | JUAN LINDO |
CIVILIZACIÓN | Y | CULTURA

Shape: Maltese cross

Size: 38 mm

Metal: Bronze

Ribbon: Blue with 2 red side stripes

*Hn4. *La Medalla de Valor Heroico*

The Medal for Heroic Valor is awarded by the
armed forces for bravery. The medal features
the bust of José Trinidad Cabañas (1805–71),
who served under Francisco Morazán as they
jointly sought to strengthen the causes of

tional Autonomous University of Honduras. He
allied himself with El Salvador in an unsuccessful attempt to defeat Rafael Carrera, the conservative president of Guatemala. Lindo was
forced out of office in 1852 and retired from
active politics.

liberalism and Latin American unity. As president, 1852–55, Cabañas boosted the economy and created the country's first public schools.

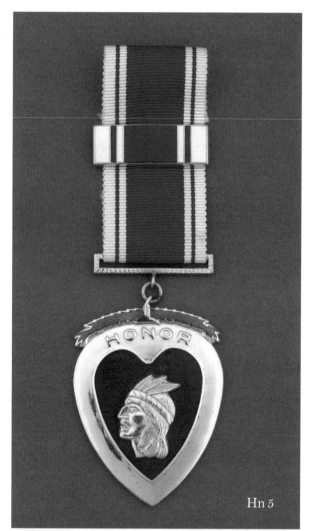

Hn 5

Obverse disc: Bust of General Cabañas, ¾ left

Obverse legend: VALOR HEROICO

Shape: Star with pointed wavy ends and leaf points in the angles, attached to an upper scroll inscribed GRAL | CABAÑOS

Size: 40 × 34 mm

Metal: Gilt

Maker: N. S. Meyer, Inc., New York

Ribbon: Yellow edged in red with a blue center stripe and 2 light blue edge stripes

*Hn5. *La Medalla de Honor*

The Medal of Honor is awarded to members of the armed forces for being wounded in the line of duty.

Obverse disc: Head of Mayan Indian, left, on a red enameled heart

Obverse inscription: HONOR

Shape: Heart surmounted by green enameled laurel branches

Size: 50 × 39 mm

Metal: Gilt

Maker: N. S. Meyer, Inc., New York

Ribbon: Red with 2 narrow white side stripes and 2 narrow white edge stripes

*Hn6. *La Estrella al Mérito*

The Merit Star is awarded for merit and service to the armed forces.

Instituted: August 19, 1955

Classes: 1st, 2nd,* 3rd*

Obverse disc: Arms of Honduras

Shape: Ball-tipped star surrounded with a green enameled wreath in the angles, suspended from a metallic bar inscribed MERITO

Size: 39 mm

Hn 6

Hn 7

Hn 8a

Metal: 1st: gilt; 2nd: silvered; 3rd, bronze

Maker: N. S. Meyer, Inc., New York

*Hn7. *La Medalla de la Patria*

The Medal of the Fatherland is awarded to members of the armed forces.

Obverse disc: Bust of Morazán, left

Shape: Concave-sided beaded cross with a laurel wreath and crossed swords in the angles

Size: 55 mm

Metal: Gilt

Ribbon: White with purple edge stripes, 2 narrow purple side stripes and 1 black center stripe

*Hn8. *La Medalla de Servicios Distinguidos*

The Medal for Distinguished Services is awarded for outstanding service to the armed forces. It is conferred in two classes, with completely different designs, produced by different makers. The gold version is awarded to persons of senior rank. September 15, 1821, was the date that Central America declared its independence from Spain.

*Hn8a. *Gold*

Obverse disc: Enameled arms of Honduras on oval disc surrounded by band reading DIOS UNION Y LIBERTAD | 15 DE SEPTIEMBRE 1821

Hn 8b

Size: 42 mm

Maker: N. S. Meyer, Inc., New York

Ribbon: Blue, red, blue, separated by 2 narrow
white stripes

*Hn9. *La Medalla del Expedicionario*

The Expeditionary's Medal is given to members of the armed forces for serving in combat.

Classes: 1st, 2nd,* 3rd*

Obverse: Honduran soldier carrying an M-1
rifle

Obverse legend: EXPEDICIONARIO above and
branches below on a band

Size: 42 mm

Metal: 1st: silver; 2nd: bronze; 3rd: white
metal

Maker: N. S. Meyer, Inc., New York

Ribbon: 2nd: blue with 2 blue side
stripes and a narrow green center stripe;
3rd: yellow edged in white with a red
center stripe and 2 black edge
stripes

Provenance: 3rd: A. Menke

Hn10. *La Cruz de Mérito de las Fuerzas Armadas*

The Merit Cross of the Armed Forces is
awarded to members of the armed forces for
distinguished conduct and long service.

Obverse: Arms of Honduras

Shape: Blue and white enameled, gilt-rimmed
Maltese cross with wavy ends suspended
from a brooch

Size: 43 mm

Metal: Gilt

Ribbon: Horizontal blue, white, and blue

Reference: http://www.medals.org.uk/
honduras/honduras011.htm, accessed May
15, 2013

Obverse legend: SERVICIOS | DISTINGUIDOS
on a circular band

Shape: Disc attached to band by enameled
flags, with laurel branches on top, suspended from a ribbon bar

Size: 45 × 42 mm

Metal: Gold

Ribbon: Blue with a red center stripe edged
in white

*Hn8b. *Gilt*

Obverse disc: 5 stars on a white enameled
field

Shape: Red enameled Maltese cross with
wavy ends and a ball-tipped triangle in each
angle, suspended from a ribbon bar

Hn 9

Hn 11

*Hn 11. *La Cruz de Conducta Ejemplar*

This Good Conduct Cross is awarded to army personnel. Similar good conduct medals are awarded to the other branches of the armed forces.

> Classes: 1st, 2nd, 3rd*
> Obverse disc: Helmet with rays on a bronzed field
> Obverse legend: CONDUCTA EJEMPLAR
> Shape: White enameled Maltese cross with 2-pointed ends and a red enameled Maltese cross with 2-pointed ends in the angles
> Size: 41 mm
> Metal: 1st: gold; 2nd: silver; 3rd: bronze
> Maker: N. S. Meyer, Inc., New York
> Ribbon: Red, white, red

Hn 12. *La Medalla al Mérito Técnico*

The Medal for Technical Merit is awarded to members of the armed forces for merit unrelated to combat.

> Classes: 1st, 2nd
> Obverse: Open book superimposed on a red and yellow flaming torch with rays
> Obverse inscription: MERITO TECNICO
> Size: 40 mm
> Metal: 1st: silver; 2nd: bronze
> Ribbon: Red, yellow, red

*Hn 13. *La Estrella del Soldado*

The Soldier's Star is awarded for merit in the army.

Obverse disc: 5 stars on a white enameled field

Obverse legend: HONOR LEALTAD | SACRIFICIO on a metallic band

Shape: Ball-tipped star with a green laurel wreath in the angles, suspended from a brooch in the shape of a rifle with a bayonet

Size: 33 mm

Metal: Silvered

Maker: N. S. Meyer, Inc., New York

Ribbon: Yellow with 2 narrow red side stripes edged in white and 1 narrow center white stripe edged in blue and red

*Hn14. *La Cruz de Vuelo*

The Flying Cross is awarded to air force personnel for service above and beyond the call of duty.

Classes: 1st,* 2nd,* 3rd

Obverse disc: Wings with 5 small stars on a white enameled field

Obverse legend: FUERZA AEREA | HONDURAS on a metallic band

Shape: Blue lacquered, metal-rimmed Maltese cross with 2-pointed ends with metallic bullet heads on the arms and a green enameled laurel wreath in the angles

Size: 44 mm

Metal: 1st: gilt; 2nd: silvered; 3rd: bronze

Maker: N. S. Meyer, Inc., New York

Ribbon: Blue, white, blue

Reference: http://www.medals.org.uk/ honduras/honduras010.htm, accessed May 15, 2013

Hn 15. *La Estrella Policial al Mérito*

The Star for Police Merit is awarded to members of the national police force for meritorious service.

Classes: 1st, 2nd
Obverse: Shield in a white enameled pentagon
Obverse inscription: HONOR POLICIAL
Shape: Ball-tipped green enameled star with rayed disc in the angles
Metal: 1st: gilt; 2nd: silvered
Maker: N. S. Meyer, Inc., New York
Ribbon: Green, white, green
Reference: http://www.medals.org.uk/ honduras/honduras001.htm, accessed May 15, 2013

*Hn 16. *La Medalla de Sacrificio Policial*

The Medal for Police Sacrifice is awarded to the survivors of members of the national police killed in the line of duty.

Obverse disc: Scales of justice on a white enameled field
Obverse legend: SACRIFICIO | POLICIAL
Shape: Red enameled cross pattée with arrowheads on each arm on a gilt disc
Size: 41 mm
Metal: Silvered
Maker: N. S. Meyer, Inc., New York
Ribbon: Blue, white, blue

Hn 16

ORDERS

HONDURAS created its first order in 1868 to support its diplomatic initiatives.

*Hn 17. *La Orden de Santa Rosa y de la Civilización*

The Order of Santa Rosa and Civilization was used principally to assist Honduras's diplomatic initiatives by conferring orders on diplomats of other countries. It was abolished by liberal President Céleo Arias, whose foreign policies instigated an invasion of El Salvador and Guatemala and tension with the world's major powers. The order is awarded in three divisions: civil, military, and religious. The design of the

Hn 17
Officer

Hn 17
Grand Cross badge (reverse)

Hn 17
Officer

three divisions is identical except for the reverse inscription.

Instituted: By decree of President José María Medina on February 21, 1868

Rescinded: By President Céleo Arias on August 6, 1872

Divisions: Diplomatic, military, religious

Grades: Grand Cross,* Grand Officer, Commander, Officer,* Knight

Obverse disc: Arms of Honduras with enameled flags

Obverse legend: Grand Cross: ORDEN DE S^A ROSA Y DE LA CIVILIZACION on a green enameled band; Officer: REPUBLICA DE HONDURAS on a green enameled band

Reverse inscription: Depending on division: MERITO CIVIL, MERITO MILITAR, or MERITO RELIGIOSO

Reverse legend: Grand Cross: REPUBLICA DE HONDURAS on a green enameled band; Officer: ORDEN DE S^A ROSA Y DE LA CIVILIZACION on a green enameled band

Shape: Ball-tipped, metallic-rimmed white

Hn 17
Grand Cross

enameled Maltese cross with 2-pointed ends and a green enameled laurel wreath in the angles, suspended from a green enameled laurel wreath

Star shape: Badge superimposed on an 8-armed, 3-part faceted silver star with a faceted arrow and 2 small rays in each angle

Size: Badge: Grand Cross: 62 mm; Officer: 42mm. Star: 85 mm

Metal: Badge: gilt; star: silver

Maker: Boulanger, Paris

Ribbon: Red with narrow center blue, white, and blue stripes

Reference: Guille 1952, 15; Werlich 1974, 235

*Hn 18. *La Orden de Francisco Morazán*

The Order of Francisco Morazán is awarded to Honduran and foreign citizens for extraordinary achievements in military, scientific, literary, artistic, and humanitarian activities. It was originally instituted with one class, but in 1954, the number of classes was increased to six. The Grand Cross with gold star is bestowed only on foreign heads of state.

José Francsico Morazán Quezada (1792–1842) was Honduras's and Central America's leading political figure in the years following Central America's independence from Mexico in 1823. Morazán allied himself with fellow liberals and took up arms against conservative authorities, leading to his memorable victory over General Justo Milla's men at the battle of La Trinidad in 1827. The following year, Morazán invaded Guatemala and defeated its conservative government. He was twice elected president of the Federal Republic of Central America, in 1830 and 1834. The federation broke up after Costa Rica, Honduras, and Nicaragua withdrew. Conservative forces under Rafael Carrera seized power in Guatemala. In 1839, Morazán was elected president of El Salvador

Hn 18
Knight

Hn 18
Knight

Hn 18
Grand Cross
with silver star

Hn 18
Grand Cross badge (reverse)

Shape: Ball-tipped, white enameled, gilt-edged Maltese cross with 2-pointed ends and a green enameled wreath in the angles, suspended from a gilt pyramid

Star shape: Badge superimposed on an 8-armed star with 3 rays in each angle

Size: Badge: Grand Cross: 56 mm; Knight: 45 mm. Star: 88 mm

Metal: Badge: gilt; silver star: silver

Ribbon: Blue with a white center stripe

Reference: Burke's Peerage, 2006, 1197–98; Werlich 1974, 234–35

*Hn19. *La Orden de José Cecilio del Valle*

The Order of José Cecilio del Valle is awarded to Hondurans for bringing honor to their country and to foreign nationals for promoting peace and international understanding and for providing distinguished service to Honduras.

The order is named after José Cecilio del Valle (1777–1834), the second-most influential Honduran political leader after Francisco Morazán. A political moderate, he was elected mayor of Guatemala City in 1821, the year that Central America proclaimed its independence from Spain. Valle wrote Central America's Declaration of Independence. When Mexico annexed Central America, Valle went to Mexico, where he was soon appointed minister of foreign affairs. In 1824, he helped to negotiate Central America's independence, and then returned to Guatemala. Valle was elected president of the Federal Republic of Central America in 1834 but died of natural causes before taking office. Although considered Honduras's most respected statesman, he never held any office in his native land.

Instituted: October 3, 1957

Regulated/modified: By Agreement No. 23 of the Military Junta on November 14, 1978

but was soon defeated by Carrera. Morazán fled into exile in South America but returned to Central America in 1842 and became head of state of Costa Rica. Later that year, Costa Ricans conspired against him, arrested him, and executed him.

Instituted: By Decree No. 102 on March 1, 1941

Modified: By Presidential Decree No. 44 on January 25, 1950

Modified: March 26, 1954

Grades: Grand Collar, Grand Cross with gold star, Grand Cross with silver star,* Grand Officer, Commander, Officer, Knight*

Obverse disc: Bust of Morazán, left, on a gilt field

Obverse legend: FRANCISCO MORAZAN | 1792–1842 on a blue enameled band

Reverse disc: 5 volcanoes with pileus and sun behind

Reverse legend: REP. DE HONDURAS | LIBRE SOBERANA E INDEPENDIENTE

Hn 19
Grand Collar

Grades: Collar,* Grand Cross with gold star,* Grand Cross with silver star, Grand Officer, Commander, Officer, Knight*

Obverse disc: Green enameled map of the western hemisphere and a gilt bust of Valle, ¾ left, on a blue enameled field

Obverse legend: ORDEN JOSE CECILIO DEL VALLE | 1777–1977 on a white enameled band

Shape: Gilt-edged, green enameled star with anchored ends and 5 rays in each angle; Grand Cross and Knight: each arm

Hn 19
Grand Cross
star and badge

Hn 19
Knight

surmounted by a star; Grand Cross and
Knight: suspended from a star

Star shape: Badge with stars superimposed on
the rays of the angles

Collar shape: Badge suspended from
oval disc with enameled arms of Honduras on a blue enameled field, and alternating discs of a scroll reading
AMERICA | DE DIA | CUANDO | ESCRIBA | DE
NOCHE | CUANDO | PIENSE; and enameled
pyramid on blue field with the legend
PROVINCIAS UNIDAS DEL CENTRO DE
AMERICA on a white enameled band

Size: Badge: Collar: 59 mm; Grand Cross,
Knight badge: 50 mm. Star: 80 mm

Metal: Gilt

Maker: Cejalvo, Madrid

Ribbon: Grand Cross with gold star:
light green with narrow yellow side
stripes; Grand Cross with silver star
and Grand Officer: light green with
silver side stripes; all other grades: light
green

Reference: Burke's Peerage 2006, 1198–99

MEXICO

MIGUEL HIDALGO Y COSTILLA, a Catholic priest, declared Mexico's independence on September 16, 1810, but he was defeated by royalist forces and executed. A year later, a royalist officer, Agustín de Iturbide, declared for independence and signed a Declaration of Independence of the Mexican Empire with representatives of the Spanish crown. The agreement was based on Iturbide's "Three Guarantees": Mexico would become an independent monarchy; Creoles and Iberian Peninsulares would enjoy equal rights; and the Catholic Church would remain the official religion. Iturbide made himself emperor and appointed an imperial regency to rule until his coronation. The regency authorized Mexico's first military medals to those who fought a resurgent royalist army. The regency later issued medals for the officers and men who swore loyalty to Iturbide and the cause of independence. After his coronation, Iturbide instituted Mexico's first imperial order, the Order of Our Lady of Guadalupe, the country's patron saint, but it was rescinded soon after he was overthrown in 1823.

For the next one hundred years of its history, Mexico lived through continuous armed conflict until the conclusion of the Mexican Revolution in 1920. At the outset, royalists and Spanish troops tried to regain control of the viceroyalty; power brokers in the capital city struggled to suppress regional interests; free trade secular liberals opposed conservatives supported by landowners and the Catholic Church; and the country faced armed conflict with American settlers in Texas (the Texas Rebellion), France (the Pastry War and the French Intervention in Mexico), and the United States (the Mexican-American War and the 1914 landing at Veracruz). Mexico, including its cities and states, issued more medals for armed conflict than any other Latin American nation.

A few Mexican leaders heavily influenced the course of the country's history. The first of these was an army officer, Antonio López de Santa Anna (1794–1876). He repeatedly led his nation into battle, demonstrating courage and resourcefulness, but not always successfully. He alienated some Mexican states by centralizing power in Mexico City, which led to regional rebellions. He abolished slavery, which affected the interests of American slaveholding plantation owners in Coahuila y Tejas and led to war over the independence of Texas. He was respected for a defense of Veracruz during the so-called Pastry War with France. He played a major role in the Mexican-American War, commanding the troops at the Battle of Buena Vista, where he lost more than half of his army. Throughout all these conflicts, Santa Anna had to face regional uprisings, especially in the Yucatán, but also in Tabasco and other states. Santa Anna authorized many medals for his officers and men who fought in these wars. While in power, he reinstituted Iturbide's Order of Our Lady of Guadalupe with a different design, but the order was rescinded after he left power in 1855.

A second influential Mexican was Benito Juárez (1806–72), who became president shortly after Santa Anna was overthrown. A Zapotec Indian and a lawyer by profession, he introduced liberal reforms that confiscated church property, disenfranchised the clergy, and established civilian control over the army. It was under his presidency that France sent another expeditionary force to Veracruz in 1862 for the purpose of installing the Hapsburg Archduke Maximilian on the throne of Mexico. The French Intervention in Mexico united all Mexicans against a common foreign enemy. The French put Maximilian on the Mexican throne, then abandoned him by 1865, as the Mexicans engaged in protracted hostilities. While he reigned, Maximilian instituted three imperial orders, all of which were rescinded following his execution. Juárez stayed on as president throughout the war and authorized many military medals for battles against the French expeditionary forces and Mexican conservatives. Many Mexican states awarded medals for their citizens who fought the French.

The third influential Mexican was General José Porfirio Díaz Mori (1830–1915), who fought Santa Anna and the French expeditionary force. He was first elected president in 1876 and remained in office until 1911, making him the longest-ruling president in the country's history. Porfirio Díaz improved internal security and strengthened the central government. He was the first president to authorize military medals for merit and loyalty not related to any particular war or battle. He did have to put down Indian insurgencies in the Yucatán, Chihuahua, and Sonora, but in each case the military medals were authorized by the affected state, not by the central government.

The Mexican Revolution broke out in 1911 and lasted nearly a decade. A number of medals were issued in connection with specific battles and important political events. The United States bombarded Veracruz during the revolution and landed troops. Mexico issued medals to its troops who opposed the American landing.

Since the end of its revolution, Mexico has been ruled mainly by the Partido Revolucionario Institucionalista, although the opposition has gained power in more recent years. During this period, the country created medals in peacetime for valor, merit, distinguished service, and loyalty. Mexico played a minor role in World War II, when it mobilized a militia for possible service in case of an invasion and for a squadron of fighters that served in the Philippines.

Mexico's only order for merit was created in 1933, and it is awarded only to foreigners. The country has never created an order for its own citizens, even in wartime.

MEDALS

War of Independence

By 1820, Spanish royalists had defeated the early forces of independence. Both Miguel Hidalgo and José María Morelos had been captured and executed. Only Vicente Guerrero had survived with his men in the extreme south. The viceroy sent one of his senior officers, Agustín de Iturbide, to defeat Guerrero. Iturbide instead made a deal with Guerrero. Their agreement created an alliance of church, military, and insurgents based on the slogan Religion, Independence, and Union. The Army of the Three Guarantees entered Mexico City on September 27, 1821, and Iturbide proclaimed Mexico's independence.

Iturbide had planned to persuade King Ferdinand VII of Spain to accept the Mexican monarchy, but the king refused. Iturbide named himself emperor instead, and an imperial regency ruled until his coronation. Spain reinforced its troops in Mexico, and the fighting resumed until Spain withdrew its last garrison from Veracruz in 1825. Mexico awarded medals for many of these battles. The first medals were awarded to Iturbide's Army of the Three Guarantees as it advanced on Mexico City in 1821. The later ones covered Spain's efforts to regain sovereignty over New Spain.

Mx1. *La Cruz de Tepeaca*

In March 1821, an insurgent general, José Joaquín de Herrera, was fighting royalist forces near Veracruz. In April, he occupied and fortified the town of Tepeaca. A royalist force under the command of Francisco Hevia took up positions outside the town. On April 21, Hevia launched an assault on the town. Both sides suffered significant casualties and both claimed victory, but Herrera abandoned Tepeaca. Herrera later became an active politician and was president of Mexico on three occasions. The imperial regency authorized a cross for the officers and men who fought there. The medal is divided into three classes, depending on the nature of the recipient's involvement in the battle.

Classes: 1st, 2nd, 3rd

Obverse disc: Church of San Francisco on a blue enameled field

Obverse legend: 1st: VIRTIO SU SANGRE | EN TEPEACA on a white enameled band; 2nd: SE DISTINGUIO | EN TEPEACA on a white enameled band; 3rd: CONCURRIO | EN TEPEACA on a white enameled band

Reverse inscription: 1821

Shape: Ball-tipped cross pattée with concave pointed ends with a gilt palm and a green enameled olive branch in the angles, suspended from olive and palm branches

Size: 46 mm

Ribbon: White; 1st: green center stripe with 2 red edge stripes; 2nd: red center stripe with 2 green edge stripes; 3rd: 1 green and 1 red edge stripe and red, white, and green center stripes

Reference: Grove 1974, 3:28, D-5; Gillingham 1940, 10; Pérez-Maldonado 1942, 19–20

Mx2. *La Cruz de Córdoba*

After abandoning Tepeaca, Herrera took up positions in Córdoba. On May 16, 1821, royalist forces under the command of Hevia attacked the town, but without success. Hevia was killed and replaced by Blas del Castillo, who continued the assault, but also in vain. Herrera received reinforcements, and Castillo withdrew on May 21, 1821. The imperial regency authorized a cross for the men of the Ninth Insurgent Division of the Army of the Three Guarantees, commanded by Herrera.

> Obverse disc: Flower on a red enameled field
>
> Reverse inscription: AÑO 1 DE LA INDEPENDENCIA on a gilt field (some specimens lack the reverse inscription)
>
> Shape: Ball-tipped, white enameled 8-pointed star surmounted by a Mexican eagle, suspended from a green enameled brooch inscribed 9° DIVISION
>
> Size: 30 mm
>
> Metal: Silver
>
> Ribbon: Green, white, red
>
> Reference: Grove 1974, 3:30, D-7; Gillingham 1940, 10; Pérez-Maldonado 1942, 21

Mx3. *La Cruz de Toluca*

In June 1821, an insurgent chief, Vicente Filisola, entered the town of Toluca after the local royalist garrison had left the town while waiting for reinforcements. Upon the arrival of these additional troops, the royalists attacked the town on June 19, but were defeated by the defenders. The royalists retreated, leaving behind their artillery and equipment.

> Obverse disc: Oval, surrounded by a red enameled band
>
> Obverse inscription: DENUE | DO EN LA | BATALLA | Y | PIEDAD | CON LOS | VENCI | DOS on a white enameled field

> Reverse disc: Oval, surrounded by a red enameled band
>
> Reverse inscription: 19 | DE JUNIO | DE 1821 | AL FRENTE | DE | TOLUCA
>
> Shape: Elongated white enameled Maltese cross with 2-pointed ends with green enameled ball-tipped points in each angle
>
> Size: 38 × 34 mm
>
> Ribbon: Red
>
> Reference: Grove 1974, 3:30, D-9; Gillingham 1940, 11; Pérez-Maldonado 1942, 22

Mx4. *La Cruz de Azcapotzalco*

Insurgent forces were closing in on Mexico City even as Iturbide was negotiating with the Spanish envoy Juan de O'Donojú. On August 19, 1821, insurgent units were probing royalist defensive positions outside Mexico City. The insurgents engaged royalist forces at the nearby town of Azcapotzalco. Both sides exchanged fire all day and suffered heavy casualties. The battle itself was indecisive. This was the last battle before the signing of the Treaty of Córdoba on August 24, which recognized Mexico's independence. The imperial regency authorized a cross for the men who fought in that battle. The medal was awarded in three classes, depending on the extent of the recipient's involvement in the battle.

> Classes: 1st: for those wounded in action; 2nd: for those who distinguished themselves in action; 3rd: for those who participated in the action
>
> Obverse disc: The church at Alzcapotzalco on a white (2nd: red; 3rd: green) field
>
> Reverse legend: 1st: VIRTIO SU | SANGRE POR LA | INDEPENDEN.ᴬ | DE MEXICO | EN | 19 DE AGOSTO | DE 1821; 2nd: SE | DISTINGUIO | EN LA | BRILLANTE | ACCION | DE 19 DE AGOSTO | DE 1821; 3rd: CONCURRIO | A LA BRILLANTE | ACCION | DE 19 DE AGOSTO | DE 1821

Shape: Cross with 5-lobed ends and 5 rays in each angle suspended from a brooch

Ribbon: 1st: red, white; 2nd: green, red; 3rd: yellow, blue

Reference: Grove 1974, 3:32–35, D-11; Pérez-Maldonado 1942, 23–24

Mx5. *La Medalla de Durango*

An insurgent army commanded by General Pedro Negrete laid siege to the city of Durango, whose governor, Diego García Conde, refused to give up the city. On August 30, the insurgents attacked and defeated the garrison, which formally surrendered a week later. This was the final battle prior to the proclamation of Mexico's independence.

Obverse: Vertical trumpet

Obverse inscription: VIVA LA UNION

Reverse inscription: A LOS | VENCEDORES | DE DURANGO | LOS NACIONALES | DE ZACATECAS | 1821

Shape: Oval

Size: 42 × 28 mm

Metal: Bronze

Reference: Grove 1974, 3:34–35, D-13; Pérez-Maldonado 1942, 25

Mx6. *La Cruz de la Independencia*

Among its early acts, the regency created two sets of medals for the officers and men who swore their loyalty to Iturbide prior to his triumphal march on Mexico City. These bore references to the triple commitment to the Catholic Church, independence from Spain, and the unity of all groups. A cross was made for senior officers, differentiated into two epochs, with variant versions known. The first epoch was given to those who swore allegiance between March 2, 1821, when the Plan de Iguala was first proclaimed, and June 15, 1821. The second epoch was awarded to those who swore allegiance between June 15 and September 2, 1821, just before Iturbide marched into Mexico City. Senior officers were given this cross; the lower ranks received the round medals described below.

Instituted: October 12, 1821

Classes: 1st, 2nd, 3rd

Epochs: 1st, 2nd

Mx6a. *Variant 1*

Obverse disc: 2 globes with a broken chain on a white enameled field, green enameled band above, red enameled band below (3rd class without enamel)

Obverse inscription: P E [S E]

Obverse legend: CONCORDIA RELIGIO | SUMA LIBERTAS on a band enameled red in the upper half and green in the lower

Reverse inscription: SPONSIONE | TRIPLICI on a white enameled field surrounded by a green enameled band with gold leaves

Shape: Ball-tipped, white enameled Maltese cross with 2-pointed ends and three 2-pointed rays in each angle suspended from an olive and palm wreath

Size: 34 mm

Metal: 1st class: gold; 2nd class: silver; 3rd class: bronze

Ribbon: Neck ribbon: 1st class, month of March only: white; rest of 1st class, 2nd class, 3rd class: green, white, red

Mx6b. *Variant 2*

Obverse inscription: SPONSIO- | NE | TRIPLISI on a white enameled field

Obverse legend: PRIMA EPOCA [SECUNDA EPOCA] on a green enameled band with laurel branches below

Reverse disc: 2 enameled globes with their connecting chains broken on a white enameled field

Mx 7b

Mx 7b

Reverse inscription: RELIGION.SVMMA.
LIBERT.CONCOR

Shape: Ball-tipped, white enameled Maltese cross with 2-pointed ends and four 2-pointed rays in each angle suspended from an olive and palm wreath

Size: 34 mm

Metal: 1st class: gold; 2nd class: silver; 3rd class: bronze

Ribbon: Neck ribbon: 1st class, month of March only: white; rest of 1st class, 2nd class, 3rd class: green, white, red

Reference: Grove 1974, 3:36, D-15, D-15v, D-20; Gillingham 1940, 7–8; Pérez-Maldonado 1942, 17–18

*Mx7. *La Medalla de la Independencia*

The Medal of Independence was awarded to officers below the rank of senior officer and for soldiers of other ranks. Like the Cross of Independence, it was issued in two epochs. For medals of each epoch, there are two varieties known, one with the inscription in Latin and the other with the inscription in Spanish.

Mx7a: *Latin legends*

Instituted: By Decree of the Imperial Regency on October 12, 1821

Classes: Junior officers, lower ranks

Epochs: 1st, 2nd

Obverse: 3 interlocking circles inscribed RELIGIO, CONCORDIA, SUMMA LIBERTAS above 2 globes with broken chains that had bound them

Obverse legend: SPONSIONE TRIPLICI | ORBEM AB ORBE SOLVIT

Reverse: Wreath tied at the base

Reverse legend: PRIMA EPOCHA [SECUNDA EPOCHA]

Size: 49 mm

Metal: Junior officers: silver; lower ranks, bronze

Maker: J. Guerrero

Ribbon: Neck ribbon; 1st, month of March only: white; rest of 1st, 2nd: green, white, red

*Mx7b: *Spanish legends*

Instituted: By Decree of the Imperial Regency on October 12, 1821

Classes: Junior officers, lower ranks*

Epochs: 1st,* 2nd*

Obverse: 3 interlocking circles inscribed RELIGION, INDEPENDENCIA, UNION above 2 globes with broken chains that had bound them

Obverse legend: CON LA TRIPLE GARANTIA | DESATO A UN ORBE DE EL OTRO

Reverse: Wreath tied at the base

Reverse legend: PRIMERA EPOCA [SEGUNDA EPOCA]

Shape: Round, with loop attached at top

Size: 49 mm

Metal: Junior officers: silver; lower ranks, bronze

Maker: J. Guerrero

Ribbon: Neck ribbon; 1st, month of March only: white; rest of 1st, 2nd: green, white, red

Reference: Grove 1974, 3:36–38, D-17–18, D-22–23; Gillingham 1940, 5–7; Pérez-Maldonado 1942, 15–16

* * *

THE SPANISH Cortes refused to accept the Treaty of Córdoba, and some royalists refused to surrender. The main holdout was the Spanish garrison at the fortress of San Juan de Ulúa dominating the strategic port of Veracruz. Spain still held on to Cuba and was able to resupply Veracruz from Havana.

Mx8. *La Cruz de Juchi*

In April 1822, a Mexican cavalry detachment under the command of Colonel Anastasio Bustamante was ordered to prevent royalist forces from regrouping. He launched a cavalry attack at Juchi (also known as Juchitepec) on April 3, forcing the royalists to surrender. Bustamante was subsequently awarded the newly created Imperial Order of Guadalupe in the grade of Grand Cross. The Juchi Cross was awarded to Bustamante's chiefs and officers.

Shape: Ball-tipped, white enameled cross with anchored ends and a small gilt diagonal cross at the juncture with an olive and palm wreath in the angles, suspended from a gilt-rimmed, white enameled brooch inscribed JUCHI

Size: 38 mm

Ribbon: Red

Reference: Grove 1974, 3:40, D-25; Gillingham 1940, 12-13; Pérez-Maldonado 1942, 35

Mx9. *La Cruz de Veracruz*

Although Spain was supposed to withdraw its troops from Veracruz under the terms of the Treaty of Córdoba, the Spanish cortés refused to ratify the agreement. The commander of the last remaining Spanish garrison in Veracruz transferred his men and supplies from the port to the fortress of San Juan de Ulúa, where he waited for reinforcements. Iturbide sent Antonio López de Santa Anna to govern Veracruz. On the late night of October 26, 1822, Santa Anna launched a surprise assault against the fortress, but the plan was poorly coordinated and abandoned. Despite the failure, two decades later Mexico authorized a cross for the officers for their courage and initiative.

Instituted: By Presidential Decree on October 29, 1840

Obverse disc: Image of the fortress at San Juan de Ulúa on a blue enameled field and inscribed below the fortress VERACRUZ

Obverse legend: VIGILANCIA Y VALOR | OCTUBRE 27 DE 1822

Reverse inscription: RECHAZO | AL ENEMIGO | EN | VERACRUZ | EN | 27 DE OCTUB^e | DE 1822

Shape: Ball-tipped, blue enameled Maltese cross with 2-pointed ends with an olive and palm wreath in the angles, suspended from a brooch in the shape of a bow

Size: 36 mm

Ribbon: Blue, white

Reference: Grove 1974, 3:41, D-27; Pérez-Maldonado 1942, 36–37

Mx10. *La Cruz de Ulúa*

The Spanish garrison at San Juan de Ulúa remained in royalist hands until late in 1825 thanks to Spain's ability to resupply its forces from Cuba by sea. In November of that year, warships purchased by Mexico in England arrived to blockade the Spanish fort. The Mexican commander, General Miguel Barragán prevented a Spanish flotilla from docking with supplies from Havana. With his provisions low and no possibility of resupply, the Spanish commander, Brigadier José Coppinger, capitulated on November 18, 1825. With the loss of San Juan de Ulúa, Spain lost its final outpost in Mexico.

Mx 11

> Instituted: By Presidential Decree on October 29, 1840
>
> Obverse disc: Image of a tower at San Juan de Ulúa on a blue enameled field
>
> Obverse legend: AL MERITO EN EL ASEDIO DE ULUA | 1825
>
> Reverse inscription: PREMIO | AL | VALOR [hand-engraved; the decree prescribes RENDICION DE ULUA EN 1825; other inscriptions are known]
>
> Shape: Gilt-rimmed, white enameled Maltese cross with convex ends (red enameled in some examples) with a laurel and palm wreath in the angles
>
> Size: 38 mm
>
> Ribbon: Yellow
>
> Reference: Grove 1974, 3:42–43, D-29, D-31; Gillingham 1940, 13; Pérez-Maldonado 1942, 38–39

Mx 11

*Mx11. *La Medalla de Zacatecas por Tampico*

Four years after the surrender of San Juan de Ulúa, Spain made one more attempt to regain its former colony. It sent a four thousand–man expeditionary force from Havana under the command of Brigadier Armando Barradas, which landed near Tampico on July 26, 1829. Barradas soon occupied Tampico itself. Mexico sent Santa Anna north by sea from Veracruz and General Manuel Tier y Terán by land to lay siege to Tampico. The first battles took place in late August. Barradas, with no hope of receiving reinforcements from Havana, capitulated on September 11, 1829. The Spaniards surrendered their weapons, while Mexico allowed them to leave Tampico by sea for Havana. Spain did not legally recognize Mexico's independence for nearly ten years, but it never again attempted to recover its colony by force of arms.

The State of Zacatecas authorized a medal for defeating Barradas at Tampico. This was the first time a Mexican state authorized a medal for a battle fought by federal forces.

Obverse: Image of mountains beneath sun and moon and above 4 flags and military trophies

Obverse legend: EL ESTADO DE ZACATECAS AL VENCEDOR DE TAMPICO | 1829

Reverse: Mexican eagle with a Phrygian cap surrounded by a laurel wreath flanked by flags and trophies

Shape: Oval

Size: 50 × 38 mm

Metal: Gold, silver, bronze*

Reference: Grove 1974, 3:44, D-35; Gillingham 1940, 13–14; Pérez-Maldonado 1942, 40–41

Mx12. *La Cruz de Tampico*

A few years later, the Mexican Congress authorized a cross in four classes to officers and enlisted men for the battle of Tampico.

Instituted: By the National Congress on April 2, 1833

Classes: 1st: general; 2nd: colonels; 3rd: lower officers; 4th: enlisted men

Obverse disc: Eagle displayed on a white enameled field

Obverse legend: ABATIO EN TAMPICO EL ORGULLO ESPAÑOL

Reverse disc: Palm branch and a saber on a white enameled field

Reverse legend: EL CONGRESO GENERAL EN 1833

Shape: Ball-tipped, 6-armed star with 2-pointed ends and 3 rays in each angle

Size: 36 mm

Metal: 1st, 2nd: gold; 3rd: gilt silver; 4th: silver

Ribbon: Green

Reference: Grove 1974, 3:45, D-37; Gillingham 1940, 11–12; Pérez-Maldonado 1942, 42

*Mx13. *La Medalla de Puebla* (*1833*)

In 1833, liberal President Valentín Gómez Farías restricted the Church's power to make ecclesiastic appointments and eliminated the military *fueros* (privileges), measures that caused a backlash from the country's conservatives in the Church and military. These measures led to the "Religión y Fueros" uprising in Morelia, led eventually by Generals Gabriel Durán and Mariano Arista. They marched on the state capital of Puebla, which was defended by a local militia under the command of the Governor Patricio Furlong. The main assault began on August 6 and lasted for several days. On the 10th, Durán and his men retreated and soon disbanded as large federal forces closed in on them. Mexico authorized a medal for the militia defenders at Puebla.

Obverse: The national eagle beneath a Phrygian cap

Obverse legend: EL GOBIERNO DE LA UNION A LOS HEROICOS DEFENSORES DE PUEBLA EN 1833

Reverse: An open book above inscription and war-club, with a bow and quiver beneath

Reverse inscription: LA FEDERACION TRIUNFANTE | EN EL ESTADO DE PUEBLA | CONTRA | LA TIRANIA Y FANATISMO | S.B.G.A. at bottom

Shape: Oval suspended by a loop from an open
   wreath pinback
Size: 48 × 38 mm, 45 × 35 mm, 39 × 30 mm*
Metal: Gold, silver, bronze*

Ribbon: Green, white, red
Reference: Grove 1974, 3:46–47, D-39–41;
   Gillingham 1940, 14; Pérez-Maldonado
   1942, 43–44

THE TEXAS REBELLION AND OTHER CONFLICTS (1835–1843)

FROM ITS earliest years, Mexico faced regional insurgencies against the central government. The most serious of these conflicts occurred in the northern state of Coahuila y Tejas, which led to the Texas Rebellion and its secession from Mexico.

The Texas Rebellion pitted American settlers in Coahuila y Tejas against Santa Anna. American settlers, many of them plantation owners, migrated to Texas at a time when the idea of Manifest Destiny was expanding America's frontiers. Coahuila y Tejas was sparsely populated. Over time, the ethnic makeup of Texas shifted dramatically in favor of Americans, who soon vastly outnumbered ethnic Mexicans. Santa Anna favored centralizing political power in Mexico, and he became concerned that these new settlers would try to secede and join the United States. He proclaimed a new constitution in 1835 that centralized power in Mexico City. Mexico abolished slavery at a time when American plantation owners in Texas grew cotton with slave labor. By October 1835, open warfare had broken out between the Mexican army, led by Santa Anna, and the Army of Texas, led by Sam Houston. The war ended with the American victory at San Jacinto and the capture of Santa Anna in 1836.

The Texans forced Santa Anna to sign the Treaty of Velasco, which recognized Texas's independence. The Mexican government never ratified the treaty, and when Santa Anna returned home, he too refused to recognize it. Raiding parties from both sides crossed the border.

*Mx14. *La Estrella por la Defensa de Texas*

Mexico awarded the Star for the Defense of Texas to its generals, chiefs, and officers who fought the Texan separatists. Medals were awarded for fighting at the battles of San Antonio, Mission, Encinal, Goliad, and others.

Instituted: August 28, 1840

Obverse disc: Eagle displayed on a white enameled field

Obverse legend: TEXAS | EN 1836 on a white enameled band

Reverse inscription: COMBATIO | POR LA | INTEGRIDAD | DEL TERRITORIO NAL. [or COMBATIO | POR LA INTE | GRIDAD DEL TER | RITORIO NA | CIONAL] on a white enameled field

Shape: Ball-tipped, gilt-rimmed, white enameled star with arrowheads in each angle, suspended from a wreath

Size: 34 mm

Metal: Gilt

Ribbon: Red, green, red

Reference: Grove 1974, 3:48, D-43; Gillingham 1940, 14–15; Pérez-Maldonado 1942, 45–47

*Mx15. *La Estrella por la Defensa de Matamoros*

Mexico awarded the Star for the Defense of Matamoros to its officers who fought a Texan incursion against Matamoros at the mouth of the Rio Grande in the spring of 1836. A Texan expedition under James Fannin Jr. headed toward Matamoros for the purpose of consolidating its supply line and also to strengthen Mexican opposition to Santa Anna. The expedition never reached Matamoros. Mexican forces under the command of General José Urrea defeated the Texans at the Battles of San Patricio, Refugio, and Coleto. Urrea captured a number of Texan prisoners, including Fannin. Urrea had negotiated an honorable surrender with Fannin, but was overruled by Santa Anna, who ordered all of the American prisoners to be shot. The execution became known as the Massacre of Goliad, an event that galvanized public opinion in favor of the Texan secessionists and contributed to Santa Anna's ultimate defeat. The officers who participated in the Massacre at Goliad may well have received this medal.

Instituted: April 27, 1836

Abolished: July 5, 1839

Obverse disc: Eagle displayed on a white enameled field

Obverse legend: MATAMOROS | EN 1836 on a white enameled band

Reverse inscription: COMBATIO | POR LA | INTEGRIDAD | DEL TERRITORIO | NAL.

Shape: Ball-tipped, white enameled star with arrowheads in each angle

Size: 34 mm

Metal: Gilt

Ribbon: Red, green, red

Reference: Grove 1974, 3:49, D-45; Gillingham 1940, 15

Mx16. *La Legión Militar Mexicana de Honor*

The Mexican Military Legion of Honor was given to officers and men who fought the Texan separatists.

Instituted: April 27, 1836

Abolished: July 5, 1839

Classes: Senior officers, officers, enlisted
men

Obverse: National eagle

Obverse legend: AL VALOR EN ____

Reverse inscription: LA PATRIA

Shape: 6-pointed star

Metal: Senior officers, officers: gold; enlisted
men: gilt silver

Ribbon: Green, white, red; senior officers:
sash; officers: neck ribbon; enlisted men:
chest ribbon

Reference: Grove 1974, 3:49, D-46

* * *

IN 1828, riots in Mexico City caused damage
to properties owned by French nationals. One
of them, a baker named Remontel, submitted
a claim for damages, one of several by French
nationals. Ten years later, France sent a naval
squadron commanded by Admiral Charles Bau-
din to force Mexico into paying an indemnity.
His squadron blockaded Mexican ports and
bombarded Veracruz, which eventually capitulated. Santa Anna came out of retirement to
lead Mexican troops against the French, losing his leg after one of the battles. The "Pastry War," better known in Mexico as the first
French intervention, went on for a few months,
and the actual fighting was limited. Mexico
eventually paid an indemnity, and the dispute
was settled.

Mx17. *La Cruz de Veracruz*

Mexico awarded the Cross of Veracruz to its
officers who defended the port during the Pastry War until its capture by the French in December 1838.

Obverse disc: A wreath with 2 swords pointed
upward

Obverse: POR SU VALOR EN VERACRUZ on a
white enameled band

Reverse legend: EL 5 DE DICIEMBRE DE on a
white enameled band

Reverse inscription: 1838 on a white enameled field

Shape: White enameled cross pattée with
concave ends and a red enameled, ball-
tipped point in each angle suspended from
a white enameled bar inscribed MERECIO
BIEN | DE LA PATRIA

Size: 38 mm

Ribbon: Red

Reference: Grove 1974, 3:49, D-47; Gillingham 1940, 16; Pérez-Maldonado 1942,
45–47

Mx18. *La Cruz de Ulúa*

The Cross of Ulúa was given to the officers
who defended Fort San Juan de Ulúa during
the bombardment by the French fleet late in
1838. An Ulúa escudo (cloth) was awarded to
the enlisted men.

Obverse disc: National eagle displayed on a
white enameled field

Obverse legend: ULUA EN 1838 on a white
enameled band

Reverse inscription: POR EL HONOR
NACIONAL [sometimes lacking]

Shape: Cross with 4 gilt towers at ends and a
green enameled wreath in the angles, suspended from a gilt oval

Size: 40 mm

Ribbon: White with red edge stripes (Grove
says blue with red edge stripes)

Reference: Grove 1974, 3:50, D-49; Gillingham 1940, 15; Pérez-Maldonado 1942,
49–50

* * *

TOWARD the end of 1839, in the northern state
of Tamaulipas, a mixed group of Texans, Co-
manches, and other Indian tribes led by Antonio Canales and Antonio Zapata rebelled

against the central government. The rebels were attacked by Mexican soldiers under the command of General Mariano Arista at Santa Rita Morelos. On March 24 and 25, 1840, the soldiers killed a number of rebels and captured Zapata, who was quickly tried and executed. Both sides signed an armistice in November 1840, and the rebellion ended.

Mx19. *La Estrella de Santa Rita Morelos*

The government awarded a star to the men who fought at Santa Rita Morelos.

> Obverse disc: National eagle displayed on a white enameled field
>
> Obverse legend: SANTA RITA MORELOS | 1840 on a white enameled band
>
> Reverse inscription: 1840
>
> Shape: Ball-tipped, white enameled star suspended from olive and palm branches
>
> Size: 32 mm
>
> Ribbon: Red with narrow green edge stripes
>
> Reference: Grove 1974, 3:51, D-52; Gillingham 1940, 18; Pérez-Maldonado 1942, 58–59

* * *

THE PASTRY WAR distracted Mexico from its protracted struggle against its own rebellious states and the Texan secessionists. When Mexico finally settled the French claims, it resumed military operations against its mutinous states, particularly Tabasco and Yucatán.

Mx20. *La Cruz de Campeche* (*1840*)

In 1839, the state of Campeche took up arms against the central government and hired Texan mercenaries with their own warships to defend against the Mexican navy. The Campeche Cross was awarded by the central government to generals, chiefs, and officers who campaigned against the Campeche federalists and their Yucatecan allies.

> Instituted: By law of August 28, 1840
>
> Obverse disc: National eagle displayed on a white enameled field
>
> Obverse legend: AL VALOR Y CONSTANCIA | EN CAMPECHE on a white enameled band
>
> Reverse inscription: 1840
>
> Shape: Ball-tipped, white enameled Maltese cross with concave pointed ends and 7 gilt rays in each angle, suspended from olive and palm branches
>
> Size: 39 mm
>
> Ribbon: Red, blue
>
> Reference: Grove 1974, 3:52, D-55; Gillingham 1940, 16; Pérez-Maldonado 1942, 51–52

Mx21. *La Cruz de Tabasco* (*1840*)

The Tabasco Cross is identical to the Campeche Cross except for its name and the ribbon. It was awarded to generals, chiefs, and officers who defeated the combined revolutionary forces of the Departments of Tabasco and Yucatán on July 27, 1840.

> Instituted: By law on August 28, 1840
>
> Obverse: National eagle displayed on a white enameled field
>
> Obverse legend: AL VALOR Y CONSTANCIA | EN TABASCO on a white enameled band
>
> Reverse inscription: 1840
>
> Shape: Ball-tipped, white enameled Maltese cross with pointed ends and 7 gilt rays in each angle, suspended from olive and palm branches
>
> Size: 39 mm
>
> Ribbon: White, green
>
> Reference: Grove 1974, 3:53, D-57; Gillingham 1940, 16–17; Pérez-Maldonado 1942, 53

* * *

THE YEAR 1840 was a particularly unstable one in Mexico, marked by rebel groups in outlying departments, the cross-border raids in the north, and a revolution in the capital city. On July 15, 1840, rebellious officers from the Mexico City garrison took the National Palace and captured President Anastasio Bustamante in the name of the Federal Constitution of 1824. Government troops, along with cadets from the Military Academy, laid siege to the rebel forces. After eleven days of fighting, they put down the uprising and freed President Bustamante.

Mx22. *La Cruz del Congreso Nacional*

The National Congress authorized three classes of the same medal, which were awarded to the officers, cadets, and enlisted men who defended the government.

Mx22a. *1st class: Officers who led the attack on the National Palace on July 15, 1840*

Instituted: By law on August 19, 1840

Obverse inscription: 15 | DE JULIO | DE | 1840 on a white enameled field surrounded by a white enameled band

Obverse legend: A LA FIDELIDAD Y LA CONSTANCIA | EL CONGRESO NACIONAL on a white enameled band

Reverse inscription: COLUMNA | DE | ATAQUE on a white enameled field

Shape: White enameled Maltese cross with 3 gold arrow feathers at the end of each arm

Size: 46 mm

Ribbon: Blue, white, blue

Mx22b. *2nd class: Officers who fought the rebels, July 15–27, 1840*

Instituted: By law on August 19, 1840

Obverse inscription: JULIO | 15 | DE 1840 on a white enameled field

Obverse legend: A LA FIDELIDAD Y AL DENUEDO EN EL COMBATE on a white enameled band

Reverse inscription: EL CON | GRESO NA | CIO- | NAL within laurel and palm branches on a white enameled field

Shape: White enameled Maltese cross with 3 gold arrow feathers at the end of each arm and five 2-pointed rays in each angle

Size: 40 mm

Ribbon: White, blue, white

Mx22c. *3rd class: Enlisted men who fought the rebels, July 15–27, 1840*

Instituted: By law on August 19, 1840

Obverse inscription: JULIO | DE 1840 on a white enameled field

Obverse legend: A LA FIDELIDAD Y VALOR on a white enameled band

Reverse inscription: EL CONGRESO NACIONAL

Shape: White enameled Maltese cross with 3 gold arrow feathers at the end of each arm and 5 rays in the angles, suspended from a metallic brooch

Ribbon: Blue

Reference: Grove 1974, 3:54–55, D-59–61; Gillingham 1940, 17; Pérez-Maldonado 1942, 57

Mx23. *La Cruz del Colegio Militar*

The Cross of the Military Academy was awarded in two classes to the cadets who defended the central government: 1st class to those who covered the Ciudadela, and 2nd class to those who occupied positions in the line of operations.

Instituted: August 19, 1840

Classes: 1st, 2nd

Obverse inscription: EN SU | NIÑEZ SALVO | A LA CAPITAL | DE LA | REPUBLICA | EN LA GLORIOSA | JORNADA DEL 15 | AL 26 DE

JULIO│DE 1840 on a white enameled
field

Reverse disc: 2 olive branches tied together
on a white enameled field

Shape: Ball-tipped, white enameled cross pattée with convex pointed ends and triangles
in the angles forming a square, and 5 rays
in each angle visible from the reverse

Size: 39 mm

Metal: Gilt

Ribbon: 1st: blue; 2nd: red

Reference: Grove 1974, 3:56, D-63–64; Gillingham 1940, 17–18; Pérez-Maldonado
1942, 54–56

*Mx24. *La Cruz de la Constancia Militar*

Mexico instituted the Cross for Military Loyalty in 1841 for the purpose of promoting loyalty to the central government among the officer corps. Regional rebellions and ambitious
caudillos often found allies among the professional officer corps, who would join the rebels.
Mexico considered this cross of honor as a distinction to recognize loyalty to the nation. This
was the first Mexican medal not associated with
a specific battle or military campaign. As such
it became the precursor of Mexico's subsequent
military medals designed to reward character
traits of loyalty, professionalism, merit, and
valor.

The Cross for Military Loyalty is awarded to
officers and enlisted men for continuous years
of military service and good conduct and comes
in three classes, with a badge and star for the
first two classes.

Instituted: June 25, 1841

Abolished: 1901

Reinstated: December 11, 1911

Classes: 1st: awarded to generals, chiefs, and
officers for 35 years of uninterrupted ser-

Mx 24

vice; 2nd: awarded to officers and chiefs
with 30 years of continuous service;* 3rd:
awarded for 25 years of continuous service,
in 2 divisions—for officers and for enlisted
men

Obverse disc: Gilt standing female on a red
enameled field (3rd enlisted men: field is not
enameled)

Obverse legend: RECOMPENSA A LA
CONSTANCIA EN EL SERVICIO MILITAR

Reverse inscription: CREADA│EN 1841│Y│
CONCEDIDA│POR│35 [30, 25] AÑOS│DE│
SERVICIO

Shape: Cross, each arm of which is formed by
3 green enameled sempervivum leaves (3rd
enlisted men: not enameled) with a palm
wreath in the angles; 1st: suspended from
eagle displayed and elevated; 2nd and 3rd:
from a brooch inscribed CONSTANCIA (1st:
on a green enameled field)

Star shape: Badge on a 32-pointed sun with 1
ray in each angle

Size: Badge: 1st: 49 × 43 mm; 2nd: 42 × 37
mm; 3rd: 42 × 35 mm. Star: 1st: 72 mm;
2nd: 60 mm

Mx 24

Mx 24

Metal: 1st, 2nd, 3rd officers: silver; 3rd enlisted men: bronze

Ribbon: 1st: generals: gold neck cord; chiefs and officers: red neck cord; 2nd, 3rd: white with green side stripes

Reference: Grove 1974, 3:158–60, D-505–10; Gillingham 1940, 21–22; Pérez-Maldonado 1942, 60–62

* * *

EVEN AS the central government in Mexico City tried to suppress internal rebels, it could not ignore the conflict along its northern border. Both Texans and Mexicans undertook cross-border raids. Mexico authorized campaign medals to the officers who fought in some of them.

Mx25. *La Cruz de Lipantitlán*

Mexico awarded the Cross of Lipantitlán for a skirmish that took place on July 7, 1842, near Matamoros. A Mexican raiding party of some five hundred men commanded by Colonel Antonio Canales crossed the Rio Grande, heading north. When they reached the Nueces River, they encountered a Texan force camped on its banks. The two sides fought an indecisive engagement with few casualties. Both sides claimed victory.

Instituted: 1842

Obverse disc: Arm with sword cutting down flag of Texas on a gray enameled field

Obverse legend: VALOR ACREDITADO EN TEXAS | JULIO 7 – 1842 on a white enameled band

Reverse legend: LIPANTITLAN | JULIO 7 DE 1842

Shape: Red enameled, 7-armed star with convex ends suspended from a metallic bar

Size: 31 mm

Ribbon: Green with a narrow horizontal red stripe

Reference: Grove 1974, 3:57, D-72; Gillingham 1940, 18; Pérez-Maldonado 1942,
63–64

* * *

IN SEPTEMBER 1842, Santa Anna, back in power again, sent a French mercenary, General Adrian Woll, with one thousand regular troops and six hundred militia to attack the town of San Antonio de Bejar in Texas. The entire incident was called "Woll's Invasion." The Mexican force surrounded the town and captured it on September 11, taking a number of prisoners, who later became known as the San Antonio Prisoners.

A hastily assembled relief force was put together under the command of Colonel Matthew Caldwell, who marched on San Antonio in an attempt to release the prisoners. On September 18, the Texan volunteers fought the Mexican force at Salado Creek, causing numerous casualties. However, Colonel Caldwell was unable to press his attack and retreated, leaving the Mexicans to return to San Antonio. As they were returning, they encountered another group of Texan volunteers commanded by Captain Nicholas Dawson. The Mexicans used their cannon, which inflicted heavy casualties and became known as the Dawson Massacre. Mexico awarded a star and a breast star to its men.

*Mx26. *La Estrella de Bejar y El Salado*

Mexico gave the Star for Bejar and El Salado to its officers who fought under General Woll at San Antonio and Salado Creek.

> Obverse disc: National eagle, displayed on a white enameled field
>
> Obverse legend: COMBATIO POR LA INTEGRIDAD DE MEXICO on a white enameled band

Mx 26

Mx 26

Reverse inscription: 11 Y 18 | SEPBRE | 1842 on a white enameled field

Reverse legend: EN BEJAR Y EL SALADO on a white enameled band

Shape: Ball-tipped, red enameled star with arrowheads in each angle

Size: 34 mm

Metal: Gilt

Ribbon: Gray, red

Reference: Grove 1974, 3:58, D-74; Gillingham 1940, 19; Pérez-Maldonado 1942, 65–66

Mx27. *La Placa de Bejar y El Salado*

Mexico also awarded a breast star to its officers for the same battles.

Obverse disc: Mexican flag flying above a flag of Texas buried under a cannon and a rifle on a white enameled field

Obverse legend: COMBATIO POR LA INTEGRIDAD DE MEXICO | EN BEJAR Y EL SALADO 11 Y 18 DE SEBRE 42 on a white enameled band

Shape: Sun of 36 rays with a ray in each angle

Size: 48 mm

Reference: Grove 1974, 3:58, D-75; Pérez-Maldonado 1942, 65–66

* * *

THE TEXAN MILITIA who were pursuing General Woll received reinforcements. Under the command of William Fisher, the militia attacked the riverine Mexican port-town of Mier. On Christmas Day, the Texans were themselves attacked by a large Mexican force under the command of General Pedro Ampudia. The Texans inflicted heavy casualties on the Mexicans but ran out of ammunition and surrendered. The Texan prisoners were force-marched south to the Perote Prison to the east of Mexico City. Santa Anna, now dictator in Mexico City, ordered that 10 percent of the Mier prisoners be shot, as determined by a hastily organized lottery. The seventeen men who drew black beans from a jar were shot on March 25, 1843. This mass execution became known as the "Black Bean Incident."

Mx28. *La Cruz de Mier*

Mexico created two similar crosses for its men for the Battle of Mier, a general one and one for those who fought under General Ampudia.

Mx28a. *General medal*

Obverse disc: Laurel and olive branches on a white enameled field

Obverse legend: VALOR | DISTINGUIDO on a white enameled band

Shape: Green enameled Maltese cross with convex ends and 3 feathered arrow ends on each arm and 5 rays in each angle, forming a square

Size: 42 mm

Ribbon: White with red and green edge stripes

Mx28b. *For those who fought under General Ampudia*

Obverse disc: AMPUDIA above laurel and olive branches on a white enameled field

Obverse legend: PERICIA | VALOR DISTINGUIDO on a white enameled band

Shape: Green enameled Maltese cross with convex ends and 3 discs and 3 feathered arrow ends on each arm and 5 rays in each angle, forming a square

Size: 42 mm

Ribbon: White with red and green edge stripes

Reference: Grove 1974, 3:59–60, D-77–78; Gillingham 1940, 19; Pérez-Maldonado 1942, 67–68

* * *

THE CENTRAL government continued its struggle to preserve national unity against regional rebellions. Yucatán, in particular, presented a challenge. It first advocated greater autonomy (see Mx20, the Campeche Cross 1840) and then proclaimed its independence in 1841. Much of the fighting took place in 1843. Medals were struck for the officers who participated in these battles.

Mx29. *La Cruz de China de Yucatán*

A Mexican army under the command of General Francisco Andrade defeated Yucatecan forces commanded by Lieutenant Colonel Manuel Oliver at China in the Department of Yucatán on February 4, 1843. This was reportedly the bloodiest single battle between the two sides during Yucatán's self-proclaimed independence (1841–48). Mexico awarded a medal to generals, chiefs, and officers who participated in the action at China.

> Instituted: By decree on August 4, 1843
> Obverse disc: Sun rising over sea and shore on a white enameled field
> Obverse legend: VENCIO EN CHINA | DE YUCATAN on a white enameled band
> Reverse: EN | 4 DE FEBRERO | DE 1843
> Shape: 4 cannons in the form of a cross with a laurel and palm wreath in the angles, suspended from a metallic band
> Size: 40 mm
> Ribbon: Blue with narrow red edge stripes
> Reference: Grove 1974, 3:61, D-80; Gillingham 1940, 20; Pérez-Maldonado 1942, 69

Mx30. *La Medalla de Tiskokob*

A government detachment under the command of Colonel Francisco Pérez was ordered to take the town of Tiskokob in the Yucatán, whose inhabitants wanted to rejoin the central government. A rebel force under López Llergo attacked Pérez on April 10, 1843, but the government forces held their ground, and the insurgents were forced to retreat. This medal was given to the town's defenders.

> Instituted: August 4, 1843
> Obverse disc: National eagle, right, with wings displayed and inverted on a white enameled field
> Obverse legend: VALOR Y CONSTANCIA | POR LA UNION NACIONAL on a white enameled band
> Reverse: VENCIO | EN | TISKOKOB | EN 10 | DE ABRIL DE | 1843
> Shape: Red enameled square with an arrowhead protruding from each side, suspended diagonally from a metallic brooch
> Size: 34 mm
> Ribbon: Red with narrow white and green edge stripes
> Reference: Grove 1974, 3:62, D-83; Gillingham 1940, 19–20; Pérez-Maldonado 1942, 70

* * *

THE YUCATECAN rebels often hired Texan mercenaries to fight the central government, and the Texans engaged Mexican ships in acts of piracy. Mexican and Texan warships fought each other at the Battles of Rio Brazos, Galveston, and Campeche, the latter of which was the largest single naval engagement of the war.

Mx31. *La Cruz Naval de Campeche*

In 1843, a Mexican fleet was blockading the port of Campeche, which had been taken over by Yucatecan insurgents. On May 16, two Texan warships allied with the Yucatecans sailed out of Campeche to engage the Mexican steam gunboats. The battle was notable in that the lead Mexican warship, the *Guadalupe*, was a modern British-built ironclad steamship with a British captain and a combined British-Mexican crew. The battle was indecisive. The Texans retreated, but they inflicted heavy casualties.

Mexico authorized the 1843 Naval Cross for Campeche for the chiefs and officers who served in the Mexican squadron. A cloth Campeche *escudo* was awarded to the enlisted men.

Instituted: By decree on August 4, 1843

Obverse disc: Enameled warship with sails

Obverse legend: ABATIO CON DENUEDO A LA ESCUADRA TEJANA on a white enameled band

Reverse inscription: EN CAMPECHE EL 16 DE MAYO 1843

Shape: Cross formed by 4 anchors, with an olive wreath in the angles, suspended diagonally from a metallic bar

Size: 32 mm

Ribbon: Green with red center stripe and red edge stripes

Reference: Grove 1974, 3:63, D-85; Gillingham 1940, 20; Pérez-Maldonado 1942, 71

Mx32. *La Cruz de Tabasco*

In July 1843, General Pedro de Ampudia attacked Yucatecan positions along the coast of Tabasco with a large force. After capturing two coastal forts, he sailed up the Grijalva River to San Juan Bautista (today's Villahermosa) on July 11. The Yucatecan rebels fled after he landed his troops. Mexico authorized a medal for its officers in this action.

Instituted: By decree on August 4, 1843

Obverse disc: Anchor flanked by 2 swords on a white enameled field

Obverse legend: VENCIO CONTRA LA INGRATITUD Y LA PERFIDIA on a white enameled band

Reverse inscription: EN | TABASCO | EL 11 | JULIO | 1843 on a white enameled field

Shape: Ball-tipped, white enameled Maltese cross with pointed ends

Size: 41 mm

Ribbon: White, light green, white

Reference: Grove 1974, 3:64, D-87; Gillingham 1940, 20; Pérez-Maldonado 1942, 72

THE MEXICAN-AMERICAN WAR (1846–1848)

THE Mexican-American War, known to Mexicans as the Intervención Estadounidense en México, was the inevitable consequence of the unresolved Texas Rebellion. Mexico refused to recognize Texas's right to secede but lacked the military strength to prevent it. After much political wrangling, the United States Congress voted to annex Texas as the twenty-eighth state on December 29, 1845. Mexico broke diplomatic relations with the United States, and both sides prepared for war.

Open hostilities broke out on April 25, 1846, when a two thousand–man Mexican cavalry detachment encountered a seventy-man U.S. patrol commanded by Captain Thornton. Sixteen Americans were killed and the rest taken prisoner, including Captain Thornton. This engagement became known as the Thornton Affair. The U.S. Congress declared war on Mexico on May 13. Fighting was concentrated on three fronts: the Pacific Coast to the tip of Baja California; the Rio Grande bordering on Texas; and the invasion route pioneered by Hernán Cortés from Veracruz through Puebla to

Mexico City. On the Pacific front, neither Mexico nor the United States is known to have struck any medals to their troops.

Northern Mexico south of the Rio Grande had seen continuous fighting going back to the Texas Rebellion. In March 1846, the American commander in Texas, General Zachary Taylor, ordered the construction of Fort Texas along the Rio Grande opposite the Mexican city of Matamoros. In May, the Mexican Army of the North under the command of General Mariano Arista laid siege to the fort. General Taylor sought to relieve the American garrison. En route to Fort Texas, he defeated a Mexican force commanded by General Arista at Palo Alto on May 9.

The following day, the fighting shifted further south to Resaca de Guerrero, where the Mexicans had settled into a stronger position. Despite facing heavy cannon fire, General Taylor's troops forced the Mexicans to withdraw. General Arista was relieved of his command on June 3 and court-martialed. Mexico authorized a medal for bravery to the officers and men who fought in the two engagements.

Mx33. *La Medalla de Palo Alto y Resaca de Guerrero*

Obverse: 2 crossed silver swords facing downward on a white enameled field

Obverse legend: COMBATIO POR LA INTEGRIDAD DEL TERRITORIO NACIONAL

Reverse inscription: PALO ALTO | MAYO 8 | LA RESACA DE GUERRERO | MAYO 9 DE | 1846 on a white enameled field

Shape: Round, surrounded by a green enameled laurel wreath, suspended from a silver eagle, right, with its wings elevated and displayed

Size: 30 mm

Ribbon: White with a narrow red center and 2 green edge stripes

Reference: Grove 1974, 3:66, D-94

* * *

GENERAL Taylor advanced south into Mexico in the late summer of 1846. His first objective was Monterrey, the largest city in northern Mexico. A newly reinforced Mexican Army of the North under the command of General Pedro de Ampudia made a stand at Monterrey. Casualties were heavy on both sides, with hand-to-hand fighting in the narrow streets. Finally, General Ampudia was cornered in the central square and forced to surrender the city in exchange for his release.

Mx34. *La Cruz de la Invasión Norteamericana (1847)*

The Cross for the North American Invasion was awarded to the Mexican troops who fought under General Ampudia at the Battle of Monterrey on September 24, 1846.

Instituted: 1847

Obverse disc: National eagle facing right on a white enameled field

Obverse legend: LA PATRIA AL MERITO | EN 1847 on a white enameled band

Reverse inscription: COMBATIO | POR LA | IN TEGRIDAD | DEL | TERRITORIO | NACIONAL on a white enameled field

Shape: Ball-tipped, red enameled Maltese cross with 2-pointed ends and 4 rays in each angle

Size: 34 mm

Reference: Grove 1974, 3:67, D-96; Gillingham 1940, 24; Pérez-Maldonado 1942, 74–76

Mx35. *La Medalla de la Invasión Norteamericana* (*1847*)

The Medal for the North American Invasion was awarded to the troops who fought on the northern front against General Taylor. The medal was not connected to any particular battle.

Obverse: Crossed swords on a white enameled field

Obverse legend: COMBATIO EN DEFENSA DE LA PATRIA on a white enameled band

Reverse inscription: AL MERITO EN 1847 on a white enameled field

Shape: Round, surrounded by green enameled oak and silver palm wreath, suspended from a silver eagle, right, with wings elevated and displayed

Size: 28 mm

Ribbon: White with a narrow red center and 2 green edge stripes

Reference: Grove 1974, 3:67, D-98; Gillingham 1940, 24; Pérez-Maldonado 1942, 74–76

Mx36. *La Estrella de Tamaulipas, 1847*

The state of Tamaulipas borders on Texas and includes the port city of Matamoros, which Taylor occupied early in his march south. The territory of Tamaulipas was in dispute between the two countries and involved in many of the cross-border raids. Mexico authorized a star for the officers who fought in these engagements.

Obverse disc: National eagle in gold on a white enameled field

Obverse legend: TAMAULIPAS | 1847 on a white enameled band

Reverse inscription: COMBATIO | POR LA | INTEGRIDAD | DEL | TERRITORIO | NAL.

Shape: Ball-tipped, white enameled star with gold arrow points in each angle, suspended from a green enameled laurel and a gold palm wreath

Size: 34 mm

Ribbon: Red with a green center stripe

Reference: Grove 1974, 3:73, D-114

* * *

HAVING consolidated his position in Monterrey, General Taylor sent part of his force to the Gulf Coast to join General Winfred Scott's advance on Mexico City. He then marched south toward Saltillo with 4,500 men on the road to Mexico City. Taylor seized the city and continued south until he was threatened by a large Mexican army commanded by Santa Anna himself.

Outnumbered by the Mexicans, Taylor took up defensive positions along the slopes of a mountain at Buena Vista, south of Saltillo. On February 22, 1847, General Ampudia led Mexican forces against the American left flank but was eventually repelled by American artillery fire. Santa Anna personally took charge and resumed the Mexican assault. By the end of the second day, Santa Anna had lost half of his army. He withdrew and returned to Mexico City. The Battle of Buena Vista was the last major battle of the war in northern Mexico.

Mx37. *La Cruz de Angostura* (*1847*)

Mexico authorized the Angostura Cross to its officers who fought in the north, and particularly the decisive Battle of Buena Vista (Angostura). At least three variants of this cross are known.

Mx37a. *Variant 1*

Instituted: April 19, 1847

Obverse disc: National eagle on a square red enameled field

Obverse legend: DEL E- | JERCI- | TO DEL | NORTE on a square white enameled band

Reverse inscription: AL | MANDO | DEL | GENERAL | SANTA-ANNA on a white enameled square field

Shape: White enameled cross with pointed ends inscribed AL VA | LOR Y | SUFRI | MIENTO on the arms with a palm and laurel branches below and 2 crossed inverted flags in the angles, suspended from a white enameled bar inscribed: ANGOSTURA 22 Y 23 DE FEBRERO DE 1847

Size: 44 × 39 mm

Ribbon: White with a center red stripe and green edge stripes

Mx37b. *Variant 2*

Obverse legend: DEL EJERCITO DEL NORTE on a square white enameled band

Reverse inscription: A | MANDO | DEL | GENERAL | SANTA-ANNA

Size: 45 × 43 mm

Mx37c. *Variant 3*

Reverse inscription: VALOR ACREDITADO 1847

Suspension bar: BATALLA DE LA ANGOSTURA

Ribbon: Red with 2 blue side stripes

Reference: Grove 1974, 3:68–69, D-100, D-100v; Gillingham 1940, 24–25; Pérez-Maldonado 1942, 80–81

* * *

ON MARCH 9, 1847, General Winfield Scott launched an amphibious assault with twelve thousand troops against Veracruz. This was the first amphibious landing in American military history. It was supported by a large fleet of steam and sail warships. The siege lasted for twelve days, and the city surrendered on March 29.

Mx38. *La Medalla de Veracruz* (*1847*)

Mexico authorized a bronze Medal for Veracruz, which it awarded to the officers and men defending the city. At least two different variants were issued.

Mx38a. *Variant 1*

Obverse: Military trophies of flags, cannon, and equipment

Obverse legend: AL PATRIOTISMO Y VALOR ACREDITADOS EN DEFENSA DE

Obverse exergue: LA H. VERACRUZ | 1847

Reverse: Laurel wreath

Size: 27 mm

Metal: Silver, bronze

Ribbon: Green, white, red

Mx38b. *Variant 2*

Obverse inscription: EL | AÑO DE | 1847 in center

Obverse legend: AL PATRIOTISMO Y AL VALOR ACREDITADOS EN DEFENSA DE LA HEROICA VERACRUZ

Size: 30 mm

Reference: Grove 1974, 3:74, D-118a–b; Gillingham 1940, 25–26; Pérez-Maldonado 1942, 82–83

* * *

SANTA ANNA marched south from Mexico City to prevent General Scott from advancing toward Puebla and Mexico City. Santa Anna set up a fortified blocking position along the road to Puebla near the hamlet of Cerro Gordo. On April 14, 1847, Scott's troops assaulted the Mexican lines. One-third of the Mexican army was killed or captured, forcing Santa Anna to retreat to Puebla, where his position was weak because the city's population opposed him. He chose to surrender the city without a fight on May 1 and retreated to Mexico City.

The next major battle took place on August 20, 1847, at the Franciscan convent of Santa María de Churubusco, barely five miles from Mexico City. The Mexicans used the convent to prevent the Americans from crossing a bridge over the Churubusco River. Scott flanked the Mexican positions on August 20. The Mexicans surrendered after suffering heavy casualties and thousands of desertions.

Mx39. *La Cruz de Churubusco*

The Churubusco Cross was awarded to the officers who fought in the battle; several variants exist. A Churubusco *escudo* was issued to the enlisted men.

Mx39a. *Variant 1*

Obverse disc: National eagle on a white enameled field

Obverse legend: DEFENSOR DE LA INDEPENDENCIA on a white enameled band

Reverse inscription: LA | PATRIA | AL MERITO | EN | 1847

Shape: Ball-tipped, gilt-rimmed, red enameled Maltese cross with 2-pointed ends suspended from a green-enameled laurel and silver palm wreath

Size: 35 mm

Metal: Gold, silver

Ribbon: 2 equal green and red stripes with 2 narrower white edge stripes

Mx39b. *Variant 2*

Obverse legend: DEFENSOR DE LA INDEPEN^A EN CHURUBUSCO on a white enameled band

Reverse inscription: LA | PATRIA | AL MERITO | 1847 surrounded by an olive wreath

Mx39c. *Variant 3*

Obverse legend: CHURUBUSCO 1847

Reverse inscription: AGOSTO 20; 8–12 Y 13 DE SEPTIEMBRE

Reference: Grove 1974, 3:71, D-108; Gillingham 1940, 26–27; Pérez-Maldonado 1942, 84–85

Mx40. *La Medalla de Churubusco* (*1847*)

Mexico awarded the Medal for Churubusco to the troops under General Pedro Anaya, who defended the village and convent at Churubusco.

Obverse: 2 crossed gold swords over a black ribbon on a white enameled field

Obverse legend: COMBATIO EN DEFENSA DE LA PATRIA

Reverse inscription: CHURUBUSCO | AGOSTO 20 | DE 1847 on a white enameled field

Shape: Round inside a gilt oak and palm wreath, suspended from a golden eagle

Size: 30 × 28 mm

Ribbon: Green, white, red, white, green

Reference: Grove 1974, 3:72, D-110

* * *

AFTER CHURUBUSCO, Scott marched on Mexico City. His first objective was to neutralize the Castle of Chapultepec, which dominated the city. The Mexicans had prepared fortified positions at Molino del Rey. They repelled the first assaults in the morning of September 8. Both sides suffered heavy casualties. Scott pressed the attacks, concentrating his forces on the center of the Mexican lines, which were eventually breached. The Mexican forces retreated to a defensive line in front of Chapultepec Castle.

On September 12, Scott launched an artillery barrage against the Chapultepec heights followed by a successful infantry assault the next day. The battle produced a final moment of patriotic courage. After the Mexicans surrendered, five young cadets led by a lieutenant continued fighting. The last surviving cadet, Juan Escutia, wrapped himself in the Mexican flag and leaped to his death from the parapets. The six men were posthumously awarded a medal for their bravery and were immortalized in Mexico's history. Mexico authorized military decorations for the men who fought the key battles at Molino del Rey and the Chapultepec Castle.

Mx41. *La Cruz de El Molino del Rey, Al Mérito*

Obverse disc: National eagle on a white enameled field within a gold circle

Obverse legend: LA PATRIA EN EL MOLINO DEL REY

Reverse inscription: LA | PATRIA | AL | MERITO | EN 1847 on a white enameled field

Shape: Ring-tipped, black enameled Maltese cross with 2-pointed ends and 5 silver rays in each angle, suspended from a green enameled laurel and silver palm wreath

Size: 33.5 mm

Ribbon: Green, red with 2 narrow white edge stripes

Reference: Grove 1974, 3:72, D-112

Mx42. *La Cruz de Chapultepec, Al Mérito*

The Cross of Chapultepec was awarded to the men for special merit during the battle.

Obverse disc: Black national eagle on a white enameled field

Obverse legend: CHAPULTEPEC | 1847 on a white enameled band

Reverse inscription: LA PATRIA | AL | MERITO on a white enameled field

Shape: Ball-tipped, red enameled Maltese cross with 2-pointed ends suspended from a green enameled laurel wreath

Size: 44 mm

Reference: Grove 1974, 3:69, D-102

Mx43. *La Cruz de Chapultepec*

The Cross of Chapultepec was awarded to the officers who participated in the defense of the castle.

Obverse disc: Gold national eagle on a white enameled field

Obverse legend: DEFENSOR DE LA INDEPENDENCIA

Reverse inscription: 8, 12 Y 13 | DE | SEPTIEMBRE | 1847

Shape: Ball-tipped, red enameled Maltese cross with 2-pointed ends and three 2-pointed rays in each angle, suspended from a green enameled oak and gilt palm wreath

Size: 36.5 mm

Ribbon: Green, red, with 2 narrow white edge stripes

Reference: Grove 1974, 3:70, D-104

Mx44. *La Medalla de Chapultepec*

The Medal of Chapultepec was awarded to all of the men who participated in the defense of the castle.

Obverse: Crossed swords tied with a ribbon on a white enameled field

Obverse legend: COMBATIO EN DEFENSA DE LA REPUBLICA on a white enameled band; variant legend: COMBATIO POR LA INTEGRIDAD DEL TERRITORIO NACIONAL

Reverse inscription: CHAPULTEPEC | 8,
12 Y 13 | DE SETIEMBRE | DE | 1847 on a
white enameled field

Shape: Round, surrounded by a green enameled laurel and gilt palm wreath, suspended
from gold eagle with wings elevated and
displayed

Size: 32 mm

Ribbon: White with a narrow center red and
2 green edge stripes

Reference: Grove 1974, 3:70, D-106; Gillingham 1940, 27; Pérez-Maldonado 1942,
86–88

Mx45. *La Cruz de Honor* (*1847*)

Mexico issued an Honor Cross to the men for
meritorious effort in the three days of fighting.

Obverse disc: National eagle on a red enameled field

Obverse legend: LA PATRIA AL
MERITO | EN 1847 on a white enameled
band

Reverse inscription: COMBATIO | POR LA |
INTEGRIDAD | DEL | TERRITORIO |
NACIONAL

Shape: Ball-tipped, red enameled Maltese
cross with 2-pointed ends and 4 rays in
each angle

Ribbon: Red, white, green

Reference: Grove 1974, 3:67, D-96; Gillingham 1940, 27

Mx46. *La Medalla de los Defensores de la República* (*1848*)

Mexico later issued a general medal for its
military who participated in either the Texas
Rebellion, the cross-border incursions, or the
Mexican-American War.

Obverse: National eagle within a laurel and
palm wreath

Obverse legend: SOCIEDAD DEFENSORES
DE LA REPUBLICA MEXICANA

Reverse inscription: COMBATIERON |
POR LA YNTEGRIDAD | DEL |
TERRITORIO NACIONAL | DESDE |
1836 A 1848

Size: 30 mm

Metal: Silver

Ribbon: Red with 2 black edge stripes

Reference: Grove 1974, 3:118, D-315a;
Pérez-Maldonado 1942, 48

* * *

ON FEBRUARY 2, 1848, Mexico and the United
States signed the Treaty of Guadalupe Hidalgo.
Under the treaty, Mexico ceded 1.36 million
square kilometers of land to the United States,
including all of Arizona, California, and New
Mexico, and most of Colorado, Nevada, and
Utah. Mexico recognized Texas's secession and
its accession to the United States. Mexico received $15 million in exchange for 55 percent
of its prewar territory.

INTERNAL STRIFE

WITH THE war over, Mexicans resumed fighting among themselves over the same issues that had divided them since becoming independent. In July 1847, the Mayan Indians in Yucatán rose up in the "Guerra de Castas." The liberal government of Yucatán,
in order to encourage more agricultural production, was selling off land for commercial agriculture that Indians had often tilled for their subsistence. Both sides committed

atrocities, with heavy fighting lasting for more than three years. A federal Mexican army was sent to restore order. The government authorized four medals to its officers and men called to intervene.

Mx47. *La Cruz de Yucatán, 1ª epoca y 2ª epoca*

The Yucatán Cross was awarded to officers, with the period of their service being distinguished by the ribbon colors.

Instituted: March 12, 1853

Classes: Superior officers, other officers

Epochs: 1st: from the beginning of the uprising until the end of 1848; 2nd: from January 1, 1849, until the end of the conflict

Obverse inscription: EL | GOBIERNO | NACIONAL on a white enameled field

Obverse legend: A LOS DEFENSORES DE LA CIVILIZACION

Reverse inscription: 1ᴬ [2ᴬ] | EPOCA | YUCATAN

Shape: Ball-tipped, white enameled Maltese cross with a laurel wreath in the angles

Size: 42 mm

Ribbon: 1st: white, red, white; 2nd: red, white, red; superior officers: neck band; other officers: worn on chest

Reference: Grove 1974, 3:78, D-134–35; Gillingham 1940, 28–29; Pérez-Maldonado 1942, 89–90

Mx48. *La Medalla de Yucatán, 1ª epoca y 2ª epoca*

The Yucatán Medal was awarded to junior officers and enlisted men for the same conflict, and the period of service was also distinguished according to ribbon color.

Instituted: March 12, 1853

Classes: Sergeants, enlisted men

Epochs: 1st: from the beginning of the uprising until the end of 1848; 2nd: from January 1, 1849, until the end of the conflict

Obverse inscription: EL | GOBIERNO | NACIONAL | 1ᴬ [2ᴬ] | EPOCA within a laurel wreath

Size: 26 mm

Metal: Sergeants: silver; enlisted men: bronze

Ribbon: 1st: white, red, white; 2nd: red, white, red

Reference: Grove 1974, 3:79, D-136a–b, D-137a–b; Gillingham 1940, 28

* * *

OTHER Indian tribes in northern Mexico had long opposed Spanish settlements on their lands. Mexico's independence did not change the dynamics of the conflict. In 1851–52, the Mexican army fought several major engagements with Indian warriors around Matamoros. Mexico authorized a cross for the generals, chiefs, officers, and troops of the army and the national guard for engaging the Indians. The Mexican Congress approved a separate medal for the same engagements.

Mx49. *La Cruz de Matamoros*

Obverse disc: White enamel

Obverse legend: NI AL INCENDIO DE SU HOGAR | SUCUMBIO on a white enameled band

Shape: Ball-tipped white enameled Maltese cross with rays in the angles, suspended from a palm and olive wreath

Size: 36 mm

Ribbon: Yellow

Reference: Grove 1974, 3:80, D-139; Gillingham 1940, 28; Pérez-Maldonado 1942, 92

Mx50. *La Medalla de la Defensa de la Frontera del Norte*

This medal was awarded for the defense of Matamoros in October 1851 and for actions at Cerralvo and Camargo on November 30 and February 22, 1852, respectively.

Instituted: May 28, 1852

Classes: Officers, enlisted men

Obverse inscription: EL | CONGRESO | MEXICANO | EN | 1852

Reverse inscription: AL | VALOR | Y | LEALTAD surrounded by a wreath

Reverse legend: ACREDITADOS EN DEFENSA DE LA FRONTERA DEL NORTE | 1851 1852

Size: 25 mm

Metal: Officers: gold; enlisted men: silver

Ribbon: White with 2 narrow green and red edge stripes on each side; worn pinned on the left chest, except for wounded men, for whom it was worn around the neck

Reference: Grove 1974, 3:80, D-141, D-141a; Gillingham 1940, 28–29; Pérez-Maldonado 1942, 92

* * *

IN JULY 1852, a French filibuster, Count Gastón Raousset de Boulbon, landed at Guaymas in northwestern Mexico with several hundred armed French followers. Raousset wanted to create an independent Republic of Sonora and occupied the city of Hermosillo. When confronted by the Mexican military, he and his men surrendered and were expelled to the United States. Two years later, Raousset landed at Guaymas again with some four hundred French and German followers. On July 13, 1854, Raousset was defeated by the local garrison commanded by José María Yañez. He was tried and executed by firing squad and his men sentenced to prison. Raousset's expedition coincided with an American filibuster, William

Walker, who landed in Guaymas in 1853. There is no evidence the two ever met, although they must have been aware of each other's ambitions.

Mx51. *La Cruz de Sonora*

Mexico awarded the Sonora Cross to the officers and men who fought Raousset during his first landing in 1852.

Classes: 1st, 2nd

Obverse disc: White enameled field

Obverse legend: AL VALOR ACREDITADO | EN SONORA 1852 on a white enameled band

Reverse inscription: EL | GOBIERNO | DE LA | REPUBLICA | MEXICANA

Shape: Ball-tipped, white enameled cross pattée with pointed ends with an olive wreath in the angles

Size: 43 mm

Metal: 1st: gold; 2nd: silver

Ribbon: Yellow with a narrow green center stripe

Reference: Grove 1974, 3:81, D-143–44; Gillingham 1940, 29; Pérez-Maldonado 1942, 93–94

*Mx52. *La Medalla del Ministerio de Hacienda*

The national government had great difficulty collecting taxes to finance its many battles against internal insurgents as well as foreign invaders. The Medal for the Ministry of Finance is believed to have been the only medal for civilians authorized before the Mexican Revolution; it was awarded to heads of the treasury office after completion of twenty years of service.

Authorized: By decree on November 7, 1853

Classes: 1st, 2nd,* 3rd

Obverse inscription: LA PATRIA | AL MERITO | EN EL | SERVICIO | DE LA | HACIENDA NACIONAL on a white enameled oval disc

Mx 52

Mx 52

Reverse inscription: MEDALLA | DE | 1ᴬ [2ᴬ, 3ᴬ] CLASE on a white enameled oval disc

Shape: 4-part Maltese cross with 5 rays in each angle, suspended from a bar

Size: 59 mm

Metal: Bronze

Reference: Grove 1974, 3:154, D-470–72

Mx53. *La Cruz de la Defensa de Guaymas*

The Cross for the Defense of Guaymas was awarded to the officers who took Raousset and his men prisoner in Guaymas on July 13, 1854.

Instituted: By a decree on August 7, 1854

Obverse disc: Sun rising behind a sea with a lighthouse in foreground

Obverse legend: COMBATIO | POR LA PATRIA on a white enameled band

Reverse inscription: GUAYMAS | JULIO 13 | DE | 1854

Shape: Ball-tipped, blue enameled cross pattée with pointed ends with laurel and palm branches in the angles, suspended from a wreath of laurel and palm

Size: 37 mm

Ribbon: Alternating 5 blue and 4 white stripes

Reference: Grove 1974, 3:82, D-148; Gillingham 1940, 29; Pérez-Maldonado 1942, 95–96

* * *

IN 1855, Mexico introduced liberal reforms, including the abolition of the special military and ecclesiastical courts (*fueros*) and confiscated Church land. Conservative forces rose up in Puebla and occupied the city. Mexican general and future president Ignacio Comonfort defeated the conservative forces at Puebla on March 23, 1856.

*Mx54. *La Medalla "Restaurador de la Paz"*

Mexico awarded the Restorer of the Peace Medal for the suppression of the conservative rebellion in 1856. The use of the term "restorer of peace" for the participants in a military operation against a domestic uprising is comparable to the practice of imperial Brazil when it referred to the Duke of Caxias as a "pacifier" in a military medal for violently crushing regional uprisings (see Br51).

Obverse inscription: RESTAURADOR | DE | LA PAZ | EN | 1856 on a white enameled field

Shape: Round, surrounded by a gilt laurel and green olive wreath

Size: 29 mm

Metal: Bronze

Ribbon: White with 2 light blue edge stripes

Reference: Grove 1974, 3:88, D-170; Gillingham 1940, 29–30; Pérez-Maldonado 1942, 97–98

Provenance: A. Menke

* * *

THE MAYAN INDIANS once again rose up in Yucatán, taking the town of Tekax on September 14, 1857. The town's garrison was too small to deter the Mayans. Volunteers from neighboring villages reinforced the garrison and they drove off the Mayans. The government authorized a cross for officers and an *escudo* for enlisted men.

Mx55. *La Cruz de Tekax*

The government awarded the Tekax Cross to Captain D. Onofre Bacelis and his fellow officers who led the garrison against the Indian insurgents.

Instituted: November 7, 1857

Obverse disc: White enameled field

Mx54

Obverse legend: POR SU VALOR Y DENUEDO EN TEKAX | LA PATRIA AGRADECIDA on a white enameled band

Reverse: 14 Y 15 | DE | SEPTIEMBRE | DE | 1857 on a white enameled field

Shape: Ball-tipped, white enameled Maltese cross with 7 gilt rays in each angle, suspended from a bar with the name of the recipient

Size: 42 mm

Ribbon: Green, white, red

Reference: Grove 1974, 3:84, D-152; Gillingham 1940, 30; Pérez-Maldonado 1942, 99–100

La Guerra de Reforma

In 1857, the struggle between the liberals and the conservatives took on the characteristics of a civil war; a period known as the Reform War. The country had two governments: a liberal, "constitutional" government, led by Benito Juárez in Guanajuato, and a conservative government in control of Mexico City, led by Félix Zuloaga. Mexican states lined up with one or the other of the two governments. Armies roamed the country fighting battles, but no medals are known to have been struck for them.

In 1860, conservative forces commanded by General Miguel Miramón laid siege to the port city of Veracruz, which was controlled by liberals. He bombarded the city but failed to take it. The liberal government authorized a medal for the defenders but could not strike it until after it regained control of Mexico City.

Mx56. *La Cruz del Bombardeo de Veracruz*

The constitutional (and liberal) government authorized a cross for the officers and men who successfully defended Veracruz in 1860 against Miramón's siege.

Instituted: By decree on June 19, 1860

Classes: 1st: officers; 2nd: enlisted men

Obverse disc: Tower of Veracruz on a white enameled field

Obverse legend: BOMBARDEO | DE VERACRUZ on a white enameled band

Reverse inscription: MARZO | DE | 1860 on a white enameled field

Shape: Ball-tipped, metallic-rimmed, green enameled star with 2-pointed ends, suspended from a laurel and palm wreath

Size: 35 mm

Metal: 1st: gold; 2nd: silver

Ribbon: Red

Reference: Grove 1974, 3:86, D-163–64; Gillingham 1940, 30; Pérez-Maldonado 1942, 103–4

* * *

In October 1861, a conservative army attacked the town of Pachuca, the capital of the state of Hidalgo, which was abandoned by its liberal garrison. However, a (liberal) Mexican army under the command of General Santiago Márquez reinforced the garrison and defeated the conservatives.

Mx57. *La Medalla de Pachuca*

Mexico authorized the Medal for Pachuca to reward its officers and men for defeating the conservative forces at Pachuca.

Instituted: By Congressional Decree on November 5, 1861

Classes: 1st: officers; 2nd: enlisted men

Obverse inscription: TRIUNFO | EN | PACHUCA | EL 20 DE OCTUBRE | DE 1861 | DEFENDIENDO LA | CONSTITUCION

Shape: Round, surrounded by a laurel wreath

Size: 25 mm

Metal: 1st: gold; 2nd: silver

Ribbon: Red, black, red

Reference: Grove 1974, 3:87, D-166, D-166a; Gillingham 1940, 30; Pérez-Maldonado 1942, 105

The French Intervention (1862–1867)

In January 1862, a combined French, Spanish, and English fleet laid siege to the port city of Veracruz as pressure to force Mexico to pay its foreign debt. After a year of negotiations, Spain and England reached agreement with Mexico and withdrew their warships. Napoleon III took advantage of American preoccupation with its Civil War to expand France's influence in the New World by overthrowing the Mexican republican government in favor of a monarchy headed by the Austrian Hapsburg Prince Maximilian. Napoleon counted on support from Mexico's conservative forces and the Church. France landed an army under the command of General Charles de Lorencez and occupied Veracruz. The French followed the same invasion route as Cortés and Scott. France's military involvement in Mexico would last another five years. The French army's advance toward Mexico City was opposed by General Ignacio Zaragoza. As he pulled back, he tried to delay the French advance by leaving a detachment in the town of Acultzingo.

Both the Mexican Empire under Maximilian and the Mexican Republic under President Benito Juárez authorized medals for their followers—all in the name of Mexico. The medals issued by both sides are included here.

*Mx58. *La Medalla de Acultzingo*

Mexico authorized the Medal of Acultzingo to the officers and men for the battle that took place there on April 28, 1862.

Mx 58

Instituted: By decree on May 21, 1862

Classes: 1st: chiefs; 2nd: other officers; 3rd: enlisted men*

Obverse inscription: LA | REPUBLICA | MEXICANA | A SUS | VALIENTES | HIJOS within a sempervivum wreath

Reverse inscription: COMBATIÓ | CON HONOR | EN LAS | CUMBRES DE | ACULTZINGO | CONTRA EL | EJÉRCITO FRANCES | EL 28 DE ABRIL | DE 1862 within a laurel wreath

Shape: Oval

Size: 26 × 21 mm

Metal: 1st: General-in-Chief: gold with a gold eagle above the ribbon; Major General and Chiefs of Brigade: gold with a wreath above the ribbon; Chiefs up to Lt. Col.: gold

Mx 58
(reverse)

without a wreath; other chiefs: gilt silver;
2nd: silver; 3rd: bronze

Engraver: S.N.G.

Ribbon: Green, white, red

Reference: Grove 1974, 3:88, D-170–72,
170ap, 170a–b; Gillingham 1940, 31; Pérez-
Maldonado 1942, 113–14

* * *

GENERAL ZARAGOZA retreated to the city of
Puebla, where he set up strong defensive positions along with General Porfirio Díaz to block
the French advance toward Mexico City. The
French army under the command of General
Charles de Laurencez laid down an artillery
barrage, but the Mexicans held their ground.
He then ordered his infantry to penetrate the
Mexican lines, but without success. Laurencez
had been led to believe that the people of Puebla
would rise up in support of the French army.
Mexican troops had neutralized the conservatives the previous day, and no support was
forthcoming. The Mexicans won the battle on
May 5, forcing the French to retreat back to
Veracruz to await reinforcements from France.
Mexico made May 5 the nation's most important national holiday. It authorized three military medals for the Mexican defenders.

*Mx59. *La Medalla de la Batalla del Cinco de Mayo* (1862)

Mexico awarded the Medal for the Battle of
May 5 to its officers and men who fought outside the Puebla city gates.

Instituted: By decree on May 21, 1862

Classes: General in Chief, Major General and
Chiefs of Brigade, other chiefs to Lt. Col.,
other chiefs, other officers,* enlisted
men*

Obverse inscription: LA | REPUBLICA |
MEXICANA | A SUS | VALIENTES HIJOS
within a sempervivum wreath

Reverse inscription: TRIUNFÓ | GLORIOSAME
NTE | DEL | EJÉRCITO FRANCES | DELANTE
DE | PUEBLA | EL 5 DE MAYO | DE 1862
within a laurel wreath

Shape: Oval

Size: 26 × 21 mm

Metal: General in Chief: gold with a gold
eagle above the ribbon; Major General
and Chiefs of Brigade: gold with a wreath
above the ribbon; Chiefs up to Lt. Col.:
gold without a wreath; other chiefs: gilt
silver; other officers: silver; enlisted men:
bronze

Engraver: S.N.G.

Ribbon: Green, white, red

Reference: Grove 1974, 3:89, D-171–72,
171ap, 171a–b; Gillingham 1940, 31–32;
Pérez-Maldonado 1942, 118–20

Mx 59

Mx 59

Mx60. *La Medalla por la Derrota de los Traidores*

The Medal for the Defeat of the Traitors was issued to the officers and men who fought the conservative forces inside Puebla on May 4, thereby preventing them from helping the French.

Instituted: December 10, 1862

Classes: Chiefs of Brigade, other chiefs to Lt. Col., other chiefs, other officers, enlisted men

Obverse inscription: LA | REPUBLICA | MEXICANA | A SUS | VALIENTES | HIJOS within a sempervivum wreath

Reverse inscription: DERROTANDO A LOS TRAIDORES | EL 4 DE MAYO | CONTRIBUYO EFICAZMENTE AL | TRIUNFO ALCANZADO EN | PUEBLA CONTRA EL | EJERCITO FRANCES | EL 5 DE MAYO DE 1862 within a laurel wreath

Size: 25 mm

Metal: Chiefs of Brigade: gold, with a wreath; other chiefs to Lt. Col.: gold, without a wreath; other chiefs: gilt silver; other officers: silver; enlisted men: bronze

Engraver: NAVALON

Ribbon: Equal green, white, and red stripes

Reference: Grove 1974, 3:90, D-173, D-173ap, D-173a–b; Gillingham 1940, 32; Pérez-Maldonado 1942, 118–20

Mx61. *La Medalla por la Defensa de la Ciudad de Puebla (1862)*

Mexico awarded the Medal for the Defense of the City of Puebla to the officers and men who defended the city against the French.

Instituted: December 10, 1862

Classes: Chiefs of Brigade, other chiefs to Lt. Col., other chiefs, other officers, enlisted men

Obverse inscription: LA | REPUBLICA | MEXICANA | A SUS | VALIENTES | HIJOS within a sempervivum wreath

Reverse inscription: DEFENDIENDO A LA CIUDAD | DE | PUEBLA CONTRIBUYO AL | GLORIOSO TRIUNFO | CONTRA | EL | EJERCITO FRANCES | EL 5 DE MAYO DE 1862

Size: 25 mm

Metal: Chiefs of Brigade: gold, with a wreath; other chiefs to Lt. Col.: gold, without a wreath; other chiefs: gilt silver; other officers: silver; enlisted men: bronze

Engraver: NAVALON

Ribbon: Green, white, red

Reference: Grove 1974, 3:90, D-172, 172ap, 172a–b; Gillingham 1940, 32; Pérez-Maldonado 1942, 118–20

* * *

THE FRENCH ARMY retreated to its base in Veracruz, where it waited for reinforcements. France sent some thirty thousand troops under the command of General Forey, who replaced Laurencez. The reinforced French army advanced following the same route as before. The Mexicans, under the command of General Jesús González Ortega, fortified their positions again in Puebla. The French laid siege to the city, which lasted for two months. The Mexican defenders were unable to receive any ammunition or supplies. On May 16, 1863, General González ordered his artillery and weapons to be destroyed and surrendered the garrison. Mexico authorized a cross and a medal for the defense of Puebla.

Mx62. *La Cruz por el Sitio de Puebla (1863)*

The Cross for the Siege of Puebla in the state of Zaragoza was awarded to officers for defending the city.

Instituted: June 14, 1863

Classes: 1st (badge and star for generals), 2nd (badge only for officers)

Obverse disc: National eagle perched on 2 flags on a red enameled field

Obverse legend: DEFENDIO PUEBLA DE ZARAGOZA EN 1863 CONTRA EL EJERCITO FRANCES on a white enameled band

Shape: Green enameled cross pattée with rounded ends suspended from a brooch

Star shape: Badge on 32-pointed sun

Size: Badge: 34 × 32 mm. Star: 55 mm

Metal: Badge: 1st: gold; 2nd: silver. Star: silver

Ribbon: White with 3 narrow green, white, and red diagonal stripes extending from lower left to upper right

Reference: Grove 1974, 3:93–94, D-179–80, D-180a; Gillingham 1940, 32–33; Pérez-Maldonado 1942, 124–27

Mx63. *La Medalla por el Sitio de Puebla* (*1863*)

The Medal for the Siege of Puebla was awarded to the men who defended Puebla during the two-month siege.

Instituted: June 14, 1863

Obverse inscription: DEFENDIO | A | PUEBLA DE ZARAGOZA | EN 1863 CONTRA | EL EJERCITO FRANCES within a laurel wreath on a white enameled field

Shape: Oval

Size: 17 × 31 mm

Metal: Gilt bronze

Ribbon: White with 3 narrow green, white, and red diagonal stripes running from lower left to upper right

Reference: Grove 1974, 3:94, D-182bp

* * *

GENERAL FOREY marched on to Mexico City. Mexico's constitutional President Benito Juárez and his cabinet retreated north and settled into the northern city of Chihuahua. From there, it organized a guerrilla war against the French and their Mexican conservative allies. With Mexico City safely in the hands of the French army, Austrian Archduke Ferdinand Maximilian of the House of Hapsburg-Lorraine accepted the Mexican throne and arrived with his Belgian wife in Veracruz on May 24, 1864.

Once in power, Maximilian instituted liberal laws favoring the indigent, a policy that aggravated his conservative allies but failed to bridge the political divide with his liberal enemies led by Benito Juárez. Maximilian tried to create a Mexican imperial court for which he adopted two grandsons of Mexico's first emperor, Agustín Iturbide. He had hoped that one of them would succeed him, as he had no issue of his own. He created three imperial orders: the revived Order of Guadalupe, the new Order of the Mexican Eagle, and the Order of Saint Charles (below, Mx122, 123, 124).

President Juárez rejected all of Maximilian's attempts at political reconciliation and organized his Army of the North with arms provided by the United States. In the south, Porfirio Díaz escaped from the French and organized his own guerrilla army. Fighting between the two sides continued unabated throughout Maximilian's reign. The fate of the monarchy was finally sealed in 1867, when Napoleon III withdrew his army from Mexico.

With the departure of the French army, the conservatives rallied their forces in Querétaro and convinced Maximilian to take command. Mexican forces converged and laid siege to the city. The imperial cavalry broke through the republican lines and rode to Mexico City for the purpose of mobilizing the garrison there to return in order to lift the siege of Querétaro.

Instead, the imperial army moved south to lift Porfirio Díaz's siege of Puebla. Díaz quickly took Puebla and then defeated the imperial army in the open. The 1867 Battle of Puebla (the third of the French Intervention) ended the conservatives hopes' of saving the monarchy. The republicans captured Maximilian and took Querétaro without firing a shot. Maximilian and his two senior generals, Miramón and Mejía, were summarily court-martialed and executed by a firing squad on June 19, 1867. The monarchy ended with Maximilian's execution.

*Mx64. *La Cruz por la Intervención Francesa*

The Cross for the French Intervention was awarded to Mexican republican officers and men who fought throughout the war against the French army and its conservative Mexican allies. The cross is not linked to any particular battle or campaign. The cross has two versions: the first for combat and the second for general support.

*Mx64a. *Version 1 (for combat)*

Instituted: August 5, 1867

Classes: 1st: generals and chiefs;* 2nd: officers; 3rd: enlisted men

Obverse inscription: COMBATIO | A LA | INTERVEN | CION FRANCESA | Y SUS ALIADOS | DESDE 1861 | HASTA 1867 on a white enameled field

Obverse legend: PREMIO | AL PATRIOTISMO on a white enameled band

Reverse inscription: SALVO LA | INDEPENDENCIA | Y LAS | INSTITUCIONES | REPUBLICA | NAS on a white enameled field

Reverse legend: DISTINTIVO | DE

Mx 64a

Mx 64a

CONSTANCIA Y VALOR on a white enameled band

Shape: Ball-tipped, red enameled Maltese cross with 7 rays in the angles, superimposed on a green enameled laurel wreath. 1st and 2nd: suspended from a national eagle, right, elevated and displayed

Size: 45 mm

Metal: 1st: gilt; 2nd: silver; 3rd: bronze with no enamel

Ribbon: White with 2 red edge stripes

*Mx64b. *Version 2 (for general support)*

Instituted: August 5, 1867

Classes: 1st: generals and chiefs; 2nd: officers; 3rd: enlisted men*

Obverse inscription: COOPERO | A LA | DEFENSA DE LA | REPUBLICA | CONTRA | EL EJERCITO | FRANCES on a white enameled field

Obverse legend: PREMIO | AL PATRIOTISMO on a white enameled band

Reverse disc: COMBATIO | POR LA | INDEPENDENCIA | Y LAS | INSTITUCIONES | REPUBLICANAS on a white enameled field

Reverse legend: DISTINTIVO | AL VALOR on a white enameled band

Shape: Ball-tipped, red enameled Maltese cross with 7 rays in the angles, superimposed on a green enameled laurel wreath

Metal: 1st: gilt; 2nd: silver; 3rd: bronze with no enamel

Ribbon: White with a narrow red diagonal stripe

Reference: Grove 1974, 3:91–93, D-175, D-175a–b, D-176, D-176a–b; Gillingham 1940, 34; Pérez-Maldonado 1942, 106–8

Mx 64b

* * *

MEXICO authorized two medals for the key battles of Puebla and Querétaro at the end of the war.

Mx 64b

Mx65. *La Cruz y Placa de Puebla* (*1867*)

The 1867 Cross and Star of Puebla were awarded for the third Battle for Puebla on April 2, 1867. Mexico also gave a gold and platinum collar of the cross to General Porfirio Díaz for commanding the Mexican forces that took the city and defeated the imperial army sent to lift the siege.

> Classes: 1st, 2nd, 3rd
> Obverse inscription: PREMIO | AL | VALOR | MILITAR on a white enameled field
> Reverse inscription: VENCIO | A LOS | DEFENSORES | DE PUEBLA | EL 2 DE ABRIL | DE 1867 on a white enameled field
> Shape: Maltese cross superimposed on a green enameled laurel wreath in the angles, suspended from a national eagle, left. The left arm is enameled green, the right arm is enameled red, and the top and bottom arms are enameled white
> Star shape: 1st: badge on a star of silver rays
> Size: 54 × 46 mm
> Metal: 1st: gold; 2nd: silver; 3rd: bronze
> Ribbon: Green, white, red
> Reference: Grove 1974, 3:95, D-186, D-186a–b; Gillingham 1940, 33; Pérez-Maldonado 1942, 143

Mx66: *La Cruz y Placa de Querétaro*

The Queretaro Cross and Star were awarded for the siege and capture of Querétaro on May 15, 1867, the final battle of the war. The cross was authorized nearly thirty years after the event. Mexico also authorized a gold collar of the cross to General Mariano Escobedo, commander of the republican forces during the siege.

> Instituted: By decree on May 10, 1894
> Classes: 1st: generals and chiefs; 2nd: officers; 3rd: enlisted men

> Obverse inscription: VENCIO | EN | QUERETARO | EN 1867 on a white enameled field
> Reverse inscription: LA | PATRIA | AGRADECIDA on a white enameled field
> Shape: Ball-tipped, 3-armed cross with 2-pointed ends, superimposed on a green enameled laurel wreath, suspended from a national eagle, right. The left arm is enameled green, upper arm is enameled white, and right arm is enameled red
> Star shape: 1st class: badge superimposed on a 6-pointed sun with 7 rays in each angle
> Size: Badge: 40 mm. Star: 60 mm
> Metal: 1st: gold; 2nd: silver; 3rd: bronze
> Ribbon: Green, white, red neck ribbon
> Reference: Grove 1974, 3:96, D-191, D-191a–b; Gillingham 1940, 33–34

Mx67. *La Medalla de los Defensores de la República*

The Medal for the Defenders of the Republic was awarded for defending Mexico against foreign invaders, during the Texas Rebellion, the first American invasion, and the French Intervention, when no other decoration was considered appropriate.

Mx67a. *Variant 1*

> Obverse: National eagle, right, within a laurel and palm wreath
> Obverse legend: SOCIEDAD DEFENSORES DE LA REPUBLICA MEXICANA
> Reverse inscription: COMBATIERON | POR LA INTEGRIDAD | DEL | TERRITORIO NACIONAL | DESDE | 1836–1848
> Size: 30 mm
> Metal: Silver
> Ribbon: Black, red, black

Mx67b. *Variant 2*

Obverse: National eagle, right, within a laurel and palm wreath

Obverse legend: SOCIEDAD DEFENSORES DE LA REPUBLICA MEXICANA

Reverse inscription: COMBATIERON | POR LA INTEGRIDAD | DEL | TERRITORIO NACIONAL | DESDE | 1836–1848 | A 1867. [Bronze lacks final period and has larger letters]

Size: 30 mm

Metal: Silver, bronze

Reference: Grove 1974, 3:118, D-315a, D-317a–b

*Mx68. *La Cruz de los Defensores de la República*

The Cross for the Defenders of the Republic replaced the Medal for the Defenders of the Republic at an uncertain date, but probably in the early twentieth century.

Obverse disc: Gilt national eagle, left, with DESDE 1836 inscribed beneath, on an enameled field of green, white, and red diagonal stripes

Obverse legend: DEFENSORES DE LA REPUBLICA on a white enameled band within a gilt laurel wreath

Reverse legend: LA PATRIA AGRADECIDA

Reverse inscription: A | SUS | DEFENSORES

Shape: Cross with red enamel edges, with 5 silvered rays in each angle

Star obverse legend: CUERPO DEFENSORES DE LA REPUBLICA | AL PATRIOTISMO

Star shape: Cross with red enameled edges and concave ends on an 8-pointed star with 6 rays in each angle

Star reverse legend: LA PATRIA AGRADECIDA

Star reverse inscription: A | SUS | DEFENSORES

Size: Badge: 59 mm. Star: 78 mm

Metal: Badge: partially gilt silver; star: gilt

Ribbon: Green, white, red silk neck cord

Reference: Grove 1974, 3:119, D-319–20

Mx 68

Mx 68

Mx 68

Mx 68

* * *

SOME MEXICAN states authorized their own medals for their citizens who fought the French and their Mexican allies.

Mx69. *Estado de Guerrero: La Medalla de Chilapa*

The Medal for Chilapa was awarded by the state of Guerrero to the men who fought the imperial forces during their twenty-day siege of the town of Chilapa in Guerrero State. A Mexican force under the command of General Vicente Jiménez broke the siege in November 1864.

Classes: 1st, 2nd, 3rd

Obverse inscription: VENCIÓ Á LOS | TRAIDORES | Y SUS ALIADOS | EL | 10 DE NOVIEMBRE DE 1864 within a laurel wreath

Reverse inscription: EL ESTADO | DE | GUERRERO A SUS | VALIENTES | HIJOS within a laurel wreath

Shape: Round, suspended from a national eagle, right

Size: 40 mm

Metal: 1st: gold; 2nd: silver; 3rd: bronze

Ribbon: Green, white, red neck ribbon

Reference: Grove 1974, 3:97, D-194, D-194a–b; Gillingham 1940, 43; Pérez-Maldonado 1942, 133

Mx70. *Estado de Guerrero: La Medalla por la Intervención Francesa*

The Medal for the French Intervention was awarded by the state of Guerrero for fighting the French. Guerrero authorized a brass medal with identical inscriptions, but without the eagle suspension.

Instituted: October 13, 1869

Classes: 1st: generals; 2nd: chiefs and officers; 3rd: enlisted men

Obverse inscription: COMBATIO | A | LA INTERVENCION | Y | AL LLAMADO | IMPERIO within an olive wreath

Reverse inscription: EL ESTADO | DE | GUERRERO A SUS | VALIENTES HIJOS within an olive wreath

Shape: Round; 1st and 2nd classes: suspended
from a national eagle elevated and displayed,
right

Size: 40 mm

Metal: 1st: gold; 2nd: silver; 3rd: brass

Ribbon: Green, white, red neck ribbon

Reference: Grove 1974, 3:9, D-196, D-196a–
b; Gillingham 1940, 43; Pérez-Maldonado
1942, 110

Mx71. *Estado de Michoacán: La Medalla por la Intervención Francesa*

The state of Michoacán authorized an elaborate
decoration for its officers and men who participated in the war.

Instituted: April 20, 1868

Classes: 1st: generals and chiefs; 2nd: other
officers; 3rd:enlisted men

Obverse inscription: MICHOACAN | AL
PATRIOTISMO | Y A LA CONSTANCIA on
metallic ribbons at the top of the medal

Shape: Irregular, following the outline of
the elements of a national eagle perched
on crossed Mexican flags beneath a laurel
half-wreath

Size: 90 × 55 mm

Metal: 1st: gold; 2nd: silver; 3rd: bronze

Ribbon: Red

Reference: Grove 1974, 3:98, D-199,
D-199a–b; Gillingham 1940, 43–44;
Pérez-Maldonado 1942, 111

*Mx72. *Estado de Oaxaca: La Medalla por la Intervención Francesa*

The state of Oaxaca in southern Mexico was
the base from which Porfirio Díaz formed his
guerrilla army. This medal was given to the
men who fought at Juchitán on September 5,
1866; Miahuatlán on October 3, 1866; and at
La Carbonera on October 18, 1866.

Mx 72

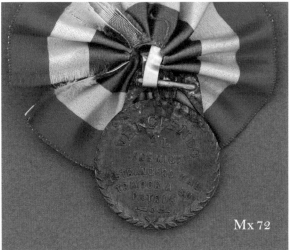

Mx 72

Instituted: By decree on January 11, 1868

Classes: 1st: generals and chiefs; 2nd: other
officers; 3rd: enlisted men*

Obverse inscription: DEFENDIO | LA |
INDEPENDENCIA | NACIONAL |
OAXACA surrounded by an olive wreath

Reverse inscription: VENCIENDO | AL |
ENEMIGO | ESTRANGERO Y AL | TRAIDOR
A SU | PATRIA

Shape: Round, suspended from a national
eagle, right

Size: 30 mm

Metal: 1st: gold; 2nd: silver; 3rd: bronze

Ribbon: Red, white, green rosette behind the eagle

Reference: Grove 1974, 3:98, D-201, D-201a–b; Gillingham 1940, 44; Pérez-Maldonado 1942, 139

Mx73. *Estado de Puebla: La Medalla de Puebla (1867)*

The state of Puebla awarded this medal to the officers and men who defeated royalist forces in the third and final battle for Puebla on April 2, 1867.

Instituted: By decree on May 7, 1869

Classes: 1st, 2nd

Obverse inscription: EL ESTADO DE PUEBLA | AL | VALOR | MILITAR within a laurel wreath

Reverse inscription: ASALTÓ LA PLAZA DE PUEBLA | VENCIENDO | A LOS | TRAIDORES | A LA PATRIA. | 2 DE ABRIL DE 1867.

Shape: Round, suspended from a ribbon bar in the shape of a Liberty cap inscribed LIBERTAS

Size: 25 mm

Metal: 1st: silver; 2nd: bronze

Ribbon: Red with white diagonal stripe running from lower left to upper right

Reference: Grove 1974, 3:99, D-203a–b; Gillingham 1940, 44–45; Pérez-Maldonado 1942, 144

Mx74. *Estado de Puebla: La Medalla por la Intervención Francesa*

The state of Puebla awarded the Medal for the French Intervention to the officers and men who fought the French between 1862 and 1867.

Instituted: By decree on May 7, 1869

Classes: 1st: generals and chiefs; 2nd: other officers; 3rd: enlisted men

Obverse inscription: EL ESTADO DE PUEBLA | PREMIA | AL VALOR | Y | LA CONSTANCIA within a laurel wreath

Reverse inscription: COMBATIO | POR LA | INDEPENDENCIA | DE SU PATRIA within a laurel wreath

Shape: Round, suspended from a ribbon bar in the form of a national eagle, right

Size: 25 mm

Metal: 1st: gold; 2nd: silver; 3rd: bronze

Engraver: L.Y. (lacking on some silver examples)

Ribbon: Green, red with a diagonal white stripe rising from lower left to upper right

Reference: Grove 1974, 3:99, D-205, D-205a–b; Gillingham 1940, 45; Pérez-Maldonado 1942, 144

*Mx75. *Estado de Puebla: Estrella "Cuique Merenti"*

The Star for the Worthy of the State of Puebla is not listed in catalogues, but it appears to be connected with the period of the French Intervention.

Obverse disc: Enameled national eagle

Obverse legend: REPUBLICA MEXICANA on a band

Reverse legend: ESTADO LIBRE Y SOBERANO DE PUEBLA

Reverse inscription: CUIQUE MERENTI surrounded by a laurel wreath

Shape: Ball-tipped star with 2-pointed ends with a ray in each angle and a laurel wreath in the angles suspended by scrollwork

Size: 45 mm

Metal: Gilt

Ribbon: Red

Provenance: A. Menke

* * *

Mx 75

Mx 75

In December 1864, a five-hundred-man French force under the command of Colonel Gazielle landed near San Pedro in Sinaloa State. Gazielle attacked the town of San Pedro, defended by four hundred Mexican troops commanded by Colonels Antonio Rosales and Joaquín Sánchez Román, on December 22, 1864. The defenders caused heavy casualties and captured nearly half of the French force, including Colonel Gazielle.

Mx76. *Estado de Sinaloa: La Cruz de San Pedro*

The state of Sinaloa awarded the Cross of San Pedro to its officers and men who defended San Pedro.

> Instituted: By decree on February 20, 1892
>
> Classes: 1st, 2nd, 3rd
>
> Obverse disc: Radiant sun with a human face
>
> Obverse legend: A LOS HEROICOS VENCEDORES DE | SAN PEDRO
>
> Obverse inscription: EL ESTADO DE | SINALOA on the upper arm
>
> Reverse disc: DICIEMBRE | 22 | DE 1864
>
> Reverse legend: PREMIO | AL VALOR Y PATRIOTISMO
>
> Shape: Cross pattée suspended from a ribbon bar and wreath
>
> Size: 35 mm
>
> Metal: 1st: gold; 2nd: silver; 3rd: bronze
>
> Ribbon: Green, white, red, white, green
>
> Reference: Grove 1974, 3:100, D-207; Gillingham 1940, 46; Pérez-Maldonado 1942, 135

Mx77. *Estado de Sinaloa: La Medalla de Sinaloa (1866)*

The state of Sinaloa awarded a medal to the men who fought under General Ramón Corona for two years against the imperial forces in Sinaloa.

Instituted: By decree on May 4, 1885

Classes: 1st: Commander in Chief; 2nd: brigade generals and other chiefs; 3rd: officers; 4th: enlisted men

Obverse: National eagle, right, within a laurel and oak wreath

Obverse legend: EL ESTADO DE SINALOA A LOS DEFENSORES DE LA INDEPENDENCIA NACIONAL

Reverse inscription: PREMIO | AL | PATRIOTISMO | NOV. 13. 1864 | A | NOV. 13. 1866

Size: 32 mm

Metal: 1st: gold; 2nd: gilt silver; 3rd: silver; 4th: bronze

Ribbon: Green, white, red, white, green

Reference: Grove 1974, 3:100, D-208; Gillingham 1940, 45 (with different inscriptions and size); Pérez-Maldonado 1942, 134

Mx78. *Estado de Tamaulipas: Cruz y Medalla*

The state of Tamaulipas along the Texas border awarded a cross to the officers and men who fought under Generals Mariano Escobedo and Gerónimo Treviño against the imperial forces commanded by General Feliciano Olivera at the Battle of Santa Gertrudis on June 16, 1866. The medals awarded to the three classes take different forms.

Authorized: By decree on October 22, 1891

Classes: 1st: generals; 2nd: other officers; 3rd: enlisted men

Mx78a. *La Cruz de la 1ª Clase*

Obverse disc: Red enameled Liberty cap on a white enameled field

Obverse legend: Outside band: COMBATIO CONTRA LA INTERVENCION | FRANCESA on a white enameled band; inside band: EN EL ESTADO DE | TAMAULIPAS on a white enameled band

Reverse inscription: EL 16 | DE JUNIO | DE | 1866

Reverse legend: CONCURRIO A LA BATALLA DE | SANTA GERTRUDIS

Shape: Red enameled cross with 2-pointed ends with laurel wreaths in the angles, suspended from a national eagle, right, displayed and inverted

Size: 47 mm

Metal: Gold

Ribbon: Divided diagonally by gold lace: lower right is white, upper left has equal diagonal green, white, and red stripes. The ribbon has 2 gold edge stripes

Mx78b. *La Cruz de la 2ª Clase*

Obverse inscription: EN EL | ESTADO | DE | TAMAULIPAS on a white enameled field

Obverse legend: COMBATIÓ CONTRA LA | INTERVENCION FRANCESA on a red enameled band

Reverse inscription: CONCURRIÓ | Á LA | BATALLA DE | S^{TA}. GERTRUDIS | EL 16 DE | JUNIO DE 1866.

Shape: Ball-tipped cross with 9 gilt flames in each angle, suspended from a national eagle, right, displayed and inverted

Size: 51 mm

Metal: Silver

Ribbon: Divided diagonally by golden lace: lower right is white; upper left has equal diagonal green, white, and red stripes

Mx78c. *La Medalla de la 3ª Clase*

Obverse inscription: COMBATIÓ | Á LA | INTERVENCIÓN | FRANCESA | EN EL ESTADO | DE | TAMA | ULIPAS within a palm and laurel wreath

Reverse inscription: CONCURRIÓ | A LA | BATALLA DE | S^{TA}. GERTRUDIS | EL 16 DE JUNIO DE | 1866.

Shape: Oval, surmounted by a national eagle, right, with the wings displayed and inverted, suspended from a ribbon bar

Size: 30 × 25 mm

Metal: Bronze

Ribbon: Divided diagonally by gold lace: lower right is white; upper left has equal diagonal green, white, and red stripes

Reference: Grove 1974, 3:101–3, D-210–12; Gillingham 1940, 46–47; Pérez-Maldonado 1942, 101–3

Mx79. *Estado de Tlaxcala: La Medalla del Asalto de Puebla* (*1867*)

The state of Tlaxcala issued the Medal for the Assault on Puebla for the successful attack on the royalist forces based in Puebla at the end of the French Intervention. The state of Tlaxcala borders on Puebla, which explains why its citizens joined the army of Porfirio Díaz in the third Battle of Puebla in 1867.

Instituted: By decree on May 2, 1868

Classes: 1st, 2nd, 3rd

Obverse inscription: EL ESTADO | DE | TLAXCALA | A SUS | VALIENTES SOLDADOS within a laurel wreath

Reverse inscription: CONCURRIO | AL | GLORIOSO ASALTO | DE | PUEBLA | EL | 2 DE ABRIL DE 1867

Size: 25 mm

Metal: 1st: gold; 2nd: silver; 3rd: brass

Engraver: Navalon

Ribbon: Green, white, red

Reference: Grove 1974, 3:103, D-214; Gillingham 1940, 46; Pérez-Maldonado 1942, 144

Mx80. *Estado de Veracruz: La Medalla de la Intervención Francesa*

The State of Veracruz awarded a medal to those who defended the city of Veracruz during the French Intervention. The French fleet bombarded the city at the outset of the war, and Veracruz then served as the main French supply hub.

Instituted: By decree on March 14, 1868

Obverse inscription: EL | ESTADO | DE | VERA CRUZ | AL | PATRIOTA | VALIENTE within a laurel wreath

Reverse inscription: COMBATIO | SIN | DESCANSO | CONTRA LOS | ENEMIGOS | DE LA | PATRIA within a laurel wreath

Shape: Oval

Size: 23 × 16.5 mm

Metal: Silver

Ribbon: Green, white, red

Reference: Grove 1974, 3:104, D-216; Gillingham 1940, 47–48; Pérez-Maldonado 1942, 144

MEDALS ISSUED BY THE IMPERIAL GOVERNMENT

EMPEROR Maximilian exercised sovereign powers in Mexico during his reign and authorized both medals and orders for his loyal supporters.

*Mx81. *La Medalla al Mérito*

The imperial government authorized one basic medal for its followers and allies. The medal was struck in a civilian and a military version, each in three classes.

Mx81a. *La Medalla al Mérito Civil* (*1863*)

Maximilian authorized the Medal for Civil Merit to his followers for political, diplomatic, and administrative service to his empire. The medal comes in two different basic designs. It is also known in different sizes ranging from 31 mm to 39 mm; in some cases, the emperor's head faces right, while in others it faces left. Four engravers are identified on the various dies.

Instituted: October 14, 1863

Classes: 1st, 2nd, 3rd

Obverse: Imperial eagle with crown, right, with its wings displayed and inverted on a white enameled field

Obverse legend: AL MERITO | CIVIL on a white enameled band

Reverse inscription: IMPERIO | MEXICANO | 1863 on a white enameled field

Shape: Round, surmounted by a metallic wreath

Size: 31 mm

Metal: 1st: gold; 2nd: silver; 3rd: bronze

Ribbon: 1st: red; 2nd: red with 2 white edge stripes; 3rd: equal green, white, and red stripes

Mx81b. *La Medalla al Mérito Civil* (*1865*)

Classes: 1st, 2nd, 3rd

Obverse: Bust of Maximilian, right (occasionally bust of Charlotte, left)

Obverse legend: MAXIMILIANO | EMPERADOR

Reverse inscription: AL | MERITO | CIVIL within an oak wreath

Size: 33 mm

Metal: 1st: gold; 2nd: silver; 3rd: bronze

Engraver: G. Navalon; E. Falot

Ribbon: 1st: red; 2nd: red with 2 white side stripes; 3rd: green, white, red

Mx81c. *La Medalla al Mérito Militar* (*1863*)

Maximilian awarded this medal to his Mexican officers and enlisted men as well as to those foreign officers and enlisted men who fought for

him against the republican Mexican forces, including the army and local militia.

Instituted: October 14, 1863

Classes: 1st, 2nd, 3rd

Obverse: Imperial eagle with a crown, right, with its wings displayed and inverted on a white enameled field

Obverse legend: AL MERITO | MILITAR on a white enameled band

Reverse inscription: IMPERIO | MEXICANO | 1863.

Size: 31 mm with variations

Metal: 1st: gold; 2nd and 3rd: silver

Ribbon: 1st: green, white, red; 2nd: red with 2 white side stripes; 3rd: green, white, red

*Mx81d. *La Medalla al Mérito Militar* (*1865*)

This medal was produced with dies bearing the names of four engravers, which vary in the portrait.

Instituted: March 10, 1865

Classes: 1st,* 2nd (2),* 3rd

Obverse: Bust of Maximilian, right (a die engraved by Stern faces left)

Obverse inscription: MAXIMILIANO | EMPERADOR

Reverse inscription: AL | MERITO | MILITAR [occasionally the "E" in "MÉRITO" is accented]

Size: 32–35 mm

Metal: 1st: silver; 2nd: bronze

Engraver: G. Navalon, E. Falot, René Stern, Charles Trotin

Ribbon: 1st: green, white, red (red according to Gillingham); 2nd: red with 2 white side stripes; 3rd: green, white red (variant: imperial crown suspension, triangular ribbon with crossed swords)

Reference: Grove 1974, 3:105–11, D-250–83; Gillingham 1940, 38–39; Pérez-Maldonado 1942, 131–32

Mx 81d

Mx 81d

MEDALS AFTER THE FRENCH INTERVENTION, 1867–1911

WITH THE end of the French Intervention, President Benito Juárez returned to Mexico City and ruled until 1876. During this period, local instability continued in much of the country, although the presidency itself was not threatened. Several states issued medals for military action within their jurisdictions.

Mx82. *Estado de Jalisco: La Medalla por la Defensa de Guadalajara (1873)*

The state of Jalisco issued three medals to the officers and men under the command of General Ramón Corona for defending the city of Guadalajara from a local guerrilla, Manuel Lozada. On January 28, 1873, Lozada, also known as the "Tiger of Alicia," threatened Guadalajara with three thousand men and artillery. Corona defeated him with 2,200 men at "La Mohonera" on the outskirts of the city. Lozada was captured and executed six months later. The state of Jalisco authorized two versions of a medal for this campaign.

Mx82a. *Version 1*

Instituted: By decrees on February 14, 1873, and January 27, 1890

Classes: 1st: General Corona; 2nd: brigade generals; 3rd: other officers; 4th: enlisted men

Obverse: Bust of General Ramón Corona, right

Reverse inscription: EL ESTADO DE JALISCO | A | LOS DEFENSORES | DE LA | SOCIEDAD | EN ENERO DE 1873. above a laurel branch

Size: 35 mm

Metal: 1st: gold; 2nd: gilt silver; 3rd; silver; 4th: bronze

Ribbon: Green, white, red

Mx82b. *Version 2*

Classes: 1st, 2nd

Obverse: National eagle perched on crossed flags surrounded by a laurel and oak wreath

Reverse inscription: EL | ESTADO | DE JALISCO Á LOS | DEFENSORES DE LA | SOCIEDAD EN | ENERO DE | 1873 within a laurel and oak wreath

Size: 31 mm

Classes: 1st: silver; 2nd: bronze

Reference: Grove 1974, 3:120–21, D-323–29; Gillingham 1940, 44; Pérez-Maldonado 1942, 150–51

Mx83. *Estado de Chihuahua: La Medalla de los Tres Castillos (1880)*

Apache Indians were carrying out attacks on residents of northeastern Chihuahua State. In 1880, the Governor, Luis Terrazas, organized a small army of four hundred volunteers and hunted them down. They killed the leader, Indio Victorio, and all his followers. The battle lasted for two days on October 14–15, 1880. The state of Chihuahua authorized a medal for the engagement.

Classes: 1st, 2nd

Obverse inscription: EL | ESTADO | DE | CHIHUAHUA | PREMIA EL VALOR | DE SUS | HIJOS within a laurel wreath

Reverse inscription: CAMPAÑA | CONTRA | LOS BARBAROS | TRES CASTILLOS | 14 Y 15 DE OBRE. | DE 1880. within a laurel wreath

Size: 34 mm

Metal: 1st: gold; 2nd: silver

Ribbon: White, red neck ribbon

Reference: Grove 1974, 3:121, D-329; Gillingham 1940, 48; Pérez-Maldonado 1942, 152–53

Mx84. *Estado de Sonora: La Medalla por la Guerra del Yaqui y del Mayo (1886)*

During the second presidency of Porfirio Díaz, Yaqui Indians under their leader José María Cajeme harassed settlers in the Valle del Mayo beginning in 1875. The Indians constructed a fort at Añil, which government forces attacked several times without success. In 1887, Mexico sent two columns of troops to Sonora and captured the fort. Cajeme retreated to another fortified town, which was also taken. The tribes stopped supporting Cajeme, and he was captured and executed. The state of Sonora awarded a medal to the officers and men who participated in this campaign.

Instituted: December 13, 1867

Obverse: National eagle, right

Obverse legend: PREMIO A LA CONSTANCIA Y AL VALOR | ESTADO DE SONORA

Reverse inscription: GUERRA | DEL YAQUI | Y | DEL MAYO | 1885 | 1886 within an oak and laurel wreath

Size: 40 mm

Metal: Silver

Engraver: J. Varón

Ribbon: White with narrow red edge stripes

Reference: Grove 1974, 3:123, D-338; Gillingham 1940, 48–49; Pérez-Maldonado 1942, 154–55

Mx85. *La Cruz de la Constancia en el Servicio Naval Militar*

The Loyalty Cross for Naval Military Service is awarded to navy officers for years of loyal service. It is similar to the Cross for Military Loyalty (Mx24), created fifty years earlier. This cross became the first of a growing number of decorations designed to reward Mexico's military for loyalty, merit, distinguished service, and professionalism in peacetime.

Instituted: By decree on May 6, 1891

Abolished: May 6, 1901

Classes: 1st: 30 years of service; 2nd: 25 years; 3rd: 20 years

Obverse disc: A gold female figure holding a sword on a red enameled oval field

Obverse legend: RECOMP. A LA CONST. | EN EL SERV. NAVAL MILITAR on a white enameled band

Reverse inscription: CREADA | EN 1891 | Y | CONCEDIDA | POR 30 [25, 20] AÑOS DE | SERVICIOS on a white enameled field

Badge shape: Badge: cross of palm leaves with each arm linked by green enameled sempervivum leaves; for 1st class, suspended from a gold national eagle, right

Star shape: 1st and 2nd: badge superimposed on a sun of 32 rays with a ray in each angle

Size: Badge: 1st: 49 × 43 mm; 2nd: 44 × 40 mm; 3rd: 42 × 35 mm. Star: 1st: 72 mm; 2nd: 62 mm

Metal: Badge: gilt. Star: silver

Ribbon: 1st: gold cord; 2nd, 3rd: white with narrow green edge stripes

Reference: Grove 1974, 3:184–86, D-605–9

Mx86. *La Medalla por Acción Distinguida, Ejército (1897)*

The Mexican army awarded the Medal for Distinguished Action to generals, chiefs, other officers, and enlisted men for merit. The medals were not associated with any particular battle or campaign.

Instituted: By Ordinance of the Army and Navy, June 15, 1897

Classes: 1st: generals; 2nd: other officers; 3rd: enlisted men

Obverse inscription: PREMIO | POR | ACCION | DISTINGUIDA | 1ᴬ [2ᴬ, 3ᴬ] CLASE within a green enameled wreath on a white enameled field

Shape: Round; 1st suspended from the national eagle, left

Size: 25 mm

Metal: 1st: gold; 2nd: silver; 3rd: bronze

Ribbon: Crimson

Reference: Grove 1974, 3:165–66, D-525–31; Pérez-Maldonado 1942, 121

Mx 87a
star

Mx 87a
badge (obverse)

Mx 87a
badge (reverse)

*Mx87. *La Estrella del Mérito Militar* (*1902*)

Mexico's Star for Military Merit is perhaps its most important single military award. A Star for Technical Military Merit was authorized at the same time for noncombat units. A navy version was authorized in 1911.

*Mx87a. *1902 Version*

Instituted: 1902

Modified: March 11, 1926

Replaced: November 19, 1929

Divisions: Officers, enlisted men, technical

Classes: 1st,* 2nd, 3rd* for each division

Obverse disc: 1ª [2ª, 3ª]; officers, technical: on a red enameled field

Obverse legend: MERITO | MILITAR; officers, technical: on a white enameled band

Reverse disc: 1902; officers, technical: on a red enameled field

Shape: Star (officers: enameled red; technical: enameled white): with laurel wreath within and 5 rays in each angle; 1st, 2nd: suspended from the national eagle, right

Star shape: Officers, technical, 1st: badge on sun of 32 rays with a ray in each angle

Size: Badge: 1st: 48 mm; 2nd, 3rd: 45 mm. Star: 75 mm

Metal: Officers, technical: silver; enlisted men: bronze

Ribbon: Officers, technical: 1st: gold silk cord; officers, 2nd, 3rd; enlisted men: 1st, 2nd, 3rd: red; technical, 2nd, 3rd: white

Mx87b. *1926 Version*

The medal for the Technical Division was modified in 1926.

    Classes: 1st, 2nd

    Obverse disc: Star on a red enameled field

    Obverse legend: MERITO TECNICO MILITAR on a white enameled band

    Reverse inscription: CREADA | POR LEY | DE 11 Mzo

    Shape: 8-pointed sun, elongated vertically, suspended from a national eagle

    Size: 46 mm

    Metal: 1st: gilt; 2nd: silver

    Ribbon: 1st: green with white side stripes; 2nd: white, green, white, green, white

*Mx87c. *1929 Version*

In 1929 a uniform medal was instituted to replace those of all divisions.

    Classes: 1st,* 2nd, 3rd*

    Obverse disc: National eagle, left, on a dark blue enameled field

    Obverse legend: MERITO MILITAR | 1ᴬ [2ᴬ, 3ᴬ] CLASE on a red enameled band

    Reverse legend: CREADA EN 1929

Mx 87c

Mx 87c

Mx 87c

Mx 87c

Shape: 8-pointed sun with 3 rays in each
angle on a dark blue enameled cross pattée

Size: 45 mm

Metal: 1st: gilt; 2nd: unknown; 3rd: silver

Ribbon: 1st: gold silk neck cord; 2nd: cobalt
blue with a narrow red center stripe; 3rd:
cobalt blue with 2 red center stripes

Reference: Grove 1974, 3:167–73, D-535–55

*Mx88. *Estado de Yucatán: La Cruz de Yucatán (1902)*

In 1896, Mayan Indians in the state of Yucatán rose up again, attacking and burning settlements. In 1899, the government appointed
General Ignacio Bravo to take charge of the
military zone. In 1901, his forces began recovering towns that had been taken by the Mayans,
and in May of that year he entered the Mayan
capital of Chan Santa Cruz, thereby ending the

war. The state of Yucatán awarded this cross to
the officers and men who "pacified" the Mayan
Indians in the Yucatán Peninsula.

Classes: 1st, 2nd,* 3rd*

Obverse inscription: PREMIO│DEL│ESTADO
DE│YUCATAN│1902 on a white enameled
field (2nd: no enamel)

Reverse inscription: CAMPAÑA│CONTRA│
LOS│MAYAS

Shape: Blue enameled Maltese cross, each arm
terminating in a white enameled lozenge,
with a laurel wreath in the angles (2nd: no
enamel)

Size: 42.5 mm

Metal: 1st: gold; 2nd: silver; 3rd: bronze

Ribbon: Light blue

Reference: Grove 1974, 3:123, D-340; Gillingham 1940, 49; Pérez-Maldonado 1942,
166–67

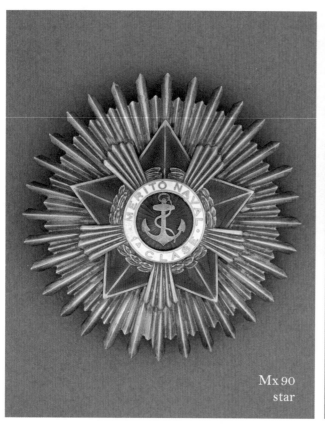

Mx 90
star

Mx 90
badge (obverse)

Mx 90
badge (reverse)

Mx89. *Estado de Sonora: La Cruz de la Campaña del Yaqui* (*1910*)

The Yaquis, an Indian tribe living mainly in the state of Sonora, frequently rebelled against Mexico's rulers, going back to the beginnings of the Spanish conquest. Their system of communal land ownership was never accepted either by the viceroy or the Mexican republic. Sonora awarded this cross for the campaign against the Yaquis, including a series of battles at Palo Parado, Laguna Prieta, Bahueca, and Mazacoba in 1899. Minor actions continued to take place for more than a decade. This was the second military decoration awarded by Sonora for military action against the Yaquis (see Mx84).

Obverse inscription: CAMPAÑA | DEL | YAQUI on a white enameled field surrounded by a green enameled band

Reverse inscription: 1899 | A | 1910 on a white enameled field surrounded by a wreath

Shape: Red enameled Maltese cross with a green enameled oak and laurel wreath in the angles, suspended from a green enameled silver ribbon bar inscribed SONORA

Size: 37 mm

Ribbon: Red with 2 white edge stripes

Reference: Grove 1974, 3:124, D-342–45; Gillingham 1940, 49; Pérez-Maldonado 1942, 156

*Mx90. *La Estrella del Mérito Naval*

The Star for Naval Merit was instituted in 1911 as the naval equivalent of the Star for Military Merit (see Mx87). The star recreated the Loyalty Cross for Naval Military Service (see Mx85) that had been abolished in 1901, but with a different design.

Instituted: By Executive Decree No. 425 on December 12, 1911

Classes: 1st,* 2nd, 3rd

Obverse disc: Anchor on a red enameled field

Obverse legend: MERITO NAVAL | 1ᴬ CLASE on a white enameled band

Reverse: 1911 on a white enameled disc surrounded by a laurel wreath

Shape: Red enameled star, with 5 rays in each angle with a laurel wreath between the rays

Star shape: Badge on sun of 32 rays with a ray in each angle

Size: Badge: 1st: 50 mm. Star: 72 mm*

Metal: 1st: gold; 2nd: silver; 3rd: bronze

Ribbon: 1st: gold cord; 2nd, 3rd: red, white

Reference: Grove 1974, 3:192, D-645–46; Mexico 1912, 18–20

From the Mexican Revolution until World War II

THE MEXICAN REVOLUTION generated a decade (1910–1920) of political instability and fighting among the contending forces. Although the revolution had its own ideological principles, the officers and men who did the fighting invariably identified themselves with one of the revolutionary leaders. They would be known as Maderistas, Orozquistas, Zapatistas, Carranzistas, and so forth.

Most medals awarded to the fighters were issued by the central government, but some were given by one of the revolutionary groups.

*Mx91. *La Cruz de Mérito Revolucionario, 1ᵉʳ Periodo (1911)*

The Cross for Revolutionary Merit was awarded to those who fought against the conservative government of President Porfirio Díaz between November 19, 1910, and May 15, 1911. This corresponds to the period between the time when Francisco Madero's forces first took up arms against Díaz and the Treaty of Ciudad Juárez under which Díaz ceded power to Madero. The cross was instituted years after the consolidation of the Mexican Revolution in 1920.

Mx91

Instituted: By Decree No. 659 on October 5, 1939

Obverse inscription: 1910 1911 | 1ᴱᴿ | PERIODO on a blue enameled field

Obverse legend: MERITO | REVOLUCIONARIO on a blue enameled band

Reverse inscription: DECRETO | NUM. 659 | DE | 5 DE OCTUBRE | DE | 1939 [lacking on some examples]

Shape: Ball-tipped, red enameled Maltese cross with 2-pointed ends and 9 rays in each angle

Size: 52 mm

Metal: Gilt

Ribbon: Red, blue, red

Reference: Grove 1974, 3:127, D-356

Mx92. *La Cruz del Plan de Ayala (1911)*

The Plan of Ayala proclaimed the political ideology of Emiliano Zapata, a revolutionary leader who advocated large-scale land reform. Zapata created his own army, the Liberation Army of the South, which helped defeat the Federal Army of President Porfirio Díaz during the Mexican Revolution. Zapata broke with Francisco Madero, the leader of the revolution, six months after Madero overthrew Díaz in May 1911. In November, Zapata drew up his Plan of Ayala, which became the political platform of his army. Zapata fought the new Mexican army controlled by Madero but never succeeded in defeating it. He instituted this cross for the officers and men of his Liberation Army of the South. Zapata was killed in a sting operation on April 10, 1919, and his army was slowly dissolved, absent his leadership.

Obverse disc: Bust of Zapata on a red enameled field

Obverse legend: EJERCITO LIBERTADOR | PLAN DE AYALA | NOV. 28 DE 1911 | ALTO MERITO REVOLUCIONARIO

Reverse disc: 2 cannons and a sheaf of grain on a blue enameled field

Shape: 7-armed, white enameled cross with pointed ends and a laurel wreath in the angles

Size: 52 mm

Ribbon: Green, white, and red silk cord worn around the neck

Reference: Grove 1974, 3:126, D-354

Mx93. *La Medalla de Valor y Abnegación (1913)*

The Medal for Valor and Sacrifice was awarded by the government of Victoriano Huerta to officers and men of the Federal Army, who fought against the Constitutionalist Army headed by Venustiano Carranza. Huerta had been a career army officer in the government of Porfirio Díaz and had once been sent to suppress Mayan insurgents in Yucatán. After the revolution, he pledged loyalty to Madero, who sent him to fight Zapata's Liberation Army of the South. Huerta overthrew Madero in a coup d'état and had him killed in February 1913. Huerta ruled until July 15, 1914, when he was forced to resign after being defeated by Victoriano Carranza.

Instituted: By Decree No. 440 on July 6,
    1913

Classes: 1st: generals and chiefs; 2nd: other
    officers; 3rd: enlisted men

Obverse disc: National eagle on a red enam-
    eled field

Obverse legend: LA REPUBLICA MEXICANA
    AL EJERCITO on a white enameled band

Shape: Green enameled laurel and oak
    wreath connected to the disc by 3 bursts
    of 5 rays

Reverse legend: PREMIO AL VALOR Y
    ABNEGACION

Metal: 1st: gold; 2nd: silver; 3rd: bronze

Ribbon: White, red suspended from a ribbon
    bar inscribed: 1913

Reference: Grove 1974, 3:129, D-365

*Mx94. *La Cruz de Mérito Revolucionario, 2° Periodo (1914)*

The second Cross of Revolutionary Merit was
awarded to the men who fought with Venustiano Carranza against the conservative government of General Huerta between February
20, 1913, and August 15, 1914. This roughly
corresponds with the period between Huerta's
usurpation of power from Madero and Huerta's
resignation under American pressure, when
Carranza assumed the presidency.

The Cross was instituted twenty years after
the consolidation of the revolution.

Instituted: By Decree No. 659 on October 5,
    1939

Obverse inscription: 1913 1914 | 2° | PERIODO
    on a red enameled field

Obverse legend: MERITO | REVOLUCIONARIO
    on a red enameled band

Reverse inscription: DECRETO | NUM. 659 |
    DE | 5 DE OCTUBRE | DE | 1939 [lacking on
    some examples]

Shape: Ball-tipped, blue enameled Maltese
    cross with 2-pointed ends and 9 rays in
    each angle

Mx 94

Mx 94

Size: 53 mm
Metal: Gilt
Ribbon: Blue, red, blue
Reference: Grove 1974, 3:127, D-357

* * *

THE UNITED STATES intervened in Mexican politics during its revolution. The American ambassador had a hand in encouraging Huerta's coup d'état. A new American president, Woodrow Wilson, changed sides, but sent the U.S. Navy and Marine Corps in April 1914 to occupy Veracruz. The marines occupied the city for six months and withdrew in November after a settlement had been negotiated. Mexico authorized three decorations for those who opposed the American invasion.

Mx95. *La Placa por la Segunda Invasión Norteamericana (1914)*

Citizen soldiers and cadets from the naval academy fought the American invasion, but with little effect. The bulk of Mexico's military was bogged down in the country's civil war. Mexico authorized a star for defending Veracruz from the U.S. Marines.

Instituted: By decree on January 3, 1927
Classes: 1st: posthumous; 2nd: chiefs and officers; 3rd: cadets and others
Obverse inscription: COMBATIO | EN DEFENSA | DE SU | PATRIA | 1914 on a white enameled field
Obverse legend: SEGUNDA INVASION | NORTEAMERICANA on a white enameled band
Reverse inscription: CREADA POR | DECRETO DEL | 3 DE ENERO DE 1927 above a wreath containing 1ᴬ [2ᴬ, 3ᴬ]
Shape: Red enameled Maltese cross set diagonally and topped with a national eagle on a 6-pointed sun

Size: 57 mm
Metal: 1st: gold; 2nd: silver; 3rd: bronze
Reference: Grove 1974, 3:130, D-367

Mx96. *La Medalla por la Escuela Naval Militar (1914)*

The Medal for the Navy Military Academy was awarded to its cadets, who fought in the streets against American marines.

Obverse inscription: LA PATRIA | A LOS HEROICOS | HIJOS DE LA | ESCUELA | NAVAL | MILITAR
Obverse legend: SEGUNDA INVASION NORTEAMERICANA | VERACRUZ ABRIL 21 DE 1914
Reverse: A national eagle perched on crossed anchors, right
Shape: Round
Size: 34 mm
Metal: Silver (some examples struck on a one peso coin)
Reference: Grove 1974, 3:131, D-371

*Mx97. *La Cruz de los Defensores de Veracruz (1914)*

The Cross for the Defenders of Veracruz was authorized nearly thirty years after the American invasion.

Instituted: By the Ministry of Defense on August 28, 1943
Obverse disc: National eagle, left. On a field enameled with the national colors
Obverse legend: DEFENSORES DE VERACRUZ | 1914 on a white enameled band
Reverse inscription: AUTORIZADA | POR LA | DEFENSA NATIONAL | SEGUN OF. 12728 | DE FECHA | 28 DE AGOSTO | 1943 | LA DIRECTIVA [lacking on some examples]
Shape: Blue, white, red enameled Maltese cross with 2-pointed ends

Mx 97

Mx 97

Size: 41 mm
Metal: Bronze
Ribbon Blue, white, red
Reference: Grove 1974, 3:131, D-373

Mx98. *Ciudad de Veracruz: La Medalla por la Segunda Invasión Norteamericana (1914)*

The City of Veracruz authorized a simple medal for those who defended the city against the American invasion.

Obverse inscription: CONTRA | LA INVASION | N. AMERICANA
Obverse legend: A LOS DEFENSORES DE LA PATRIA | EN ABRIL DE 1914
Reverse: Arms of Veracruz
Size: 50 mm
Metal: Silver
Reference: Grove 1974, 3:130, D-369

Mx99. *La Cruz Constitucionalista (1916)*

Mexico awarded the Constitutionalist Cross to the officers and men of the Constitutionalist Army, which defeated the Federal Army under President Victoriano Huerta. The Constitutionalist Army sought to preserve the 1857 constitution closely identified with Benito Juárez. In 1916, Carranza, as chief of the Constitutionalist Army, convoked the Constitutional Convention in Querétaro for the purpose of rectifying the 1857 constitution. The liberal 1917 constitution was adopted, and Carranza was elected president. The Constitutionalist Army went on to fight renegade caudillos like Pancho Villa in the north and Emiliano Zapata in the south.

Classes: 1st, 2nd
Obverse disc: National eagle, right
Obverse legend: LA REPUBLICA MEXICANA | AL EJERCITO

Shape: 3-armed cross of rays linked by an oak and laurel wreath, suspended from a bar with the bust of Benito Juárez and the dates 1857 and 1916

Size: 39 mm

Metal: 1st: silver; 2nd: bronze

Reference: Grove 1974, 3:144, D-425

Mx100. *Ciudad Juárez: La Medalla de la Ciudad Juárez (1919)*

The city of Ciudad Juárez awarded this medal to the men who defended it from an attack by Pancho Villa's troops on the night of June 14, 1919. The garrison in Ciudad Juárez was loyal to Mexican President Carranza. Villa's men also fired on American troops in El Paso, who crossed the border, but returned to El Paso as soon as they had chased Villa's men away.

Obverse disc: Green, white, and red enameled vertical stripes

Obverse legend: C. JUAREZ | A SUS VALIENTES DEFENSORES

Shape: Round laurel wreath suspended from a bar inscribed: 14–15 JUNIO 1919

Size: 35 mm

Metal: Silver

Reference: Grove 1974, 3:144, D-427

*Mx101. *La Cruz a la Lealtad, Carranza (1920)*

President Venustiano Carranza was forced out of office on May 7, 1920, and later assassinated on his way to safety in Veracruz. Mexico awarded this medal to Carranza's followers who accompanied him on his last day.

Obverse inscription: A LA LEALTAD | MAYO | DE | 1920 on a white enameled field

Shape: Ball-tipped, purple enameled Maltese cross with 2-pointed ends and dark red enameled trefoils and a gilt laurel wreath in

Mx 101

the angles, suspended from a national eagle, left

Size: 46 × 43 mm

Ribbon: Purple with narrow green, white, red center stripes

Reference: Grove 1974, 3:145, D-430

*Mx102. *La Cruz al Valor Heróico (1926)*

The Cross for Heroic Valor was one of several military medals for valor and merit instituted in 1926 by General Joaquín Amaro Domínguez, then the secretary of war. General Amaro was an important revolutionary army officer, who set out to professionalize the Mexican military. The army in particular had often been used to

Mx 102

Mx 102

promote the personal or ideological ambitions of Mexican caudillos and leaders. Amaro created military academies to form an elite corps of professional military officers similar to what existed in France and the United States. The army and navy versions of this cross are identical.

> Instituted: By law on March 11, 1926
>
> Classes: 1st, 2nd, 3rd*
>
> Obverse disc: 1ª [2ª, 3ª] on a red enameled field
>
> Obverse legend: VALOR | HEROICO on a white enameled band
>
> Reverse inscription: CREADA | POR LEY | DE 11 Mzo | DE 1926
>
> Shape: Red enameled cross pattée with pointed ends and 5 rays in each angle
>
> Size: 46 mm
>
> Ribbon: 1st: red; 2nd: red, white, red, white, red; 3rd: white with red edge stripes
>
> Reference: Grove 1974, 3:174, D-558–60

*Mx103. *La Estrella del Mérito Naval* (*1926*)

The Medal for Naval Merit is awarded to navy personnel for merit. It was also created by General Amaro as part of his efforts to professionalize the Mexican military.

> Instituted: By law on March 11, 1926
>
> Modified: December 17, 1945
>
> Classes: 1st, 2nd*
>
> Obverse: Silver (2nd: gilt) anchor above silver (2nd: gilt) oak and laurel branches
>
> Obverse legend: MERITO NAVAL on a blue enameled band behind anchor
>
> Reverse inscription: CREADA | POR LEY | DE 11 DE Mzo | DE 1926
>
> Shape: 8-pointed star, suspended from a national eagle, left (after 1945, eagle is perched on crossed anchors)
>
> Size: 49 mm

Metal: 1st: gilt; 2nd: silvered

Ribbon: 1st: blue with 2 narrow white edge stripes; 2nd: white, blue, white, blue, white

Reference: Grove 1974, 3:194, D-653–56

*Mx 104. *La Estrella del Mérito Aeronáutico* (1929)

The Star for Aeronautical Merit was the first Mexican medal for its air force. It was instituted while General Amaro was secretary of war.

Instituted: By decree on September 28, 1929

Classes: 1st,* 2nd,* 3rd

Obverse disc: Winged propeller on a red enameled field (on some examples, MERITO inscribed beneath)

Obverse legend: 1ᴬ [2ᴬ, 3ᴬ] CLASE AERONAUTICO on a white enameled band

Reverse legend: CREADA POR DECRETO DEL 28 DE SEP. DE 1929 [on some examples as an inscription on 4 lines]

Shape: Green, white, red enameled 6-pointed star with the tips connected by a laurel wreath, suspended from a national eagle, left

Size: 40 mm

Metal: 1st: gilt; 2nd: silvered; 3rd: bronze

Ribbon: 1st: purple; 2nd: purple with white center stripe; 3rd: purple with 2 white side stripes, suspended from bar with laurel leaves

Reference: Grove 1974, 3:176, D-570–72

Mx 104

Mx 104

WORLD WAR II

IN RESPONSE to German U-boat attacks on two of its oil tankers, Mexico declared war on the Axis powers in 1942.

*Mx 105. *La Cruz de Voluntarios de 1942 y del SMN*

The Cross for Volunteers of 1942 rewarded those who volunteered for the Servicio Militar Nacional and those enlisted under the draft instituted that year.

> Obverse disc: Helmeted head, left, cactus to left and to right
> Obverse legend: VOLUNTARIOS DE 1942 | Y DEL SMN on a red enameled band
> Shape: Blue enameled Maltese cross with 2-pointed ends and crossed swords in the angles
> Size: 47 mm
> Metal: Gilt
> Ribbon: Blue, with yellow and red side stripes
> Provenance: A. Menke

Mx 106. *La Cruz del Mérito Especial (1943)*

The Medal for Special Merit is awarded to navy personnel for service above and beyond the call of duty.

> Instituted: By decree on November 1, 1943
> Obverse disc: Gilt helmsman's wheel with a national eagle in center on a white enameled field
> Obverse legend: LA ARMADA DE MEXICO | POR MERITO ESPECIAL in blue letters on a white enameled band
> Reverse inscription: CREADA | POR | DECRETO | DE 1º DE NOV. DE | 1943
> Shape: Ball-tipped Maltese cross

Mx 105

> Size: 53 mm
> Metal: Gilt
> Ribbon: Yellow, blue, yellow
> Reference: Grove 1974, 3:197, D-674

*Mx 107. *La Medalla por Servicio en Lejano Oriente*

In 1944, Mexico sent a squadron of fighter planes to the Philippines.

> Obverse: Radiant sun in disc with stars to left, right, and below, with an enameled

Mx 107

airplane above, surrounded by an orange enameled band

Obverse legend: SERVICIO EN EL LEJANO ORIENTE on a maroon enameled band

Size: 37 mm

Metal: Gilt

Ribbon: White, red with a central green pointed panel

Provenance: A. Menke

*Mx108. *La Medalla del Mérito Técnico Naval (1945)*

The Medal for Naval Technical Merit is awarded to navy noncombat personnel for merit.

Instituted: By law on December 17, 1945

Classes: 1st,* 2nd*

Obverse disc: Silver anchor on a blue enameled field

Obverse legend: MERITO TECNICO NAVAL on a white enameled band edged in red

Reverse inscription: CREADA POR LEY | DE | 17 DIC. | 1945

Shape: Square set diagonally with rayed square in the angles suspended from a national eagle, left, perched on crossed anchors above laurel branches

Size: 45 mm

Metal: 1st: gilt; 2nd: silvered

Ribbon: 1st: blue; 2nd blue, white, blue

Reference: Grove 1974, 3:193, D-650–51

*Mx109. *La Estrella del Mérito Aeronáutico Naval (1945)*

The Star for Naval Aeronautical Merit is awarded to navy personnel for merit.

Instituted: By law on December 17, 1945

Classes: 1st,* 2nd*

Obverse disc: Vertical anchor and horizontal propeller on a red enameled field

Obverse legend: MERITO AERONAUTICO | NAVAL

Reverse inscription: CREADA POR LEY | DE | 17 DIC. | 1945

Shape: Star suspended from a national eagle, left, perched on crossed anchors above laurel branches

Size: 44 mm

Metal: 1st: gilt; 2nd: silvered

Ribbon: 1st: dark green; 2nd: green with white center stripe

Reference: Grove 1974, 3:196

*Mx110. *La Medalla de Operaciones Navales de Guerra (1949)*

The Medal for Naval War Operations was awarded to navy personnel for patrolling the Gulf of Mexico against enemy submarines during World War II.

Mx 108

Mx 108

Mx 109

Mx 109

Mx 110

Instituted: By decree on March 1, 1949

Classes: 1st,* 2nd*

Reverse inscription: On the suspension bar: OPERACIONES NAVALES DE | GUERRA 1942–1945. 1ᴬ [2ᴬ] CLASE | CREADA POR DECRETO DE | 1º DE MARZO DE 1949

Shape: Crossed anchors suspended from bar with enameled multicolored diagonal lines

Size: 34 × 36 mm

Metal: 1st: gilt; 2nd: silver

Ribbon: 1st : blue, yellow, blue, yellow, blue; 2nd: yellow, blue, yellow, blue, yellow

Reference: Grove 1974, 3:198, D-676–77

*Mx 111. *La Cruz de Guerra* (1949)

The War Cross was awarded for meritorious military service at no personal risk of death.

Instituted: By decree on July 25, 1949

Classes: 1st,* 2nd,* 3rd*

Obverse disc: Head of Cuauhtémoc, left (right on some examples), on a red enameled field

Obverse inscription: CRUZ DE GUERRA | PRIMERA [SEGUNDA, TERCERA] on a white enameled band (gilt or silvered on some examples)

Reverse inscription: CREADA POR DECRETO | DE 25 | DE JULIO DE | 1949 [lacking on some examples]

Shape: Red enameled cross with jagged ends

Metal: 1st: gilt; 2nd: silver; 3rd: bronze

Ribbon: Red

Reference: Grove 1974, 3:175, D-564–66

*Mx 112. *La Legión de Honor* (1951)

The Mexican Military Legion of Honor (see Mx 16) was originally created in 1836 and rescinded in 1839. The present Legion of Honor was formed by decree on February 1, 1949. The decoration of the Legion of Honor was instituted in 1951. The decoration recognizes the sacrifices of Mexico's military in defending the country against internal and external

Mx 111

Mx 111

Mx 112

Mx 112

enemies. It may be awarded after completing thirty years of military service. Members of the armed forces who fought in the Pacific during World War II, who received the medal for naval operations between 1942 and 1945, or who received the medal for naval aviation were eligible to be admitted to the Legion of Honor.

Instituted: By Presidential Decree on May 3, 1951

Obverse: Bust of Cuauhtémoc, ¾ right, on a light blue enameled field

Obverse legend: LEGION DE HONOR on a red enameled band

Reverse inscription: POR DECRETO PRESIDENCIAL | DEL 3 DE | MAYO DE | 1951

Shape: Red enameled cross with forked ends over a design of the Aztec calendar stone suspended from the national eagle, left

Size: 52 mm

Metal: Gilt

Ribbon: Light blue with narrow yellow edge stripes

Reference: Grove 1974, 3:147, D-348

Mx113. *La Medalla de Honor Belisario Domínguez*

The Belisario Domínguez Medal is awarded to Mexican citizens who have distinguished themselves in the service of the country or of humanity. One medal is awarded each year on October 7 by the Mexican Senate in session. It is named for Senator Domínguez, who had his tongue cut out on October 7, 1913, for speaking out against then President Huerta.

Instituted: By Presidential Decree on January 3, 1953

Obverse: Bust of Belisario Domínguez, facing

Obverse legend: ENOBLECIDO A LA PATRIA | 7 DE OCTUBRE 1913

Reverse: National eagle, left

Reverse legend: ESTADOS UNIDOS
MEXICANOS | H. CAMARA DE SENADORES
1952 1953
Shape: Round, surrounded by laurel wreath
Size: 48 mm
Metal: Gold
Ribbon: Green, white, red neck ribbon
Reference: Grove 1974, 3:155, D-476

Mx114. *La Estrella y Placa del Cuerpo Médico Militar*

The Badge and Breast Star of the Military Medical Corps are awarded to army medical personnel for merit.

Obverse disc: National eagle on a pink enameled field

Obverse legend: REPUBLICA MEXICANA | CUERPO MED. MILIT.

Shape: Pink enameled star with 2-pointed ends suspended from a laurel wreath

Star disc: Serpent entwined around a mirror on a white enameled field

Star legend: REPUBLICA MEXICANA | CUERPO MEDICO MILITAR on an inner white enameled band, SERVI | CIOS | HECHOS | A LA HU | MANIDAD on an outer white enameled band

Star shape: Pink-enameled star with 2-pointed ends and 3 rays in each angle

Size: Badge: 39 mm. Star: 65 mm

Ribbon: Red, brown, red

Reference: Grove 1974, 3:182–83, D-598–99; Gillingham 1940, 23; Pérez-Maldonado 1942, 73

Mx115. *La Cruz y Placa para Divisionarios*

This cross and breast star are awarded to division-level army generals and navy admirals who have already reached the highest rank in

their service. No promotion is possible, so the badge of this award carries with it an additional 100-peso monthly pension, while the breast star carries with it an additional 200-peso monthly pension. The medal and breast star are identical for the army and the navy.

Obverse inscription: HEROI | CIDAD on a white enameled field

Reverse inscription: PERICIA on a white enameled field

Shape: White enameled cross with a red enameled eagle in each angle

Star shape: Badge on an 8-pointed star with 5 rays in each angle

Size: Badge: 32 mm. Star: 70 mm

Ribbon: 5 red and 4 white stripes

Reference: Grove 1974, 3:181, 205, D-596–97, 696–97

Mx116. *La Condecoración por Mérito contra el Narcotráfico*

Because of the growing power of the drug cartels in Mexico, the government has often called on its armed forces to combat drug-related violence. The Decoration for Merit against Drug Trafficking is awarded to military personnel and civilians for fighting drug trafficking and violence.

Classes: Order, 1st, 2nd, 3rd

Obverse disc: Gilt map of Mexico

Obverse legend: MERITO EN CAMPANA | NARCOTRAFICO on a white enameled band

Shape: Red enameled cross pattée with 8-pointed star with multiple blunt rays in the center suspended by small Mexican eagle

Ribbon: Order: green with large center black stripe overlaid by diagonal green, red, white stripes; 1st: green with wide black center stripe; 2nd: green, black, green, black,

green; 3rd: green black, green. All 3 classes
have a gilt bar on the ribbon inscribed
MEXICO

Reference: http://www.en.wikipedia.org/
wiki/Military_decorations_of_Mexico,
accessed May 4, 2013

*Mx117. *La Medalla de Valor Heróico por el Terremoto de 1985*

On September 19, 1985, Mexico suffered a cat-
astrophic earthquake. This medal appears to
have been awarded to those who responded.

Obverse disc: National eagle

Obverse inscription: ESTADOS UNIDOS
MEXICANOS

Reverse inscription: RECONOCIMIENTO |
NACIONAL | 19 DE | SEPTIEMBRE

Shape: 4-pointed star with 3 rays in each
angle

Size: 50 mm

Metal: Gilt

Ribbon: Red with diagonal band green,
white, red

CIVIL DEFENSE MEDALS

MEXICO created a civil defense force in Mexico City on August 14, 1942, the Comité Central de la Defensa Civil del Distrito Federal, three months after Mexico declared war on the Axis Powers. German submarines had already sunk three Mexican tankers, and the country was concerned about the possibility of the war reaching its shores. The civil defense force created a militia and authorized its first medal for these volunteers. As the danger of war receded, the civil defense force became increasingly involved in protecting the civilian population from natural disasters.

*Mx118. *La Medalla por la Milicia de la Defensa Civil*

The first act of the civil defense force was the establishment of an armed militia to defend the country against possible attack by Nazi Germany.

Obverse: Enameled image of militia man with a rifle in his right hand and his left hand resting on a map of Mexico

Obverse legend: MEXICO | CONFIA EN SUS HIJOS on a blue enameled band surrounded by a laurel wreath

Reverse inscription: MAYO 28 DE 1942 | COMITE CENTRAL | DE LA | DEFENSA CIVIL DEL D.F. | AL ENTUSIASMO PATRIOTICO | SEPTIEMBRE 15 DE 1943

Size: 43 mm

Metal: Gilt

Mx118

Mx118

Mx119

Ribbon: Red with a center white stripe and a narrow white stripe to the right

*Mx119. *La Medalla al Patriotismo de la Defensa Civil*

Obverse: Disc with DC in a white enameled triangle within a blue enameled band with the legend AL PATRIOTISMO within the arms of a green and white enameled V flanked by laurel branches

Obverse inscription: COMITE CENTRAL | DE LA | DEFENSA CIVIL DEL D.F. on a blue scroll

Size: 45 × 35 mm

Metal: Gilt

Ribbon: Light red, white with a red center left side stripe

ORDERS

MEXICO's earliest orders were imperial, so Mexicans have traditionally looked upon them as instruments and symbols of monarchical power. The country's only republican order dates back to 1933, and it is awarded exclusively to foreigners.

Mexico became independent on September 28, 1821, under the leadership of Agustín de Iturbide. A monarchist himself, Iturbide tried but failed to persuade King Ferdinand VII to accept the Mexican throne. Ferdinand not only refused, but he prohibited any member of his family from accepting. Lacking a suitable candidate to assume the throne, Iturbide had himself coronated as emperor.

Iturbide set out to create the trappings of a royal court, including an imperial order to bestow on his loyal supporters.

Mx120. *La Orden Imperial de Guadalupe*

The Imperial Order of Guadalupe was Mexico's first order. It only existed for the one remaining year of Iturbide's reign, so it is unlikely that many orders were actually bestowed. The order was rescinded (and recreated) twice during the nineteenth century. It became obsolete when its Grand Master, Emperor Maximilian, was executed on June 19, 1867.

For his new order Iturbide chose Mexico's most revered religious symbol, Our Lady of

Guadalupe, the Church's icon of the Virgin Mary. His choice helped Iturbide cement his relationship with the Church. It also strengthened Mexico's sense of independence, because Guadalupe is a Mexican saint. The peasant who first reported this vision was a converted Nahautl-speaking Indian.

Instituted: By Decree of the Regent on February 20, 1822

Annulled: February 1823

Grand Master: Emperor

Grades: Grand Cross (50), Knight (100), Supernumerary Knight

Obverse disc: Virgin of Guadalupe on a white enameled oval field

Obverse legend: RELIGION YNDEPENDENCIA UNION on a green enameled band (ribbon for the star)

Reverse inscription: AL | PATRIOTIS | MO | HEROICO on a red enameled field

Shape: Ball-tipped, 3-pointed cross pattée with a laurel wreath in the angles, suspended from the national eagle perched on an imperial crown

Metal: Gold

Ribbon: Green, white, and red

Reference: Grove 1974, 3:6–8, O-6–9

Mx121. *La Distinguida Orden de Guadalupe*

The Imperial Order of Guadalupe was restored as the Distinguished Order of Guadalupe by General Antonio López de Santa Anna in 1853 with new statutes. He made it a republican order and changed its design, but he retained the medallion with the Virgin of Guadalupe and the legend. The crown below the national eagle was removed. Santa Anna limited the number of Grand Cross members to twenty-four, the number of Commanders to one hundred, and placed no limit on the number of Knights.

Instituted: By a decree signed by General Santa Anna, November 11, 1853

Rescinded: 1855

Grand Master: General Santa Anna

Grades: Collar, Grand Cross (24), Commander (100), Knight

Obverse: Virgin of Guadalupe on a white enameled oval field

Obverse legend: RELIGION INDEPENDENCIA UNION on a green enameled band

Reverse inscription: AL PATRIOTISMO | HEROICO on a white enameled field

Shape: Ball-tipped, green, white, and red enameled cross pattée with rays and olive and palm wreaths in the angles, suspended from the national eagle, right.

Star shape: Badge on a ball-tipped, 8-pointed star with 7 ball-tipped rays in each angle

Collar: Badge suspended from national eagle, right; the chain consists of alternate eagles with outspread wings and small wreaths around the monogram "I S", which stands for Iturbide and Santa Anna

Size: Badge: Grand Cross: 55 × 50 mm; Knight: 40 × 38 mm. Star: 90 mm

Metal: Gold

Ribbon: Blue with violet edge stripes

Reference: Grove 1974, 3:9–12, O-11–14

*Mx122. *La Orden de Guadalupe*

When the French army occupied Mexico City in 1863, it created a regency in anticipation of Maximilian's becoming emperor of Mexico. One of the regency's first acts was to restore the Order of Guadalupe, an event that Maximilian ratified on April 10, 1864. Maximilian retained Santa Anna's design for the order, but with the crown restored. The only historically interesting difference between the two versions of the Order were the initials on the chain of the collar. Santa Anna designed a monogram with the initials "I S" (Iturbide and Santa Anna).

Mx 122
Grand Cross star

Maximilian changed the monogram to "A Y" for Agustín de Iturbide. Maximilian adopted two of Iturbide's grandsons, one of whom he hoped would succeed him as emperor, as he himself was without issue. The legend "Religión Independencia Unión" recalls the three guarantees of Iturbide.

Whereas Iturbide and Santa Anna both considered the order to be a military decoration, Maximilian added a civilian version. The Order of Guadalupe was definitively dissolved with the execution of Maximilian in Querétaro in 1867. Two medals issued to celebrate the reestablishment of the order are catalogued here as well.

Restored: By Decree of the Regent on July 1, 1863

Confirmed: By Maximilian in Miramar on April 10, 1865

Modified: By Maximilian on April 10, 1865 (creation of civilian version)

Dissolved: June 19, 1867

Grand Master: Emperor Maximilian

Grades: Collar, Grand Cross (30),* Grand Officer (100), Commander (150), Knight, Military* and Civil*

Obverse: Virgin of Guadalupe on a white enameled oval field

Obverse legend: RELIGION INDEPENDENCIA UNION on a green enameled band

Reverse inscription: AL | PATRIOTISMO | HEROICO [AL | MERITO | Y | VIRTUDES on the civilian version] on a white enameled field

Shape: Ball-tipped, green, white, and red enameled cross pattée with rays and olive and palm wreaths in the angles, suspended from the national eagle, right, with an imperial crown on its head

Mx 122
Grand Cross badge (miniature)

Mx 122
Grand Cross badge (miniature)

Mx 122
Knight (military and civil)

Mx 122
Knight (military and civil)

Mx 122a

Mx 122a

Star shape: Badge on an 8-pointed star with 7
   rays in each angle

Collar: Badge suspended from national eagle,
   right; the chain consists of alternate eagles
   with outspread wings and small wreaths
   around the monogram A Y

Size: Badge: 55 × 50 mm, 40 × 37 mm; miniature: 12 × 10 mm.* Star: 90 × 85 mm, 82 ×
   82 mm. Sizes vary slightly according to the
   maker

Metal: Gold, silver

Makers: Rothe, Vienna; Halley, Paris

Ribbon: Blue with violet edge stripes

Reference: Grove 1974, 3:13–19, O-16–27;
   Gillingham 1940, 8–9

*Mx122a. La Medalla de Oro por el Restablecimiento de la Orden de Guadalupe

The Latin inscription means "He has not done
thus for every nation."

Obverse: Virgin of Guadalupe

Obverse legend: N.S.D. Guadalupe de Mexico
   A 1803

Reverse inscription: NON FECIT | TALITER |
   OMNINATIONI

Shape: Oval, looped

Size: 35 × 28 mm

Metal: Gold

*Mx122b. La Medalla de Maximiliano por el Restablecimiento de la Orden de Guadalupe

Obverse: Head of Maximilian, left

Obverse legend: MAXIMILIANO EMPERADOR
   | 1865

Reverse: Virgin of Guadalupe

Reverse legend: NON FECIT TALITER OMNI
   NATIONI

Engraver: Ocampo

Size: 28 mm

Metal: Silver

Mx 122b

Mx 122b

* * *

MAXIMILIAN created two more orders during his reign: the Order of the Mexican Eagle and the Order of Saint Charles. Both orders ceased

to exist following his execution, and neither was revived later.

*Mx 123. *La Orden del Aguila Mexicana*

The Order of the Mexican Eagle was awarded for outstanding merit and extraordinary service to the state and to the emperor.

Instituted: By Imperial Decree on January 1, 1865

Grand Master: Emperor Maximilian

Grades: Collar (12), Grand Cross (25),* Grand Officer (50), Commander (100), Officer (200), Knight

Badge shape: Partially enameled gilt national eagle, left, suspended from an imperial crown

Star shape: Disc with national eagle, right, wearing imperial crown, surrounded by 2 bands set with round colored stones on a

Mx 123
Grand Cross badge (reverse)

Mx 123
Grand Cross

faceted cross with floriated ends and rectangular green stones set at the ends, with 7 faceted rays in each angle

Size: Badge: 45 × 38 mm, 30 × 28 mm. Star: 90 mm

Metal: Gold, silver

Maker: C. F. Rothe, Vienna

Ribbon: Green with 2 narrow red side stripes

Reference: Grove 1974, 3:20–22, O-30–33

*Mx 124. *La Orden Imperial de San Carlos*

Maximilian created the Imperial Order of Saint Charles in 1865 on the same day that he modified the Order of Guadalupe. He designed the order for his wife, the Empress Carlota, and it was awarded only to women for acts of charity and civil merit.

Instituted: By Imperial Decree on April 10, 1865

Grades: 1st,* 2nd

Obverse inscription: SAN CARLOS on a green enameled Latin cross

Reverse inscription: HUMILITAS on a green enameled Latin cross

Shape: White enameled Latin cross with floriated ends

Size: 1st: 63 × 48 mm; 2nd: 50 × 43 mm

Metal: Gold, silver

Ribbon: Red

Reference: Grove 1974, 3:22–23

* * *

ALL OF Mexico's imperial orders ceased to exist when Maximilian was executed in 1867, and none were restored. Today's only Mexican republican orders are the Order of the Aztec Eagle, which is awarded exclusively to foreigners, and the Order of Honor and Merit of the Mexican Red Cross, which has semi-official status.

*Mx125. *La Orden del Aguila Azteca*

The Order of the Aztec Eagle is awarded only to foreign citizens. It falls within the jurisdiction of the secretary of foreign affairs. The collar of the order is awarded only to heads of state. The first order was awarded in 1933 to Niceto Alcalá Zamora, president of the Second Spanish Republic. Many orders have been bestowed on foreign diplomats stationed in Mexico City at the time of their departure. The grade awarded follows standard diplomatic protocol.

Instituted: By decree on December 29, 1933

Grades: Collar, 1st class (Grand Cross),* 2nd class (Grand Officer), Star (Commander), Encomienda (Officer), and Insignia (Knight)*

Obverse disc: Gilt Aztec eagle with a red enameled serpent in its beak on a light blue enameled field surrounded by a red enameled band

Shape: Star with ornamented arms in the angles

Star shape: Disc on star with a small point in each angle

Size: Badge: 1st: 62 mm;* Encomienda: 48 mm; Insignia: 41mm;* Star: 61 mm*

Metal: Gilt

Ribbon: Yellow, with width varying with grade

Reference: Grove 1974, 3:24–27, O-40–44

Mx 125 Knight

Mx 125
Grand Cross
1st class

ORDER OF THE MEXICAN RED CROSS

THE MEXICAN Red Cross has been providing disaster relief assistance for more than one hundred years. Its beginnings date back to 1909, when a group of philanthropists led by Luz González Cosío de López provided emergency assistance for people in Monterrey affected by heavy rains. President Porfirio Díaz signed Decree No. 401 on February 21, 1910, officially recognizing the Mexican Red Cross. The International Committee of the Red Cross gave its recognition in 1912. The Mexican Red Cross awards its own order for meritorious service.

Mx 126
Grand Cross

*Mx126. *La Orden de Honor y Mérito de la Cruz Roja Mexicana*

In the absence of documentation, the names of the grades have been assigned on the basis of ribbon and design.

Grades: Grand Cross,* Knight,* Dame,* Member*

Obverse disc: Grand Cross, Knight: National eagle, left, on a green enameled field; Dame, Member: red enameled cross on a white enameled field

Obverse legend: CRUZ ROJA | MEXICANA on a white enameled band (green for Dame)

Mx 126
Grand Cross badge (reverse)

Mx 126
Dame

Mx 126
Knight

Mx 126
Member

Shape: Grand Cross: red enameled, gilt-rimmed cross with a star in each angle on a faceted 8-pointed star with 5 rays in each angle suspended from a green enameled laurel wreath; Knight: red enameled, gilt-rimmed cross with a wreath in the angles on a faceted 8-pointed star, suspended from a green enameled laurel wreath; Dame: ball-tipped, red enameled Maltese cross with gilt rim and center and 2-pointed ends with a laurel wreath in the angles; Member: ball-tipped Maltese cross with 7 rays and red enameled points on each arm and 2-pointed ends, with a laurel wreath between the arms suspended from a green enameled laurel wreath

Size: Badge: Grand Cross: 86 mm; Knight: 55 mm; Dame: 43 mm; Member: 48 mm. Star: 90 mm

Metal: Badge: Grand Cross: silver; Knight, Dame, Member: gilt. Star: gilt

Ribbon: Grand Cross, Knight, Member: White, red, white, red, white; Dame: red bow

Recipient: Grand Cross badge: José Mora, 1954

NICARAGUA

NICARAGUA declared its independence from Spain on September 15, 1821, becoming part of the Mexican Empire along with the rest of Central America. In 1823, Nicaragua joined the United Provinces of Central America and remained a member until 1838, when it was dissolved. Nicaraguans divided politically between liberals based in León and conservatives based in Granada, causing decades of civil war. Nicaragua is not known to have authorized any military medals for this conflict.

The first award attributed to Nicaragua is the Order of Greytown, also known as the Ordre Américain de San Juan. On July 13, 1854, a U.S. Navy sloop-of-war, the USS *Cyane*, shelled and heavily damaged the Nicaraguan town of San Juan del Norte, also known as Greytown in English. The Order of Greytown was instituted shortly thereafter. The literature generally classifies the order under Nicaragua on the grounds that the city of San Juan del Norte authorized it according to the certificates awarding the order. In fact, the order's origins remain a matter of controversy.

U.S. Marines landed in Bluefields on May 27, 1910, and occupied Nicaragua off and on until 1933. Toward the end of their occupation, the marines battled guerrilla forces led by Augusto César Sandino, a Nicaraguan whose name was later used by a coalition of revolutionary groups to overthrow the government of Anastasio Somoza. Before leaving, the marines organized and trained a Nicaraguan National Guard under Anastasio Somoza García, establishing a political dynasty that lasted more than forty years. The Somozas created Nicaragua's first military medals and orders of merit.

In 1979, a national insurgent group, the Frente Sandinista de Liberación Nacional (FSLN) defeated Somoza's national guard and forced Anastasio Somoza Debayle (the son of the founder of the regime) to flee the country. The Sandinistas ruled the country as a revolutionary dictatorship until 1990, when free elections were held.

Nicaragua's system of official awards can be divided into two periods: from 1932 until 1979 during the reign of the Somoza clan and after that date by a new array of orders and medals authorized by the Sandinistas and their successors. The official awards under the Somozas recognized traditional values of military valor and personal merit; the Sandinistas used their awards to promote their revolutionary ideals, while postrevolutionary administrations have chosen a middle ground.

Since 1990, different political leaders have been elected to the presidency, sometimes by the country's traditional parties and sometimes by the Sandinistas. Each president has modified the design of the country's official awards in keeping with his or her ideology.

MEDALS

Ni1. *La Cruz de Servicio Distinguido*

The Cross of Distinguished Service was awarded to Nicaraguan and foreign citizens for distinguished services to the nation.

Instituted: September 16, 1932

Obverse: Arms of Nicaragua

Obverse inscription: SERVICIO DISTINGUIDO

Reverse inscription: REPUBLICA DE NICARAGUA

Shape: Cross with 1 ray in each angle

Size: 40 mm

Metal: Gold, bronze

Ribbon: White with light blue edges and a light blue center stripe edged in red

Reference: Flores Donaire 2002, 200

*Ni2. *La Cruz de Valor*

The Cross of Valor was Nicaragua's highest military decoration and was awarded to Nicaraguan military who assisted the U.S. Marines against insurgents led by Augusto Sandino.

Instituted: September 16, 1932

Obverse inscription: CRUZ DE VALOR within a wreath

Shape: 3-armed Maltese cross with the bottom arm in the shape of a triangle containing the arms of Nicaragua. The left arm is inscribed REPUBLICA, the upper arm DE, and the right arm NICARAGUA

Size: 36 mm; miniature: 18 mm*

Metal: Bronze

Ribbon: Alternating 3 light blue and 2 white stripes with the center light blue stripe edged in red

Reference: Flores Donaire 2002, 188

Ni2

Ni3. *La Medalla del Mérito del Congreso*

The Congressional Medal for Merit is awarded for meritorious public service.

Instituted: May 7, 1937

Obverse: Arms of Nicaragua in a triangle

Obverse legend: MEDALLA DEL MERITO | CONGRESO DE NICARAGUA

Reverse: [Name of recipient]

Size: 30 mm

Metal: Gilt

Ribbon: Blue, white, blue

Reference: Flores Donaire 2002, 218

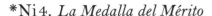

Ni4

Ni5

Ni5

*Ni4. *La Medalla del Mérito*

The Medal of Merit, which includes pins and a hat badge, was issued to officers of the United States and Nicaraguan forces during service in Nicaragua from 1926 to 1933.

    Obverse: Arms of Nicaragua
    Obverse inscription: MERITO
    Shape: Triangle
    Size: 38 × 41 mm
    Metal: Copper
    Maker: N. S. Meyer, New York
    Reference: Flores Donaire 2002, 188

*Ni5. *La Condecoración Presidente Somoza*

The President Somoza Decoration was awarded for loyalty to the president and for civil and military merit. It was abolished under the Sandinista administration.

    Instituted: 1957
    Obverse: Bust of Anastasio Somoza García, right
    Obverse legend: CONDECORACIÓN PRESIDENTE SOMOZA
    Reverse inscription: HONOR | A LA | LEALTAD

Size: 31 mm
Metal: Bronze
Reference: Flores Donaire 2002, 210
Provenance: Humberto Flores

* * *

Following the Sandinista victory in 1979, the government of Nicaragua instituted many Sandinista military medals. The Sandinistas expanded the size of the Nicaraguan army far beyond the former National Guard, which had been controlled by the Somoza dynasty. The Sandinistas introduced important changes to the country's system of medals. Many of the new Nicaraguan medals came with pentagonal ribbons patterned after the Cuban model. The standard size of a Sandinista medal was 30 mm, much as in Cuba. Most of the new medals were named after Sandinista militants who had died, often in combat. It is not known what modifications were made to the Sandinista medals after their leaders were voted out of office in 1990.

Ni6. *La Medalla "Patria Libre o Morir"*

The medal "Free Fatherland or Death" was issued for meritorious service in the military.

Instituted: 1982
Obverse: Soldier holding a rifle while throwing a hand grenade
Obverse inscription: PATRIA LIBRE O MORIR
Size: 31 mm
Metal: Gold-plated ferronickel
Ribbon: Red, black
Reference: Flores Donaire 2002, 263

Ni7. *La Medalla del Ejército Sandinista*

The Medal of the Sandinista Army was awarded to military and civilian workers for meritorious service.

Instituted: 1983
Obverse: Helicopter, tank, soldier
Obverse legend: EJERCITO POPULAR SANDINISTA | CUMPLIMIENTO DEL DEBER
Size: 28.5 mm
Metal: Gold-plated ferronickel
Ribbon: Pentagonal; red, blue, white
Reference: Flores Donaire 2002, 263

Ni8. *La Medalla de Oscar Turcios*

The Medal of Oscar Turcios was awarded for outstanding performance in directing military operations and guiding troops during combat.

The medal is named after Oscar Ariel Turcios Chavarria, who was a member of the Sandinista National Directorate at the time he was killed by the Nicaraguan National Guard in 1973. Turcios was sent as a student to the Patricio Lumumba University in Moscow, but was expelled, reportedly for Maoist tendencies. On his return to Nicaragua, he joined the FSLN. He rose in the ranks until 1965, when he was promoted to the National Directorate in charge of military operations.

Instituted: By order No. 08 of the Ministry of Defense on April 30, 1988
Obverse: Bust of Turcios, ¾ right
Obverse legend: OSCAR TURCIOS
Reverse: Arms of Nicaragua
Reverse legend: REPUBLICA DE NICARAGUA | AMERICA CENTRAL
Size: 35 mm
Metal: Gold-plated ferronickel
Ribbon: Pentagonal; red, blue, white, blue, black
Reference: Flores Donaire 2002, 265

*Ni9. *La Medalla de Camilo Ortega S.*

The Medal of Camilo Ortega S. was awarded to Sandinista military personnel who distinguished themselves in combat.

Ni 9

The medal was named after Camilo Antonio Ortega Saavedra (1950–78), a Sandinista militant and younger brother of Daniel Ortega. He joined the FSLN in 1966 and was made a unit commander of an urban guerrilla group. He traveled and trained in Cuba before returning to Nicaragua. He led a group of guerrillas that took the city of Granada in the last days of the Somoza dynasty. He was killed by National Guard troops in a shoot-out near Managua.

Classes: 1st, 2nd, 3rd*

Obverse: White enameled bust of Ortega, facing (not enameled for 3rd); inscribed on either side of his head: FSLN and EPS

Obverse legend: Variant 1: FSLN EPS | CAMILO ORTEGA S.; on Variant 2, FSLN EPS appears as an inscription flanking the bust

Size: 30 mm

Metal: 1st: gold-plated ferronickel; 2nd: silvered; 3rd: bronze ferronickel

Ribbon: Pentagonal; light blue, white

Reference: Flores Donaire 2002, 266–67

Provenance: Variant 1: A. Menke; Variant 2: Humberto Flores

*Ni10. *La Medalla de Hilario Sanchez V.*

The Medal of Hilario Sanchez V. was awarded to officers for outstanding service in military planning.

Sanchez was a guerrilla commander during the Sandinista war against the Somoza dynasty. Hilario Sanchez Vásquez was one of three guerrillas who murdered the deputy commander of the National Guard in Managua in 1978.

Classes: 1st,* 2nd

Obverse: Bust of Sanchez; inscribed on either side of his head: FSLN and EPS

Ni 10

Ni 11

Ni 11

Obverse legend: HILARIO SANCHEZ V

Size: 30 mm

Metal: 1st: gold-plated ferronickel; 2nd: silver-plated ferronickel

Ribbon: Pentagonal; dark blue, white

Reference: Flores Donaire 2002, 268

Provenance: A. Menke

THE MINISTERIO de Gobernación, or Home Office, is an umbrella ministry that includes both the Ministry of the Interior (security forces) and the National Police, each of which issued its own medals.

*Ni 11. *La Medalla de Cumplimiento de Misión Internacionalista "Enrique Schmidt"*

The Enrique Schmidt Medal for Completion of an Internationalist Mission was awarded to foreign nationals for distinguished service to the state.

Enrique Schmidt was a Sandinista militant put in command of an elite unit of the Ministry of the Interior, the Tropas Pablo Ubeda (TPU), directly under Tomás Borge. Schmidt led his unit against Contra forces, resulting in his death.

Classes: 1st,* 2nd

Obverse: Enameled bust of Enrique Schmidt, facing

Obverse legend: CUMPLIMIENTO DE MISION INTERNACIONALISTA

Ni 12

Ni 12

Obverse inscription: ENRIQUE | SCHMIDT

Reverse inscription: MINISTERIO DEL INTERIOR | REPUBLICA DE NICARAGUA

Size: 31 mm

Metal: 1st: gold-plated ferronickel; 2nd: silver-plated ferronickel

Ribbon: Pentagonal; light blue, white, with a medalet with the roman numeral of the class in the center

Reference: Flores Donaire 2002, 277–78

Provenance: Humberto Flores

*Ni 12. *La Medalla al Mérito por Servicio Distinguido "Marco Somarriba"*

The Ministry of the Interior awarded the Marco Somarriba Medal of Merit for Distinguished Service to its personnel.

Marco Somarriba was a Sandinista militant who fought with the FSLN against the Somoza family. He later worked in the Ministry of the Interior under Tomás Borge, coordinating assistance from the security services of several Warsaw Pact countries. He died in uncertain circumstances.

Classes: 1st, 2nd,* 3rd

Obverse: Enameled bust of Somarriba, ¾ left, within a pentagon

Obverse legend: MARCO SOMARRIBA | AL MERITO

Reverse inscription: MINISTERIO DEL INTERIOR | REPUBLICA DE NICARAGUA

Size: 30 mm

Metal: 1st: gold-plated ferronickel; 2nd: silver-plated ferronickel; 3rd: bronze-plated ferronickel

Ribbon: Pentagonal; yellow with a star with the roman numeral of the class in the center

Reference: Flores Donaire 2002, 278–79

Provenance: Humberto Flores

*Ni 13. *La Medalla al Valor "Pedro Arauz Palacios"*

The Ministry of the Interior awarded the Pedro Arauz Palacios Medal for Valor for distinguished service by its personnel.

Pedro Arauz joined the FSLN as a student. He staged the first hijacking of a Nicaraguan airliner to Cuba and later became coordinator of the northern front. He was captured and killed near Managua in 1977.

Classes: 1st,* 2nd, 3rd

Obverse: Enameled bust of Palacios, facing

Ni 13

Ni 13

Ni 14

Obverse legend: PEDRO ARAUZ PALACIOS | AL VALOR

Reverse inscription: MINISTERIO DEL INTERIOR | REPUBLICA DE NICARAGUA

Size: 30 mm

Metal: 1st: gold-plated ferronickel; 2nd: silver-plated ferronickel; 3rd: bronze-plated ferronickel

Ribbon: Pentagonal; blue, white

Reference: Flores Donaire 2002, 282–83

Provenance: Humberto Flores

*Ni 14. *La Medalla de Servicio Distinguido "Saul Alvarez R."*

The Medal for Distinguished Service "Saul Alvarez R." is awarded by the National Police to its personnel.

Saúl Alvarez Ramírez was a Sandinista militant. Following the Sandinista takeover, he became an officer in the National Police. He was killed by Sandinista strikers opposed to the government of Violeta Chamorro. His killing, by supporters of Daniel Ortega, produced resentment within the Sandinista movement.

Classes: 1st, 2nd,* 3rd

Obverse: Enameled bust of Alvarez, facing

Obverse legend: SAUL ALVAREZ R. | SERVICIO DISTINGUIDO

Size: 30 mm

Metal: 1st: gold-plated ferronickel; 2nd: silver-plated ferronickel; 3rd: bronze-plated ferronickel

Ribbon: Blue, white, yellow with a star with the roman numeral of the class in the center

Reference: Flores Donaire 2002, 286

Provenance: Humberto Flores

Ni15. *La Medalla al Mérito Aéreo*

The Medal for Air Merit is awarded to air force personnel and officers of friendly countries for service of importance to the air force.

Classes: 1st, 2nd

Ribbon: Blue, narrow white, light blue

Ni16. *La Medalla al Mérito Naval*

The Medal for Naval Merit is awarded to navy personnel and officers of friendly foreign countries for service of importance to the navy.

Classes: 1st, 2nd

Metal: 1st: gilt; 2nd: silvered

Ribbon: Red, blue, white

Ni17. *La Medalla de Honor al Mérito de Sanidad Militar*

The Medal of Honor for Merit of the Military Medical Corps is awarded to medical personnel for service of interest to the armed forces.

Classes: 1st, 2nd

Metal: 1st: gilt; 2nd: silvered

Ribbon: 1st: yellow with red Greek cross; 2nd: white with red Greek cross

Ni18. *La Medalla de Honor al Mérito Militar "Soldado de la Patria"*

The Medal of Honor for Military Merit "Soldier of the Fatherland" is awarded to military

attachés serving in Nicaragua from friendly countries for promoting friendship and cooperation with the Nicaraguan armed forces. The medal is also given to military personnel and civilians of friendly foreign countries who have cooperated with the Nicaraguan armed forces in responding to natural disasters and protecting the environment.

Ni19. *La Medalla de Amistad Policial*

The Medal for Police Friendship is awarded by the National Police for contributions to public order and security. The medal is given to nationals and foreigners.

Instituted: By Ministerial Order No. 018-95 and Decree No. 64-90 on August 31, 1995

Classes: 1st, 2nd, 3rd

Obverse: Arms of Nicaragua on a white enameled shield

Obverse inscription: MINISTERO DE GOBERNACION | POLICIA NACIONAL | NICARAGUA

Obverse legend: AMISTAD POLICIAL: PRIMER GRADO [SEGUNDO GRADO, TERCER GRADO]

Size: 31 mm

Metal: 1st: gold-plated ferronickel; 2nd: silver-plated ferronickel; 3rd: bronze-plated ferronickel

Ribbon: White with 2 narrow side blue stripes

Reference: Flores Donaire 2002, 287

Ni20. *La Medalla al Cumplimiento de Misión Internacional*

The Medal for Completion of an International Mission is awarded to members of the armed forces for participating in an international peacekeeping operation. Nicaragua sent 230 military personnel to Iraq in 2003 as part of Operation Iraqi Freedom, mainly engineers and medical personnel.

Obverse: Map of globe with Nicaragua
   enlarged

Obverse legend: MEDALLA AL
   CUMPLIMIENTO DE MISION
   INTERNACIONAL

Reverse: National flag of Nicaragua

Reverse legend: EJERCITO DE NICARAGUA

Size: 31 mm

Metal: Gilt

Ribbon: Blue with narrow center red stripe
   edged in white

Reference: "Nicaraguan Medal for Completion of an International Mission," *Journal of
   the Orders and Medals Society of America* 63,
   no. 4 (July–August 2012): 42

ORDERS

OUR REVIEW of Nicaraguan orders begins with the Order of Greytown, instituted in 1857. Greytown is the English name for San Juan del Norte, where the San
Juan River enters the Caribbean Sea. The order was supposed to have been awarded to
people who helped rebuild the town following its destruction by the USS *Cyane* in 1854.

Nicaragua instituted its first official order in 1947, and several more orders were
founded over the next thirty years. In 1979, a new Sandinista-dominated government
took power and created a new array of orders and medals more suited to its ideology. In
1990, Violeta Chamorro was elected president, and she introduced significant changes
to the Sandinista orders. We have documented these changes as best we could with the
information available to us.

*Ni21. La Orden de San Juan de Nicarahia [Greytown]

The Order of San Juan of Nicarahia, or Greytown in English, was reportedly given to those
who helped rebuild the town of San Juan del
Norte following a bombardment by the American warship USS *Cyane* on July 13, 1854. The
British gave the name of Greytown to the village of San Juan del Norte in 1848 in honor
of Sir Charles Grey, governor of Jamaica. The
British were making economic forays along Nicaragua's Mosquito Coast, and British troops
briefly occupied the town. They were consider-
ing building an interoceanic canal up the San
Juan River and across Nicaragua to the Pacific
coast. However, the British were mindful of
American interests in the region, and the two
countries signed the Clayton-Bulwer Treaty
on April 19, 1850, with each nation relinquish-
ing its exclusive right to a Nicaraguan canal.

An American businessman, Cornelius
Vanderbilt, began transporting people and
cargo by boat and wagon from the Caribbean to
the Pacific Ocean through Nicaragua with his
Accessory Transit Company, whose base of operations was in San Juan del Norte. For a time
Vanderbilt worked with the American adventurer, William Walker, when he became president of Nicaragua in 1856 (see Allen Menke's
article, in this volume, for other medals associated with Walker). However, the two soon became enemies when Walker in effect confiscated
Vanderbilt's canal company and transferred
control to two other American businessmen.

Ni 21
Grand Cross

Ni 21
Grand Cross badge (reverse)

Napoleon III of France had considerable interest in projecting French influence in the New World by building an interoceanic canal through Nicaragua, and he had written extensively on the subject before becoming emperor. Francisco Castellón, a president of the country in 1854–55, offered to extend commercial advantages to him if he would undertake to build the canal.

The Order of Greytown was instituted on May 1, 1857, the same day that Walker was deposed as president of Nicaragua. The precise origins, names of sponsors, and purpose of this order remain the subject of historical debate. It was not a Nicaraguan order. It was probably made in Paris, as the certificates awarding the order were written in French, and the letterhead read "Ordre Américain de San Juan." It was administered from Paris, in the name of the residents of Greytown, and the certificates were signed by the president of the order's council, a M. Martin, mayor of San Juan del Norte, who was a French citizen. The Library's collection includes the certificate of the order bestowed on M. Martin.

The inscription on the obverse of the Order of Greytown indicates in Latin that it was designed to recognize people for assisting in the rebuilding of the town following the bombardment by the USS *Cyane*. However, the elegant design, the fine craftsmanship of the order, and its probable manufacture in Paris suggest a higher purpose, most likely related to one of the competing efforts to build an interoceanic canal through Nicaragua. This hypothesis warrants additional research that exceeds the scope of this catalogue.

Instituted: May 1, 1857

Grades: Grand Cross,* Commander,* Officer, Knight

Obverse disc: 2 crossed torches tied with a

Ni 21
Commander

Ni 21
Commander

knot on a blue enameled disc surrounded by a green enameled wreath

Obverse legend: CIVES | URBIS REPARATÆ MEMORES

Reverse disc: Star on a blue enameled disc surrounded by a green enameled wreath

Reverse inscription: 1854 | 1857

Shape: Ball-tipped, 8-armed, white enameled star with metallic stripes down the center of each arm and a green enameled wreath between the arms, suspended from a tower with a blue enameled band inscribed GREY-TOWN [GREY TOWN on Commander] on front and back

Star shape: Badge on 8-pointed faceted star with 5 rays in each angle

Size: Badge: Grand Cross: 60 mm; Commander: 40 mm. Star: 82 mm

Metal: Silver

Ribbon: Crimson with a dark blue center stripe and 2 dark blue edge stripes

Reference: Flores Donaire 2002, 177

* * *

THE FIRST order known to have been instituted by Nicaragua goes back to the post–World War II period during the government of Anastasio Somoza García.

*Ni 22. *La Orden de Rubén Darío*

The Order of Rubén Darío is Nicaragua's highest award. It was instituted by Anastasio Somoza García, the first of the Somoza dynasty, a few months before leaving office. It recognizes outstanding merit in the political, economic, social, technological, cultural, and spiritual fields. The order may be bestowed on both foreigners and nationals. The current statutes were approved in 2002 during the presidency of Arnoldo Alemán of the Constitutional Liberal Party. Rubén Darío was born in León, the birthplace of the Liberal Party.

Ni 22
Collar

The order is named for Rubén Darío García Sarmiento (1867–1916), Nicaragua's best-known poet and writer. Raised in Nicaragua by an uncle, he earned a living as a journalist, part-time diplomat, and writer. He befriended Hispanic writers in many Latin American and European countries. Toward the end of his life, he read poetry at Columbia University in New York. He initiated the Hispanic literary movement known as *modernismo*. Over the years, his addiction to alcohol ruined his health, and he died prematurely at the age of forty-nine.

Instituted: February 15, 1947

Regulated: By Executive Decree No. 49 on October 5, 1951

Abolished: By Decree No. 276 of the Sandinista junta on January 31, 1980

Restored: By Law No. 433 on July 2, 2002

Statutes: Approved on September 17, 2002

Grand Master: President of the Republic

Ni 22
Grand Cross

Ni22
Knight

Grades: Collar,* Grand Cross,* Grand Officer, Commander, Officer, Knight*

Obverse disc: Bust of Rubén Darío, ¾ left, on a blue enameled disc surrounded by a wreath

Shape: Blue enameled Maltese cross with pointed ends with white enameled lyres in the upper and lower arms and white enameled swans in the side arms, and 3 rays in each angle, suspended from an enameled disc with the arms of Nicaragua in a triangle surrounded by the legend REPUBLICA DE NICARAGUA│AMERICA CENTRAL

Star disc: Bust of Rubén Darío, ¾ left, on a blue enameled disc

Star legend: ORDEN DE RUBEN DARIO

Star shape: Blue enameled Maltese cross with pointed ends with the enameled arms of Nicaragua in a triangle in the upper arm, a white enameled lyre in the lower arms, and white enameled swans in the side arms, and a green enameled wreath in the angles, on a 9-part cross with 3 rays in each angle

Collar: Badge on collar of alternating links of enameled lyres and swans within scrollwork

Size: Badge:Collar: 65 × 59 mm; Grand Cross: 49 × 43 mm; Knight: 50 × 48 mm. Star: 77 mm

Metal: Collar, Knight: gilt; Grand Cross: gilt silver

Maker: Collar, Knight: Cejalvo, Madrid

Ribbon: Blue, white

Reference: Flores Donaire 2002, 195–96; Burke's Peerage 2006, 1422–24

Ni23. *La Orden de la Independencia Cultural "Rubén Darío"*

The Order of Cultural Independence "Rubén Darío" was created by the Sandinista government as a replacement for the original Order of Rubén Darío. It remained the country's highest award for literary, artistic, and cultural merit. It is believed that this order was rescinded in 2002 and the original 1947 order reinstated.

Instituted: By Governmental Junta Decree No. 927 on January 21, 1982

Obverse: Bust of Darío, ¾ right

Obverse legend: REPUBLICA DE NICARAGUA │AMERICA CENTRAL

Size: 37 mm

Metal: Gilt

Ribbon: Blue, white

Reference: Flores Donaire 2002, 225

Ni24
Commander

*Ni24. *La Orden de José de Marcoleta*

The Order of José de Marcoleta was originally authorized in 1947 and was modified under the Sandinistas in the middle of their war against the Contra insurgents. It is Nicaragua's highest order for achievement in diplomacy and international relations to promote peace, international friendship and the defense of Nicaragua's sovereignty and territorial integrity. The country's diplomatic officers can receive the order after twenty-five years of service. It is also awarded frequently to foreign diplomats on the basis of reciprocity and after a minimum two-year tour of duty in Nicaragua.

The order is named after José de Marcoleta y de Casaus (1802–81), a Spanish-born diplomat, who first served in the Spanish diplomatic service at the Russian Court. Retired at a young age from the service for health reasons, Nicaragua appointed him to represent the nation in France. Marcoleta signed a contract with the future Napoleon III creating a canal company, but it is not clear whether the company was actually created. In 1848, he was appointed chargé d'affaires to negotiate a solution to Britain's claim to the Mosquito Coast and to San Juan del Norte. In 1849, while in the United States, he undermined a joint American-British plan giving the south bank of the San Juan River to Costa Rica. In 1850, he was named minister plenipotentiary in Spain, where he signed a treaty with Spain recognizing Nicaragua's independence and territorial integrity, including the Mosquito Coast. He died in Paris in 1881 at the age of forty-nine.

Instituted: 1947

Modified: By Agreement No. 86 of the Ministry of Foreign Affairs on July 23, 1986

Modified: By Presidential Decree No. 6-97 on February 3, 1997

Modified: By Decree No. 64-2000 on July 27, 2000

Grand Master: President of the Republic

Grades: Collar, Grand Cross, Grand Officer, Commander*, Officer, Knight

Obverse disc: Bust of Marcoleta, ¾ right

Obverse legend: ORDEN JOSE T. DE MARCOLETA | NICARAGUA

Shape: White enameled 2-pointed Maltese cross superimposed on a larger blue enameled 2-pointed Maltese cross with 7 gold rays in the angles

Star shape: Same as badge, superimposed on 3 faceted rays in the angles

Size: Grand Cross: 61 mm (after 1986, 70 mm); Commander: 67 mm

Metal: Gilt

Maker: Indústrias de la Riva, Guatemala City

Ribbon: Blue, white, blue

Reference: Flores Donaire 2002, 229–30; Burke's Peerage 2006, 1424–25

Provenance: Humberto Flores

Ni25. *La Orden General José Dolores Estrada, Batalla de San Jacinto*

The Order General José Dolores Estrada, Battle of San Jacinto is awarded to Nicaraguan and foreign nationals in recognition of outstanding service to the nation or humanity or as a stimulus for political or diplomatic merit. It was originally called simply the Order of San Jacinto, but its name was changed to the present one in 1991.

The order recognizes Nicaraguan General José Dolores Estrada (1792–1869), who defeated the forces of American filibuster William Walker at the Hacienda San Jacinto on September 15, 1856.

Instituted: By Executive Decree on September 11, 1956

Modified: By Law No. 123 on February 20, 1991, changing the name *Orden de San Jacinto* to *Orden General José Dolores Estrada, Batalla de San Jacinto*

Regulated: By Presidential Decree No. 24-91 on June 11, 1991

Grades: Collar, Grand Cross, Grand Officer, Commander, Officer, Knight

Obverse: Bust of Estrada, facing, on a red enameled field

Obverse legend: GENERAL JOSE DOLORES ESTRADA | BATALLA DE SAN JACINTO

Shape: White and blue enameled star with pointed ends and a burning torch in each angle, and suspended from an oval wreath

Ribbon: Blue, white

Reference: Flores Donaire 2002, 210, 234–35; Burke's Peerage 2006, 1425

*Ni26. *La Orden de Miguel Larreynaga*

The Order of Miguel Larreynaga was awarded to foreigners and nationals for service to Nicaragua in the fields of diplomacy and international relations. Anastasio Somoza Debayle, a liberal from León, instituted the order in 1968, during his presidency. It was rescinded by the Sandinistas in 1980.

The order is named for Miguel Larreynaga (1772–1847), a liberal Nicaraguan humanist born in León. He left Nicaragua at an early age and played an important role in the fight for independence from Spain and in the early years of the Central American Federation and in Mexico.

Instituted: By Executive Decree No 1,491 on September 16, 1968

Regulated: By Executive Decree on April 10, 1969

Rescinded: By the Sandinista government on February 6, 1980

Grades: Grand Collar,* Grand Cross,* Grand Officer, Commander, Officer, Knight*

Ni 26
Grand Collar

Obverse disc: Bust of Larreynaga, ¾ left, on a red enameled disc

Obverse legend: ORDEN DE MIGUEL LARREYNAGA on a white enameled band

Shape: 5-armed blue and white enameled 2-pointed star with 3 rays in each angle, suspended from an enameled disc with the arms of Nicaragua in a triangle surrounded by the legend REPUBLICA DE NICARAGUA | AMERICA CENTRAL

Collar: Interlocking bows interspersed with discs with the arms of Nicaragua in a triangle surrounded by the legend REPUBLICA DE NICARAGUA | AMERICA CENTRAL within concentric blue, white, blue enameled bands within a green enameled wreath

Size: Badge: Collar: 55 mm; Grand Cross, Knight: 46 mm. Star: 70 mm

Metal: Gilt

Maker: Collar, Knight: Cejalvo, Madrid

Ribbon: Red, gold

Reference: Flores Donaire 2002, 216

Ni 26
Grand Cross

Ni 26
Knight

* * *

THE FRENTE Sandinista de Liberación Nacional, which came to power in 1979, issued orders in keeping with its political ideology. In 1990, the Sandinistas lost the elections to Violeta Chamorro, a conservative. Mrs. Chamorro modified some of them. A few years later, the Sandinistas returned to power again and are be-

lieved to have modified Mrs. Chamorro's modifications. The extent and frequency of these modifications need to be clarified.

Ni27. *La Orden Carlos Fonseca Amador*

The Order Carlos Fonseca Amador is awarded to those considered to share the ideals of the Sandinista revolution. It recognizes the founder and early leader of the Frente Sandinista de Liberación Nacional. Fonseca was influenced by the Cuban Revolution and committed himself to the armed struggle against the ruling Somoza family. He trained in Cuba and traveled to the Soviet Union. He was killed in combat in 1976, three years before the Sandinistas seized power.

Instituted: 1980

Obverse disc: Bust of Fonseca, ½ right, on a white enameled field

Shape: 5-pointed star with the letters O, C, F (Orden Carlos Fonseca) respectively, on the left red enameled arm, on the top red and black enameled arm, and on the right black enameled arm, suspended from a black and red enameled bar inscribed with the letters FSLN

Size: 44 mm

Metal: Gilt

Reference: Flores Donaire 2002, 225

Ni28. *La Orden Augusto C. Sandino*

This order honors the memory of Augusto C. Sandino, who fought the U.S. Marine occupation of Nicaragua for nearly six years. Sandino was a Nicaraguan nationalist and not a revolutionary, although the Sandinistas appropriated his name to promote their cause. Sandino was finally murdered by two officers of the newly created National Guard commanded by Anastasio Somoza García.

The order is divided into three grades, each named for an important battle in Nicaraguan history. The Battle of San Jacinto was the engagement in which General José Estrada defeated William Walker in 1856; the Battle of Coyotepe took place in 1912 between U.S. Marines and Nicaraguan nationalists opposed to the American occupation; the Battle of Ocotal was fought in July 1927 between U.S. Marines and Augusto Sandino.

Instituted: By Decree of the Governmental Junta No. 851 on October 28, 1981

Grades: "Batalla de San Jacinto," "Batalla de Coyotepe," "Batalla de Ocotal"

Obverse: Bust of Sandino, ¾ left

Obverse legend: REPUBLICA DE NICARAGUA | PATRIA LIBRE O MORIR

Size: 45 mm

Metal: Gilt

Ribbon: Blue, white

Reference: Flores Donaire 2002, 224

Ni29. *La Orden "Commandante José Benito Escobar"*

The Order "Commander José Benito Escobar" was established as the country's highest order, awarded to workers for distinguished achievements in their employment. Escobar was a union activist and cofounder of the Sandinista movement. He died in 1978 near the border with Honduras. It is not known whether this order was modified after the Sandinistas were voted out of office.

Instituted: By Executive Decree No. 1,092 of the Council of State on August 11, 1982

Reference: Flores Donaire 2002, 226

Ni30. *La Orden "General Francisco Estrada"*

The Order "General Francisco Estrada" was created three years after the Sandinistas took power and was designed to encourage revolutionary action against international imperialism. Francisco Estrada was a senior military commander in Sandino's guerrilla army, known as the Ejército Defensor de la Soberanía Nacional de Nicaragua. He played a central role in fighting the U.S. Marines, and he was killed in combat.

Instituted: By Executive Decree No. 1,093 of
the Council of State on August 11, 1982

Reference: Flores Donaire 2002, 227

Ni31. *La Orden "Eduardo Green Sinclair"*

The Order "Eduardo Green Sinclair" has been
awarded to promote athletic achievements.
Green was a baseball player who represented
Nicaragua in international competition in the
1950s and played briefly in the American minor
leagues.

Instituted: By Executive Decree No. 1,094 of
the Council of State on August 11, 1982

Obverse: H with red enameled rings above
and below

Obverse inscription: REPUBLICA DE
NICARAGUA | AMERICA CENTRAL

Size: 32 mm

Metal: Gold plated ferronickel

Ribbon: Blue, white, blue, suspended from
a bar engraved ORDEN | EDUARDO GREEN
SINCLAIR

Reference: Flores Donaire 2002, 226

Ni32. *La Orden "Miguel Ramírez Goyena"*

The Miguel Ramírez Goyena Order was created by the Sandinista government to recognize Nicaraguan and foreign nationals for their
scientific and humanist development in favor
of the Sandinista Revolution. It is not known
what happened to this order after the Sandinistas were voted out of office.

The order is named after Miguel Ramírez
Goyena (1857–1927) a Nicaraguan scientist,
botanist, and teacher. His best-known work,
La flora nicaraguense, classified all of his country's plants.

Instituted: By Executive Decree No. 1,095 of
the Council of State on August 11, 1982

Obverse: Enameled geometric design

Obverse legend: REPUBLICA DE NICARAGUA
| AMERICA CENTRAL

Size: 32 mm

Metal: Gold-plated ferronickel

Ribbon: Blue, white, blue suspended from a
bar inscribed ORDEN | MIGUEL RAMIREZ
GOYENA

Reference: Flores Donaire 2002, 227

Ni33. *La Orden Bernardino Díaz Ochoa*

The Bernardino Díaz Ochoa Order was established as the country's highest award to farm
workers who improved agricultural productivity for the benefit of the revolutionary society.
It has three grades, two recognizing dates important to the Sandinista government and one
bearing the name of a Sandinista agricultural
cooperative.

Ochoa was a rural union organizer and cham-
pion of workers' rights who organized peasants
against the government in rural areas during
the Sandinista insurgency. He was killed during the uprising.

Instituted: By Law No. 35 on December 22,
1987

Regulated: By Presidential Accord No. 126 on
May 20, 1988

Grades: A: July 16, Agrarian Reform Day;
B: September 3, Anniversary of Ochoa's
death; C: Sandinista Cooperatives of
Wiwilí

Obverse: Bust of Ochoa, facing

Obverse legend: REPUBLICA DE NICARAGUA
| PATRIA LIBRE O MORIR

Size: 42 mm

Metal: A: gilt; B: silver; C: bronze

Ribbon: Blue white, blue, suspended from a
bar inscribed ORDEN | BERNARDINO DIAZ
OCHOA

Reference: Flores Donaire 2002, 231

Ni34. *La Orden Centenario de Azul*

The Centennial of Azul Order was created in 1988 to celebrate the centennial of the publication of Rubén Darío's book titled *Azul*, which established his reputation as a leader of literary modernism. It is awarded for the promotion of Hispanic literary culture, particularly that related to Darío.

> Instituted: January 18, 1988
>
> Grades: Grand Cross, Commander, Official
>
> Obverse: Bust of Darío, facing, on a blue enameled field
>
> Obverse inscription: CENTENARIO DE AZUL | RUBEN DARIO
>
> Shape: 8-pointed star with 5 rays in each angle
>
> Size: 55 mm. Star: 78 mm
>
> Metal: Gilt
>
> Ribbon: Blue, with gold stripe on its center
>
> Reference: Flores Donaire 2002, 232

Ni35. *La Orden Pedro Joaquín Chamorro*

The order was created to honor the memory of Pedro Joaquín Chamorro, who was murdered in the last days of the Somoza dynasty. It is awarded by the National Assembly to persons who perform distinguished service in defense of democracy and liberty. This was the first order created during the presidency of Violeta Chamorro.

Chamorro, who came from a conservative family, was the owner and editor of the newspaper *La Prensa*. His assassination in 1978 dramatically increased public support for the Sandinista insurgency and sparked a general uprising that overthrew Somoza on July 19, 1979. When the Sandinistas agreed to general elections in 1990, his widow, Violeta, won the election and took power from the Sandinistas.

> Instituted: By Presidential Law No. 126 on April 8, 1991
>
> Grades: Collar, Grand Cross, Grand Officer, Commander, Officer, Knight
>
> Obverse: Bust of Chamorro, facing
>
> Obverse legend: ASAMBLEA NACIONAL | REPUBLICA DE NICARAGUA on a blue enameled band
>
> Shape: Oval sun with 17 blunt rays suspended from a disc with the arms of Nicaragua in a triangle on a blue and white enameled field
>
> Size: Collar badge: 90 × 65 mm
>
> Metal: Collar: gold
>
> Reference: Flores Donaire 2002, 236–37

Ni36. *La Orden Ejército de Nicaragua*

The Army of Nicaragua Order is issued for excellence in the organization, planning, and direction of military operations. It recognizes senior officers, civilian executives, and foreign dignitaries for their service to the Nicaraguan army.

> Instituted: September 2, 1998
>
> Obverse disc: Arms of Nicaragua within a laurel wreath. Inscribed on a white enameled band above: EJERCITO; and below: PATRIA Y LIBERTAD
>
> Obverse legend: REPUBLICA DE NICARAGUA | AMERICA CENTRAL
>
> Shape: Breast star: blue and white enameled Maltese cross with 2-pointed ends and 3 rays in each angle
>
> Size: 58 mm
>
> Metal: Gilt
>
> Reference: Flores Donaire 2002, 274

Ni37. *La Orden Cultural José de la Cruz Mena*

The José de la Cruz Mena Cultural Order is the highest decoration awarded by the National

Assembly to Nicaraguan and foreign citizens for artistic achievement as composers, interpreters, promoters, and researchers of Nicaraguan music.

José de la Cruz Mena (1874–1907) was born in León. He became Nicaragua's most revered composer of classical and popular music, in particular the waltz, which he adapted from German and Austrian melodies. He contracted leprosy at an early age and composed his music for the rest of his life physically isolated outside León. He was widely admired, particularly in his hometown, where the Municipal Theater is named after him. His compositions are often considered the musical equivalent of Rubén Darío's poetry. Nicknamed "the Divine Leper," de la Cruz died of leprosy at the age of thirty-three.

Instituted: By Decree Law No. 619 of the National Assembly on May 15, 2007

Reference: Nicaragua, Law No. 619 on May 15, 2007; http://www.es.wikipedia.org/Jose_de_la_Cruz_Mena, accessed October 25, 2012

PANAMA

PANAMA's history and destiny have been determined by its location between two major oceans. Because of Panama's importance to the silver trade, Spain created an Audiencia Real de Panamá in 1538. When Latin America gained its independence in the early nineteenth century, most of the initial political boundaries followed the jurisdictional limits of the Audiencias Reales. In Panama's case, Spain had incorporated it into the new Viceroyalty of Nueva Granada in 1739 after the Bourbon reforms. Thus, when Bolívar defeated the royalist forces at the Battle of Boyacá, Panama was incorporated into the new Republic of Gran Colombia. However, the mere existence of the Audiencia Real in Panama created a sense of legal and even political independence, which was reinforced by poor land communications between Bogotá and Panama City.

By the late nineteenth century, France, Great Britain, and the United States had become interested in opening a sea route between the two oceans in either Panama or Nicaragua. Count Ferdinand de Lesseps of France, who had completed the sea-level Suez Canal ten years earlier, took the initiative and sponsored a canal through Panama with his newly created Panama Canal Company. Lesseps negotiated an agreement primarily with the leaders of Panama, despite the fact that it was still a province of Colombia. By 1880, he had raised money and started the engineering studies. The government of Panama, while still a province of Colombia, instituted a medal for Lesseps and his team of engineers. The associated certificate was signed by the president of the "Sovereign" State of Panama. Lesseps struggled to raise more money for his canal, but skyrocketing costs discouraged new investors, and the company filed for bankruptcy.

As the French lost interest in Panama, the United States became more involved. It undertook to negotiate an agreement with Colombia to build a canal, but it was not ratified by Colombia. A French shareholder of the original French Panama Canal Company, Phillipe Bunau-Varilla, encouraged the United States to back Panamanian rebels seeking independence from Colombia as an alternative solution. The Panamanians declared independence, and later that year the two sides signed the Hay–Bunau-Varilla Treaty, giving the United States the right to build, operate, and defend the canal. The United States built and then administered the canal in the Canal Zone under American law. The American army established permanent bases there to defend the canal, which was of strategic importance to the United States. During the long period of American administration of the canal, the Panamanian government did not create any military medals for merit, but it did create several civilian orders recognizing diplomatic, cultural, and political service to the nation.

The dominant American presence in Panama eventually led to tensions with the country's nationalist elements, particularly in the military. In 1968, a populist Panamanian officer, Omar Torrijos, staged a coup d'état and began pressing the United States to return the canal to Panama. After lengthy negotiations brokered by the Organization of American States, the two sides signed the Torrijos-Carter Treaties in 1977, whereby the United States pledged to turn over the canal and the Canal Zone to Panamanian sovereignty at the end of 1999.

Panama created its first military medals for meritorious service after Torrijos's coup d'état as well as several orders awarded for cultural service to the nation. After Torrijos's death in 1981, Panama began promoting a national identity through new orders recognizing the country's literature, art, music, athletes, and folk culture.

MEDALS

THE FIRST Panamanian medal dates back to 1879, when the country authorized Count Ferdinand de Lesseps and his engineers to study the feasibility of a sea-level canal through Panama. The medal was instituted by President Dámaso Cervero, and the accompanying certificates were issued in the name of "El Presidente del Estado Soberano de Panamá en los Estados Unidos de Colombia."

*Pa1. *La Medalla en Honor del Señor Conde Ferdinand de Lesseps*

The Medal Honoring Count Ferdinand de Lesseps was awarded to the study team hired by Lesseps to prepare the first engineering studies of a sea-level canal through the isthmus of Panama.

Instituted: By Law 41 of 1879

Regulated: By Presidential Decree of the Sovereign State of Panama in the United States of Colombia, January 17, 1880

Classes: Gold, silver,* bronze

Obverse: Arms of Panama on a shield between the red, blue, and yellow enameled flags of Colombia

Obverse inscription: LIBERTAD Y ORDEN on a white enameled band above the shield and FEY Y | PERSEVERANCIA | ESTADOS UNIDOS DE COLOMBIA beneath the shield

Reverse inscription: 1º DE ENERO DE 1880 | INAUGURACION | DE LOS ESTUDIOS DEFINITIVOS | PARA LA APERTURA | DEL CANAL INTEROCEANICO | DE COLON A PANAMA | POR EL CONDE | FERDINAND | DE | LESSEPS

Shape: Shield attached to an eagle, facing right, with wings outstretched, suspended from a green enameled laurel wreath

Pa 1

Pa 1

Size: 45 × 40 mm

Metal: Gold, silver, bronze

Designer: O. Roty

Ribbon: Red with yellow, blue, red edge stripes

Reference: Posada 1938, 143–44

* * *

PANAMA next instituted a medal for World War I, after it declared war on the Central Powers. Panama had neither the ability to, nor any interest in, fighting a war four thousand miles to the east, so it must have been pressured by the United States to declare war. Panama authorized its first medal as an independent nation, which was awarded to the military of countries that did fight the Central Powers.

Pa2. *La Medalla de la Solidaridad 1917–1918*

The Solidarity Medal was awarded by the government of Panama to allied combatants who fought in World War I. Panama declared war on the Central Powers on April 7, 1917, one day after the U.S. Congress did.

Instituted: 1918

Classes: 1st: commanders in chief of allied armies; 2nd: generals and senior officers; 3rd: all other ranks

Obverse: Female figure representing the republic holding a shield bearing the arms of Panama, standing in front of altar marked PATRIA and inscribed LA GUERRA DEL DERECHO

Reverse: Arms of Panama flanked by 4 flags with eagle above, inscribed 1917 at top and 1918 at bottom

Size: 36 mm

Metal: 1st: gold; 2nd: silver; 3rd: bronze

Ribbon: Red, with a blue center stripe edged in white

Pa 3

* * *

ON OCTOBER 11, 1968, the Panamanian National Guard, led by Lieutenant Colonel Omar Torrijos Herrera orchestrated a coup d'état, overthrowing the recently elected president, Arnulfo Arias Madrid. The country's constitution was annulled, and Torrijos imposed a dictatorial government with a leftist and nationalist agenda of social and economic reforms. Torrijos set out to recover Panamanian sovereignty over the Panama Canal, which he finally accomplished in 1977. He died in a plane crash in 1981. Panama created two essentially identical medals—one for distinguished service and one for being killed in the line of duty—for members of National Guard, who remained loyal to him.

*Pa3. *La Medalla por Servicios Distinguidos*

Obverse: Shield with crossed bayonets and sword on an enameled field divided horizontally blue, white, red

Obverse inscription: 11 OCTUBRE DE 1968 | TODO POR LA PATRIA

Shape: 4-pointed star with 3 rays in each angle within a laurel wreath

Size: 50 mm

Metal: Gilt

Maker: N. S. Meyer, New York

Pa 4

*Pa4. *La Medalla "Caido en Cumplimiento del Deber"*

Obverse: Shield with crossed bayonets and sword on an enameled field divided horizontally blue, white, red

Obverse inscription: 11 OCTUBRE DE 1968 | TODO POR LA PATRIA

Shape: 4-pointed star with 3 rays in each angle within a laurel wreath

Size: 50 mm

Metal: Gilt

Maker: N. S. Meyer, New York

Ribbon: Blue, white, red

ORDERS

PANAMA has instituted at least seventeen official orders for merit, covering a full range of meritorious services rendered in the political, diplomatic, military, and cultural arenas. Most of these orders have been instituted after the death of Omar Torrijos in 1981.

Panama historically depended on the United States, first to guarantee its independence from Colombia, and then to build, operate, and defend the Panama Canal. In addition, Panama has no central bank and uses the United States dollar as its main currency. Panamanian political leaders have sought to create a sense of a Panamanian nationality and identity through the institution of new orders for service to the nation. Panamanian orders promote a sense of Panamanian history, culture, and governance. In so doing, the country honors its most distinguished citizens, presents them as role models for the general population, and simultaneously identifies itself with their accomplishments.

*Pa5. *La Orden de Vasco Nuñez de Balboa*

The Order of Vasco Nuñez de Balboa is awarded to nationals and foreigners for service in the fields of diplomacy and international relations. As a militarily weak nation, Panama has had to rely on diplomatic and legal means to promote its national interests.

The order is named after the Spanish explorer who first crossed the isthmus and saw the Pacific Ocean in 1513. Panama became the key transit route for silver mined in Peru, providing unprecedented wealth for the Spanish monarchs. Panama's location as a transit hub has dominated its economic and political history to this day.

Instituted: By Decree No. 28 and Law No. 27 in 1937

Reformed: By Law No. 94 on July 1, 1941

Grade: Extraordinary Grand Cross, Grand Cross,* Grand Officer, Commander, Knight

Obverse disc: Gilt bust of Balboa, left, on a white enameled field

Obverse legend: ORDEN DE VASCO NUÑEZ DE BALBOA

Reverse: Map of Panama

Reverse legend: REPUBLICA DE PANAMA

Shape: White enameled cross pattée with

Pa 5
Grand Cross

Pa 5
Grand Cross badge (reverse)

president of the republic. The Grand Collar is restricted to heads of state. Recipients include Queen Elizabeth II; José López Portillo, president of Mexico; Frà Andrew Bertie, grand master of the Order of Saint John of Jerusalem; and Fernando Henrique Cardoso, president of Brazil. The Library's example of the Grand Cross was awarded in 1972 to Robert S. Willis, class of 1946, Resident Vice President of the First National City Bank of New York, and was donated by him in 2012.

Manuel Amador Guerrero (1833–1909) was Panama's first president after the nation achieved independence from Colombia in 1903. The order is Panama's highest award.

Instituted: By Law No. 22 on October 29, 1953

Grades: Gold Collar, Grand Collar, Grand Cross,* Grand Officer, Commander

Obverse disc: Gilt bust of Guerrero, ¾ right, on a white enameled field

Obverse legend: ORDEN DE MANUEL AMADOR GUERRERO

pointed ends with a green enameled wreath in the angles

Star shape: Same as badge, on a silver 8-pointed star with 6 rays in each angle

Size: Badge: 58 mm. Star: 80 mm

Metal: Badge: gilt silver. Star: silver

Ribbon: Purple with a narrow yellow center stripe

Reference: Burke's Peerage 2006, 1451

*Pa6. *La Orden de Manuel Amador Guerrero*

The Manuel Amador Guerrero Order was created on the fiftieth anniversary of Panama's independence. It is awarded for merit in the civic, scientific, artistic, and humanitarian fields to Panamanian and foreign civilians and military personnel. The gold collar is bestowed on the

Pa 6
Grand Cross badge (reverse)

Reverse legend: REPUBLICA DE PANAMA

Shape: White-enameled cross with an angled band with an Indian design in the angles

Star shape: Same as badge, on a 12-rayed silver star of 2-pointed and diagonal-ended rays, with 6 small rays in each angle

Size: Badge: 61 × 54 mm. Star: 80 × 77 mm

Metal: Badge: gilt silver. Star: silver

Ribbon: Yellow with narrow red, white, and blue center stripes

Reference: Burke's Peerage 2006, 1450

Provenance: Gift of Robert S. Willis, Princeton University class of 1946

Pa7. *La Orden de Manuel José Hurtado*

The Order of Manuel José Hurtado is Panama's highest order in the field of education. It is awarded every December 1 to the country's best educator and student. Hurtado (1821–87) was a civil engineer and educator. He is considered to be the founder of Panama's public education system.

Instituted: By Decree No. 412 on November 27, 1959

Modified: By Resolution No. 1,046 in 1997, 1,027 in 1998, 2,106 in 2004, and 469 in 2011

Obverse disc: Gilt bust of Hurtado

Obverse legend: MANUEL JOSE HURTADO | PADRE DE LA EDUCACION PANAMENA

Reverse: 1959 [and the year the order was bestowed]

Size: 70 mm

Metal: Silver

Ribbon: Purple with a narrow yellow center stripe

Reference: http://www.en.wikipedia.org/wiki/Category:Orders_decorations_and_medals_of_Panama; http://www.protocolo.org/internacional/america/Ordenes_y_Medallas_de_Primera_Clase_Otorgadas_por_el_Gobierno, accessed April 1, 2012

Pa8. *La Orden "Octavio Méndez Pereira"*

The Octavio Méndez Pereira Order is awarded to Panamanian citizens and foreigners who have made a significant contribution to the arts, literature, science, and education in Panama, or have otherwise served to promote Panamanian culture.

Octavio Méndez Pereira (1887–1954) was a respected Panamanian writer, educator, essayist, and diplomat. He was a cofounder of the University of Panama and served as its first president. He authored many scholarly books and is recognized for his knowledge about Spanish writer Miguel Cervantes.

Instituted: By Law No. 18 on February 1, 1966

Regulated: By decree on March 11, 1971

Grand Master: President of the Republic

Grades: Collar, Grand Cross, Grand Officer, Commander, Knight

Reference: http://gmic.co.uk/index.php?app=core&module=attach&section=attach&attach_rel_module=post&attach_id=97325, accessed April 4, 2012

Pa9. *La Orden "Belisario Porras"*

The Belisario Porras Order is awarded to Panamanian citizens for serving the cause of Omar Torrijos's government through civic action, or for exceptional scientific, literary, artistic, humanitarian, or heroic merit. This is the first Panamanian order instituted by Omar Torrijos after he overthrew his country's constitutional government in 1968.

Belisario Porras (1856–1942) was a three-term president of Panama. He initiated the country's shift from a rural agrarian economy to one based on international trade and services. He is credited with creating the National Archives and with drafting the country's penal code. He was a leader of Panama's

Liberal Party, which favored free trade and a market economy.

Instituted: By Cabinet Decree No. 132 on May 28, 1970

Grand Master: President of the Republic

Grades: Collar, Grand Cross, Grand Officer, Commander

Ribbon: Red, white, blue

Reference: http://www.gmic.co.uk/index .php/topic/21149-panama/Panama-Gentleman's Military Interest Club, accessed April 4, 2012

Pa10. *La Orden "General de División Omar Torrijos Herrera"*

The Order of Division General Omar Torrijos Herrera is awarded to Panamanian and foreign nationals for eminent service to the state; for civic virtues; for special merit in the fields of literary science, the arts, or humanities; as well as for heroic acts and recognition of a distinguished military performance.

The order is named after General Omar Torrijos Herrera (1929–81), a former commander of the Panamanian National Guard and leader of Panama from 1968 to 1981. Torrijos came to power through a coup d'état that he orchestrated against a democratically elected president, Arnulfo Arias. Politically, Torrijos was considered both a nationalist and a populist. He is best known for having negotiated the Torrijos-Carter Treaties, which returned the Canal Zone to Panamanian sovereignty on December 31, 1999. He died in a plane crash in 1981. The order was created in the year following Torrijos's death.

Instituted: By Law No. 23 on December 14, 1982

Regulated: By Executive Decree No. 336 on July 13, 1995

Modified: By Executive Decree No. 1, on January 11, 2006, making the President of the Republic the Grand Master of the Order

Grades: Civil: Extraordinary Grand Cross, Grand Cross, Grand Officer, Commander; Military: Grand Cross for Officer, Silver Grand Cross, Knight

Ribbon: Blue with 2 narrow white edge stripes

Reference: http://www.protocolo.org/ internacional/america/Ordenes_y_Medallas _de_Primera_Clase_Otorgadas_por_el_ Gobierno, accessed April 1, 2012; http:/ www.docs.panama.justia.com/23 de 1982-dec-21-19, accessed April 4, 2012

Pa11. *La Orden Nacional por Mérito y Honor al Trabajo*

The National Order of Merit and Honor for Labor is awarded annually on May 1 by the Ministry of Labor. The council of the order decides the basis for awarding each medal.

Instituted: By Law No. 10 of the Legislative Assembly on August 9, 1985

Reference: http://www.docs.panama.justia .com, accessed April 5, 2012

Pa12. *La Orden "José de la Cruz Herrera"*

The José de la Cruz Herrera Order is awarded annually to the graduating students with the best overall grade-point average at each of the country's leading universities. It is named after José de la Cruz Herrera (1876–1961), philosopher, writer, historian, editor, teacher, and diplomat. Toward the end of his career, he was appointed consul in Buenos Aires and wrote a three-volume history of Simón Bolívar.

Instituted: By Law No. 14 on July 13, 1992

Obverse: Bust of de la Cruz

Obverse legend: JOSE DE LA CRUZ HERRERA EDUCADOR FILOSOFO HUMANISTA

Reverse: JOSE DE LA CRUZ GARACHINE 1876–BUENOS AIRES 1961 [with space available to inscribe the name of the recipient, the university, and the year of graduation]

Size: 40 mm

Metal: Gilt

Pa13. *La Orden "Maria Ossa de Amador"*

The Maria Ossa de Amador Order is awarded to Panamanians who have made important contributions to social, philanthropic, educational, cultural, sporting, artistic, scientific, humanitarian, or community service and who have exhibited exceptional civic, moral, and ethical virtues.

Maria Ossa de Amador was the wife of Panama's first president, Manuel Amador Guerrero. She is credited with having helped design Panama's national flag and was widely respected for promoting social services among the country's most vulnerable citizens.

Instituted: By Executive Decree No. 135 on September 18, 1996

Grand Master: First Lady of the Republic

Grade: Grand Medal of Merit

Obverse: Bust of Maria Ossa de Amador

Reference: http://gacetas-procuraduria-admin.gob.pa, accessed April 3, 2012

Pa14. *La Orden Rogelio Sinán de Literatura*

The Rogelio Sinán Order is awarded every two years for the best work of literature by a Panamanian writer. Rogelio Sinán was the nom de plume of Bernardo Domínguez Alba (1902–94), one of Panama's most distinguished authors and poets.

Instituted: By Law No.14 in 2001 and Decree No. 47 in 2002

Obverse: Bust of Sinán

Ribbon: Purple with a narrow yellow center stripe

Reference: http://es.wikipedia.org/wiki/Rogelio_Sinán, accessed April 1, 2012

Pa15. *La Orden Cacique Urracá*

The Cacique Urracá Order is awarded to Panamanian citizens and foreigners for merit in improving the human rights of indigenous peoples. It is named after a Guaymi Indian chieftain, Urracá, who fought the Spaniards in the early years of the conquest. He was captured by the Spaniards, but he escaped and continued fighting until his death in 1531.

Instituted: By Law No. 52 in 2002

Obverse: Bust of Cacique Urracá

Reference: http://www.asamblea.gob.pa/2002_09_24_a_comi_indigena, accessed April 4, 2012

Pa16. *La Orden "Arnulfo Arias Madrid"*

The Arnulfo Arias Madrid Order is awarded to Panamanian citizens and foreigners for meritorious service in the development of democracy, literature, science, the humanities, and the arts and for accomplishments of value for a sustainable society.

The order is named after Arnulfo Arias Madrid (1901–88), a politician, physician, and writer. He was elected three times to the presidency but was overthrown on each occasion by the Panamanian military before his term of office expired.

Instituted: By Law No. 1 on January 8, 2003

Grand Master: President of the Republic

Grades: Grand Collar, Grand Cross, Grand Officer

Obverse disc: Bust of Arias on a white-enameled field

Obverse legend: ORDEN ARNULFO ARIAS MADRID

Reverse inscription: REPUBLICA DE PANAMA

Shape: White enameled cross

Size: Badge: 80 mm

Metal: Gilt

Ribbon: Red with 2 narrow blue edge stripes

Reference: http://docs.panama.justia.com/ federales/leyes/1-de-2003-jan-5-2003.pdf, accessed April 4, 2012

Pa17. *La Orden "Marta Matamoros"*

The Marta Matamoros Order is awarded to Panamanian workers who promote the encouragement, defense, and exercise of women's rights. Marta María Matamoros (1909–2005) was a defender of women's rights and improved working conditions for women. She early on organized women's labor unions and fought for maternity leave within the country's labor laws.

Instituted: By Decree No. 81 on January 8, 2006

Grand Master: President of the Republic

Obverse: Bust of Marta Matamoros

Reference: http://www.es.wikipedia.org/wiki/ Marta/Matamoros, accessed April 4, 2012

Pa18. *La Orden al Atletismo Irving J. Saladino A.*

The Irving J. Saladino A. Order for Athletics is awarded to outstanding Panamanian athletes. Recipients must be Panamanian citizens and excel at a sport either in Panama or abroad. The recipient must be between twelve and twenty-five years old.

The order is named after Irving Jair Saladino Arande (b. 1983), a Panamanian athlete. Saladino won the gold medal for the high jump at the Olympic Games in Beijing in 2008, the first and only time Panama has won an Olympic gold medal.

Instituted: By Law No. 1 on January 2, 2007

Obverse: Bust of Saladino

Reverse: Arms of Panama

Reference: http://www.asamblea.gob .pa/2006_P_261, accessed April 5, 2012

Pa19. *La Orden Nacional "Dr. Ricardo J. Alfaro"*

The Dr. Ricardo J. Alfaro National Order is awarded to Panamanian and foreign nationals who have demonstrated civic virtue in promoting peace, national identity, and human rights through legal means.

Ricardo J. Alfaro (1882–1971) was a Panamanian civil servant, diplomat, and negotiator of international treaties. He led the team that produced the Spanish version of the United Nations Universal Declaration of Human Rights in 1948.

Instituted: By Executive Decree No. 85 on June 9, 2008

Grand Master: President of the Republic

Grades: Grand Collar, Grand Cross, Grand Officer

Obverse: Bust of Alfaro

Reference: http://www.gacetaoficial.gob.pa/ pdf/Temp/14575pdf, accessed April 5, 2012

Pa20. *La Orden Manuel Zárate*

The Manuel Zárate Order is awarded annually to a Panamanian citizen for significant contributions to the search, discovery, knowledge, and conservation of Panamanian folklore. It is given simultaneously with the Dora Pérez de Zárate Prize to performers for the outstanding presentation of Panamanian folklore.

Pa 21
1st, 2nd, 3rd grades

Manuel Zárate (1899–1968) and his wife Dora promoted popular folkloric instrumental music, dance, and song. The order is administered by the National Cultural Institute, which annually awards the order and prize at the end of the National Festival of the "Mejorana," held every year in the town of Guararé, Zárate's birthplace.

Instituted: By Law No. 40 on June 30, 2009
Obverse: Bust of Manuel Zárate

Reference: http://www.glin.gov/download .action?fulltext, accessed April 4, 2012; http://www.gacetaoficial.gob.pa/ pdfTemp/18499.pdf, accessed April 5, 2012

*Pa 21. *La Orden del Halcón Gris*

The Order of the Gray Falcon was instituted during the government of Manuel Noriega.

Grades: 1st,* 2nd,* 3rd,* 4th

Obverse: Red enameled shield with gray enameled falcon

Obverse inscription: HALCON GRIS

Shape: Cross pattée with red, white, blue enamel outlines, 3 pointed concave rays in each angle; 1st: star within wreath on upper arm; 2nd: star on upper arm, 3rd: no star

Size: 50 mm

Metal: Gilt

Ribbon: Red, white, blue neck ribbon

PARAGUAY

PARAGUAY differs from the rest of Latin America in several important ways. It is the only country in the New World that never had direct access to the sea. It is the only one whose entire population speaks the language of its indigenous people. Paraguay is the only Latin American country to fight a major war with every one of its neighbors.

Shortly after Buenos Aires overthrew the Spanish viceroy, Paraguay declared its independence on May 14, 1811. The country's first leaders imposed economic self-reliance and a social structure without a racially elite upper class. Paraguay escaped the many internal wars between centralists and regional interests that dogged its neighbors. Consequently, Paraguay never awarded any medals for fighting its own people, again unlike it neighbors.

Paraguay fought two major wars: the Triple Alliance War and the Chaco War. In both cases a self-reliant Guarani-speaking nation engaged in protracted combat with larger neighbors. The Triple Alliance War caused cataclysmic casualties among Paraguay's male population and a humiliating loss of national territory. The Chaco War preserved the country's territorial integrity and restored the nation's confidence in itself. Almost all of Paraguay's medals until after World War II were related to these two wars. The country has remained at peace with its neighbors for the past eighty years. Paraguay has created a modest array of orders and medals for peacetime.

MEDALS

PARAGUAY never instituted any medals for defending its independence, since its separation from Spain was never contested by the royalists. Spain had no garrison in Paraguay, and there was no wealth worth fighting for anyway. Paraguay's declaration of independence included its separation from the Viceroyalty of La Plata. Buenos Aires attempted to retake Paraguay but had no more success than it did with Bolivia. Paraguay did not authorize any medals until the Triple Alliance War.

The Triple Alliance War began when the Brazilian Empire invaded Uruguay in 1864 to support its Colorado allies. Paraguay was allied with the Blancos and retaliated by attacking a Brazilian fort at Nova Coimbra on the Paraguay River just north of the border. The important fighting took place to the south, where Paraguay launched an offensive through Argentina and occupied the riverine port of Corrientes.

THE TRIPLE ALLIANCE WAR (1864–1870)

THIS WAR pitted Paraguay against the combined forces of Argentina, Brazil, and Uruguay. Paraguay struck the first blow in the north by assaulting the Brazilian fort at Coimbra in Matto Grosso on the Paraguay River. The Paraguayans encountered stiff resistance, but soon overwhelmed the outnumbered garrison and advanced north. They made a separate push south to Corrientes in Argentina along the Paraná River, with the goal of linking up with their allies, the Uruguayan Blancos. The Paraguayans pushed forward along both fronts but lacked the logistical ability to sustain a military operation outside its borders.

Brazil mobilized its forces and led the allied counterattack up the Paraná River, with the objective of invading Paraguay and overthrowing Francisco Solano López. Solano López authorized five campaign medals to his men, who fought with tenacity and personal sacrifice against a superior enemy. All of these medals were made in Paraguay under primitive conditions, as the country had no mint. All of Paraguay's medals during the nineteenth century were awarded for this war.

*Py1. *La Medalla de Riachuelo*

The allies quickly organized for war in 1865, as Paraguayan troops penetrated further into both Argentina and Brazil. Led by Brazil, they began moving warships and troop transports up the Paraná River to Corrientes. Solano López sent his own fleet down the river to attack the Brazilian warships anchored at Riachuelo, just south of Corrientes, and moved his Second Horse Artillery into hidden posi-

tions near the river to provide covering fire. The Paraguayans nearly won the engagement, but after a three-day battle on June 11–13, the Brazilians destroyed much of the Paraguayan fleet. The battle was the largest naval engagement in Latin American history.

Solano López authorized his country's first medal from his field headquarters in Humaitá to the men of the Second Horse Artillery Regiment.

Instituted: By Presidential Decree on July 2, 1865

Classes: Chiefs, officers,* enlisted men*

Obverse inscription: EL | MARISCAL | PRESIDENTE above crossed cannons and cannon balls

Obverse legend: AL 2o REGIMENTO DE ARTILLERIA A CABALLO within a laurel wreath

Reverse: RIACHUELO | 11 Y 13 JUNIO / 1865

Size: 30 mm

Metal: Chiefs: cast gold; officers: cast silver; enlisted men: cast copper

Ribbon: Black with narrow white edge stripes

Reference: Pratt Mayans 2007, 39–41; Gillingham 1932, 137–38

Provenance: Silver: A. Menke

Py 2

*Py2. La. Cruz de Corrales

The allies moved their forces up closer to the Paraguayan border and by the end of 1865 had entered Paraguayan territory near where the Paraguay and Paraná Rivers meet north of Corrientes. Solano López placed himself in strong defensive positions but lacked the manpower to sustain a major counterattack. Instead, he resorted to guerrilla tactics, ambushes, and unexpected sorties. On January 31, 1866, he sent a major raiding party across the Paraná River from his fort at Itapiru to attack an Argentine force near Corrales in Argentina. The Argentines anticipated the Paraguayan attack and laid an ambush. However, the Paraguayans detected the ambush early on, and the two sides fought a bloody, inconclusive battle. The Paraguayans returned to their base the following morning in good order. Solano López was pleased with the performance of his troops and authorized the Cross of Corrales from his field headquarters in Paso de la Patria.

Instituted: By Presidential Decree on February 13, 1866

Classes: Officers, enlisted men*

Obverse inscription: 31 | ENERO | 1866

Obverse legend: VENCIO EN CORRALES within a laurel wreath

Shape: Latin cross with trilobe ends, metallic inserts below ends

Size: 58 × 44 mm

Metal: Officers: silver with gold inserts; enlisted men: copper with silver inserts

Ribbon: Blue, white, blue

Reference: Pratt Mayans 2007, 35–36; Gillingham 1932, 138

Provenance: A. Menke

*Py3. La Medalla de Tataiyba

Numerous battles and skirmishes were fought during the two years that the allies moved up the Paraguay River toward the key Paraguayan fortress at Humaitá. On October 21, 1867, a Paraguayan cavalry regiment was ambushed by a superior Brazilian force at Tataiyba. The Paraguayans suffered heavy casualties but managed to get back to their lines. Solano López was pleased with the resourcefulness and resolve of his men and authorized a medal from his field headquarters at Paso Pucú for the survivors.

Instituted: By Presidential Decree on October 24, 1867

Classes: Chiefs, officers,* enlisted men

Obverse: Mounted cavalryman with lance

Obverse legend: EL MARISCAL LOPEZ A LOS VALIENTES DE TATAIYBA

Reverse inscription: 21 | DE | OCTUBRE | 1867 within a laurel wreath

Size: 30 mm

Metal: Chiefs: gold; officers: silver; enlisted men: copper

Ribbon: Red, yellow

Py3

Py3

Reference: Pratt Mayans 2007, 45–47; Gillingham 1932, 140

Provenance: A. Menke

*Py4. *La Medalla de Tuiuti*

The allies sought to flank the Humaitá fortress by land. López lacked the forces to defeat
them, but he undertook a daring attack on the
allied supply hub at Tuiuti on November 3. His
troops achieved total surprise and routed the
camp's garrison. The Paraguayans captured
military supplies, but they suffered heavy casualties. From his headquarters at Paso Pucú,
Solano López authorized a medal for all the
men who fought at Tuiuti.

Instituted: By Presidential Decree on November 15, 1867

Classes: Chiefs, officers, enlisted men*

Obverse: Military trophies and flags

Obverse legend: EL MARISCAL LOPEZ A LOS
BRAVOS DE TUIUTI

Reverse inscription: 3 | DE | NOVIEMBRE | 1867
within a laurel wreath

Size: 35 mm

Metal: Chiefs: gold; officers: silver; enlisted
men: bronze

Ribbon: Green, blue

Designer: Charles [signature on the medal]

Reference: Pratt Mayans 2007, 51–53;
Gillingham 1932, 138–40

*Py5. *La Cruz de Acaiuasá*

By mid-1868, Argentine and Brazilian troops
were operating in the Chaco across the river
from Humaitá. Both sides were laying ambushes. A Paraguayan ambush on July 18, 1868,
caused heavy casualties to an Argentine force at
Acaiuasá. Solano López authorized a cross from
his field headquarters at San Fernando for that
action. The battle did little to change the direction of the war, but it highlighted Paraguay's
resourcefulness in slowing the allied advance.

Py 4

Py 4

Py 5

Py 5

Instituted: By Presidential Decree on July 24, 1868

Grades: 1st: chiefs; 2nd: officers; 3rd: enlisted men* (no 1st or 2nd known to exist)

Obverse disc: Star

Obverse legend: ACAIUASA 18 DE JULIO | 1868

Reverse disc: Star

Reverse legend: A LA DECISION Y BRAVURA

Shape: Ball-tipped Maltese cross with 2-pointed ends

Size: 38 mm

Metal: 1st: gold with blue enamel; 2nd: silver with gold adornments; 3rd: silver

Ribbon: 6 alternating blue and red stripes

Reference: Pratt Mayans 2007, 57–59; Gillingham 1932, 140

Provenance: A. Menke

*Py6. *La Medalla de la Campaña de Amambay*

President Solano López awarded the Medal for the Amambay Campaign in the last days of his

government to his remaining loyal troops. His enemies had occupied his capital city and were hunting him down in the hilly lands of Mbaracayu in the northeastern Amambay region. Solano López was shot and killed by Brazilian soldiers less than a week after he signed this decree. He had called for making gold medals with diamonds and rubies, but this luxury far exceeded the financial means of the country's treasury. The medal was officially instituted seventy-five years later.

Authorized: By Presidential Decree on February 25, 1870

Instituted: By Presidential Order No. 21 on March 1, 1945

Classes: 1st, 2nd, 3rd*

Obverse: Star within laurel wreath

Obverse legend: VENCIO PENURIAS Y FATIGAS

Reverse: 5 hills

Reverse legend: EL MARISCAL LOPEZ

Reverse inscription: CAMPAÑA | DE | AMAMBAY | 1870

Size: 37 × 27 mm

Metal: 1st: silver; 2nd: bronze; 3rd: copper

Ribbon: Orange with red edge stripes

Engraver: Chiola

Provenance: A. Menke

Reference: Pratt Mayans 2007, 236–37

*Py7. *La Medalla Conmemorativa al General Bernardino Caballero*

The Commemorative Medal to General Bernardino Caballero recognized his military leadership in the Triple Alliance War. The reverse of the medal lists the following battles in which he commanded the Paraguayans: Isla Tayi (October 3, 1867), Tataiyba (October 21, 1867), Acaiausá (July 18, 1868), Ytororó (December 6, 1868), Abaí (December 11, 1868), Lomas Valentinas (December 12, 1868), and Rubio Ñu (August 16, 1869).

Classes: Chiefs, officers,* enlisted men

Obverse: Bust of General Caballero, ¾ right

Obverse legend: GENERAL B CABALLERO

Reverse: Sitting lion beneath Liberty cap

Reverse legend: ITORORO | RUBIO ÑU | LOMAS
VALENTINAS | ACAYUAZA | ISLA TAYI |
ABAY | TATAYIBA

Reverse inscription: PAZ Y JUSTICIA

Shape: Irregular

Size: 32 mm, but uneven

Metal: Chiefs: gold; officers: silver; enlisted
men: bronze

Ribbon: Blue, white, red

Engraver: J. Gottuzzo

Provenance: A. Menke

* * *

THE END of the Triple Alliance War brought foreign occupation. The allies would not allow Paraguay to have a regular army until the turn of the century, when they permitted the country to reorganize its armed forces.

*Py8. *La Medalla de la Guardia Nacional*

In 1901, Paraguay authorized a medal for its National Guard. The country had instituted mandatory military service for men between the ages of eighteen and twenty, followed by a tour in the reserves until the age of twenty-eight, then the National Guard until the age of thirty-nine, and finally in the Territorial Guard until the age of forty-five.

Py 8

Py 8

Instituted: 1901

Classes: Chiefs,* officers,* enlisted men

Obverse: Soldier holding a rifle

Obverse legend: ORGANIZACIÓN
   DE LA GUARDIA NACIONAL │ 1ᴬ
   CIRCUNSCRIPCIÓN

Reverse: Lion in front of a Liberty cap surrounded by a wreath and topped by a star

Reverse legend: REPÚBLICA DEL
   PARAGUAY │ 25 DE NOVIEMBRE
   1901

Size: 28 mm

Metal: Chiefs: gold;* officers: silver;*
   enlisted men: bronze

Engraver: Chiefs: BYR

The Chaco War (1932–1935)

Paraguayan and Bolivian troops had been skirmishing in the Chaco for some years. Few people lived there, but rumors circulated of oil riches. The war started on June 15, 1932, when Bolivian soldiers attacked a small Paraguayan fort on Lake Pitiantuta. The Paraguayans retook the fort one month later, and hostilities began in earnest.

The Bolivians had the advantage in equipment and population size, but they lacked competent political and military leadership. Bolivia's officer corps consisted mainly of Spanish-speaking creoles, while the bulk of its foot soldiers were Aymara or Quechua-speaking Indians from the Altiplano. The Paraguayans had the advantage of a more unified and competent political and military leadership. Its officers and men were mainly mestizos and could communicate with each other in either Spanish or Guarani. Paraguay's supply lines into the Chaco were much shorter, and a rail line existed from Puerto Casado on the Paraguay River into the heart of the Chaco.

The Paraguayans took the offensive early on and gradually moved northwest toward Bolivia. The war was finally settled by international mediation. The Paraguayans were awarded 80 percent of the Chaco, but the 20 percent that went to Bolivia contained most of the oil and gas.

Paraguay authorized three medals for those who participated in the war. None of the medals were for specific battles.

*Py9. *La Medalla por la Entrega de Oro*

Paraguay had a small tax base to pay for the war against Bolivia in the Chaco. The government called on women to donate their gold wedding rings to the treasury to help cover the war bills. The government created an iron medal in recognition of the women who made this contribution.

Obverse: Star within palm and laurel branches

Obverse inscription: ENTREGÓ ORO PARA LA VICTORIA | LA PATRIA | AGRADECIDA | 1932 | 1933

Obverse legend: REPUBLICA DEL PARAGUAY

Reverse: [Number of recipient engraved] 149

Shape: Shield

Size: 30 × 30 mm

Metal: Iron

Ribbon: Red, white, blue

Provenance: A. Menke

*Py9a. *La Argolla de la Victoria*

The government made an iron replacement ring for the women who received the above medal.

Inscription: ORO DEFENSA [star] NACIONAL

Shape: Wedding band given to the wife as a replacement for the wedding ring she gave to pay for the war

Metal: Iron

Provenance: A. Menke

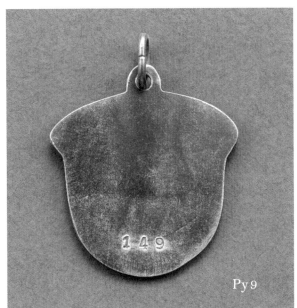

Py 9

Py 9

Py 9a

Py 9a

Py 9a

*Py10. *La Cruz del Defensor*

The Defender's Cross was awarded to individuals and units from both the army and the navy for meritorious service in the war. The medal was awarded to any man involved in the conflict, even if he did not directly engage in combat. The medal was also awarded to those killed in action, hospitalized, wounded, or mutilated while on active duty. For merit above and beyond the call of duty, the government awarded a distinction consisting of a gilt metallic palm attached to the medal's ribbon. The accompanying certificate detailed the circumstances of the special distinctions.

The medal could also be conferred on entire units, and they too were eligible to receive a special distinction. A regimental or ship distinction added a steel pin with parallel bars on the ribbon. A division or naval task force distinction added a silver star on the ribbon. An army or fleet distinction added a gold star. A field army would receive a gold star surrounded by a laurel and olive wreath. When a unit received this medal, it was placed on the unit's banner.

Py 10

Instituted: By Law No. 1,339 on August 10, 1933

Regulated: By Presidential Decree No. 49,326 on October 3, 1933

Modified: Decree No. 7,813 on December 22, 1936, authorizing the Commander of the Army in the Chaco to award the Chaco Cross to all officers who had already received the Defender's Cross

Modified: Decree No. 572 on December 22, 1936, awarding the Defender's Cross to all officers and enlisted men who participated in the Chaco War

Classes: Officers, enlisted men*

Obverse inscription: CRUZ | DEL DEFENSOR

Py 10

Shape: Cross superimposed on a cross pattée with a wreath in the angles, small star between palm and laurel branches in the upper arm

Size: 38 mm

Metal: Officers: silver; enlisted men: bronze

Ribbon: Blue with narrow red and white edge stripes on both sides; some were issued with ribbons with the Paraguayan colors—red, white, blue. Officers: neck ribbon; enlisted men: chest ribbon

Reference: Pratt Mayans 2007, 179–83, 198–200

*Py11. *La Cruz del Chaco*

The Chaco Cross was awarded to individuals or military units from the army and navy that participated in the Chaco War. The rules for awarding the medal were similar to those set out for the Defender's Cross.

Instituted: By Law No. 1,339 on August 10, 1933

Regulated: By Presidential Decree No. 49,326 on October 3, 1933

Classes: Officers, enlisted men*

Obverse disc: Star between palm and laurel branches

Obverse legend: CRUZ DEL CHACO

Reverse inscription: REPUBLICA | DEL | PARAGUAY

Shape: 2 superimposed crosses with crossed swords in the angles

Size: 45 mm

Metal: Officers: silver; enlisted men: bronze*

Ribbon: Red with narrow red, white, and blue edge stripes; some were issued with the Paraguayan national colors—red, white, blue

Reference: Pratt Mayans 2007, 179–96

Py 11

Py 11

*Py12. *La Medalla del Reconocimiento Paraguayo*

The Medal of Paraguayan Recognition was awarded to individuals and institutions that cooperated in the defense of the nation but were not members of the armed forces. When the medal was awarded to an institution, it was attached to that institution's banner. Individuals working at that institution had the right to wear a ribbon bar.

> Instituted: By Law No. 1,339 on August 10, 1933
>
> Regulated: By Decree No. 10,801 on December 16, 1938
>
> Modified: By Decree No. 11,934 on February 18, 1939 (changing the inscription on the reverse from relief to incuse)

Classes: Chiefs, officers, enlisted men*

Obverse: Star between palm and laurel branches

Obverse legend: MEDALLA DE RECONOCIMIENTO PARAGUAYO

Reverse inscription: REPÚBLICA | DEL | PARAGUAY | 1932 | 1935 surrounded by a wreath

Shape: Oval

Size: 41 × 30 mm

Metal: Chiefs: gold; officers: copper; enlisted men: bronze

Ribbon: Olive green with narrow red, white, and blue edge stripes; some were issued with the Paraguayan national colors—red, white, blue

Maker: Casa José F. Piana, Buenos Aires

Reference: Pratt Mayans 2007, 208–14

Py 13

Py 13

*Py13. *La Medalla Conmemorativa de la Victoria de Boquerón*

The Commemorative Medal for the Victory at Boquerón was awarded to officers, enlisted men, and military units that participated in the Battle

of Boquerón in 1932. The war had just broken out, and the Paraguayans were anxious to take as much territory as possible before the Bolivians were able to move their heavy weaponry into the Chaco. On September 9, 1932, Colonel (later Marshal) Estigarribia attacked the Bolivian fort at Boquerón. After a three weeks' siege, Estigarribia launched an all-out assault and took the fort on September 29.

> Instituted: By Decree Law No. 15,714 on November 25, 1942
>
> Awarded: By Decree No. 7,390 on September 29, 1949, to institutional recipients
>
> Awarded: By Decree No. 7,391 on September 29, 1949, to officers and enlisted men
>
> Classes: Chiefs, officers,* enlisted men
>
> Obverse: Star between palm and laurel branches
>
> Obverse legend: REPUBLICA DEL PARAGUAY
>
> Reverse inscription: BOQUERON | 29-IX-32 within a laurel wreath
>
> Size: 30 mm
>
> Metal: Chiefs, officers: silver; enlisted men: bronze
>
> Ribbon: Chiefs, officers: yellow with red edge stripes; enlisted men: red, white, blue
>
> Reference: Pratt Mayans 2007, 216–19

* * *

AFTER THE Chaco War, Paraguay had no further need for military medals in wartime. The country authorized new medals for good conduct, length of service, merit, professionalism, and loyalty.

*Py14. *La Medalla del Ministerio de Defensa Nacional*

The available literature contains no information on this medal.

Py 14

Py 14

Obverse: Star on red, white, blue enameled field between palm and laurel branches

Obverse legend: REPUBLICA DEL PARAGUAY

Reverse: Wreath

Reverse legend: MINISTERIO DE DEFENSA NACIONAL

Shape: Octagonal

Size: 32 × 30 mm

Metal: Silver

Ribbon: Horizontal red and blue stripes divided by a narrow white stripe; bronze palm frond attached

Py15. *La Medalla de Honor al Mérito de las Fuerzas Armadas*

The Medal of Honor for Merit of the Armed Forces is the most important of a series of medals for merit awarded to members of the armed forces and its different branches.

Instituted: By General Order No. 10 on March 5, 1955

Obverse: An open wreath with the arms of Paraguay near the top

Reverse inscription: HONOR / AL / MERITO

Reverse legend: REPUBLICA DEL PARAGUAY / FF.AA. DE LA NACION

Shape: Oval

Size: 35 × 29 mm

Metal: Gilt

Ribbon: Red with blue, white, and red edge stripes

Reference: Pratt Mayans 2007, 265–71

Py16. *La Medalla de Honor al Mérito de la Policia Nacional*

The Medal of Honor for Merit of the National Police serves the same purpose as the previous medal for the armed forces.

Obverse disc: Relief map of Paraguay

Obverse legend: ORDEN Y PATRIA | POLICIA PARAGUAY

Shape: Star within laurel branches

Size: 35 mm

Metal: Gilt

Ribbon: Red, white, blue

Reference: Pratt Mayans 2007, 281

ORDERS

PARAGUAY has two orders of merit, one for the military and one for both civilians and the military.

*Py17. *La Orden Nacional del Mérito*

The National Order of Merit is Paraguay's highest award and also its oldest. It is bestowed on both civilians and military personnel, including both Paraguayan and foreign nationals. It was originally instituted by Solano López shortly after he declared war on Argentina during the Triple Alliance War, and he bestowed the order on his officers for courage in battle. He originally intended to make several grades but was technically only able to make one grade in chased gold. The decoration was a five-pointed, ball-tipped star with crossed cannon in the angles and superimposed on a laurel wreath. The ribbon was purple with narrow red, white, and blue stripes on either side.

The order fell into disuse following Paraguay's defeat but was reestablished in 1939. It was modified in that same year to limit the number of Grand Cross recipients to 50, Grand Officer to 150, Commander to 200, Officer to 250, and Knight to 350. Although originally intended for military officers, the new statutes made both civilians and the military eligible to receive it.

Instituted: On April 8, 1865 (for military recipients only)

Reestablished: By Law No. 125 on June 23, 1939, making foreigners eligible, changing the date on the reverse to 1939, and changing the diameters of all grades

Modified: By Decree No. 18,221 on November 22, 1939, limiting the number of awards per grade

Modified: By Law No. 394 on September 7, 1956, increasing the number of grades from

Py 17
Officer

Py 17
Officer

Py 17
Collar

5 to 7, limiting the Collar to heads of state, annulling Law No. 125 and Decree No. 18,221, and changing the date on the reverse to 1865

Grand Master: President of the Republic

Grades: Collar,* Extraordinary Grand Cross, Grand Cross,* Grand Officer, Commander, Officer,* Knight

Obverse disc: Collar: bust of Francisco Solano López, facing; other grades: lion's head

Obverse legend: Collar: MARISCAL FRANCISCO SOLANO LOPEZ | HONOR ET GLORIA; other grades: HONOR | ET GLORIA

Reverse disc: Collar: 1865 [or 1939] on a gilt field

Reverse legend: PRAEMIVM | MERITI

Shape: Ball-tipped, white enameled star with 3 rays in each angle and a green enameled wreath in the angles, suspended by ribbons from a green enameled wreath

Py 17
Collar
(reverse)

Py 17
Grand
Cross

Py 17
Grand
Cross
badge
(reverse)

Star shape: Like badge but not enameled, 5 rays in each angle

Collar shape: Alternating links of badge and star

Size: Badge: Collar: 70 × 63 mm; Extraordinary Grand Cross, Grand Cross, Grand Officer, Commander: 70 × 60 mm; Officer, Knight: 47 × 41 mm. Star: Extraordinary Grand Cross, Grand Cross: 95 mm

Metal: Badge: gilt. Star: silver

Maker: Collar: Casa Mazzetti, Buenos Aires

Ribbon: Red with blue, white, and red center stripes edged in white

Reference: Pratt Mayans 2007, 241–62; Burke's Peerage 2006, 1453–55; Gillingham 1932, 336–37; Werlich 1974, 337–38

*Py 18. *La Orden al Mérito Militar*

The Order of Military Merit is Paraguay's second-highest military award. It may be awarded to foreign military personnel on the basis of reciprocity, provided the recipient served in Paraguay for at least two years.

Instituted: February 18, 1957

Grand Master: President of the Republic

Grades: Grand Cross,* Grand Officer, Commander, Officer, Knight*

Obverse disc: Star between palm and laurel branches

Obverse legend: REPUBLICA DEL PARAGUAY | AL MERITO MILITAR

Reverse legend: VENCER O MORIR

Shape: Ball-tipped star

Star shape: Badge with 3 rays in each angle

Size: Badge: 48 mm. Star: 72 mm

Metal: Badge: white metal; disc is gilt bronze except for Knight. Star: white metal, disc gilt bronze

Ribbon: Red, white

Reference: Pratt Mayans 2007, 272–73; Burke's Peerage 2006, 1453–54; Werlich 1974, 338

Py 18
Grand
Cross badge (reverse)

Py 18
Grand
Cross

Py 18
Knight

Py 18
Knight

*Py 19. *La Orden del Teniente José María Fariña*

The Order of Lieutenant José María Fariña is a navy order for meritorious service to the Navy. Lieutenant Fariña (1836–1915) joined the Paraguayan navy and fought in the Triple Alliance War. He commanded a flotilla of small gunboats that bombarded the Brazilian fort at Coimbra, the first battle of the war. He is best known for having damaged larger Brazilian warships with his boat armed with one cannon at the Battle of Riachuelo.

Obverse disc: Bust of Fariña, left

Obverse legend: TTE 1º JOSE MARIA FARIÑA on a blue enameled band

Shape: White enameled star with anchors in the angles

Size: 55 mm

Metal: Gilt

Ribbon: Light blue with red, white, blue side stripes; neck ribbon

Provenance: A. Menke

Py 19

Py 20

*Py20. *La Orden del Teniente Silvio Pettirossi*

The Order of Lieutenant Silvio Pettirossi is an air force order for meritorious service to the air force. Silvio Pettirossi (1887–1917) was an aviation pioneer famous for his aerobatic prowess.

Obverse disc: Bust of Pettirossi with aviator's glasses, ¾ right

Obverse legend: TTE 1º SILVIO PETTIROSSI on a blue enameled band

Star shape: White enameled star with eagles with displayed wings in the angles on an 8-pointed sun with convex ends and 5 rays with convex ends in each angle

Size: 75 mm

Metal: Gilt star on white metal sun

Provenance: A. Menke

PERU

ARGENTINE General José Francisco de San Martín proclaimed Peru's independence in Lima on July 28, 1821, after the Spanish viceroy La Serna withdrew royalist forces from the city. He awarded Peru's first medals for fighting the royalists as well as its first order of merit—the Order of the Sun, an order that remains today Peru's highest award. Independence could not be consolidated, however, as royalist forces had regrouped in the high Andes, where they were supported by part of the Indian population. The royalists outnumbered San Martín's own army, and he preferred to support irregular Peruvian revolutionaries rather than face the royalists directly. San Martín turned to Bolívar for help. The two met in Guayaquil but failed to coordinate their efforts. Instead, San Martín resigned his commission and left in permanent exile for Europe.

Bolívar assumed the role of liberator and trained a new army, which defeated the royalist army at the Battle of Ayacucho in 1824. Peru awarded military medals for the officers and men from five Latin American countries who fought at Ayacucho. Spain still maintained a garrison inside the Real Felipe fortress in Callao, which held out for two years before surrendering. Peru authorized a medal for the siege of Callao, which ended Spain's military presence in South America.

Spain's defeat did not bring peace to Peru. Ambitious political leaders jockeyed for power inside the country and sought to expand Peru's frontiers, first at the expense of Ecuador and then Bolivia. Gran Colombia defeated the Peruvians at the Battle of Tarqui and annexed Ecuador. Peru's relations with Bolivia proved more complicated. Caudillos from both countries fought each other for the right to lead a union of both nations. General Andrés de Santa Cruz briefly succeeded in creating a Peru-Bolivian Confederation, which led to a war with Chile. The Confederation was forced to disband. Peru awarded several medals to its military who fought in the War of the Confederation. Peru also fought a running naval war, known as the Chincha Islands War, against a Spanish squadron. The war ended in 1866, when the Spanish squadron withdrew following an exchange of fire with the Peruvian coastal defenses at Callao. Peru awarded medals to its military for the naval battle at Abtao and the defense of Callao.

Peru and Bolivia continued searching for ways to forge a closer union, signing an ill-fated secret mutual defense treaty, aimed primarily at Chile. When Bolivia became embroiled in a dispute over taxing Chilean mines in Bolivian territory, the existence of this treaty became known, and Chile declared war. The War of the Pacific proved disastrous for Peru. Its ally Bolivia withdrew its troops soon after the war started, leaving Peru alone to face the Chilean invasion. Peru authorized at least one military medal during the war.

Peru has remained at peace with its neighbors ever since, except for several border skirmishes with Ecuador over poorly marked frontiers. Peru authorized medals in connection with this conflict. Peru's security problems in the past fifty years have been caused by a Maoist insurgency known as the Sendero Luminoso and by drug traffickers operating in the eastern slopes of the Andes.

After World War II, Peru began to institute an array of orders of merit for its military and diplomatic services and for meritorious service to the state. Peru established these orders as part of its long-standing efforts to create a functioning democratic government.

MEDALS

PERU began issuing military medals shortly after it declared independence. José de San Martín, acting as Protector of Peru, authorized the country's first medals for that war, although many of them were awarded to soldiers from other Latin American countries who participated in the struggle to defeat the royalists.

Pe1. *La Medalla al Batallón Numancia*

Because of the numerical inferiority of his forces, San Martín encouraged royalist units to join his army. The defection of the Numancia Battalion was the most important royalist military unit to abandon the viceroy. The battalion had been formed in New Granada and consisted mainly of native American troops under the command of Colonel Thomas Heres. It had been sent to Peru with modern weaponry to reinforce the viceroy in Lima. San Martín sent allies to encourage the men to defect. On December 2, 1820, Colonel Heres joined San Martín with his entire battalion. His defection made it possible for San Martín to occupy Lima. San Martín, who had not yet been named Protector of Peru, created a medal on his own initia-

tive as commander in chief. It was struck at the Lima mint.

Instituted: By Decree of San Martín on December 4, 1820

Obverse: Crossed sword and dagger within a wreath

Obverse legend: A LA LEALTAD DE LOS MAS BRAVOS

Reverse: Radiant sun

Reverse legend: Radiant sun surrounded by inscription LIMA | EJERCITO LIBERTADOR

Shape: Reversed letter S, suspended by a ring

Metal: Gold

Ribbon: Red, white

Maker: Casa Nacional de la Moneda, Lima

Reference: Argentina 1910, *33–35*; Gillingham 1932, *146–47*

Pe2. *La Medalla de Pasco*

The Spanish viceroy in Lima sent a force under the command of Diego Reilly to intercept a joint Peruvian-Chilean division led by a Chilean officer, Alvarez de Arenales. The revolutionaries attacked O'Reilly's defensive positions and dislodged them in a successful bayonet charge near the town of Cerro de Pasco on December 6, 1820. San Martín, as "liberator," authorized his second medal to the victors at Pasco.

Instituted: By decree of San Martín on December 6, 1820

Classes: Chiefs, officers

Obverse: Rising sun surrounded by palm and laurel branches

Obverse inscription: A LOS | VENCED° | RES DE | PASCO

Reverse inscription: DIC. 6 | DE | 1820

Shape: Oval attached to a bar

Size: 27.5 × 24 mm

Metal: Chiefs: gold; officers: silver

Ribbon: Red, white

Reference: Argentina 1910, 3:35–40; Gillingham 1932, 147

Pe3. *La Medalla por la Batalla de Pichincha*

The Peruvian government authorized its first military medal for Peruvian officers and soldiers who fought at the Battle of Pichincha in Ecuador on May 24, 1822. Revolutionary forces included a Gran Colombian division, a Peruvian division sent by San Martín, and Ecuadorean troops—all under the command of General Antonio José de Sucre. The revolutionaries were marching toward Quito, which was defended by royalist forces under Melchor de Aymenich. When Aymenich spotted the allied forces marching across the side of the Pichincha volcano, he launched an attack that nearly succeeded. But a British battalion appeared on the battlefield at a critical moment, and the momentum shifted to the allies. Aymenich capitulated the next day. The Battle of Pichincha was one of the key revolutionary victories, as it allowed the Cabildo of Quito to declare Ecuador's independence. Peru authorized a medal for its officers and men who fought at Pichincha.

Instituted: By Supreme Decree on July 1, 1822

Classes: Chiefs, officers, noncommissioned officers, enlisted men

Obverse inscription: A LOS LIBERTADORES DE QUITO above military trophies

Reverse inscription: LA PATRIA AGRADECIDA above military trophies

Metal: Chiefs, officers: gold; noncommissioned officers, enlisted men silver

Ribbon: Neck ribbon; chiefs, officers, noncommissioned officers: red; enlisted men: white

Reference: Argentina 1910, 3:83; Gillingham 1932, 147–50; Dargent Chamot 2012, 8–9

Pe4. *La Medalla a las Partidas de Guerrilla*

San Martín authorized the Medal for Guerrilla Bands for the Peruvian officers and men who fought a guerrilla war against the royalists. This is Peru's first military medal that San Martín created after being named Protector of Peru.

Instituted: By decree of San Martín on October 1, 1821

Classes: Officers, enlisted men

Obverse: Shield beneath laurel branches

Obverse legend: EL | VALOR | ES MI | DIVISA

Reverse: Radiant sun

Reverse legend: A LAS PARTIDAS DE GUERRILLA

Shape: Oval

Size: 40 × 37 mm

Metal: Officers: gold; enlisted men: silver

Ribbon: White, red

Reference: Argentina 1910, 3:54; Gillingham 1932, 143–44; Posada 1938, 65–66

Pe5. *La Medalla de Zepita*

The Spanish viceroy in Lima sent General Jerónimo Valdés to intercept Santa Cruz, who had just occupied La Paz on August 8, 1823. Learning of Valdés's presence in Puno, Santa Cruz advanced, and the two armies fought an indecisive battle near the village of Zepita on August 25. A cavalry squadron of hussars, who had fought at the Battle of Pichincha, played a critical role in the battle. Valdés retreated, leaving Santa Cruz in control of the battlefield and also of upper Peru. Santa Cruz authorized a medal for his officers and men who fought at Zepita.

Instituted: By decree of Santa Cruz on August 28, 1823

Classes: Chiefs, officers, enlisted men

Obverse inscription: EN LA | CUNA DE | LOS TIRANOS | LABRE | SU | SEPULCRO above floral branches, all within a border of dots

Reverse inscription: ZEPITA | AGOSTO | 25 DE 1823 within a laurel wreath

Shape: Irregular pentagon

Size: 30 × 25 mm

Metal: Chiefs, officers: gold; enlisted men: silver

Ribbon: Red, white

Pe5a. *Variant issued for hussars*

Instituted: By decree of Santa Cruz on August 28, 1823

Classes: Chiefs, officers, enlisted men

Obverse inscription: AL VALOR DE LOS HUSARES DE ZEPITA above branches

Reverse inscription: ZEPITA 25 DE AGOSTO DE 1823 within a laurel wreath

Shape: Inverted pentagon

Size: 30 × 25 mm

Metal: Chiefs, officers: gold; enlisted men: silver

Reference: Argentina 1910, 3:82–97; Gillingham 1932, 151; Dargent Chamot 2012, 9

Pe6. *La Cruz de Junín*

Bolívar's army of liberation began its march from Trujillo in July 1824 up into the central highlands. On August 6, a royalist cavalry squadron under the command of General Jean Canterac attacked a revolutionary cavalry force under General Guillermo Miller near Junín. The battle was fought with steel only, reportedly without a shot being fired. Miller carried the day, causing moderate casualties but heavy desertions within the royalist ranks. The Peruvian Congress authorized the Cross of Junín for the officers and men who fought there. This was the last major confrontation between the two sides before the decisive Battle of Ayacucho.

Instituted: By Congressional Decree on March 28, 1828, and September 18, 1828

Classes: Chiefs, officers, enlisted men

Obverse inscription: BATALLA DE JUNIN on a white enameled field

Reverse disc: 2 crossed swords united by 2 lances with banners

Shape: Ball-tipped, red enameled, white-rimmed, 5-armed star with 2-pointed ends and a laurel wreath in the angles suspended from a gold laurel brooch (the silver medal has no brooch)

Metal: Chiefs, officers: gold; enlisted men: silver

Ribbon: Red, white, red

Reference: Gillingham 1932, 151–52; Dargent Chamot 2012, 10

*Pe7. *La Medalla de Ayacucho*

Peru authorized the Medal for Ayacucho for the decisive victory, which consolidated its independence more than three years after San Martín had proclaimed it in 1821. Bolívar's army of liberation, commanded by Antonio José de Sucre, was engaged in a campaign of maneuvers in the high Andes with a royalist army under Viceroy La Serna. The two armies met on the plains around Ayacucho on December 9, 1824. The opposing troops were disciplined and well led. The viceroy advanced in three columns, one of which attacked the revolutionary army's right flank, commanded by Colombian General José María Córdova (a modern Colombian order has been named after him; see Co31). The revolutionary troops stood their ground and counterattacked. The battle was short, but decisive. The revolutionary forces carried the day, capturing the viceroy and all of his senior officers. The battle destroyed the last remaining Spanish field army in South America after three hundred years of colonial rule. See also the medals of Bolivia (Bo1) and Colombia (Co8, 9) for the same battle. This medal was struck in different sizes using different metals and was signed by at least two different engravers.

Instituted: By a law of the Constitutional Congress on February 12, 1825

Classes: Chiefs (2),* officers, enlisted men

Obverse: Uniformed bust of Bolívar, right

Obverse legend: A SU LIBERTADOR SIMON BOLIVAR

Reverse: Peruvian arms superimposed on battle flags with a laurel wreath above and palm branches below (wreath and palm lacking on some varieties)

Reverse legend: EL PERU RESTAURADO EN AYACUCHO ANO DE 1824

Shape: Oval (some strikes were round)

Pe7

Pe 7
(reverse)

Size: 35 × 32 mm; 31 × 28 mm (round medals were 30 mm)

Metal: Chiefs, officers: gold, gilt; enlisted men: silver

Ribbon: Red, white; possibly red, yellow, green for Bolivian officers

Engravers: 35 × 32 mm: Mᴸ.vᵒ. Gᵒ (Manuel Villavicencio); 31 × 28 mm: A.D. (Atanasio Davalos)

Reference: Argentina 1910, 3:114–19; Gillingham 1932, 152–54; Gianelloni 1974, 16–18; Dargent Chamot 2012, 11–12

Pe8. *La Medalla del Peru a Simón Bolívar por la Batalla de Ayacucho*

Obverse: 2 laurel branches

Obverse legend: AYACUCHO

Shape: Oval

Size: 27 × 22 mm

Metal: Gold, silver

Reference: Argentina 1910, 3:114–15; Gillingham, 1932, 154; Gianelloni 1974, 16–18

Pe9. *La Cruz de Ayacucho*

The Cross of Ayacucho was awarded to the officers and men who fought in the battle. The literature contains different descriptions of this decoration.

Instituted: By Supreme Decree on December 27, 1824

Regulated: By decree signed by Agustín Gamarra on May 16, 1830

Classes: Generals, chiefs, officers, enlisted men

Obverse disc: Laureate bust of Bolívar, left

Obverse legend: SIMON | BOLIVAR on a blue enameled band and surrounded by 18 brilliants

Reverse: REPUBLICA DEL PERU

Shape: Ball-tipped, white enameled, 5-armed star with 2-pointed ends and a laurel wreath between the arms, suspended from a laurel wreath

Metal: Generals: enameled, with semiprecious stones; chiefs, officers: gold; enlisted men: silver

Ribbon: Red, white. Generals, chiefs, officers: neck ribbon; enlisted men: short chest ribbon

Reference: Argentina 1910, 3:343–44; Gillingham 1932, 155; Dargent Chamot 2012, 10–11; Gianelloni 1974, 16–18

Pe10. *La Medalla de La Toma del Callao*

Despite the royalist defeat at the Battle of Ayacucho, General José Ramón Rodil, the Spanish commander of the Real Felipe, the fortress dominating the port of Callao, refused to surrender, hoping for reinforcements from Spain. Peruvian General Bartolomé Salón laid siege to the fort. Rodil finally surrendered on January 19, 1826, as his supplies ran out and it was clear he would not receive any reinforcements. Peru authorized a medal for the officers and men who laid siege to the fort. Several different medal designs were struck. This description is believed to be the most common version.

> Instituted: By decree on February 1, 1826
>
> Classes: Chiefs, officers, enlisted men
>
> Obverse: Peruvian flag flying from the top of a fort surrounded by a laurel wreath
>
> Obverse inscription: TOMA DEL CALLAO EN 1826
>
> Shape: Oval, suspended from palm and laurel branches
>
> Size: 31.5 × 27.5 mm
>
> Metal: Chiefs, officers: gold; enlisted men: silver
>
> Ribbon: Red, white
>
> Reference: Argentina 1910, 3:122–23; Gillingham 1932, 155–56; Dargent Chamot 2012, 12

* * *

RODIL'S surrender ended Spanish military power in Peru. Like the rest of Latin America, Peru became divided between liberals and conservatives. This struggle became intertwined with an effort to unite Peru and Bolivia into a single confederation. Bolivia's president Andrés

de Santa Cruz plotted with Peruvian caudillos to establish a confederation. In Lima, one of the Peruvian caudillos, Felipe Santiago Salaverry, declared himself supreme chief in a coup d'état against the titular president General José Ruiz de Orbegoso, who was campaigning in the south. Orbegoso then joined forces with Santa Cruz, causing Salaverry to lead his forces south to face this combined threat.

Pe11. *La Cruz de la Defensa de Uchumayo*

The Battle of Uchumayo was the most important of a series of skirmishes between Salaverry and Santa Cruz. It was fought around the bridge of Uchumayo near Arequipa on February 4, 1836. Santa Cruz attacked Salaverry's lines but failed to penetrate them.

The battle was indecisive, but the Bolivians retreated. Salaverry was executed following the Battle of Socabaya on February 7, so it is not clear who would have authorized this medal.

> Obverse legend: DEFENSA DE HUCHUMAYO on a white enameled band
>
> Reverse inscription: FEBRERO 4 DE 1836
>
> Shape: Ball-tipped cross with 3-pointed ends, suspended from a laurel wreath
>
> Metal: Gold
>
> Ribbon: Red, white, red
>
> Reference: Dargent Chamot 2012, 13–14; http://www.medals.org.uk/peru/peru02.htm, accessed April 7, 2012

THE WAR OF THE CONFEDERATION (1836–1839)

THE WAR of the Confederation pitted Chile and its Peruvian allies against the Peru-Bolivia Confederation, whose president was Andrés de Santa Cruz. Chile opposed the formation of the Confederation, but Santa Cruz refused to break it up. Chile declared war in December 1836. Peru was a divided nation. It had been split up into a northern and southern Peru. The Peruvians themselves were also divided; some wanted to expel the Chileans, some opposed the Bolivians, while some wanted to get rid of both the Chileans and the Bolivians.

The first Chilean invasion ended in defeat, and the country's troops returned home. In early 1838, Chile sent a second expedition and joined allied Peruvian forces opposed to the Peru-Bolivia Confederation. The Chileans defeated units of the Confederation army on September 18 at Matucana in the foothills of the Andes east of Lima.

Pe12. *La Batalla de Matucana*

Agustín Gamarra, who became president of Peru a second time after the defeat of the Peru-Bolivian Confederation, authorized a medal for the officers and men from Chile and Peru who defeated the Confederation forces at Matucana on September 18, 1838.

Instituted: By Decree No. 278 of Agustín Gamarra on September 24, 1838
Classes: Chiefs, officers, enlisted men
Obverse inscription: EL PERU AL TRIUNFO HEROICO EN MATUCANA
Shape: Hexagon
Metal: Chiefs, officers: gold; enlisted men: silver
Reference: Dargent Chamot 2012, 15

THE CHINCHA ISLANDS WAR (1864–1866)

THE PERU-BOLIVIAN Confederation was dissolved following the Battle of Yungay. Peru's next foreign war involved a Spanish naval squadron that visited the west coast of Latin America in 1863, a conflict known as the Chincha Islands War. A minor brawl involving Spanish citizens in Peru set in motion a series of unrelated events that brought Chile and Peru into a state of war with Spain.

The Spanish fleet, initially commanded by Admiral Luis Hernández Pinzón, dominated the sea with its superior firepower. The Spaniards lacked the troops to launch a ground war, and they lacked a port to resupply and support their ships. Spain took the military initiative by occupying the Chincha Islands, from which Peru was exporting bird guano for the international fertilizer market. The outgunned Peruvian-Chilean ships took refuge at Abtao in shallow waters off Chiloé in southern Chile. Two Spanish ironclad steamships, the *Villa de Madrid* and the *Blanca*, bombarded the allied ships but could not get close enough, owing to their greater displacement.

Pe13. *La Estrella de Abtao*

Peru authorized a star for the officers of the allied ships involved in the naval combat at Abtao.

Obverse inscription: ABTAO 7 FEB 1866
Reverse inscription: LA PATRIA RECONOCIDA
Shape: White enameled, 6-pointed star with rays in the angles
Metal: Gold

Pe 15a

Pe 15a

Ribbon: Red with a narrow white center
stripe

Reference: Gillingham 1932, 158–59

Pe14. *La Medalla de Abtao*

Peru also gave a silver medal for the same battle, probably for the sailors.

Obverse: Inscribed on a shield: A LOS |
VENCEDORES | EN | ABTAO, superimposed on
trophies of war and crossed flags and surmounted by a sun

Reverse inscription: 7 DE FEBRERO 1866 | 57
CANONES CONTRA 92

Shape: Oval

Size: 32 × 26 mm

Metal: Silver

Reference: Gillingham 1932, 159

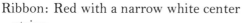

THE SPANISH warships from Abtao joined the
rest of the Spanish fleet that was blockading
Callao.

*Pe15. *La Estrella de Callao*

On May 2, 1866, the Spanish fleet bombarded
the port of Callao all day, inflicting heavy casualties, but the Peruvian shore batteries also
scored damaging hits on the Spanish warships.
The Spanish commander had nowhere to repair
his vessels and no troops to capture the port,
so he sailed away, and the fighting ended. Peru
authorized a star for its officers, which is known
in two variant forms.

*Pe15a. *Variant 1*

Obverse inscription: CALLAO | 2 DE MAYO |
DE 1866 on a white enameled disc

Reverse inscription: FUÉ | UNO DE MIS |
DEFENSORES on a white enameled
disc

Shape: White enameled, 6-armed star
with 2-pointed ends and 3 rays in each
angle

Size: 31 mm

Metal: Gold

Pe 15b   Pe 15b

*Pe15b. *Variant 2*

Classes: Generals,* officers*

Obverse disc: Fortress on a white enameled field

Obverse legend: CALLAO 2 DE MAYO DE | 1866 on a white enameled band

Reverse legend: 50 CANONES CONTRA 500

on a white enameled band (lacking in some versions)

Shape: Ball-tipped, red enameled star suspended from a green enameled laurel wreath

Size: 34 mm; 29 mm

Metal: Generals: gold; officers: silver

Ribbon: White with 2 red stripes

Reference: Gillingham 1932, 159–60

THE WAR OF THE PACIFIC (1879–1883)

THE WAR of the Pacific was started after Bolivia imposed taxes on Chilean miners operating on Bolivian soil, in contravention of an agreement between the two countries. Prior to this, Peru and Bolivia had signed a secret mutual defense treaty.

Chile declared war on Bolivia and Peru on April 5, 1879 (see also the chapter on Chile in this volume).

Pe16. *La Legión del Mérito*

Peru created the Legion of Merit during the War of the Pacific. It came in a military and civilian version. The military version was awarded for exceptional or distinguished service at sea or on land. The third class was given collectively to military units. The civil decoration was awarded for the sciences and arts, industry, and philanthropic works.

Instituted: By decree on May 26, 1880

Classes: 1st, 2nd, 3rd

Obverse: LA REPUBLICA AL MERITO MILITAR [military]; LA REPUBLICA AL MERITO CIVIL [civil]

Reverse: [The place and date of the award are inscribed]

Shape: Cross on a green enameled wreath; wreath is gold in the 2nd class and steel in the 3rd class

Metal: Military: steel; civil: silver

Ribbon: Military: red; civil: light blue

Reference: Gillingham 1932, 160–61

* * *

THE WAR of the Pacific lasted for four years and ended with the Treaty of Ancón on October 20, 1883. Chile occupied Peru for most of that time while it fought an irregular army led by General Andrés Avelino Cáceres, until the Battle of Huamachuco on July 10, 1883. Peru is only known to have authorized one medal—for the Battle of Tarapacá, nearly twenty years after the war ended.

Pe17. *La Medalla de Tarapacá*

The land war began in November 1879, when the Chilean army, commanded by Luis Arteaga, landed at Pisagua and began marching toward the port of Iquique. The Peruvians, led by Juan Buendia, sought to block the Chilean advance. They met on November 27, 1879. The Peruvians won the battle, as the Chileans retreated, but the Peruvians decided to return to Arica, leaving the Chileans in control of Tarapacá. In 1901, Peru authorized a medal for its troops that fought at the Battle of Tarapacá.

Instituted: By law on November 20, 1901

Obverse: Arms of Peru above palm and laurel branches

Obverse legend: BENEMERITA SOCIEDAD | - VENCEDORES | EN TARAPACA

Reverse: 1879 surrounded by a laurel wreath

Metal: Bronze

Ribbon: Red, white, red

Reference: Certificate awarding the medal on July 28, 1902

* * *

PERU engaged in hostilities with its northern neighbors over their poorly marked borders. In 1932, Colombia and Peru fought a war over disputed territory in the confluence of the Putumayo and Amazon rivers, centering on the town of Liticia. The war was settled diplomatically, and neither country is known to have authorized medals specifically for this conflict.

THE PERU-ECUADOR BORDER WAR OF 1941

THE BORDER war with Ecuador lasted a few weeks in July 1941 and produced few casualties. The fighting took place along Peru's poorly marked northern border with Ecuador from the upper Amazon to the Pacific coast. Peruvian troops entered into and occupied territory claimed by Ecuador. The two countries fought several skirmishes but quickly agreed to a cease-fire. Both countries signed the Rio de Janeiro Protocol in 1942, which called for the Peruvian troops to withdraw. However, the protocol did not definitively mark the border between the two countries. The Peruvian navy issued two medals to the men who fought in the war.

*Pe18. *La Medalla del Combatiente*

Divisions: Frente Interno, Frente Externo

Classes: Frente Interno: Combatiente,* Combatiente Especial,*Combatiente Extraordiario; Frente Externo: Combatiente*

Obverse: Anchor

Obverse legend: MARINA DE GUERRA DEL PERU

Reverse inscription: COMBATIENTE; COMBATIENTE | ESPECIAL; COMBATIENTE | FRENTE | EXTERNO

Size: Combatiente: 30 mm; Combatiente Especial, Combatiente Frente Externo: 32 mm

Metal: Gilt

Maker: Zuloeta

Ribbon: Combatiente: orange with a center blue stripe edged in yellow; Combatiente Especial: green with a center blue stripe edged in yellow; Combatiente Frente Externo: light blue with a center blue stripe edged in red, white, red

Provenance: Combatiente Frente Externo: A. Menke

Pe 18

Pe 18

*Pe19. *La Medalla "Honor al Mérito" de la Marina de Guerra del Peru*

Obverse: Arms of Peru superimposed on crossed anchors

Obverse inscription: MARINA DE GUERRA DEL PERU on a scroll

Reverse inscription: HONOR | AL | MERITO with an oak and laurel wreath

Size: 31 mm

Metal: Gilt

Ribbon: Blue, yellow with narrow red, white, red center stripes

Pe20. *La Medalla Conmemorativa de la Guerra del 1941*

Peru issued a commemorative medal twenty-five years after the war.

Instituted: 1966

Obverse: A winged female warrior holding a sword in one hand and a wreath in the other

Obverse legend: CAMPANA MILITAR | MCMXLI

Reverse: Crossed swords beneath the Peruvian arms

Reverse inscription: 1941–1966 | 25 ANIVERSARIO | VENCEDOR

Size: 41 mm

Metal: Bronze

Ribbon: Yellow with narrow red, white, and red center stripes

* * *

ASIDE from the minor border war with Ecuador, Peru has remained at peace with its neighbors since the end of the War of the Pacific. In recent years, the country has been faced with an internal insurrection known as the Sendero Luminoso and continuous violence by drug traffickers on the eastern slopes of the Andes. The military played a major role in controlling both problems, but the national police have also been given an important role in the struggle.

Pe 19

Pe 19

MEDALS OF MERIT IN PEACETIME

*Pe21. *La Medalla al Mérito Jorge Chávez Dartnell*

The Medal for Merit Jorge Chávez Dartnell recognizes outstanding service to Peruvian aviation. It is awarded to Peruvian and foreign civilians and military personnel.

The medal is named after Jorge Chávez Dartnell (1887–1910), a Franco-Peruvian aviation pioneer. Chávez died in a crash landing while attempting to be the first pilot to fly over the Alps from Switzerland to Italy. His remains were returned to Peru on September 28, 1957. The international airport in Lima is named after him.

> Instituted: By Decree No. 1, on January 4, 1966
>
> Obverse: Early high-wing, single-motor plane over mountains above the date: 1910
>
> Reverse inscription: HOMENAJE | A | JORGE CHAVEZ | LIMA | 28 IX 1957
>
> Shape: Shield with winged shield below, joined to the suspension bar by laurel leaves
>
> Size: 42 × 35 mm
>
> Metal: Bronze
>
> Ribbon: Blue with a red-edged white center stripe
>
> Reference: http://www.medals.org.uk/peru/peru013.htm, accessed April 15, 2012

*Pe22. *La Medalla del Combatiente Marescal Andrés A. Cáceres*

The Marshal Andrés A. Cáceres Combatants Medal is awarded to army personnel for honor, distinction, and merit. It has been awarded to aging veterans of the 1932–33 war with Colombia and the border skirmishes with Ecuador.

The medal is named after a Peruvian army

Pe21

Pe21

Pe 22

Pe 23

Pe 22

COMBATIENTE | mcal. ANDRES A CACERES on a red enameled band, surrounded by a green enameled laurel wreath

Reverse disc: Rayed sun with upraised sword behind, flanked by palm and laurel branches

Shape: Maltese cross with convex ends and 5 rays in each angle

Size: 53 mm

Metal: Gilt

Ribbon: Red, white, red with suspension bar denoting class

*Pe23. *La Medalla al Mérito de la Policía de Investigaciones del Perú*

The Medal of Merit of Peru's Investigative Police was awarded to its members for meritorious service.

Obverse: Star of the Order of Merit of the Investigative Police, laurel branch below

Obverse inscription: AL | MERITO | PIP

Size: 35 mm

officer who organized an army in the Andes after Chile occupied Lima during the War of the Pacific. He was finally defeated at the battle of Yungay (see Ch9–10).

Classes: Honor, Distinction, Merit*

Obverse disc: Bust of Cáceres, ¾ left

Obverse legend: MEDALLA DEL

Metal: Silver

Ribbon: Red, white, red

Pe24. *La Medalla al Defensor de la Democracia*

The Medal for the Defender of Democracy is awarded to members of the armed forces, the National Police of Peru, the self-defense committees, and civilians killed, wounded, or incapacitated in the fight against terrorism.

Instituted: By Supreme Decree No. 026-2011-PCM on March 26, 2011

ORDERS

*Pe25. *La Orden del Sol*

General San Martín authorized the Order of the Sun, Peru's first order of merit, shortly after he was proclaimed Protector of Peru. He intended that it replace the Spanish Order of Isabella la Católica for the purpose of rewarding officers who had distinguished themselves during Peru's War of Independence. He awarded the order to Peruvian, Argentine, and Chilean officers.

Pe25a. *San Martín version*

Instituted: By decree signed by San Martín at the Palacio Protectoral de Lima on October 8, 1821

Discontinued: By Decree of the Constitutional Congress on March 9, 1825

Grand Master: President of the Republic

Grades: Fundador, Benemerito, Asociado

Obverse inscription: In the upper part, inscribed in red on a white enameled band: EL PERU; in the lower part, inscribed in white on a red enameled band: A SUS LIBERTADORES

Shape: Round

Size: 33 mm

Metal: Gold, silver

Ribbon: White

* * *

THE ORDER was reestablished as the Order of the Sun of Peru by President Augusto B. Leguía, nearly one hundred years later. It is designed to reward nationals and foreigners, civilians and military, for meritorious service to the nation. It remains today Peru's highest award for merit. Recipients of the Grand Cross with diamonds include Ernesto Zedillo, president of Mexico; Lucio Gutierrez, president of Ecuador; Álvaro Uribe Vélez, president of Colombia; and Carlos Mesa, president of Bolivia.

As is the case of most official orders of merit, the Order of the Sun of Peru can be rescinded under certain circumstances. A onetime president of Peru, Alberto Fujimori, had his membership in the order rescinded by the council of the order for having established a dictatorship. Fujimori had been Grand Master of the order.

The order was originally made by Arthus Bertrand, Paris, but was later transferred to Le Maître, Paris, and to the Casa Nacional de la Moneda, Lima.

*Pe25b. *Leguía version, Variant 1*

Reestablished: By Supreme Decree on April 14, 1921

Modified: By Law No. 4,685 on August 31, 1923

Regulated: September 6, 1923

Pe 25b
Commander

Pe 25b
Commander

Grades: Grand Cross with diamonds, Grand
Cross, Grand Officer, Commander,* Officer,
Knight

Obverse inscription: EL SOL | DEL | PERU on a
white enameled disc

Reverse inscription: 1066 [engraved]

Shape: 12-armed star with scrollwork design,
with a ray in each angle

Size: Commander: 40 mm

Metal: Bronze

Ribbon: Dark burgundy

*Pe 25c. *Leguía version, Variant 2*

Grades: Grand Cross with diamonds, Grand
Cross,* Grand Officer, Commander, Officer,
Knight*

Obverse disc: Arms of Peru surrounded by
a laurel wreath (green enameled on Grand
Cross)

Obverse legend: EL SOL DEL PERÚ [on a red
enameled band] | 1821 [on a white enameled
band

Shape: Sun of eighteen 5-part arms with

Pe 25c
Grand Cross

2-pointed ends, suspended from a green enameled laurel wreath

Size: Badge: Grand cross: 61 mm; Knight: 40 mm. Star: 76 mm

Metal: Gilt

Maker: Le Maître et Fils, Paris

Ribbon: Dark burgundy

Reference: Zamora Botta 2012, 4–5; Ugarteche 1966; Gillingham 1932, 145–46; Burke's Peerage 2006, 1456–58; Werlich 1974, 338–39

Pe 25c
Knight

*Pe26. *La Orden Militar de Ayacucho*

The Military Order of Ayacucho is awarded to military and national security personnel for extraordinary military merit and for length of service. It is the country's highest military award.

Instituted: By Law No. 7,563 on November 30, 1944

Modified: By Law No. 25,135

Regulated: Supreme Decree No. 016-DE-SG

Grades: Grand Cross* (Ross collection has two examples, one standard and one with gems),* Grand Officer, Commander, Officer,* Knight

Obverse rectangle: Bust of Bolívar, ¾ left, on a white enameled field curved to top and bottom

Obverse inscription: REPUBLICA | DEL | PERU on a red enameled field [AYACUCHO | 1824 below bust on star]

Reverse rectangle: Bust of Sucre, ¾ left

Reverse inscription: AYACUCHO | 1824 on a red enameled field

Badge shape: Vertical rectangle superimposed on a laurel wreath on a white enameled band on a horizontal crossbar, 3 red and white enameled flags to left and right above, eight 3-part rays above; Knight badge suspended from trophies

Star shape: Same as badge, with gemstones in rays and flags on some examples

Size: Badge: Grand Cross: 69 × 53 mm; Officer: 42 × 31 mm. Star: 82 × 69 mm; with gems: 85 × 73 mm

Metal: Gilt; example with gems: gilt silver

Maker: Casa de Moneda, Lima; example with gems has swan hallmark

Ribbon: Red with a center white stripe

Reference: Burke's Peerage 2006, 1460–61; Werlich 1974, 339–40

Pe 26
Grand Cross star (obverse)

Pe 26
Grand Cross star with gems

Pe 26
Grand Cross badge (obverse)

Pe 26
Grand Cross badge (reverse)

Pe 26
Officer

Pe 26
Officer

*Pe27. *La Orden de Mérito Policial*

The Order of Police Merit is awarded to members of the National Police for a wide range of meritorious services, including promotions and length of service.

Instituted: 1945

Grades: Grand Cross, Grand Officer, Commander, Officer, Knight*

Obverse disc: Intertwined letters PM on a red enameled field

Shape: White enameled cross with 2-pointed ends

Size: 36 mm

Metal: Silver gilt (hallmarked 925)

Ribbon: Red

Pe 27
Knight

Pe 28
Grand Cross star

Pe 28 Knight

*Pe28. *La Orden al Mérito de la Guardia Civil del Perú*

The Order of Merit of the Peruvian Civil Guard was awarded to its members for a range of meritorious services. The Civil Guard was merged into the National Police in 1988.

Instituted: 1945

Disbanded: By Law No. 24,949 on December 7, 1988

Grades: Grand Cross (star),* Grand Officer, Commander, Officer, Knight (2)*

Obverse disc: Laureate warrior head, left, with vertical bayonet

Obverse legend: MERITO | GUARDIA CIVIL DEL PERU on a red enameled band

Shape: Cross surmounting an 18-rayed, 3-part sun with 2-pointed ends and a band in the angles suspended from a green enameled wreath

Star shape: White enameled Greek cross with band with 7 gems in each angle, surmount-

ing a 20-rayed, 5-part sun with 2-pointed ends and a band in the angles

Size: Badge: Knight: 41 mm. Star: Grand Cross: 76 mm

Metal: Gilt; silvered

Ribbon: Red with 3 narrow white stripes

*Pe29. *La Cruz Peruana al Mérito Naval*

The Peruvian Cross for Naval Merit is awarded for extraordinary naval merit. It may be conferred on Peruvian and foreign nationals.

Instituted: By Law No. 10,678 in October 1946

Regulated: By Ministerial Resolution No. 0.811-84-MA | CG on June 19, 1984

Modified: By Ministerial Resolution No. 1,164-2004-DE | MGP on November 9, 2004

Grades: Grand Cross,* Grand Officer, Commander, Knight (2)*

Pe 29
Grand Cross

Pe 29
Grand Cross star (reverse)

Pe 29
Grand Cross badge (reverse)

Pe 29
Knight

Pe 29
Knight

Pe 30
Grand Cross star (obverse)

Pe 30
Grand Cross star (reverse)

Obverse: Blue enameled anchor superimposed on a white enameled, gold-edged Latin cross surmounted by a small sun (variant: red enameled cross)

Obverse inscription: PERU

Shape: 16-rayed, 5-part sun with 2-pointed ends

Size: Badge: Grand Cross 47 mm; Knight: 40 mm. Star: 65 mm

Metal: Grand Cross: gilt; Knight: silver, silvered

Maker: Casa de Moneda, Lima

Ribbon: Dark blue with yellow edge stripes and a red-edged center white stripe

Reference: Werlich 1965, 340; http://www .medals.org.uk/peru/peru006.htm, accessed April 15, 2012

Provenance: Red enameled variant: A. Menke

*Pe30. *La Cruz Peruana al Mérito Aeronáutico*

The Cross of Aeronautical Merit is awarded for outstanding achievements in aviation and the air force. It is conferred on Peruvian citizens and foreigners.

Instituted: By Law No. 12,372 in October 1946

Regulated: Supreme Resolution No. 0.262-77-AE

Grades: Grand Cross (star),* Grand Officer, Commander, Officer, Knight*

Obverse disc: Gilt arms of Peru with wings on a blue enameled disc surrounded by a 5-part, 8-armed sun with 3-poined ends and a ray in each angle

Reverse disc: Concentric circles of red, white, and red enamel

Reverse legend: AL MERITO AERONAUTICO

Shape: Blue-and-white enameled cross pattée with convex ends and a wreath in the angles, suspended from a ribbon bar

Size: Badge: Officer, Knight: 42 mm. Star: 78 mm

Metal: Gilt silver

Ribbon: Blue with 3 narrow white center stripes and 2 white side stripes with small version of badge

Pe 30
Knight

Pe 31
Officer

Pe 30
Knight

Pe 31
Officer

Reference: http://www.medals.org.uk/peru/peru007.htm, accessed April 15, 2012

*Pe31. *La Orden al Mérito Agrícola*

The Order of Agricultural Merit is awarded for outstanding service in the field of agriculture.

Instituted: By Supreme Decree No. 01 on January 5, 1948

Modified: By Supreme Decree No. 30 on May 2, 1953

Grade: Grand Cross, Grand Officer, Commander, Officer,* Knight

Obverse: Octagonal medallion with a tractor in front of a sun rising behind mountains

Obverse legend: MERITO AGRICOLA | REPUBLICA PERUANA on a red enameled band

Reverse inscription: AL | MERITO

Shape: Green enameled, gilt-edged, 8-armed star with 2-pointed ends with points at the bases of each arm and laurel branches in the angles, suspended from a laurel branch

Size: 40 mm

Metal: Gilt silver

Maker: Casa Nacional de la Moneda, Lima

Ribbon: Dark green with yellow side stripes

Reference: http://www.medals.org.uk/peru/peru019.htm, accessed April 14, 2012

*Pe32. *La Cruz Peruana al Mérito Militar*

The Peruvian Cross for Military Merit is awarded to members of the armed forces for distinguished service in defense of the country. This cross recognizes Colonel Francisco Bolognesi, who commanded the Peruvian forces defending Arica from the Chileans during the War of the Pacific. Bolognesi was a career officer in the Peruvian army. He was killed during the final Chilean assault against the rock outcropping at Arica known as the Moro on June 7, 1880. In 1951, the Peruvian government named him the Patron of the Army.

Instituted: By Law No. 10,961 in February 1949

Regulated: Supreme Resolution No. 1,825-GU-AG

Grades: Grand Cross,* Grand Officer, Commander, Officer,* Knight*

Pe 32
Grand Cross star (obverse)

Pe 32
Grand Cross star (reverse)

Pe 32
Officer and Knight (obverse)

Pe 32
Officer and Knight (reverse)

Obverse disc: Bust of Colonel Bolognesi, ¾ left

Obverse legend: CRUZ PERUANA | AL MERITO MILITAR on a white enameled band, surrounded by a green enameled wreath

Reverse disc: Bust of Colonel Bolognesi, ¾ left

Reverse legend: CORONEL | FRANCISCO BOLOGNESI on a white enameled band, surrounded by a green enameled wreath

Shape: Red enameled cross pattée with 5 arrow rays in each angle, suspended from a green enameled wreath (Knight not enameled)

Star shape: Same as badge, but with diamonds in wreath; reverse inscription: CORONEL | FRANCISCO BOLOGNESI

Size: Badge: 51 mm. Star: 80 mm

Metal: Grand Cross: gilt silver; Officer: silver; Knight: bronze

Maker: Zuloeta S.A., Lima

Ribbon: Yellow with white center stripe edged in red

Reference: http://www.medals.org/uk/peru/peru004.htm, accessed April 15, 2012

*Pe33. *La Orden de Palmas Magisteriales*

The Decoration of Magisterial Palms is awarded to professionals in the field of education who have made an exemplary contribution to education, science, culture, and technology.

Instituted: By Decree Law No. 11,192 on October 11, 1949

Regulated: By Supreme Decree No. 007-2005-ED on February 16, 2005

Pe 33
Collar

Grades: Educator (collar),* Master (Commander),* Amauta

Obverse disc: Rayed sun

Obverse legend: PALMAS MAGISTERIALES | DEL PERU on a white enameled band; collar: on a red enameled disc

Shape: White-and-red enameled cross pattée with convex ends and a ray on each arm and a wreath in the angles

Collar shape: Badge on a red enameled disc flanked by palm and laurel branches on an 8-rayed sun with 3 rays in each angle, suspended from a collar of oblong links with wreaths

Pe 33
Commander

Size: Educator: 111 mm; Master: 43 mm
Designer: Armando Pareja Landeo
Maker: Casa de Moneda, Lima
Ribbon: Green neck ribbon
Reference: Peru 1949; Peru 2005

*Pe34. *La Orden al Mérito por Servicios Distinguidos*

The Order of Merit for Distinguished Services was created by a military junta to recognize Peruvians who contribute to promote the prestige of Peru in the fields of the arts, science, industry, and business. It is awarded to Peruvian citizens as well as foreigners.

The order was designed by Fortunato Quesada, whose letter of description accompanies the second example of the star in the Ross Collection.

Instituted: By Legislative Decree No. 11,474 on July 18, 1950
Regulated: By Presidential Decree No. 552 on December 6, 1951
Grades: Grand Cross (2 stars),* Grand Officer, Commander, Officer, Knight*
Obverse disc: Original design of the arms of Peru: rectangular sun (imitating Inca style) rising above mountains and sea, flanked by palm and laurel branches
Obverse legend: AL MERITO POR SERVICIOS DISTINGUIDOS | REPUBLICA PERUANA on red enameled scrolls on a white enameled band
Shape: Top: 2-headed condor in style based on a mythological bird of the Chavin culture; bottom: condor claws with 13 wings of condor plumage on either side
Size: Badge: Grand Cross: 58 × 53 mm; Knight: 38 × 33 mm. Star: 78 × 70 mm

Pe 34
Grand Cross

Pe 34
Grand Cross star (alternate)

Pe 34
Knight

Pe 34
Grand Cross badge (reverse)

Metal: Grand Cross: gilt; Knight: silver
Designer: Fortunato Quesada
Maker: Casa Nacional de Moneda, Lima
Ribbon: Purple
Reference: Burke's Peerage 2006, 1458–59;
    Werlich 1974, 339

*Pe35. *La Orden de Hipólito Unánue*

The Order of Hipólito Unánue is awarded to
medical professionals who have made progress
in the medical sciences and improvements in
public health, such as in the fight against epidemics. The order is named for José Hipólito
Unánue y Pavón (1755–1833), a Peruvian

Pe 35
Grand Cross

Pe 35
Knight

physician, university professor, and politician. Unánue was appointed to cabinet positions under San Martín, and he created today's Faculty of Medicine at the National University of San Marco. He was one of the founders of the original Order of the Sun and received it in recognition of his service to the nation.

Instituted: By Supreme Decree No. 169-SP on October 22, 1955

Regulated: By Supreme Resolution No. 176-69-SA/DS on November 7, 1969

Modified: By Supreme Resolution No. 013-2004-SA on October 22, 2004, replacing Supreme Resolution No. 176-69-SA/DS

Grand Master: President of the Republic

Grades: Grand Cross,* Grand Officer, Commander, Officer, Knight*

Obverse disc: Bust of Unánue, ¾ right

Obverse legend: ORDEN HIPOLITO
    UNANUE|REPUBLICA PERUANA on a red
    enameled band; on star: ORDEN HIPOLITO
    UNANUE|REPUBLICA DEL PERU

Shape: Violet enameled, gilt-edged, 3-part
    Maltese cross with 3-pointed ends and
    3 rays in each angle, suspended from a
    wreath

Size: Badge: 40 mm. Star: 80 mm

Metal: Grand Cross, Grand Officer: gilt;
    Commander, Officer: silver

Maker: Grand Cross star: Zuloeta, S.A.,
    Lima; Grand Cross badge and Knight: Casa
    Nacional de la Moneda, Lima

Ribbon: Purple with red edge stripes

Reference: http://www.medals.org.uk/peru/
    peru009.htm, accessed April 14, 2012

Pe 36
Grand Cross star

*Pe36. *La Orden de Daniel Alcides Carrión*

The Order of Daniel Alcides Carrión is awarded
for exemplary service in social work, medicine,
and health-related science. It is named after
Daniel Alcides Carrión (1857–85), a Peruvian
medical student who fatally experimented on
himself to discover the link between Oroya
fever and the disease verruga peruana (Peruvian wart).

Instituted: By Supreme Decree No. 8 DGS on
    July 20, 1957

Modified: By Supreme Decree No. 00.132-62
    on September 3, 1969

Grand Master: Minister of Public Health

Grades: Grand Cross,* Grand Officer, Com-
    mander, Knight*

Obverse disc: Bust of Carrión, ¾ right, signed
    R. PELLETIER

Obverse legend: DANIEL. A CARRION

Shape: Disc surrounded by an oak and laurel
    wreath surmounted by a purple enameled
    cross

Pe 36
Grand
Cross badge

Size: Grand Cross badge: 58 × 52 mm. Star:
    72 × 63 mm; Knight: 46 × 40 mm

Metal: Gilt silver

Designer: R. Pelletier

Pe 36
Knight

Maker: Casa Nacional de Moneda, Lima

Ribbon: White with a wide purple center stripe and 2 narrow purple edge stripes

Reference: http://www.medals.org.uk/peru/peru017.htm, accessed April 14, 2012

*Pe 37. *La Orden del Trabajo*

The Order of Labor is awarded to workers, employees, and academics for improving the welfare of workers, labor harmony, labor legislation, and social security. The original decree called for promoting social peace and creating better labor standards than required by law,

but these provisions were partially rescinded in 1965.

Instituted: By Law No. 15,195 on November 4, 1964

Modified: By Law No. 20,585 on September 10, 1965, rescinding parts of Law No. 15,195

Regulated: By Supreme Decree No. 003-74-TR

Modified: By Supreme Decree No. 039-85-TR

Modified: By Supreme Decree No. 001-2010-TR

Grades: Grand Cross, Grand Officer, Commander,* Officer, Knight

Badge: Semicircle with image of a man with tools surmounted by an upside-down trapezoid flanked by waves

Pe 37
Commander

Obverse legend: ORDEN DEL TRABAJO

Obverse inscription: AMA | SUA | AMA | LLULLA | AMA | QELLA

Grand Cross star: An artistic design featuring 2 clasped hands and 3 crossed shovels with silvered handles; inscribed within the design: ARMONIA JUSTICIA PRODUCTIVIDAD ORDEN DEL TRABAJO REPUBLICA PERUANA

Size: Knight: 56 × 35 mm

Metal: Knight: patinated silver

Designer: Armando Pareja Landeo

Maker: Casa Nacional de Moneda, Lima

Ribbon: Grand Cross: green with yellow and red edges; Commander: homespun ribbon of burgundy with green and yellow center stripes

Provenance: Commander: Jorge Barclay (recipient)

Reference: http://www.medals.org.uk/peru/peru021.htm, accessed April 15, 2012

Pe 38
Grand Cross star (obverse)

*Pe38. *La Orden del Gran Almirante Miguel Grau*

The Order of Grand Admiral Miguel Grau is awarded to navy personnel for merit. It is named after Miguel Grau (1834–79), who fought the Chilean navy during the War of the Pacific. He commanded the *Huáscar*, one of two Peruvian ironclads, which sank the Chilean warship *Esmeralda* in the first naval engagement of the war. The Chilean navy later captured the *Huáscar* in the Bay of Angamos. Admiral Grau was killed during the battle, along with many of his officers and men.

Instituted: By Supreme Decree No. 015-69-MA on August 13, 1969

Regulated: By Ministerial Resolution No. 0.789-78-MA/CG on August 18, 1978

Modified: By Ministerial Resolution No. 1,165-2004-DE/MGP on November 9, 2004

Pe 38
Grand Cross star (reverse)

Modified: By Supreme Decree No. 003-2010-DE on March 29, 2010

Grades: Grand Cross,* Grand Officer, Commander, Officer, Knight

Obverse disc: Bust of Grau, ¾ right, on a blue enameled field

Obverse legend: GRAN ALMIRANTE GRAU | 8 OCTUBRE 1879

Reverse legend: Star: ARMADA DEL PERU

Reverse inscription: Star: GRAN | CRUZ

Shape: Crossed anchors above an 8-armed, 3-part star with five 3-part rays in each angle

Size: Grand Cross star: 73 mm

Metal: Gilt silver

Maker: Zuloeta S.A., Lima

Reference: http://www.medals.org.uk/peru/ peru022.htm, accessed April 15, 2012

*Pe39. *La Orden al Mérito de la Policía de Investigaciones del Perú*

The Order of Merit of the Investigative Police (PIP) of Peru was awarded to its personnel for outstanding merit to the institution. The PIP was disbanded in 1988 and later merged with the National Police of Peru.

Instituted: By Decree Law No. 17,799 on September 2, 1969

Discontinued: By Law No. 24,949 on December 17, 1988

Grand Master: President of the Republic

Grades: Grand Cross,* Grand Officer, Commander, Officer, Knight*

Obverse disc: Enameled arms of Peru flanked by branches and surmounted by a small oval wreath on an oval green enameled field

Obverse legend: POLICIA DE INVESTIGACIONES DEL PERU [on a red enameled band] | AL MERITO [on a white enameled band]

Badge shape: 8-armed star with 3 rays in each angle, suspended from crossed laurel branches

Size: Badge: Grand Cross: 58 mm; Knight: 47 mm. Star: 78 mm

Pe39 Knight

Metal: Grand Cross: gilt; Knight: silver

Ribbon: Green with narrow white side stripes

Reference: http://docs.peru.justia.com/ 17799-sep-2-1969-1.pdf, accessed September 12, 2012

*Pe40. *La Orden al Mérito de la Guardia Republicana del Perú*

The Order of Merit of the Republican Guard of Peru was awarded to its personnel for outstanding service to the institution. The Republican Guard was merged into the National Police in 1988.

Pe 39
Grand Cross

Pe 40
Grand Cross star

Pe 40
Knight

Instituted: By Decree Law No. 18,164, on March 3, 1970

Disbanded: By Law No. 24,949 on December 7, 1988

Grand Master: President of the Republic

Grades: Grand Cross (star),* Grand Officer, Commander, Officer, Knight*

Obverse disc: Arms of Peru on a blue enameled disc (for the Grand Cross) surrounded by a stylized wreath

Obverse legend: Knight: GUARDIA REPUBLICANA | PERU

Star obverse legend: AL MERITO | GUARDIA REPUBLICANA DEL PERU on a white enameled band

Shape: 6-armed star with flat ends and 4 flat-ended rays in each angle

Size: Badge: Knight: 60 mm. Star: 67 mm

Metal: Grand Cross: gilt; Knight: silver

Ribbon: Light blue with white side stripes

Engraver: Armando Pareja Landeo

Maker: Casa Nacional de la Moneda, Lima

Reference: http://www.docs.peru.justia.com/ 18,164-mar-3-1970.pdf; accessed September 12, 2012

*Pe41. *La Orden del Capitán José A. Quiñones*

The Order of Captain José A. Quiñones is awarded for meritorious service to the Peruvian air force. It may also be bestowed under exceptional circumstances to personnel of the armed forces and the police for service to the air force.

José Abelardo Quiñones Gonzales (1914–41) was one of Peru's most renowned military pilots. Quiñones first distinguished himself as an acrobatic pilot by flying his biplane upside-down near the ground. During the Peru-Ecuador Border War of 1941, his squadron

Pe 41
Grand Cross star

was sent north to attack Ecuadorean positions. On July 23, 1941, while attacking Ecuadorean forces, his plane was disabled by antiaircraft fire at Quebrada Seca. Instead of jumping out in his parachute, he reportedly chose to crash his plane into an enemy gun emplacement. Years later, the Chamber of Deputies declared him a national hero by Law No. 16,126 on May 10, 1966. July 23 is still celebrated as National Air Force Day.

Instituted: By Decree Law No. 21,207 on July 8, 1975

Regulated: By Ministerial Resolution No. 0.811-84-MA-CG

Modified: By Ministerial Resolution No. 1,164-2004-DE-MGP

Grades: Grand Cross (star),* Grand Officer, Commander, Officer, Knight

Obverse disc: Bust of Captain Quiñones, ¾ left, on an oval, blue enameled field

Obverse legend: CAPITAN FAP. JOSE A. QUIÑONES | 23 JULIO 1941 on a red enameled band

Shape: 8-armed faceted star with 5 faceted rays in each angle

Size: Star: 90 × 80 mm

Metal: Gilt silver

Reference: http://www.medals.org.uk/peru/peru026.htm, accessed April 15, 2012

*Pe42. *La Orden al Mérito de la Policía Nacional del Perú*

The Order of Merit of the National Police of Peru was instituted in 1990 as a replacement for three earlier orders: Pe28, Pe39, and Pe40. It is awarded to members of the National Police of

Peru for meritorious service. In extraordinary cases, the order may be bestowed on members of the armed forces, individuals, or even national and foreign institutions. National Police recipients are eligible for a bonus of between 5 percent and 20 percent of their basic salary, depending on grade.

Instituted: By Supreme Decree No. 017-90-IN on June 28, 1990

Regulated: On July 12, 1990

Grand Master: President of the Republic

Grades: Grand Cross,* Grand Officer, Commander, Officer, Knight

Obverse disc: Enameled arms of Peru on a white enameled field

Obverse legend: MERITO | POLICIAL separated by single gilt circles on a red enameled field, surrounded by a green enameled wreath; miniature: MERITO | PNP

Badge shape: White enameled, silvered-edged Maltese cross with 2-pointed ends and four 2-pointed rays in each angle, suspended from a green enameled laurel branch

Star shape: Same as the badge, but has 3 gems on each side of the band, separating the words of the legend

Size: Badge: Grand Cross: 64 mm. Star: 80 mm

Metal: Gilt

Ribbon: Light green edged in white

Reference: http://www.scribd.com/doc/59915188/to-de-Condecoracion-de-La-Orden-Al-Merito-Pnp, accessed September 12, 2012

Pe43. *La Orden al Mérito del Servicio Diplomático José Gregorio Paz Soldán*

The Order of Diplomatic Merit José Gregorio Paz Soldán is awarded for distinguished diplomatic service and for outstanding contributions to the foreign policy of Peru. It is

Pe 42
Grand Cross

the highest order awarded by the Ministry of Foreign Affairs.

José Gregorio Paz Soldán (1808–75) was a lawyer, diplomat, journalist, and politician, and a three-time Minister of Foreign Affairs of Peru. He created Peru's diplomatic service by opening embassies in neighboring countries, the United States, and England. He organized Latin America's first congress of ministers of foreign affairs in Lima.

Instituted: By Supreme Decree No. 050-2004-RE on August 31, 2004

Grand Master: Minister of Foreign Relations

Grade: Grand Cross, Grand Officer, Commander, Officer, Knight

Obverse: Arms of the Peruvian Diplomatic Service in relief

Obverse legend: AL MERITO DEL SERVICIO DIPLOMATICO DEL PERU | JOSE GREGORIO PAZ SOLDAN on a red enameled band

Size: Badge: Grand Cross and Grand Officer: 80 mm; Commander: 60 mm; Officer and Knight: 40 mm

Ribbon: Blue

Reference: Peru 2004; http://www.medals.org.uk/peru/peru018.htm, accessed April 15, 2012

Pe 44
Grand Cross star

*Pe44. *La Orden del Servicio Civil del Estado "Libertador Ramón Castilla"*

The Order for the Civil Service of the State "Liberator Ramón Castilla" is awarded to civil servants of the central government for meritorious service. It is Peru's highest distinction for civil servants.

The order is named for a four-time president of Peru, Ramón Castilla (1797–1867), who joined Bolívar as an officer during the War of Independence and fought in the Battle of Ayacucho. An active officer, he fought in many of the caudillo wars on the side of the liberals. As president, he is regarded as a good administrator. He is best known for having abolished slavery in Peru.

Regulated: By Supreme Decree No. 01-94-JUS in 1994

Grand Master: President of the Republic

Grade: Grand Cross,* Grand Officer, Commander,* Officer, Knight,* Member

Obverse: Bust of Ramón Castilla, right, signed R. PELLETIER

Obverse inscription: RAMON CASTILLA [below bust]; MORALIDAD | EFICIENCIA [below disc]

Pe 44
Commander

Pe 44
Knight

Obverse legend: REPUBLICA PERUANA [on a red enameled band]; SERVICIO CIVIL DEL ESTADO [on a red enameled band, separated by a white enameled band]

Shape: Oval disc surrounded by a palm and laurel wreath

Size: Grand Cross star: 80 × 60 mm; Commander: 55 × 44 mm; Knight: 41 × 33 mm

Metal: Grand Cross and Commander: bronzed silver; Knight: silver

Designer: R. Pelletier

Maker: Casa Nacional de la Moneda, Lima

Ribbon: Blue with narrow red edge stripes

Reference: http://www.inst.servis.gub.pe/ files/normas%20legales/DS%20001-94 -DS001-94-JUS.pdf, accessed September 19, 2012

*Pe45. *La Orden del Mérito Industrial*

The Order of Industrial Merit is awarded to business leaders for meritorious service in expanding the national economy.

Regulated: By Supreme Decree No. 003-74-TR in 1974

Grades: Grand Cross (star),* Grand Officer, Commander, Officer, Knight

Obverse disc: Female head, right, with designs on a metallic field

Obverse legend: ORDEN DEL MERITO | INDUSTRIAL on a white enameled band

Shape: Disc is surrounded by 12 white enameled gears, on an 8-pointed rayed star

Size: 77 mm

Metal: Gilt silver

Designer: Armando Pareja Landeo

Maker: Casa Nacional de la Moneda, Lima

Reference: http://www.medals.org.uk/peru/ peru020.htm, accessed April 14, 2012

Pe 45
Grand Cross star

Pe 46

*Pe46. *La Orden al Mérito Turístico*

The Order of Tourism Merit is awarded to business leaders for developing the country's tourist potential.

> Obverse disc: Stylized man with arms outstretched on a field enameled with horizontal purple, blue, turquoise bands

Obverse legend: AL MERITO TURISTICO

Shape: Cross with long vertical arms and a convex-ended ray on each arm, with a convex-ended ray in each angle

Size: 75 × 65 mm

Metal: White metal

Maker: Casa Nacional de Moneda, Lima

URURGUAY

URUGUAY's early history was influenced by the territorial rivalry between the Empire of Portugal and the Empire of Spain. Montevideo itself was founded by Spain as a counterweight to the Portuguese settlement at Colonia to the west. This rivalry continued between the Empire of Brazil and the United Provinces of the River Plate during and after the wars of independence.

Buenos Aires liberated Montevideo on June 23, 1814, after a siege lasting nearly two years. Brazil, ever concerned about republican activism in Uruguay, occupied Montevideo in 1817 and then annexed the entire country as the Province of Cisplatina. The Uruguayans revolted once more and declared their independence from Brazil on May 25, 1825. This led to the five-hundred-day Cisplatine War that pitted Brazil against Argentina. The Treaty of Montevideo in 1828 ended the war and recognized Uruguay's independence.

After independence, the Uruguayans divided themselves between the rural, conservative Blanco Party and the liberal Montevideo free traders forming the Colorado Party. The Blancos were more numerous, but the Colorados were more cohesive. Both sides allied themselves with one of their neighbors. The conflict turned into a virtual civil war lasting some twelve years, from 1840 until 1852, and became known as the Guerra Grande. The Blancos laid siege to Montevideo during most of that period. The war finally ended inconclusively in 1852.

With the fighting over, the Blancos and Colorados resumed their feuding. Each side sought allies abroad. In 1865, Brazil invaded Uruguay in support of the Colorados. Paraguay responded by invading both Brazil and Argentina. The Triple Alliance War lasted until the death of the Paraguayan dictator in 1870. The Blancos and Colorados again resumed their rivalry, but this time they agreed to divide up the territory in accordance with their relative strength, and the country began to develop economically with an influx of immigrants from Europe.

Uruguay evolved into a functioning democracy and was never again forced into armed conflict with its neighbors. The country went through a brief period of military dictatorship in reaction to a left-wing insurgency led by the Tupamaros, an urban guerrilla group. Today, Uruguay maintains a small professional army that plays a prominent role in United Nations peacekeeping operations.

MEDALS

THE WAR OF INDEPENDENCE (1811–1828)

URUGUAY's path to independence started in 1811, when the country's national hero, José Gervasio Artigas, first raised the banner of rebellion against Spain. Artigas formed an army and defeated the royalists at the Battle of Las Piedras on May 18, 1811. Uruguay lacked the population and economic strength to consolidate its independence alone. Artigas unsuccessfully sought to ally himself with Buenos Aires and then organized the *Liga Federal* (Federal League) in 1814, naming himself "Protector." In so doing, he inserted his country into the bitter struggle between the unitarians and federalists in the United Provinces of the River Plate.

Montevideo was key to liberating Uruguay. Spain used the port as its main naval base in the South Atlantic and could thus deliver supplies and reinforcements not only to the city, but also to its forces in upper Peru (today's Bolivia). Artigas laid siege to Montevideo, while a fleet from the United Provinces challenged the Spanish warships anchored there. In May 1814, the Spanish ships sailed out of the port and did battle with the republican fleet commanded by Guillermo Brown. The Spanish fleet was decisively defeated, and Montevideo surrendered on May 20. The Battle of Montevideo undermined Spain's ability to maintain a strong military presence in the River Plate.

Uy1. *La Condecoración "La Patria a los Libertadores de Montevideo"*

Uruguay authorized a medal for the officers who participated in the siege and surrender of Montevideo in 1814.

Instituted: 1814

Obverse: LA | PATRIA | A LOS | LIBERTADORES | DE | MONTEVIDEO | 1814

Shape: Oval

Metal: Bronze

Reference: http://www.fraymacho.blogspot.com/2012/05/condecoraciones.html, accessed July 18, 2012

* * *

THE FEDERAL LEAGUE with Artigas as its self-proclaimed "Protector" was backed by six provinces, four of which were inside Argentina. However, the Brazilian emperor regarded republican activism as a threat and invaded Uruguay, occupying Montevideo in early 1817. The Brazilians defeated Artigas at the Battle of Tacuarembó. Four years later, Brazil annexed the country as the Provincia Cisplatina. In 1822, the Brazilian Empire declared itself independent of the Kingdom of Portugal.

In 1825, Uruguay again declared for independence, this time from the Empire of Brazil with the support of Buenos Aires. Uruguayan irregulars fought with the Argentine army and navy against Brazil in the Cisplatine War (1825–28).

The Uruguayan effort to free itself finally co-alesced around Juan Antonio Lavalleja, who landed at Playa de la Agraciada with thirty-two rebels on April 19, 1825. They became known as the *Treinta y Tres Orientales*, and they soon attracted sufficient volunteers to take to the field and challenge the Brazilians. Six months later, they defeated a Brazilian army at the Battle of Sarandí on October 12, 1825.

Their victory followed by less than one month an equally important success by Uruguayan forces under the command of José Fructuoso Rivera at the Battle of Rincón de las Gallinas. A third key battle was at Ituzaingó (Ytusaingó) on February 20, 1827, which pitted a Brazilian army against a joint Argentine-Uruguayan force. The Uruguayan contingent under the command of Lavalleja took the brunt of the first Brazilian thrust and successfully counterattacked. The battle itself was inconclusive, but the Brazilians abandoned their plan to march on to Buenos Aires. While there were other important battles, particularly at sea, these three were the ones with the greatest Uruguayan participation.

Great Britain finally mediated the 1828 Treaty of Montevideo, which ended the war. This treaty consolidated Uruguay's political independence.

*Uy2. *La Medalla de Sarandí*

Uruguay struck two medals for the land battles in the Cisplatine War that ended in victory for its forces.

> Obverse: Arms of Uruguay surrounded by a wreath
>
> Obverse legend: ESTADO ORIENTAL DEL URUGUAY
>
> Reverse: SARANDI | YTUSAINGO | RINCON DE LAS | GALLINAS surrounded by a wreath
>
> Size: 38 mm
>
> Metal: Bronze
>
> Ribbon: None; trace of removed pin on reverse

Uy3. *La Condecoración a los Vencedores de Ituzaingó*

> Obverse: Shield with 20 | DE | FEBRERO | 1827 surmounted by a Liberty cap, with 3 lances to either side above, and banners beneath

Obverse legend: LA PATRIA A LOS
VENCEDORES EN YTUZAINGO
Shape: Oval
Metal: Bronze, repoussé

Reference: http://www.fraymacho.blogspot
.com/2012/05/condecoraciones.html,
accessed July 18, 2012

THE GREAT WAR (1839–1852)

URUGUAYANS divided themselves politically between the Blanco and Colorado parties. The Blanco Party was supported by rural landowners and the Argentine dictator Juan Manuel de Rosas. The Colorados drew their support from merchants in Montevideo allied with Britain, France, and Brazil. Fighting went on for more than a dozen years, during which the Blancos laid siege to Montevideo, which was controlled by the Colorados. Finally, in 1851, Uruguay and Brazil were joined by the Argentine Province of Entre Rios, and they all declared war on the Argentine dictator Rosas.

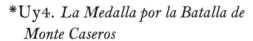
*Uy4. *La Medalla por la Batalla de Monte Caseros*

The Battle of Monte Caseros was fought in Buenos Aires Province on February 3, 1852. The allies had a numerical superiority with thirty thousand men under arms, although only the Brazilian contingent consisted of trained professionals. Uruguay sent a contingent of 1,500 men and artillery. Argentine caudillo Justo José de Urquiza from Entre Rios provided 80 percent of the allied manpower. The battle lasted for only three hours, but it ended in a decisive victory for the allies. Rosas was slightly wounded. He resigned and boarded a British warship for exile in Europe. Urquiza entered

Buenos Aires and went on to become a constitutional president of the Argentine Confederation. The Uruguayan government authorized a medal for the allied officers and men who fought in the Battle of Monte Caseros.

Instituted: By President Suarez, on February 13, 1852

Classes: Chiefs, officers, enlisted men*

Obverse legend: EL GOBIERNO DE LA REPUBLICA ORIENTAL DEL URUGUAY

Obverse inscription: AL | VENCEDOR | EN MONTE | CASEROS

Reverse inscription: 3 DE | FEBRERO | DE | 1852

Shape: Oval

Size: 40 × 30 mm

Metal: Chiefs: gold; officers: silver; enlisted men: bronze

Ribbon: Light blue

Reference: Gillingham 1932, 163; http://www.medals.org.uk/uruguay/uruguay005.htm, accessed July 8, 2012

THE WAR AGAINST AGUIRRE (1864–1865)

THE WAR against Aguirre pitted the Uruguayan Blanco Party under President Atanasio Aguirre against the Empire of Brazil, Argentina, and the Uruguayan Colorado Party under Venancio Flores. The war was both a continuation of the decades' long internal struggle between the Colorado and Blanco parties and a prelude to the War of the Triple Alliance.

*Uy5. *La Medalla por la Defensa de Paysandú*

Pedro II of Brazil gave his support to the Uruguayan Colorados in their long-standing struggle against the Blancos and issued an ultimatum to Uruguayan President Aguirre. The ultimatum was rejected, and Brazil invaded Uruguay. In December 1864, the Brazilians laid siege to Paysandú, a port town on the Uruguay River, which controlled traffic up and down that waterway. Despite being outnumbered in men and equipment, the Uruguayan defenders held out for one month. Following the town's surrender on January 2, the senior Uruguayan officers, including General Leandro Gómez, were executed by the Colorados. The Brazilian invasion of Uruguay convinced Paraguayan dictator Francisco Solano López to attack Brazil and declare war on Argentina, which led to the

Triple Alliance War, the bloodiest military conflict in Latin American history.

The Medal for the Defense of Paysandú was awarded by the Uruguayan government to the surviving Blanco troops from that siege. It is known in three variant forms.

*Uy5a. *Variant 1*

Obverse: Bust of General Leandro Gómez, left

Obverse legend: GENERAL LEANDRO GOMEZ | GEFE DE LA PLAZA

Reverse: Arms of Uruguay

Reverse legend: DEFENSA NACIONAL | 1864 PAYSANDU 1865

Size: 30 mm

Metal: Silver, bronze*

*Uy5b. *Variant 2*

Obverse: Bust of General Leandro Gomez, left, laurel branches beneath

Uy 5a

Uy 5a

Uy 5b

Uy 5b

Obverse legend: Gᴿᴬᴸ ʟᴇᴀɴᴅʀᴏ ɢᴏᴍᴇᴢ

Reverse legend: ʜᴇʀᴏɪᴄᴀ ᴅᴇꜰᴇɴꜱᴀ | 1865

Reverse inscription: ᴅᴇ | ᴘᴀʏꜱᴀɴᴅᴜ́

Size: 27 mm

Metal: Gilt

*Uy5c. *Variant 3*

Obverse: Bust of General Leandro Gómez,
left

Reverse: Laurel branch

Reverse inscription: ʜᴏɴᴏʀ ᴀʟ ʜᴇʀᴏᴇ |
ʟᴇᴀɴᴅʀᴏ ɢᴏᴍᴇᴢ | ᴘᴀʏꜱᴀɴᴅᴜ́ | 2 ᴇɴᴇʀᴏ
1865

Size: 27 mm

Metal: Gilt

Reference: Gillingham 1932, 166; http://
www.medals.org.uk/uruguay/uruguay00
.htm, accessed July 8, 2012

Tʜᴇ Tʀɪᴘʟᴇ Aʟʟɪᴀɴᴄᴇ Wᴀʀ (1864–1870)

Pᴀʀᴀɢᴜᴀʏᴀɴ dictator Solano López had allied his country with the Blancos. When Brazil invaded Uruguay, Solano López responded by attacking the Brazilian fort at Coimbra in Matto Grosso on the Paraguay River. He also declared war on Argentina and marched south along the Paraná River, taking the riverine port of Corrientes. He then detached a large force to advance south along the Uruguay River.

*Uy6. *La Medalla por Yatay*

The Yatay Medal was awarded to the Uruguayan troops who defeated a Paraguayan army in the Battle of Yatay on August 17, 1865. A ten thousand–man Paraguayan army crossed the Argentine province of Misiones and reached the Uruguay River under the command of Colonel Antonio Estigarribia. The Paraguayan strategy was to invade Rio Grande do Sul, free the slaves, and march down the river to invade

Uy 6

Uy 6

Uruguay, where they hoped to join their Blanco allies. Estigarribia split his army and marched south along both banks of the river. A Uruguayan force under the command of Uruguayan President Venancio Flores marched north and defeated the Paraguayans on the west bank of the river at Yatay.

The Paraguayans suffered heavy casualties. Estigarribia concentrated his forces in Uruguayana and waited for instructions from Solano López. This gave Brazil time to bring up its army to lay siege to Estigarribia's position. Estigarribia never received any orders from Solano López and surrendered.

The Battle of Yatay was strategically important because it cut short the Paraguayan invasion south and the Paraguayans were never again able to mount a major offensive. The battle was significant for Uruguay because its soldiers played the leading role in defeating the Paraguayans. Because of its small population, the Uruguayans usually made up only a small part of the allied forces facing the Paraguayans.

Instituted: By decree on September 30, 1865

Classes: Chiefs,* officers,* enlisted men*

Obverse: Arms of Uruguay surrounded by battle flags, rising sun above

Obverse legend: VENCEDORES | DEL YATAY

Reverse inscription: 17 | DE | AGOSTO | DE | 1865 surrounded by a laurel wreath

Shape: Oval

Size: 33 × 28 mm

Metal: Chiefs: gold; officers: silver; enlisted men: copper

Ribbon: 4 blue and 5 white stripes

Reference: Gillingham 1932, 164–66; http://www.portalguarani.com/detalles_museos_exposiciones.php?id=91&id_exposicion=277, accessed July 7, 2012

*Uy7. *La Cruz de la República Oriental del Uruguay al Ejército Aliado contra el Paraguay*

The Medal of the Oriental Republic of Uruguay to the Allied Army against Paraguay was authorized and bestowed more than twenty years

Uy7

Uy 7
(reverses)

after the war ended. It was given to the troops of the three allied nations that defeated Paraguay as part of a reciprocal exchange of medals.

Instituted: By Presidential Decree on April 4, 1891

Classes: Chiefs,* officers,* enlisted men*

Obverse disc: Arms of Uruguay

Obverse legend: CAMPANA DEL PARAGUAY | 1865–1869

Reverse inscription: A LAS | VIRTUDES | MILITARES

Reverse legend: REPUBLICA ORIENTAL DEL URUGUAY

Shape: Cross with expanding pointed ends with a wreath in the angles, suspended from a radiant sun

Size: 45 mm, 42 mm

Metal: Badge: iron. Suspension sun: chiefs: gold; officers: silver; enlisted men: bronze

Ribbon: Red

Reference: Gillingham 1932, 164–66; Pratt Mayans 2007, 160–64; http://www .portalguarani.com/detalles_museos_ exposiciones.php?id=27, accessed April 18, 2012

POSTBELLUM URUGUAY

THE END OF the Triple Alliance War allowed Uruguayans to focus on building their nation without military intervention from either Argentina or Brazil. The Blancos and Colorados never resolved their differences, but they argued in the Congress rather than on the battlefield. The country was able to build a credible record of peaceful democratic government. With the exception of the 1891 commemorative medal for its allies in the Triple Alliance War, Uruguay did not authorize any new military medals until well after the end of World War II. The country broke diplomatic relations with the Central Powers during World War I but never fought.

At the height of the Cold War, political rivalries in Uruguay upset the democratic balance, and the period was marked by official repression and guerrilla warfare. In 1973, the Uruguayan military staged a coup d'état and arrested much of the leadership of the Tupamaro *Movimiento de Liberación Nacional*. A military junta ruled Uruguay until 1985, when constitutional rule was reestablished. During that time, the junta created the Order of the Oriental Republic of Uruguay (see below) and three military orders, but no military or police medals.

After the end of the cold war, Uruguay built up a small, professional military force, which it has sent around the world in support of UN peacekeeping missions. This has allowed the country to defray the cost of its military to the United Nations without impinging on the many social benefits enjoyed by Uruguayan citizens. The Uruguayan military has supervised elections in turbulent countries, engaged in rescue operations, disarmed local militias, controlled smuggling, imposed law and order, and separated armed rivals—all at the behest of the UN Security Council and as part of the United Nations peacekeeping budget. Uruguayan military have operated in Guatemala, Honduras-Nicaragua, Mozambique, Rwanda, Liberia, Angola, Tajikistan, Iran-Iraq, Cambodia, the Sinai Peninsula, the western Sahara, the Democratic Republic of the Congo, Sierra Leone, Iraq-Kuwait, Ethiopia-Eritrea, India-Pakistan, East Timor, Cyprus, and Georgia.

The Uruguayan troops have suffered casualties, both killed and wounded, during these operations. They have received military medals for merit and courage from the host countries and from the United Nations, as well as newly authorized Uruguayan military medals. Some of the medals were awarded posthumously.

*Uy8. *La Medalla al Mérito Aeronáutico*

The Medal for Aeronautical Merit is awarded mainly to air force officers for meritorious service in developing aviation in Uruguay. It may be awarded to other individuals for the same purpose.

Instituted: By Decree No. 770/76 of the Ministry of National Defense in 1976

Obverse: Eagle with upraised wings holding ribbon inscribed LIBERTAD, PAZ, TRABAJO | R.O. DEL URUGUAY | 1893 all beneath the bust of a man, ¾ left, with a half oak branch on the left and a half laurel branch on the right above the eagle's wings

Reverse inscription: AL | MERITO | AERONAUTICO

Reverse legend: FUERZA AEREA URUGUAYA | [engraved name of recipient]

Uy 8

Uy 8

Size: 35 mm

Metal: Gilt

Ribbon: Blue with white center stripe edged in red

Recipient: Brig. Gral. (Av.) Juan C. Jorge

Uy9. *La Medalla al Mérito Militar*

The Medal for Military Merit is given to civilians and military personnel, both national and foreign, for distinguished service or relevant personal action that deserves recognition by the army.

Instituted: By Decree No. 511/991 on September 17, 1991

Classes: 1st (heroism); 2nd (distinguished valor)

Reverse inscription: HEROISMO AL VALOR MILITAR

Shape: Cross

Size: 40 mm

Metal: 1st: gilt; 2nd: silver

Ribbon: Blue, white, red

Reference: Uruguay 2007

Uy10. *La Medalla del 18 de Mayo de 1811*

The Medal of May 18, 1811, is awarded to civilians and military personnel, both national and foreign, for distinguished service. It is named after the date of the Battle of Las Piedras, when Artigas won his first major battle against the royalists.

Instituted: By Decree No. 469 on December 16, 1997

Classes: 1st, 2nd, 3rd

Obverse: Blue, white, and blue circles within each other; a red stripe runs from upper left to lower right

Ribbon: White with 2 red side stripes, each edged in blue

Uy11. *La Medalla al Valor Militar*

The Medal for Military Valor is awarded to Uruguayan military personnel for outstanding accomplishments while on active duty or which by their nature raise the image and prestige of the army, or which denote acts of valor or heroism. The medal is awarded in two classes, according to the importance of the accomplishment. Rank is not a factor in awarding this medal.

Instituted: By Decree No. 227/07 on June 25, 2007

Grades: 1st (Heroism); 2nd (Outstanding Valor)

Obverse disc: Stylized sun with 8 rays above a laurel and olive wreath, on a blue enameled field

Reverse legend: MEDALLA AL VALOR MILITAR

Shape: Cross (1st: red enameled)

Size: 40 mm

Metal: 1st: gilt; 2nd: silver

Ribbon: Blue, white, red

Reference: http://archivo.presidencia .gub.uy/_Web/decretos/2007/06/ ASUNTO152_28%2005%202007_ 00001.PDF, accessed April 21, 2012

ORDERS

FOR MOST of its history, Uruguay chose not to authorize orders of state for merit. Orders had been associated with monarchy and nobility in the minds of Uruguayan republicans. This attitude changed during the military junta that ruled Uruguay from 1972 to 1985, under which four orders of state were authorized. These orders were officially rescinded in 1985, but the three military ones are still being awarded. A fifth award, known as Protector de los Pueblos Libres General José Artígas, is said to have been instituted for the struggle against terrorism and subversion, but no reference to specific legislation or executive regulation is known.

*Uy12. *La Orden Militar al Mérito Aeronáutico*

The Military Order of Aeronautical Merit is awarded to civilians and military personnel, both national and foreign, for outstanding services to the country's aviation. In 1978, the air force bestowed the order on the First Engineer Combat Battalion of the Army for its work in building the international airport of Montevideo.

Instituted: By Decree No. 770 on November 24, 1976

Rescinded: By Law No. 15,738 on March 6, 1985

Divisions: Military, civilian

Grades: Grand Cross,* Grand Officer,* Commander, Officer, Knight

Obverse: 8-pointed sun with rays in the angles

Reverse inscription: AL | MERITO | AERONAUTICO

Shape: Blue enameled Maltese cross (civilian) with crossed swords (military), suspended from eagle in flight

Star shape: 8-pointed sun on a blue

Uy 12
Grand
Cross
(military)

Uy 12
Grand Cross (military) badge
(reverse)

Uy 12
Grand Officer
(civilian)

enameled field with legend AL MERITO
AERONAUTICO on a blue enameled band on
an 8-pointed star with 5 rays in each angle

Size: Badge: 60 mm. Star: 90 mm

Metal: Badge: gilt. Star: silvered

Ribbon: Red with white center stripe and narrow white edge stripes

Maker: N. S. Meyer, Inc., New York

Reference: http://www.parlamento.gub.uy/
leyes/ley15738.htm, accessed April 18, 2012

*Uy13. *La Orden Militar al Mérito de los Tenientes de Artigas*

The Order of Military Merit of the Companions
of Artigas was instituted by the military junta.
It was given to military and civilian personnel,
both foreign and national, who provided distinguished service to the army. A law modifying

the order a year later broadened the eligibility
to include service to the Uruguayan air force.

Instituted: By Law No. 14,955 on November
13, 1979

Modified: By Law No. 15,066 on October 7,
1980

Rescinded: By Law No. 15,738 on March 6,
1985

Grand Master: President of the Republic

Divisions: Military, civilian

Grades: Grand Cross, Grand Officer,* Commander,* Officer,* Knight*

Obverse disc: Grand Officer: enameled arms
of Uruguay on a white enameled field surrounded by a blue enameled band with a
red diagonal stripe; Commander, Officer,
Knight: 8-pointed sun

Reverse inscription: ORDEN | MILITAR | AL |
MERITO

Shape: Blue enameled Maltese cross (civilian)
with crossed swords (military); Commander:
suspended from eagle in flight

Star shape: 8-pointed sun on a blue enameled

Uy 13
Grand Officer
(civilian)

Uy 13
Commander
(military)

Uy 13
Commander
(military)

Uy 13
Officer
(military)

Uy 13
Officer
(military)

Uy 13
Knight

Uy 13
Knight

field with legend ORDEN MILITAR AL MERITO on a blue enameled band on an 8-pointed star with 5 rays in each angle

Size: Badge: Grand Officer: 62 mm; Commander: 60 mm; Officer: 43 mm; Knight: 40 mm. Star: 80 mm

Metal: Badge: Grand Officer, Commander, Officer: gilt; Knight: silvered. Star: silvered

Ribbon: Red with narrow white and blue edge stripes

Maker: N. S. Meyer, Inc., New York

Reference: http://www.en.wikipedia.org/wiki/Order_of_Military_Merit_of_the_Companions_of_Artigas, accessed July 8, 2012

Uy 14. *La Orden "Honor al Mérito Naval Comandante Pedro Campbell"*

The Order "Honor for Naval Merit Commander Pedro Campbell" was awarded to national or foreign military personnel or civilians who had performed an important service to the navy. The award could also be given to military units, public and private institutions, national or foreign, for performing a service the navy wished to recognize.

Pedro Campbell (1780–1832) was born in Ireland. He joined the British army and was sent to the South Atlantic in 1807 to participate in the assault on Buenos Aires and Montevideo. Campbell deserted and joined the revolutionary forces of José Artigas. He became known commonly as the Irish Gaucho. In 1818, Artigas made Campbell commander of Uruguay's naval forces. He later accepted a letter of marque from Artigas and became a corsair, capturing many commercial vessels.

The Uruguayan Navy has also taken an active part in United Nations peacekeeping operations around the world. From 1991 to 1993, it conducted river patrols in Cambodia. In 2001, the navy provided river patrols in the Democratic Republic of the Congo and was called on to rescue passengers from river boats. The president of Uruguay bestowed the Order "Honor for Naval Merit Commander Pedro Campbell" on the Uruguayan Riverine Patrol Company in the Congo. In 2004, the navy supplied coastal patrols along the Haitian coast and intercepted marijuana shipments from Jamaica.

Instituted: By Law No. 15,068 on October 14, 1980

Rescinded: By Law No. 15,738 on March 6, 1985

Grades: Great Medal, Medal

Reference: http://www.parlamento.gub.uy/ leyes/ley15068.htm, accessed April 18, 2012; http://www.armada.mil.uy/armada_ misiones_de_paz.html, accessed July 18, 2012

*Uy15. *La Orden de la República Oriental del Uruguay*

The Order of the Eastern Republic of Uruguay was instituted in the last year of the military junta and was rescinded shortly after constitutional rule returned to the country in 1985. It was awarded to foreign citizens in recognition of their meritorious contributions to the nation on the basis of reciprocity. The order was headed by the president of the republic, without the title of grand master.

Instituted: By Law No. 15,529 on February 21, 1984

Rescinded: By Law No. 15,738 on March 6, 1985

President: President of the Republic

Grades: Collar, Grand Cross,* Sash (for ladies only), Commander, Officer, Knight*

Obverse disc: Blue and white enameled arms of Uruguay surrounded by a wreath and on a ribbon below: ORDEN DE LA REPUBLICA

Uy 15
Knight

Shape: Blue and white enameled cross with 6 rays in the angles

Star shape: Blue and white enameled cross superimposed on an 8-pointed star with 6 rays in each angle

Size: Badge: 51 mm. Star: 92 mm

Metal: Grand Cross: gilt; Knight: silver

Ribbon: Blue, white

Maker: Cejalvo, Madrid

Reference: http://www.parlamento.gub.uy/ leyes/ley15529.htm>, accessed April 18, 2012; http://www.gmic.co.uk/index.php/ topic/54205-order-of-the-eastern-republic-of-uruguay, accessed June 26, 2012

Uy 15
Grand Cross

VENEZUELA

VENEZUELA proclaimed its independence on July 5, 1811. The initial revolutionary enthusiasm was not shared by all Venezuelans, however, and a year later royalist forces reestablished colonial rule in Caracas. Venezuela's liberator, Simón Bolívar went into exile, but he raised another army, returned, and defeated the royalists at Cúcuta. Bolívar triumphantly entered Caracas in 1813. Like his compatriot, Francisco de Miranda, Bolívar dreamed of a united Spanish American republic, and he next led his army to liberate New Granada (today's Colombia). In December 1814, he occupied Bogotá, but Spanish reinforcements forced him into exile again.

In 1816, Bolívar set sail from Haiti back to Venezuela. He allied himself with José Antonio Páez, the leader of the *llaneros*, a Venezuelan version of the Argentine gaucho. Bolívar made a historic march over the Andes with these *llaneros* and defeated the royalists at the historic Battle of Boyacá on August 7, 1819. Bolívar returned once again to Venezuela and defeated the royalists at the key Battle of Carabobo on June 24, 1821. With Venezuela securely independent, Bolívar left to liberate the rest of South America.

Independence did not bring peace to Venezuela. The country became a battleground for regional caudillos, starting with José Antonio Páez. He proclaimed himself president of Venezuela following the dissolution of Gran Colombia in 1830 and allied himself with the creole conservative elite. He was succeeded by the Monagas brothers, who ruled with the backing of the liberals. In 1854, José Tadeo Monagas instituted the Medal of the Bust of Bolívar, the country's first decoration and the precursor of the Order of the Bust of Bolívar, Venezuela's highest award today.

For another hundred years, caudillos competed for power. All of the country's medals until after World War II were awarded for fighting among Venezuelans. Sometimes, a victorious caudillo would award a medal to his officers and men for defeating the government forces of his predecessors. They generally described their movements as revolutionary, with names such as the Revolución de Marzo (1858), the Revolución de las Reformas, the Revolución Federal, or the Revolución Azul, among others. The issues were similar to those in many other Latin American countries. Few Venezuelan presidents finished their constitutional terms during this period.

It was not until 1958, when Rómulo Betancourt was elected president, that Venezuela finally managed to break its long history of caudillo rule. Since Betancourt's presidency, every Venezuelan president has served his full term, and power has been peacefully transferred to another democratically elected president.

The institutionalization of Venezuela's democratic government has led to the creation of new orders of merit. Many of these orders were named after heroes of the War of Independence, such as Francisco de Miranda, Luis Brión, Rafael Urdaneta, José Antonio Páez, and José Félix Ribas. None of them were named after Venezuela's numerous caudillos.

Venezuela's recent president, Hugo Chávez, sought to promote his Bolivarian Revolution, somewhat patterned after the Cuban Revolution. Chávez restructured some of Venezuela's medals and orders. His orders were modified to promote his ideology rather than to reward service to the nation per se. As many of these medals and orders have been created quite recently, and we have seen neither descriptions nor the medals themselves, we are not able to include them here.

MEDALS

VENEZUELA began to authorize military medals at the beginning of the Federal War (1859–63), the country's worst civil conflict. None of Venezuela's nineteenth-century military medals were awarded for fighting an external enemy. Venezuela has not fought a foreign war since it became independent. All of its medals were awarded for domestic conflict. The civil war continued under different names and with differing intensities for generations. Venezuela did not begin to create medals for merit in peacetime until after World War II.

THE FEDERAL WAR (1859–1863)

THE FEDERAL WAR pitted liberal insurgents under Juan Crisóstomo Falcón against the conservative government. The war ended with the treaty of Coche in 1863, and Juan Falcón became president.

Ve1. *La Medalla de Santa Inés*

The Medal for Santa Inés was awarded to the officers and men of Juan Falcón's federalist army, which defeated the conservative forces of the central government near Santa Inés on December 1, 1859. This was the first of the decisive battles of the five-year Federal War between Venezuela's conservatives and liberals. Falcón instituted the medal shortly after the battle, but years before he became president.

Instituted: December 19, 1859

Modified: By Presidential Decree on February 3, 1864

Classes: Generals, chiefs, officers, enlisted men

Obverse: Image of Santa Inés surrounded by 20 stars

Reverse inscription: VENCEDOR EL 10 DE DICIEMBRE DE 1859

Shape: Oval

Metal: Gold, silver, bronze

Ribbon: Chiefs: blue, red, yellow; division generals: yellow; brigade generals: yellow, red; colonels: yellow; commanders: red; captains, lieutenants, enlisted men: blue

Reference: Pérez Tenreiro 1968, 42–43

Ve2. *La Medalla al Valor Militar*

The Medal for Military Valor was created by Juan Falcón to reward his officers at the end of Venezuela's civil war.

Instituted: October 2, 1863

Obverse inscription: AL VALOR surrounded by a laurel wreath

Reverse inscription: VENEZUELA REGENERADA

Shape: Round

Metal: Gold

Ribbon: Blue, red, yellow

Reference: Pérez Tenreiro 1968, 41–42

Ve3. *La Estrella de la Federación*

The Star of the Federation was awarded to generals, chiefs, and officers who fought in the Federal War against the central government. To be eligible, a candidate had to have fought and won at least three separate military engagements between February 20, 1859, and June 15, 1863.

Instituted: February 5, 1864

Obverse: DF [for *Dios* and *Federación*]

Reference: Pérez Tenreiro 1968, 44

Ve4. *La Medalla de la Asamblea Nacional Constituyente*

The Medal of the Constitutional National Assembly was awarded to all the chiefs and officers of the federal army, who remained loyal to the federalist cause from 1859 to 1864.

Instituted: By Decree on April 8, 1864

Obverse Image of Liberty

Reverse: 20 stars

Reverse inscription: LA ASAMBLEA CONSTITUYENTE 1864 A LOS GUARDIANES DE LA CONSTITUCION

Metal: Gold

Reference: Pérez Tenreiro 1968, 44–45

THE BLUE REVOLUTION (1867–1868)

FALCÓN'S victory at the end of the Federal War did not bring peace to Venezuela. Regional caudillos took up arms against him. By late 1867, the insurgency, led by General Miguel Antonio Rojas, became more organized. The insurgents flew a blue flag, which gave the name to the Blue Revolution. In April 1868, Falcón resigned and went into exile in Curaçao. In May, Rojas entered Caracas with his army. After much political bickering, general José Ruperto Monagas was named provisional president.

Ve5. *La Medalla de los Libertadores de Caracas*

The Medal for the Liberators of Caracas was awarded to the generals, chiefs, officers, and noncommissioned officers who belonged to the army that took Caracas on June 25, 1868.

> Instituted: By Presidential Decree No. 1,638 on July 5, 1868
>
> Classes: Generals, chiefs, commissioned officers, noncommissioned officers

> Obverse inscription: LIBERTADOR DE CARACAS
>
> Reverse inscription: UNION Y LIBERTAD
>
> Shape: Oval
>
> Metal: Generals, chiefs: gold; commissioned officers: silver; noncommissioned officers: copper
>
> Ribbon: Blue
>
> Reference: Pérez Tenreiro 1968, 45–46

THE APRIL REVOLUTION (1870–1877)

IN FEBRUARY 1870, Antonio Guzmán Blanco (1829–99), son of the founder of the Venezuelan Liberal Party, landed in Venezuela with his forces and quickly gained support from local caudillos. In April, he defeated the forces of interim president Guillermo Tell Villegas, took Caracas, and installed himself as provisional president with extraordinary powers. Guzmán ruled for the next seven years as a dictator.

Ve6. *La Medalla de la Campaña de Apure*

President Guzmán Blanco authorized the Medal for the Apure Campaign, which was awarded to the chiefs and officers who participated in the campaign for Apure against the conservative forces.

> Instituted: By Presidential Decree on December 18, 1872
>
> Classes: Generals, colonels, other officers
>
> Obverse inscription: EL GENERAL GUZMAN BLANCO PRESIDENTE DE LA REPUBLICA A LOS VALIENTES DEL EJERCITO VENCEDOR DE APURE surrounded by a laurel wreath
>
> Reverse inscription: GRAN BATALLA DE APURE
>
> Size: 40 mm
>
> Metal: Generals, colonels: gold; other officers: silver
>
> Reference: Pérez Tenreiro 1968, 47

Ve7. *La Medalla de la Campaña de Potrerito y Tinaquillo*

Conservative forces commanded by General Matías Salazar continued to fight the central government after the battle of Apure. The government forces engaged Matías in what became known as the Campaign of Potrerito y Tinaquillo during April and May 1872. The Medal for the Campaign was given to the victorious chiefs and officers.

> Instituted: By Presidential Decree on December 18, 1872
>
> Classes: Generals, colonels, other officers
>
> Obverse inscription: CAMPANA | DE | POTRERITO | I TINAQUILLO surrounded by a laurel wreath
>
> Reverse inscription: EL GENERAL | GUZMAN | BLANCO PRESIDENTE | DE LA REPUBLICA | A EL EJERCITO | VENCEDOR | EN

POTRERITO │ I TINAQUILLO surrounded
by a laurel wreath

Size: 40 mm

Metal: Generals, colonels: gold; other officers:
silver

Reference: Pérez Tenreiro 1968, 48

Ve8. *La Medalla de la Campaña de 1874, Llamada de la "Lealtad"*

In October 1874, another insurgency took shape
among disaffected liberals and a few conservatives, commanded by General León Colina. By
early 1875, the rebellion had been suppressed,
and Colina surrendered. Guzmán awarded the
"Loyalty" Medal for the 1874 Campaign, for
bravery and loyalty.

Instituted: By Presidential Decree on July 30,
1876

Classes: Military and civilian chiefs, their
subordinates

Obverse inscription: GUZMAN A LA LEALTAD
DE [name of recipient] surrounded by a laurel wreath

Reverse inscription: CAMPANA DE 1874
surrounded by a laurel wreath

Shape: Oval

Size: 40 × 30 mm

Metal: Military and civilian chiefs: gold; subordinates: silver

Reference: Pérez Tenreiro 1968, 51

*Ve9. *La Estrella de la Regeneración de Venezuela*

The Star of the Regeneration of Venezuela
was awarded to military personnel and civilians who participated in the capture of Caracas by the forces of Antonio Guzmán Blanco
on April 27, 1870. The medal was also given to
those who supported the seventy-day campaign
during Guzmán's self-proclaimed "Regenera-

Ve 9

Ve 9

tion of the Fatherland," and to persons who
helped consolidate his power after he became
president. The medals that were issued at the

time did not always exactly fit the description below.

Instituted: September 1, 1876

Class: Officer*

Obverse inscription: 27 | DE ABRIL | DE 1870

Obverse legend: REGENERACION DE VENEZUELA

Reverse legend: GUZMAN BLANCO Á [name of the recipient]

Shape: Green enameled star

Size: 40 mm

Metal: Gilt

Ribbon: Yellow

Reference: Pérez Tenreiro 1968, 52

Ve10. *La Medalla de "La Guardia"*

General Guzmán Blanco authorized this medal for the chiefs and officers of the "La Guardia" Regiment for its loyalty and services from 1870 to the date of his decree.

Instituted: By Presidential Decree 2,014 on January 18, 1877

Obverse: Bust of Guzmán Blanco

Reverse inscription: GUZMAN BLANCO A LOS JEFES Y OFICIALES DE LA GUARDIA 1877

Shape: Oval

Size: 40 × 30 mm

Metal: Gold

Reference: Pérez Tenreiro 1968, 53

THE LEGALISTIC REVOLUTION (1892)

IN EARLY 1892, President Raimundo Andueza Palacio, a political independent, sought to increase the presidential term from two to four years. A caudillo, general Joaquín Sinforiano de Jesús Crespo, a former liberal president, raised an army in opposition, defeated Andueza's forces, and entered Caracas at the head of his army. During his presidency, Crespo and the National Assembly authorized at least three medals for his military personnel and civilian supporters.

Ve11. *La Medalla de Jobo Mocho*

The Medal of Jobo Mocho was created by Crespo to reward the chiefs, officers, and enlisted men who fought in the Battle of Jobo Mocho on April 15, 1892.

Instituted: By Executive Resolution of Joaquín Crespo on February 11, 1893

Obverse inscription: COMBATE | DE | JOBO MOCHO | 15 DE ABRIL | DE 1892

Reverse: Arms of Venezuela

Reverse legend: REVOLUCION NACIONAL

Size: 30 mm

Metal: Bronze

Ribbon: Blue, red, yellow

Designer: E. Pastells

Reference: Pérez Tenreiro 1968, 56–58

Ve12. *La Medalla a las Mujeres Venezolanas*

The Medal for Venezuelan Women was created to recognize the widows, wives, mothers, and sisters of the chiefs, who sent men to fight for the revolutionary army, and the women who supported Crespo's second term in office.

Instituted: By Joaquín Crespo on March 15, 1893

Obverse: Image of Liberty beneath the 7 stars of the federation and above "1892"

Reverse: Arms of Venezuela

Reverse legend: EL GOBIERNO DE LA
REVOLUCION A LAS DIGNAS HIJAS DE
LA PATRIA

Shape: Oval

Size: 54 × 37 mm

Grades: Gold, silver, white metal

Reference: Pérez Tenreiro 1968, 58–59

Ve13. *La Medalla de la Gratitud Nacional*

The National Assembly created the Medal of National Gratitude for the chiefs, officers, and enlisted men of the army who fought with General Crespo against the army of president Andueza Palacio in 1892.

> Instituted: By Decree of the National Assembly on June 19, 1893
>
> Classes: 1st: chiefs; 2nd: officers; 3rd: enlisted men
>
> Obverse: Arms of Venezuela
>
> Obverse legend: ACUERDO DE LA ASAMBLEA NACIONAL 1893
>
> Reverse inscription: LA PATRIA AGRADECIDA A SUS DEFENSORES
>
> Size: 30 mm
>
> Metal: 1st: gold; 2nd: silver; 3rd: nickel
>
> Ribbon: Blue, red, yellow
>
> Reference: Pérez Tenreiro 1968, 59

* * *

Ve14. *La Estrella de Tocuyito*

General Cipriano Castro awarded the Medal of Tocuyito to the chiefs, officers, and enlisted men who fought with his Army of Liberal Restauration in the Battle of Tocuyito on September 14, 1899. One month later, Castro overthrew the government of Ignacio Andrade.

> Instituted: By General Cipriano Castro on September 1, 1900

Classes: 1st: chiefs; 2nd: officers; 3rd: enlisted men

Obverse: Arms of Venezuela

Obverse legend: DECRETO DEL JEFE SUPREMO DE LA REPUBLICA

Reverse inscription: LA NACION AGRADECIDA A SUS DEFENSORES surrounded by a laurel wreath

Shape: Star

Metal: 1st: gold; 2nd: silver; 3rd: bronze

Ribbon: Blue, red, yellow

Reference: Pérez Tenreiro 1968, 60

* * *

NO MORE medals are known to have been created until after World War II, when the country began instituting medals for merit unrelated to specific historical events.

*Ve15. *La Cruz de las Fuerzas Aéreas Venezolanas*

President Rómolo Ernesto Betancourt authorized Venezuela's first military medal for the air force barely two months after he took office in a coup d'état.

The Cross of the Venezuelan Air Force is given to both Venezuelan and foreign military for distinguished service to the Venezuelan air force. The cross may be conferred upon a foreign banner rather than an individual. The three classes of this medal are awarded for differing levels of merit, not for rank. The design of all three grades was changed in 1952.

> Instituted: By Decree No. 84 of the Junta Revolucionaria on December 10, 1945
>
> Regulated: April 23, 1947
>
> Regulated: By Presidential Decree No. 5 on December 5, 1952; Decree No. 84 was annulled
>
> Chief: President of the Republic
>
> Classes: 1st: for heroism in the face of the

Ve 15a

Ve 15b

Ve 15b

enemy with a favorable outcome or for the writing of a book used for training purposes; 2nd: for boldness in the face of the enemy, even if the outcome is not entirely favorable, or for efficient performance; 3rd: for heroic acts under any circumstance, or for winning a sporting event, or for being top student in a training class

*Ve15a. *Variant 1*

Obverse disc: FAV

Obverse: A gilt propeller is etched at the end of each arm

Shape: Maltese cross with a gilt propeller at the end of each arm and a laurel wreath in the angles, suspended by a ribbon from wings displayed with the arms of Venezuela in the center

Size: 42 mm

Metal: 1st: gilt;* 2nd: silvered;* 3rd: copper*

Ribbon: Yellow, blue, red

*Ve15b. *Variant 2*

Obverse disc: FAV

Reverse inscription: 10 DE | DICIEMBRE | DE 1920

Shape: Green enameled cross pattée with a gilt propeller at the end of each arm and a laurel wreath in the angles, attached to wings displayed with the arms of Venezuela in the center

Size: 41 mm

Metal: Gilt

Ribbon: Green with 2 blue side stripes; 1st: neck ribbon; 2nd: suspension ribbon;* 3rd: no ribbon, pinback*

Reference: Pérez Tenreiro 1968, 115–30

*Ve16. *La Cruz de las Fuerzas Armadas de Cooperación*

Also known as the Cross of the National Guard, this cross is conferred on members of the National Guard for outstanding service. The cross

may also be conferred on servicemen from the other branches of the armed forces, as well as civilians. The minister of defense and the commander in chief of the armed forces receive the 1st class of the order because of their rank. Other recipients receive the class corresponding to the level of merit. Eligibility requirements are similar to those of the Cross of the Venezuelan Air Force.

Instituted: By Decree No. 434 of the Government Junta on August 2, 1952

Regulated: By Presidential Decree on December 5, 1952

Classes: 1st,* 2nd, 3rd*

Obverse disc: Arms of the Venezuelan National Guard on a red enameled field

Obverse legend: EL HONOR ES SU DIVISA on a red enameled band

Reverse legend: FUERZAS ARMADAS DE COOPERACION | VENEZUELA

Shape: White enameled, gilt-edged Maltese cross with 2-pointed ends, attached to a half wreath

Size: 59 mm

Metal: Gilt

Ribbon: Red with narrow yellow edge stripes; 1st: neck ribbon

Reference: Pérez Tenreiro 1968, 68–70; http://venciclopedia.com/index.php?title= Cruz_de_las_Fuerzas_Armadas_de_ Cooperación, accessed April 25, 2012

*Ve17. *La Cruz de las Fuerzas Terrestres Venezolanas*

The Cross for Land Forces is a military decoration for distinguished service in the army. It is often also called the *Cruz del Ejército Venezolano*. The cross is also bestowed on civilians.

Instituted: By Decree No. 418 of the Government Junta on June 23, 1952

Regulated: By Presidential Decree No. 3 on December 5, 1952

Ve 16

Ve 16

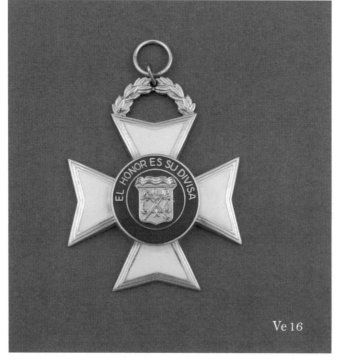

Ve 16

Ve 16

Ve 17a

Ve 17a

*Ve 17a. *Variant 1*

Classes: 1st,* 2nd,* 3rd*

Obverse inscription: HONOR | AL | MERITO surrounded by a green enameled wreath

Reverse inscription: FUERZAS TERRESTRES | DE | VENEZUELA surrounded by a wreath

Shape: Ball-tipped Maltese cross with double concave ends; 1st: enameled green; 2nd: enameled red and white; 3rd: enameled white

Size: 50 mm

Metal: Gilt

Maker: N. S. Meyer, New York

Ribbon: Green with white center stripe

Ve 17b

Ve 17b

*Ve17b. *Variant 2*

Obverse inscription: HONOR | AL | MERITO surrounded by a green enameled wreath

Reverse legend: CRUZ DEL EJERCITO | VENEZOLANO surrounded by a wreath

Shape: Ball-tipped, red enameled Maltese cross with double concave ends

Size: 54 mm

Metal: Gilt

Ribbon: Yellow with narrow red edge stripes

Reference: Pérez Tenreiro 1968, 66–67, 149–58

*Ve18. *La Medalla Naval "Almirante Luis Brión"*

The Naval Medal "Admiral Luis Brión" is awarded for professional and academic achievement in the navy. It may be given to civilians as well as military personnel and to Venezuelan as well as foreign citizens. The medal comes in only one class.

The medal was named after Admiral Luis Brión (1782–1821), who fought in the War of Independence. Born in Curaçao, Brión was a businessman who took up the cause of Venezuelan independence in 1813. He joined the Venezuelan navy and rose to the rank of admiral. He commanded the small fleet of schooners that transported Bolívar and his officers from Les Cayes in Haiti to Venezuela in 1816. He later liberated Guayana in eastern Venezuela and became its first governor. He died of tuberculosis in Curaçao.

Obverse disc: Crowned shield with Arms of Venezuela

Obverse legend: 24 DE JULIO DE 1820 | NAVIGARE NECESSE | VIVERE NECESSE

Reverse legend: MEDALLA NAVAL | ALMIRANTE BRION inscribed on outer band

Shape: 4-pointed star with 3 rays in each angle within a band

Size: 38 mm

Metal: Bronze

Ribbon: Blue, red

Reference: http://venciclopedia.com/index.php?title=Medalla_Naval_Almirante_Luis_Brión, accessed April 26, 2012

*Ve19. *La Medalla del Paso de los Andes*

The Medal for the Crossing of the Andes recognizes a strong work ethic. It is named after the epic crossing of the Andes by the forces of Simón Bolívar during the War of Independence,

Ve 18

Ve 19

Ve 18

Obverse: Man on horseback, right

Obverse legend: PASO DE LOS ANDES | ESPIRITU DE TRABAJO

Size: 32 mm

Metal: Silvered

Maker: N. S. Meyer, Inc., New York

Ribbon: Yellow with 3 narrow black center stripes

Reference: http://webspace.webring-com/ people/we/emlynccs/Pag_Militares/EJV_ Medalla_Paso_de_los_Andes-htm, accessed August 21, 2012

*Ve20. *La Medalla de Honor Augusto Pinaud de la Cruz Roja Venezolana*

when he crossed into Colombia from Venezuela to defeat the Spanish forces at the Battle of Boyacá. The award is bestowed annually on June 24 (Army Day) to army officers.

The Venezuelan Red Cross awards the Augusto Pinaud Medal of Honor for service to the institution. Augusto Pinaud was a Venezuelan physician.

Obverse: Red enameled cross on a white field
Obverse legend: CRUZ ROJA VENEZOLANA |
  1895 on a blue enameled band surrounded
  by a wreath
Reverse: Arms of Venezuela

Reverse legend: AUGUSTO PINAUD | HONOR
  AL MERITO
Size: 46 mm
Metal: Gilt
Ribbon: Red neck ribbon

ORDERS

THE WAR of Independence in Venezuela went on for more than a decade, and the fortunes of war favored one side and then the other. The first attempt to create a republican order was made by Francisco de Miranda during the First Republic on May 24, 1812, when he authorized the *Orden Civil y Militar del Mérito*. Miranda intended that his order take the form of a badge, but no examples have survived, and there is no documentation confirming that the badges were ever made.

Ve21. *La Orden de los Libertadores de Venezuela*

The Order of the Liberators of Venezuela was awarded to military officers from Gran Colombia and Venezuela who distinguished themselves fighting for the cause of independence. It is the first republican order.

Instituted: By Bolívar on October 22, 1813

Obverse: LIBERTADOR DE VENEZUELA

Reverse: SIMON BOLIVAR

Shape: 7-armed star (for the 7 provinces of Venezuela)

Metal: Gold

Ribbon: Yellow cord

Reference: Pérez-Tenreiro 1968, 6–11; Gillingham 1932, 167

*Ve22. *La Orden del Libertador*

The Order of the Liberator is Venezuela's highest official award. It is given to civilians and military personnel, both national and foreign, for service to Venezuela. It was first created as a medal (*Medalla de Distinción*) in 1854 by José Gregorio Monagas. The medal was designed with the bust of Bolívar on the obverse disc. The order itself was not created until 1880. Some of the decrees establishing the order referred to the "Bust of the Liberator" as having originated in Peru in 1825, when an order by that name was instituted. Venezuelan historians dispute this and argue that the Venezuelan Medal of Distinction became the basis for instituting the Order of the Liberator.

Lately, the order has often been awarded for political reasons related to President Hugo Chávez's policy of promoting his Bolivarian Revolution. Recent recipients of the Grand Cross include Mahmoud Ahmadinejad, Bashar al-Assad, and Muammar al-Gaddafi.

Instituted: By Legislative Decree on March 11, 1854 (the Medal of Distinction)

Modified: September 14, 1880 (creating the Order of the Liberator)

Confirmed: By Law on May 3, 1881

Revised: By Decree on December 29, 1881

Revised: On June 19, 1912 (Council of the Order established)

Regulated: On June 15, 1922 (current statutes approved)

Chief: President of the Republic

Grades: Collar,* Grand Cross,* Grand Officer, Officer,* Knight

Obverse disc: Bust of Bolívar, right

Obverse legend: SIMON BOLIVAR, laurel branches below, on a blue enameled band

Reverse: Arms of Venezuela

Shape: Oval with twenty-eight 2-pointed rays

Star shape: 8-pointed faceted star with 5 rays in each angle

Collar: Badge suspended from silhouette disc with arms of Venezuela within green

Ve22
Grand Cross
badge (reverse)

Ve 22
Collar

Ve 22
Grand Cross

Ve 22
Officer

Ve 22
Officer

enameled laurel wreath with reversed fleur de lys at bottom, suspended from collar of alternating discs connected by double chain: intertwined ornate letters S and B in red and blue enamel; arms of Venezuela within green enameled laurel wreath

Size: Badge: Collar: 47 × 44 mm; Grand Cross: 52 × 47 mm; Knight: 52 × 47 mm. Star: 86 × 80 mm

Metal: Badges, collar: gilt bronze. Star: silver

Makers: Star: Le Mâitre, Paris; Arthus Bertrand, Paris; Halley, Paris; G. Wolfers, Brussels; S. Picard & Cia., Caracas; Gathmann Hnos., Caracas; J. C. Ammé & Cia., Caracas; La Royale, Rio de Janeiro; Russell Uniform Co., New York; N. S. Meyer, New York

Ribbon: Red, light blue, yellow

Reference: Pérez Tenreiro 1968, 63–78; Gillingham 1932, 167–69

*Ve23. *La Orden al Mérito*

The Order of Merit is given to Venezuelan and foreign civilians and military personnel for service to the nation. The Venezuelan Congress instituted this order in 1861, the day before general José Antonio Páez replaced Pedro Gual Escandón as president.

Instituted: By Congressional Decree on August 28, 1861

Grades: Grand Cross, Commander, Knight*

Obverse disc: Arms of Venezuela

Obverse legend: REPUBLICA DE VENEZUELA on a blue enameled band

Reverse inscription: 29 AGOSTO 1861

Reverse legend: HONOR AL MERITO on a blue enameled band

Shape: Ball-tipped, 6-pointed, white enameled, star with a green enameled wreath in the angles

Ve 23
Knight

Ve 23
Knight

Size: 42 mm

Metal: Gilt

Ribbon: Red with narrow light blue edge
   stripes

Reference: Gillingham 1932, 170

Provenance: A. Menke

Ve24. *La Legión de la Defensa Nacional*

The National Defense Legion is awarded to
both civilian and military personnel for defending Venezuela's sovereignty and independence. The award was authorized and awarded
by the Senate and was bestowed only in the
months following its institution, in response
to a blockade imposed by several European navies. Venezuela had defaulted on some of its
obligations to European creditors, and their
governments were threatening military action
unless payments were brought current. It was
never given for any other purpose. The first
grade was awarded only to heads of state, and
the number of awards was limited to twenty-
five. The second grade was limited to fifty recipients, while there was no limit on the third
grade.

Instituted: By Congressional Decree on
   April 11, 1903

Grades: 1st, 2nd, 3rd

Obverse disc: Arms of Venezuela

Reverse inscription: DEFENSA
   NACIONAL

Shape: Cross: 1st: enameled yellow; 2nd:
   enameled blue; 3rd: enameled red

Size: 35 mm

Metal: Gilt

Ribbon: 1st: white sash with narrow yellow,
   blue, red center stripes; 2nd, 3rd: neck
   ribbon; red, blue, yellow

Reference: Pérez Tenreiro 1968, 78–80;
   Gillingham 1932, 170

*Ve25. *La Orden de Francisco de Miranda*

The Order of Francisco de Miranda is awarded to Venezuelan citizens and foreign nationals for exceptional merit in science, progress of the country, and the humanities, or for outstanding merit. When awarded for combat, the badge is suspended from a laurel wreath with crossed swords.

Instituted: By Congressional Decree on June 23, 1943

Regulated: By law on July 14, 2006, which repealed the Decree of June 23, 1943

Chief: President of the Republic

Grades: Grand Cross,* Commander, Knight*

Obverse disc: Bust of Miranda, left, on oval disc

Obverse legend: FRANCISCO DE MIRANDA with laurel branches beneath on a red enameled band

Reverse disc: Arms of Venezuela

Shape: 5-part Maltese cross with 2-pointed ends and a 5-part, 2-pointed ray in each angle joined by a band

Ve 25
Knight

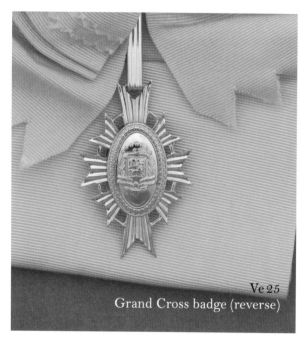

Ve 25
Grand Cross badge (reverse)

Ve 25
Knight

Ve 25
Grand Cross

Ve 26
1st grade

Ve 26
3rd grade

Star: FRANCISCO | DE | MIRANDA on red enameled disc surrounded by a silver wreath on an 8-pointed star with 5 rays in each angle

Size: Badge: Grand Cross: 45 × 38 mm; Knight 61 × 43 mm. Star: 80 mm

Metal: Gilt

Maker: N. S. Meyer, Inc., New York

Ribbon: Yellow

Reference: Pérez Tenreiro 1968, 85–91

*Ve26. *La Orden al Mérito Naval*

The Order of Naval Merit is given to Venezuelan and foreign military for distinguished service rendered to the Venezuelan navy. Acts of heroism represent the most important reason for awarding this order. Decisions on which grade to confer are based on the degree of heroism, not on the rank of the recipient. Other reasons for awarding the order are writing books used in teaching by the navy, carrying out difficult missions in peacetime, and efficient execution of professional functions. Foreigners may receive the order based on providing a valuable service to the Venezuelan navy. The minister of defense and the commander in chief of the navy receive the order based on their titles.

Instituted: By law on June 21, 1948

Regulated: By Decree No. 4 on December 5, 1952

Regulated: By Presidential Decree No. 476 on January 20, 1961; Decree No. 4 on December 5, 1952, was annulled

Chief: President of the Republic

Grades: 1st,* 2nd, 3rd*

Shape: Blue enameled, gilt-rimmed Maltese cross with 2-pointed ends and crossed blue enameled anchors in the angles suspended from 2 crossed blue enameled cannons

Size: 62 × 54 mm

Metal: Gilt

Maker: Distintivos Venezolanos

Ribbon: Blue, red, blue; 1st class: neck ribbon; 2nd class has a rosette attached to the red stripe

Reference: Pérez Tenreiro 1968, 135–46; http://venciclopedia.com/index.php?title=Orden_al_Mérito_Naval, accessed April 26, 2012

Ve27. *La Orden al Mérito del Ejército*

The Army Order of Merit is awarded to Venezuelan and foreign citizens for rendering service to the army. It may be given to military personnel from the other branches of the armed forces. Only one grade was authorized.

Instituted: 1948

Obverse: Arms of the army surrounded by 3 concentric black, red, and black enameled ovals, which in turn are surrounded by an enameled laurel wreath; below the wreath is a ribbon with HONOR on black enamel, EJERCITO on red enamel, and MERITO on black enamel

Reverse legend: MEDALLA ORDEN AL MERITO | DEL EJERCITO on a red enameled band

Shape: Oval

Metal: Gilt

Ribbon: Blue with 3 narrow red side and center stripes

Reference: http://venciclopedia.com/index.php?title=Orden_al_Mérito_del_Ejército, accessed April 26, 2012

*Ve28. *La Orden al Mérito en el Trabajo*

The Order of Labor Merit is awarded to employees and workers who have distinguished themselves by their efficiency, preparation, and perseverance in their work and for their support to Chávez's Bolivarian Revolution. The three classes of the order have been named after three men and three women. It may be awarded to Venezuelan and foreign citizens. It is not apparent how the appearance of the order differs for men and women.

Instituted: By law on April 28, 1954

Regulated: By Presidential Decree No. 173 on November 20, 1954

Modified: By Decree No. 6,043 on April 29, 2008, consolidating previous reforms and changing the design

Grades: Men: 1st: Alfredo Maneiro for 25 years' work;* 2nd: Antonio "Pope" for 16–25 years' work; 3rd: Pedro Pascual Abarca for 5–15 years' work; women: 1st: Eumalia Hernández for 25 years' work; 2nd: Carmen Clemente Travieso for 16–25 years' work; 3rd: Argelia Laya for 5–15 years' work

Obverse disc: Ploughman with ox to left, oil derrick above, book with calipers flanked by branches below

Reverse disc: Arms of Venezuela

Reverse legend: ORDEN AL MERITO EN EL TRABAJO | VENEZUELA

Shape: Cross with round arms bracketed by 2 rays on each side

Size: 61 mm

Metal: Gilt

Ribbon: 1st: yellow, blue; 2nd: yellow, red; 3rd: blue, red; all are neck ribbons

Reference: Pérez Tenreiro 1968, 175–91

Ve 28
1st grade

Ve 28
1st grade

Ve29. *La Orden del 27 de Junio*

The Order of June 27 was created in 1957 by Venezuelan dictator Marcos Pérez Jiménez to replace the Medal of Honor of June 27 (founded in 1949). The order recognizes distinguished service in education and years of teaching. It is awarded only to teachers in active service. Teachers who had previously been awarded the Medal of Honor of June 27 were eligible to receive the order. Recipients are required to pay for it: 250 bolivares for 1st grade, 150 for 2nd grade, and 100 for 3rd grade.

Instituted: By Legislative Decree on May 17, 1957; the decree annulled Decree No. 165 of June 22, 1949, which had created the Medal of Honor of June 27

Regulated: By Decree Law No. 561 on July 12, 1957

Grades: 1st: 30 years' service; 2nd: 20 years' service; 3rd: 15 years' service

Obverse: Open book from which a hand holds a lit torch with lines emanating from the flame

Obverse legend: XXVII VI MDCCCLXX

Reverse inscription: LA REPUBLICA DE VENEZUELA HONRA A LOS EDUCADORES, surrounded by a laurel wreath

Size: 40 mm

Metal: 1st: gold; 2nd: silver; 3rd: bronze

Ribbon: 1st: dark green with a narrow yellow center stripe; 2nd: dark green with a narrow blue center stripe; 3rd: dark green with a narrow red center stripe

Reference: Pérez Tenreiro 1968, 173–78

*Ve30. *La Orden de Andrés Bello*

The Order of Andrés Bello is awarded to persons for their contributions to education, scientific research, literature, and the arts. It may also be bestowed on persons who have aided cultural advances. It replaces the Medal of Public Instruction created in 1920.

The order is named for Andrés de Jesús María y José Bello López (1781–1865). Bello was perhaps Venezuela's most accomplished intellectual, although he lived most of his adult life in London and Santiago, Chile. He became a humanist, poet, legislator, philosopher, and educator. He left Venezuela in 1810 and never returned. He knew Miranda and Bolívar but remained in London throughout his country's War of Independence.

In 1843, he accepted a position with the Chilean Foreign Affairs Ministry in Santiago in the days of Diego Portales. He went on to become a senator, which position he used to create the University of Chile, that country's first university. He was made its first president, a title he held until his death. Bello wrote the first Spanish grammar for Hispanic Americans, and he drafted Chile's *Código Civil,* which was later adapted to Colombia and Ecuador. He died at the age of eighty-three in Santiago.

Instituted: By Congressional Decree on October 14, 1965; the Executive Decree of May 27, 1920, creating the Medal of Public Instruction was annulled

Regulated: By Presidential Decree No. 571 on June 17, 1966

Grades: Collar,* 1st class (Grand Cross),*

2nd class (Grand Officer), 3rd class (Knight)*

Obverse disc: Bust of Bello, ¾ left

Obverse legend: ANDRES BELLO, branches beneath, on a blue enameled band

Reverse disc: Open book that reads: EDUCACION CIENCIAS LETRAS ARTES

Reverse legend: REPUBLICA DE VENEZUELA on a blue enameled band

Shape: 7-armed, white enameled star superimposed on a 7-pointed gilt sun with 4 rays in each angle

Ve 30
Knight

Ve 30
Knight

Ve 30
Collar

Ve 30
Grand
Cross

Ve 30
Collar badge (reverse)

Ve 30
Grand Cross badge (reverse)

Star: Open book that reads: EDUCACION CIENCIAS LETRAS ARTES surrounded by the legend REPUBLICA DE VENEZUELA on a blue enameled band on a 7-pointed silver sun with 5 rays in each angle

Collar: Badge suspended from small 7-pointed sun with 2 rays in each angle, suspended from open book that reads: EDUCACION CIENCIAS LETRAS ARTES suspended from collar of alternating discs connected by double chain: script letters A and B in red and blue enamel; open book as above

Size: Badge: 45 mm. Star: Collar: 87 × 83 mm; Grand Cross: 78 mm

Metal: Badge: gilt. Star: silver

Maker: Collar star: Russell Uniform Co., New York

Ribbon: Purple with a very light blue center stripe

Reference: Pérez Tenreiro 1968, 115–17

Provenance: Grand Cross: A. Menke

*Ve31. *La Orden al Mérito Aeronáutico "Teniente Carlos Meyer Baldó"*

The Order of Aeronautical Merit "Lieutenant Carlos Meyer Baldó" is awarded to members of the air force for exceptional service. It only has one class.

The order is named for Carlos Meyer Baldó (1896–1933), a Venezuelan of German origin, who flew against the allies during World War I. He returned to Venezuela ten years after the war ended and was made a lieutenant in the Venezuelan air force. He died in an aviation accident in 1933.

Instituted: October 7, 1968

Obverse disc: Bust of Meyer Baldó, ¾ right

Reverse inscription: TTE CARLOS | MEYER BALDÓ | 1896–1933

Shape: Maltese cross with striated arms and

Ve 31

Ve 31

2-pointed ends and a wreath in the angles and a wreath in the angles and suspended from a bar with a propeller

Size: 51 mm

Metal: Gilt bronze

Ribbon: Light blue, hanging behind medal

Reference: http://venciclopedia.com/index .php?title=Orden_al_Mérito_Aeronáutico_ Teniente_Carlos_Meyer_Baldó, accessed April 26, 2012

Ve32. *La Orden Henri Pittier*

The Henri Pittier Order is awarded to persons who distinguish themselves in studying, teaching, and publishing works on the conservation of renewable natural resources, or who render preeminent service to agricultural research.

The order is named after Henri François Pittier (1857–1950), a Swiss botanist and naturalist, who became a pioneer in establishing national parks in Venezuela. He is credited with

writing nearly three hundred publications in the fields of botany, meteorology, ethnography, and linguistics.

Instituted: By Congressional Decree on August 5, 1974

Grades: 1st, 2nd, 3rd

Ribbon: Honey brown with a yellow center stripe

Reference: http://web.laoriental.com/ leyes/221-239/L227TOCapO.htm, accessed April 26, 2012

Ve33. *La Orden Brígido Iriarte*

The Brígido Iriarte Order is awarded to persons who render distinguished service to Venezuelan sports. It is named after Brígido Iriarte (1921–1984), a Venezuelan athlete. He participated in the 1955 and 1959 Pan American Games and the Helsinki Olympics. He competed in the men's long jump, javelin throw, and decathlon.

> Instituted: By law on July 2, 1985
>
> Grades: 1st, 2nd, 3rd
>
> Obverse: Bust of Iriarte, left, above inscription BRIGIDO IRIARTE
>
> Obverse legend: INSTITUTO NACIONAL DE DEPORTES
>
> Metal: 1st: gold; 2nd, 3rd: bronze
>
> Ribbon: Green, white
>
> Reference: http://venezuela.justia.com/ federales/leyes/ley, accessed April 26, 2012

Ve34. *La Orden José Félix Ribas*

The Order of José Félix Ribas is given to young people for outstanding participation in cultural, artistic, scientific, technological, pedagogical, environmental, and sporting activities that contribute to the development of humankind and of the nation.

Recipients are required to have strengthened the socialist state or promoted regional integration. The order is bestowed every year on February 12, "Youth Day."

The order is named after José Félix Ribas (1775–1815), a hero of the War of Independence. Ribas was born and educated in Caracas. He married an aunt of Bolívar and sympathized with the republican cause. He joined Miranda's *Sociedad Patriótica* and became involved in republican politics. Although not a military man, he was given a command. He won the Battle of La Victoria on February 12, 1814, against a royalist force of irregular *llaneros*. Ribas's troops were inexperienced university students and young recruits, whom he motivated before the battle with the words: "No podemos optar entre vencer o morir, es necesario vencer." The date of this battle was chosen for the annual Youth Day celebration in Ribas's name.

> Instituted: By Congress on July 28, 1987
>
> Reformed: By Law of the National Assembly on February 18, 2010
>
> Grades: 1st: international relevance; 2nd: Latin American relevance; 3rd: Venezuelan relevance
>
> Obverse inscription: ORDEN JOSE FELIX RIBAS
>
> Obverse legend: NO PODEMOS OPTAR ENTRE VENCER O MORIR | NECESARIO ES VENCER
>
> Reverse: Arms of Venezuela
>
> Reverse legend: MINISTERIO DEL PODER POPULAR DEL DESPACHO DE LA PRESIDENCIA DE LA REPUBLICA BOLIVARIANA DE VENEZUELA-INSTITUTO NACIONAL DEL PODER POPULAR DE LA JUVENTUD
>
> Metal: 1st: gold; 2nd: silver; 3rd: bronze
>
> Ribbon: 1st: red; 2nd: blue; 3rd: yellow
>
> Reference: http://www.SANC-REF-CREAC-ORDEN-JOSE-FELIX-RIVAS 18-02-10. pdf, accessed August 5, 2012; http://web .laoriental.com/leyes/001-019/ L018TOCapO.htm, accessed April 27, 2012

*Ve35. *La Orden de la Estrella de Carabobo*

The Star of Carabobo is a military decoration that recognizes outstanding service by members of the army. It may also be bestowed on members of the other branches of the armed forces as well as civilians. The order has also been conferred on foreign officials for promoting trade with Venezuela. The medal comes in one class.

The medal commemorates the Battle of Carabobo fought on June 24, 1821, between Spanish royalist forces under General La Torre and a revolutionary army led by Simón Bolívar. The revolutionaries carried the day, inflicting heavy casualties on the royalist troops, who retreated behind the defensive walls of Puerto Cabello.

Ve 35

Ve 35

The *llaneros* of General Páez played a critical role by punching through the royalist lines and attacking their rear. The battle allowed Bolívar to march on Caracas and finally achieve Venezuela's independence.

> Obverse disc: Arms of the Venezuelan army surrounded by decorative band
>
> Reverse legend: ESTRELLA DE CARABOBO
>
> Shape: Disc with 8 balls and 3 concentric bands from which emanates an 8-pointed star with 3 rays in each angle
>
> Size: 61 mm
>
> Metal: Silvered
>
> Maker: N. S. Meyer, Inc., New York
>
> Ribbon: Blue, red, blue

Ve36. *La Orden General de Brigada Francisco Conde*

The order was named after General Francisco Conde, a Venezuelan general, who fought in the War of Independence. In 1810, Conde joined the revolutionary army as a sergeant and fought in many engagements against the royalist forces. He gradually ascended in the ranks to brigadier general. At different times in his military career, he fought with Miranda, Bolívar, Páez, and Urdaneta. He later went into politics, rising to minister of war. His career ended when he sided with an insurgency, which failed, and he then retired from political life.

Ve 37

Ve 37

Grades: 1st, 2nd, 3rd

Obverse disc: Bust of Conde, facing

Shape: Red enameled star

Ribbon: Red with narrow black edge stripes; 1st: with black, red rosette over a white horizontal stripe; 2nd: with black, red rosette

*Ve37. *La Orden Militar de la Defensa Nacional*

Grades: Commander, Officer,* Knight

Obverse: Arms of Venezuela on a silver oval

Obverse legend: GLORIA AL BRAVO PUEBLO on a red enameled band surrounded by branches and stars on a blue enameled band

Reverse legend: ORDEN MILITAR DE LA DEFENSA NACIONAL

Shape: 26-pointed sun, surrounded by a wreath with red enameled arabesques at top and sides and a downward pointing arrow at bottom

Size: 95 × 75 mm

Metal: Gilt

Provenance: A. Menke

BIBLIOGRAPHY

Introductions & Bibliographies

CLAIN-STEFANELLI, Elvira E. 1985. *Numismatic Bibliography.* Pp. 1333–86. Munich.

HENNING, Eckhart, and Dietrick HERFURTH. 2010. *Orden und Ehrenzeichen: Handbuch der Phaleristik.* Cologne.

JACOB, Jeffrey R. 1978. *Court Jewelers of the World.* Cherry Hill, N.J.

LASLO, Alexander J. 1995. *A Glossary of Terms Used in Phaleristics: The Science, Study, and Collecting of the Insignia of Orders, Decorations and Medals.* Albuquerque, New Mex.

MULDER, C. P., and A. A. PURVES. 1999. *Bibliography of Orders and Decorations.* Copenhagen.

SCHARFENBERG, Gerd, and Günter THIEDE. 2010. *Lexikon der Ordenskunde: Von Adlerschild bis Zitronenorden.* Munich.

SUETENS, Ivo. 1969. *Bibliographie numismatique: Supplément; Ordres et décorations.* Cercle d'Études Numismatiques, Travaux 4. Brussels.

National Regulations & Publications

ARGENTINA. 1910. Ministerio de Guerra. *Historia de los premios militares: Republica de Argentina.* 3 vols. Buenos Aires.

———. 1969. Ministerio de Relaciones Exteriores y Culto. *Condecoraciones.* Buenos Aires.

BOLIVIA. 1866. *Anuario de disposiciones administrativas.* Official ed. January. La Paz.

———. 1970. *Gaceta oficial del gobierno plurinacional de Bolivia, edición No. 514, 10 de julio de 1970.* Decreto Supremo No. 9,305.

BRAZIL. 1968. Ministério do Exército. *Medalhística militar brasileira.* Rio de Janeiro.

———. 1983. Marinha do Brasil. Serviço de Documentação Geral. *Medalhas e condecorações.* Rio de Janeiro.

———. 1995. Presidência da Republica, Casa Civil. *Decreto No. 1,711 de novembro de 1995.* Brasilia.

CHILE. 1996. Carabineros de Chile. Consejo Asesor Superior. *Reglamento para el otrorgamiento y uso de condecoraciones, medallas y sus distintivos en las Fuerzas de Orden y Seguridad Publico.* Vol. 8. Santiago.

———. 2005. Ministerio de Defensa Nacional. Estado Mayor de Defensa Nacional. *Reglamento para el otorgamiento y uso de condecoraciones, medallas y sus distintivos en las Fuerzas Armadas.* DNL-907. Santiago.

COLOMBIA. 2010. Ministerio de Defensa Nacional. Decreto Numero 4,444. November 29.

———. 2011. Ministerio de Defensa Nacional. Decreto Numero 2,066. June 13.

DOMINICAN REPUBLIC. 1939. *Ley y reglamento de la Orden de Cristobal Colón.* Pp. 3–11. Santo Domingo.

———. 2001. *Gaceta oficial.* October 31.

ECUADOR. 1934. Ministerio de Relaciones Exteriores. *Decretos y reglamentos codificados relativos al mérito y a la antiguedad.* Pp. 3–5. Quito.

704   Bibliography

ECUADOR. 2002. *Registro oficial.* No. 671, Decree No. 3,110. September 26.

———. 2005. Armada del Ecuador. Orden General No. 116, October 4. *Reglamento general de condecoraciones militares.* Pp. 7–13. Guayaquil.

EL SALVADOR. 1946. Ministerio de Relaciones Exteriores. *Reglamento de la Orden Nacional "José Matias Delgado."* Decreto legislativo, No. 85, August 14. San Salvador.

———. 1969. *Diario oficial* (198, 225), October 24. Ley de Condecoraciones Militares, Decreto Ley No. 520, October 21. San Salvador.

———. 1973. *Diario oficial* (209, 241), November 12. Decreto Ejecutivo No. 82, June 10. San Salvador.

———. 1988. Ministerio de Relaciones Exteriores. *Manual de ceremonial.* Pp. 61–66. San Salvador.

———. 1998. *Diario oficial* (338, 15), January 23. Decree No. 4 of November 27, 1997. San Salvador.

GUATEMALA. 1982. *Acuerdo gubernativo* (No. 43). Pp. 3–5. Guatemala City.

MEXICO. 1912. "Ordenanza General de la Armada." *Diario Oficial* 1, January 8.

PERU. 1949. Decree Law No. 11,192, October 11. Lima.

———. 2004. Resolución Ministerial No. 0.890-2004-RE, November 2; Decreto Supremo No. 050-2004-RE. Lima.

———. 2005. Supreme Decree No. 007-2005-ED, February 16. Lima.

URUGUAY. 2007. *Boletín de la Defensa Nacional,* vol. 192, year 76. No. 10,922, July 4. Montevideo.

Catalogues & Studies

AMERICAN NUMISMATIC SOCIETY. 2006–7. *Medals, Orders and Decorations from the Collection of the American Numismatic Society.* 3 vols. London. Auction catalogue by Morton & Eden.

ARISTA-SALADO, Maikel. 2010–11. *Condecoraciones cubanas.* 3 vols. Bloomington, Ind.

BANCO CENTRAL DE BOLIVIA. 1999. *Monedas, medallas y billetes de Bolivia.* La Paz.

BARAC, Borna. 2009. *Reference Catalogue of Orders, Medals and Decorations of the World. Part I: Iron Book, A–D.* Zagreb.

———. 2010. *Reference Catalogue of Orders, Medals and Decorations of the World. Part II: Bronze Book, D–G.* Zagreb.

BOSCO, Paul. 1980. "The Silver Proclamation Coinage of the Bolivian Republic." *Numismatic Quarterly* (December).

BRAZIL. 1952. Museo Histórico Nacional. *Medalhas.* Rio de Janeiro.

BRINKMANN, Juergen. 2012. *Orden: Condecoraciones de Chile.* 2 vols. Santiago.

BURKE'S PEERAGE AND GENTRY. 2006. *World Orders of Knighthood and Merit.* Edited by Guy Stair Sainty and Rafal Heydel-Mankoo. 2 vols., continuously paginated. Wilmington, Del.

DARGENT CHAMOT, Eduardo. 2012. *Premios de la independencia y la confederación.* Lima.

DERMAN, Alberto J. 2007. *Colección de medallas Alberto J. "Coco" Derman.* Auction catalogue by Cayón Subastas, December.

DOS SANTOS, Francesco. 1937. *Medalhas militares brasileiras.* Rio de Janeiro.

EMERING, Ed. 2013. "The American Phalanx," *OMSA Journal* 64, no. 1 (January–February): 33–34.

ÉTIENNE, Francis E. 1954. *Les decorations haïtiennes à travers l'histoire*. Port-au-Prince.

EYZAGUIRRE, Jaime. 1934. *Historia de la Orden "al Merito" de Chile*. Santiago.

FLORES DONAIRE, Luis Humberto, 2002. *Nicaragua: Its Coins, Paper Money, Medals and Tokens*. Managua.

FLOYD, Jeffrey B. 2004. *Brazil*. Alexandria, Va.

FONSECA, Alvaro Augusto da, and João MACEDO E CHAVES. 1945. *Ordens honorificas portuguesas*. Lisbon.

GIANELLONI, Luis. 1974. "Las medallas conmemorativas de Ayacucho." *Numismática* (Lima) 19:16–18.

GILLINGHAM, Harrold E. 1932. *South American Decorations and War Medals*. American Numismatic Society Numismatic Notes and Monographs 56. New York.

———. 1940. *Mexican Decorations of Honour*. American Numismatic Society Numismatic Notes and Monographs 89. New York.

GROVE, Frank W. 1974. *Medals of Mexico*. Vol. 3: *Orders, Awards and Military Decorations*. Guadalajara, Mexico.

GUILLE, L. F. 1952. *The Decorations and Medals of the Central American Countries*. Wood End, Ardeley, Stevenage, United Kingdom.

LILL, George, III. 1986. *Caudillismo as Demonstrated by Bolivian Propaganda Coinage*. Chicago.

MARTÍNEZ LANELA, José Félix. 1996. *Premios militares*. Buenos Aires.

MEDINA, José Toribio. 1901. *Las medallas chilenas*. Santiago.

MEILI, Julio. 1890. *Collecçao numismatica de Julio Meili: As medalhas referentes ao Imperio do Brasil*. Zurich.

MUSSO AMBROSI, Luis Alberto. 1976. *Uruguay-Brasil u sus medallas*. Montevideo.

NICARAGUAN MEDAL. 2012. "Nicaraguan Medal for Completion of an International Mission." *Journal of the Orders and Medals Society of America* 63, no. 4 (July–August): 42.

PARDO, Oscar. 1972. *Condecoraciones argentina: La Orden del Libertador San Martín*. Buenos Aires.

PÉREZ-MALDONADO, Carlos. 1942. *Condecoraciones mexicanas y sus historia*. Monterrey.

PÉREZ TENREIRO, Tomás. 1968. *Condecoraciones nacionales*. Caracas.

POSADA, Eduardo. 1938. *Numismática colombiana: Medallas y condecoraciones*. 2nd edition. Bogotá.

PRATT MAYANS, Miguel Ángel. 2007. *Condecoraciones y medallas de las guerras del Paraguay*. Asunción.

PROBER, Kurt. 1951. *Historia numismática de la República Dominicana*. Rio de Janeiro.

———. 1957. *Historia numismática de Guatemala*. 2nd ed. Guatemala City.

RODRÍGUEZ CABRER, Miguel Antonio. 2001. *Ceremoniales, condecoraciones nacionales y jefes de protocolo en la República Dominicana*. Santo Domingo.

ROSA, Alejandro. 1891. *Colleción de leyes, decretos y otros documentos sobre condecoraciones militares, medallas conmemorativas, moneda metalica de algunos paises de la America del Sur*. Buenos Aires.

———. 1898. *Estudios historico-numismáticos: Medallas y monedas de la Republica Argentina*. Buenos Aires.

SALBACH, Oscar. 1911. *Coins and Medals of Latin America*. Auction sale in 2 parts by Jacques Schulman. February 2, September 9. Amsterdam.

SCHULMAN. 1970. Auction sale by the firm of Jacques Schulman. November 24. Amsterdam.

Speir, Daniel E. 2010. "The High Cost of Defeat: Bolivia, Peru and the War of the Pacific." *Journal of the Orders and Medals Society of America* 61, no. 5.

Ugarteche, Pedro. 1966. *La Orden del Sol del Perú 1821–1825*. Lima.

Urquidi, José Mariano. 1921. *Nuevo compendio de la historia de Bolivia*. La Paz.

Urquiza, Eduardo de. 1928. *Historia numismática de la Campaña Libertadora (Argentina–Brasil–Uruguay)*. Buenos Aires.

Werlich, Robert. 1974. *Orders and Decorations of All Nations: Ancient, Modern; Civil and Military*. 2nd ed. Washington, D.C.

Zamora Botta, Jorge. 2012. *La Orden del Sol del Peru*. Lima.

PRINTED AND BOUND BY

THE TIEN WAH PRESS, LTD.

SINGAPORE

∗

DESIGNED AND COMPOSED BY

MARK ARGETSINGER

HOLYOKE

MASSACHUSETTS